PEARSON ALWAYS LEARNING

D1309466

Marvin L. Bittinger

Elementary Algebra
Math 017

Fifth Custom Edition for
Community College of Philadelphia

Taken from:
Introductory Algebra, Eleventh Edition
by Marvin L. Bittinger

Taken from:

Introductory Algebra, Eleventh Edition
by Marvin L. Bittinger

Published by Addison-Wesley
Upper Saddle River, New Jersey 07458

This special edition published in cooperation with Pearson Learning Solutions.

Pearson Learning Solutions, 501 Boylston Street, Suite 900, Boston, MA 02116
A Pearson Education Company
www.pearsoned.com

Printed in the United States of America

1 2 3 4 5 6 7 8 9 10 V0ZN 18 17 16 15 14 13

000200010271854183

AW

PEARSON

ISBN 10: 1-269-60745-6
ISBN 13: 978-1-269-60745-2

Community College of Philadelphia

Welcome to Distance Education

Distance Education online and hybrid courses use the Canvas online learning system. New Canvas users should create their Canvas password prior to the first day of the class. However, **you will not be able to access your Distance Education courses until the first day of the class**.

If you already have a Canvas account from a prior semester, you may continue to use your Canvas username and password.

If you are setting up your Canvas account for the first time, do the following:

1. Go to CCP's Canvas site: http://ccp.instructure.com There is also a link to Canvas on the MyCCP login page called "Canvas LMS".

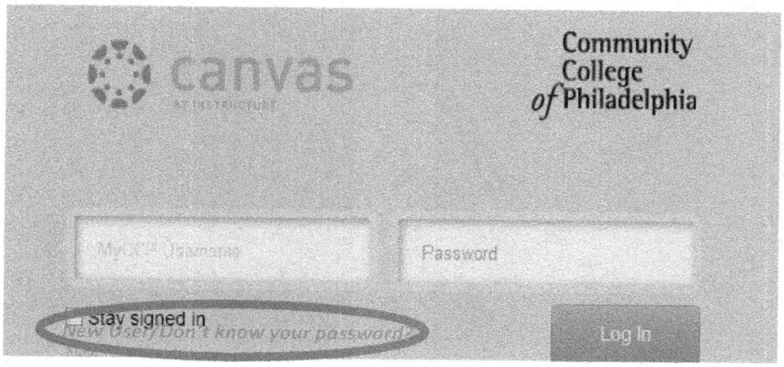

If you are a new Canvas user, do not enter any information in the boxes labeled "MyCCP Username" and "Password". Click on the "**New User/Don't know your password**" link (This is found under the "MyCCP Username" box, pictured left).

2. On the **next screen**, enter your CCP email address and click **Request Password**.

In a few minutes, you will get an email from Canvas in your CCP email account with a link to set your password. Click on that link and type your new password in both boxes.

2. Go to CCP's Canvas site: http://ccp.instructure.com (Please bookmark this link.)

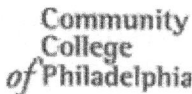

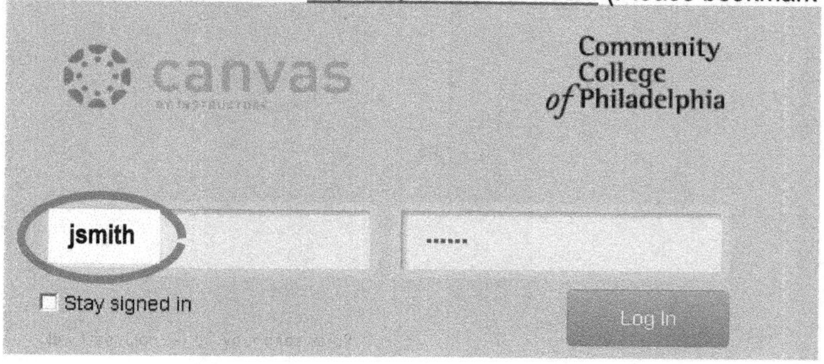

Enter your **MyCCP Username** (for example, **jsmith**) and the password you just set. Click on Log In.

NOTE: Your username is NOT your full email address! **Do not use @ccp.edu in the username box!**

If you have a problem with the sign in process, please contact the Office of Distance Education, via email at distance_ed@ccp.edu, or call the Help desk at 215-496-6000.

Community College of Philadelphia

Math 017 Students

To access your MyLabsPlus account:

1. Go to www.ccp.mylabsplus.com – You must use IE as your browser
2. In the Log In space, enter your J number – use upper case J
3. In the Password space, enter "password"
4. Click on Log In
5. At the Welcome Screen, find and click on MyProfile in the upper right

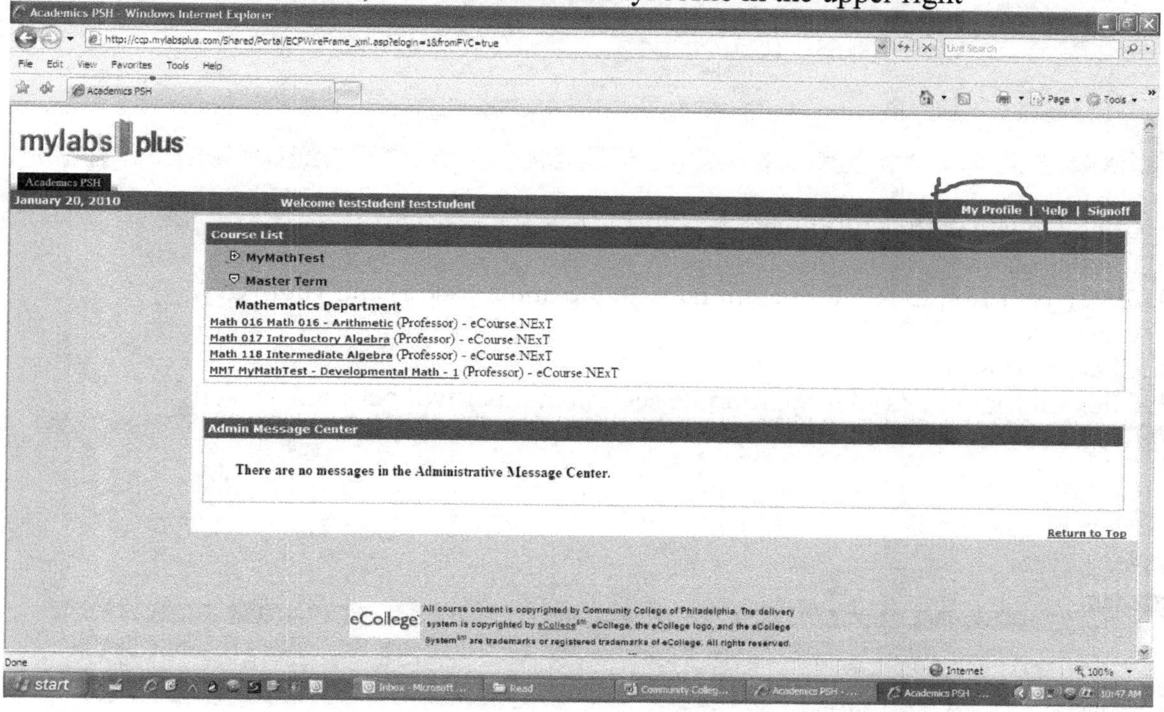

6. In the Old Password space, enter "password"
7. Create and Verify a New Password for your account

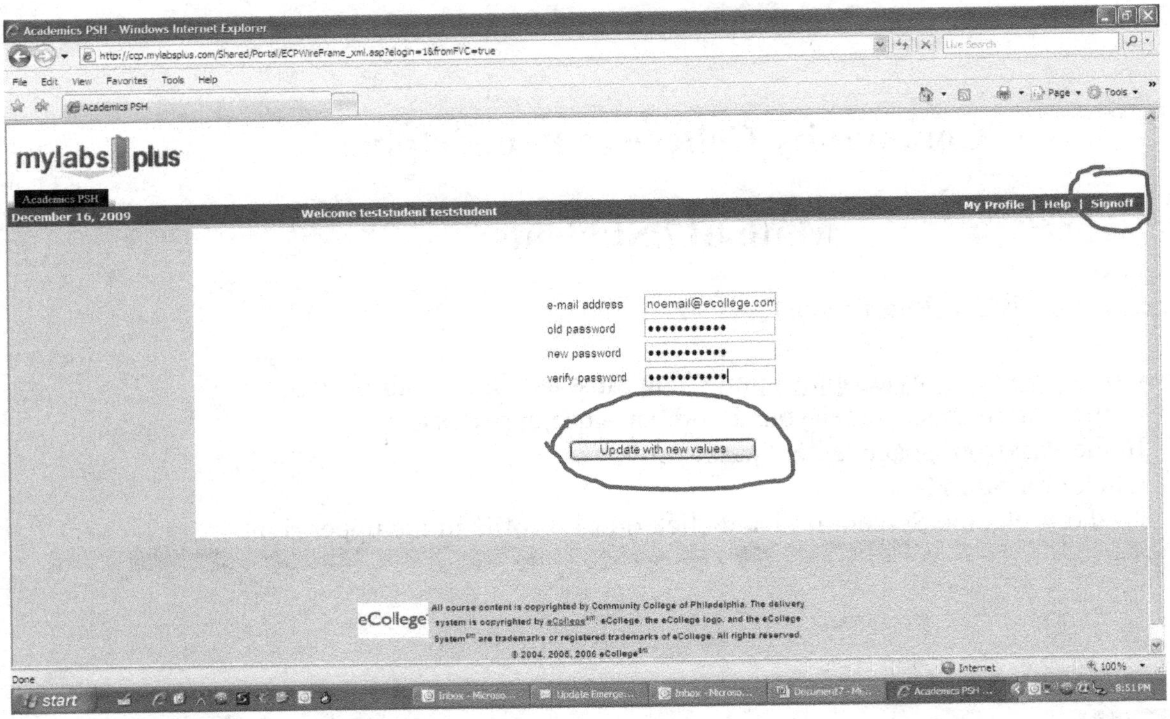

8. Click Update with new Values
9. Click Sign off
10. Enter your Log In (CCP Student ID with the upper case J) and your NEW Password
11. Click on Log In
12. Click on Math 017 (your appropriate section number will be listed as well)

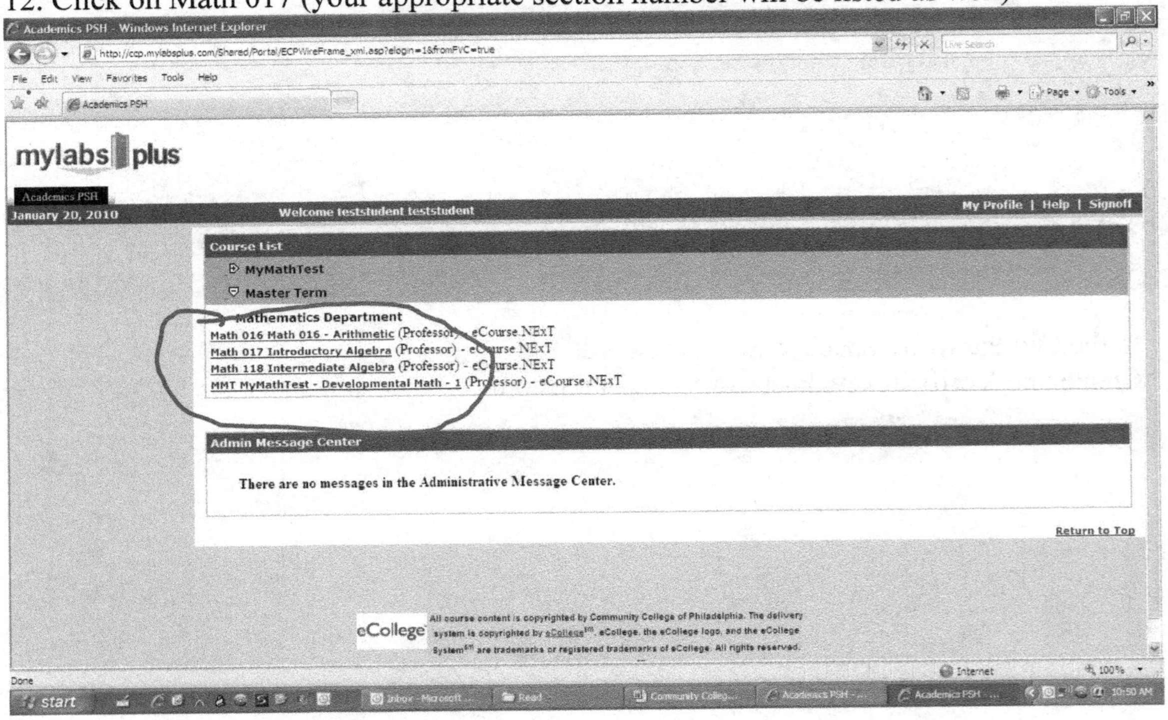

13. On the left side, click on Study Plan
14. Click on the MML Study Plan link in the middle of the screen

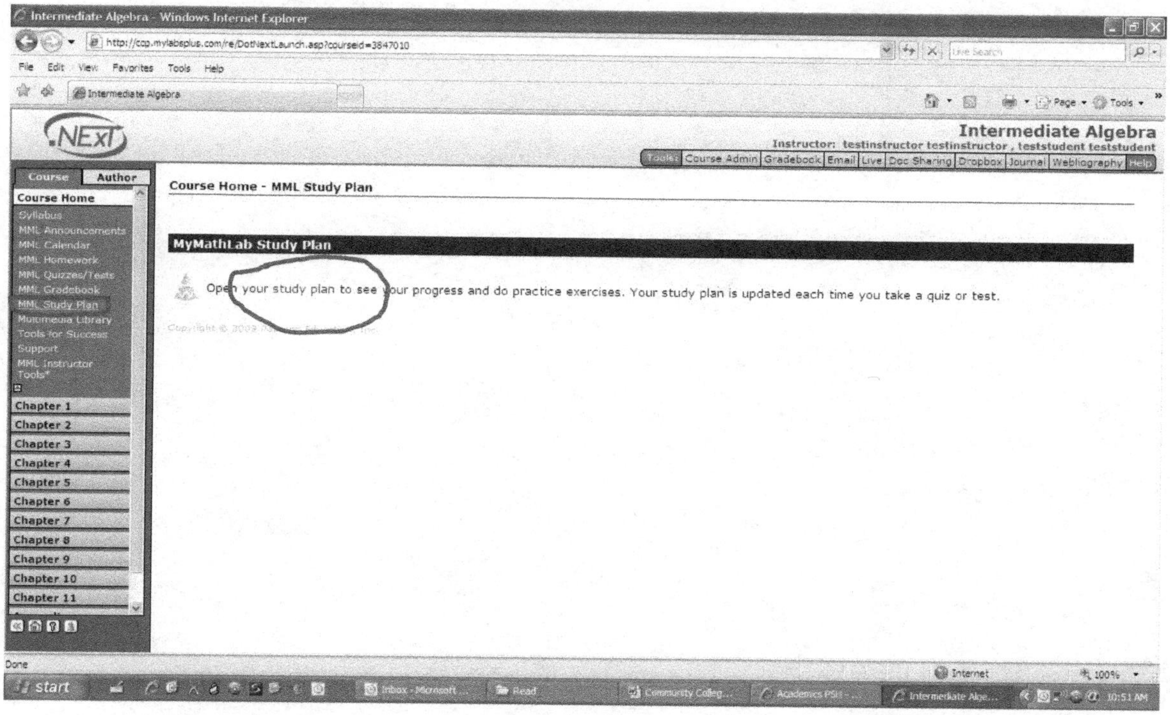

15. You will see the Licensing agreement, scroll to the bottom and click on: I Accept.
16. You will be prompted for an access code, click on Access Code and enter the access code packaged with your Textbook.
    -If you do not have an Access Code you purchase one on line, click on Buy Access Now
    -The Access code will look something like this:
    HSEMSA-QUIPU-PRAYS-ADMAN-TANIS-MOLES

Once you have entered the Access Code successfully, you will not need it again. You will have full access to all the on line materials for your course.

Once in the course materials, click on the Study Plan, Tools for Success and Multimedia Library to find tutorials, tools and practice problems that will help you understand the material covered in this class.

Contents

3 Polynomials: Operations 213

4 Polynomials: Factoring 297

Appendix

Author's Note to Students

Welcome to *Introductory Algebra*. Having a solid grasp of the mathematical skills taught in this book will enrich your life in many ways, both personally and professionally, including increasing your earning power and enabling you to make wise decisions about your personal finances.

As I wrote this text, I was guided by the desire to do everything possible to help you learn its concepts and skills. The material in this book has been developed and refined with feedback from users of the ten previous editions so that you can benefit from their class-tested strategies for success. Regardless of your past experiences in mathematics courses, I encourage you to consider this course as a fresh start and to approach it with a positive attitude.

One of the most important things you can do to ensure your success in this course is to allow enough time for it. This includes time spent in class and time spent out of class studying and doing homework. To help you derive the greatest benefit from this textbook, from your study time, and from the many other learning resources available to you, I have included an organizer card at the front of the book. This card serves as a handy reference for contact information for your instructor, fellow students, and campus learning resources, as well as a weekly planner. It also includes a list of the Study Tips that appear throughout the text. You might find it helpful to read all of these tips as you begin your course work.

Knowing that your time is both valuable and limited, I have designed this objective-based text to help you learn quickly and efficiently. You are led through the development of each concept, then presented with one or more examples of the corresponding skills, and finally given the opportunity to use these skills by doing the interactive margin exercises that appear on the page beside the examples. For quick assessment of your understanding, you can check your answers with the answers placed at the bottom of the page. This innovative feature, along with illustrations designed to help you visualize mathematical concepts and the extensive exercise sets keyed to section objectives, gives you the support and reinforcement you need to be successful in your math course.

To help apply and retain your knowledge, take advantage of the new Skill to Review exercises when they appear at the beginning of a section and the comprehensive mid-chapter reviews, summary and reviews, and cumulative reviews. Read through the list of supplementary material available to students that appears in the preface to make sure you get the most out of your learning experience, and investigate other learning resources that may be available to you.

Give yourself the best opportunity to succeed by spending the time required to learn. I hope you enjoy learning this material and that you will find it of benefit.

Best wishes for success!
Marv Bittinger

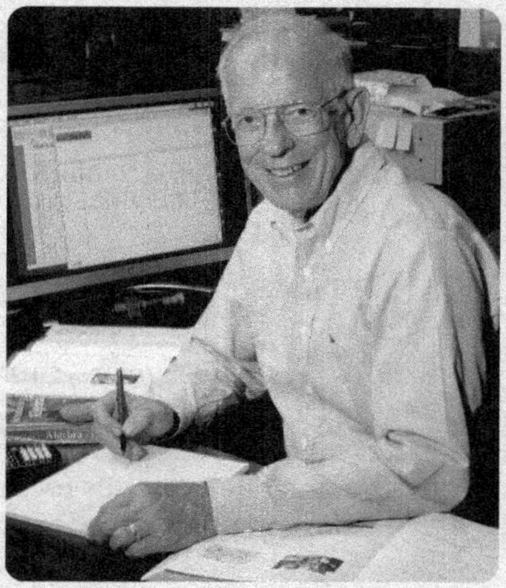

Related Bittinger Paperback Titles

- Bittinger: *Fundamental College Mathematics,* 5th Edition
- Bittinger: *Basic College Mathematics,* 11th Edition
- Bittinger/Penna: *Basic College Mathematics with Early Integers,* 2nd Edition
- Bittinger: *Intermediate Algebra,* 11th Edition
- Bittinger/Beecher: *Introductory and Intermediate Algebra,* 4th Edition

Accuracy
Students rely on accurate textbooks, and my users value the Bittinger reputation for accuracy. All Bittinger titles go through an exhaustive checking process to ensure accuracy in the problem sets, mathematical art, and accompanying supplements.

Preface

New in This Edition

To maximize retention of the concepts and skills presented, five highly effective review features are included in the 11th edition. Student success is increased when review is integrated throughout each chapter.

Five Types of Integrated Review

Skill to Review exercises, found at the beginning of most sections, link to a section objective. These exercises offer a just-in-time review of a previously presented skill that relates to new material in the section. For convenient studying, section and objective references are followed by two practice exercises for immediate review and reinforcement. Exercise answers are given at the bottom of the page for immediate feedback.

Skill Maintenance Exercises, found in each exercise set, review concepts from other sections in the text to prepare students for their final examination. Section and objective references appear next to each Skill Maintenance exercise. All Skill Maintenance answers are included in the text.

A Mid-Chapter Review reinforces understanding of the mathematical concepts and skills just covered before students move on to new material. Section and objective references are included. Exercise types include Concept Reinforcement, Guided Solutions, Mixed Review, and Understanding Through Discussion and Writing. Answers to all exercises in the Mid-Chapter Review are given at the back of the book.

The Chapter Summary and Review at the end of each chapter is expanded to provide more comprehensive in-text practice and review.

- **Key Terms, Properties, and Formulas** are highlighted, with page references for convenient review.
- **Concept Reinforcement** offers true/false questions to enhance students' understanding of mathematical concepts.
- **Important Concepts** are listed by section objectives, followed by *worked-out examples* for reference and review and *similar practice exercises* for students to solve.
- **Review Exercises**, including Synthesis exercises and two new multiple-choice exercises, are organized by objective and cover the whole chapter.
- **Understanding Through Discussion and Writing** exercises strengthen understanding by giving students a chance to express their thoughts in spoken or written form.

Section and objective references for all exercises are included. Answers to all exercises in the Summary and Review are given at the back of the book.

Chapter Tests, including Synthesis questions and a new multiple-choice question, allow students to review and test their comprehension of chapter skills prior to taking an instructor's exam. Answers to all questions in the Chapter Tests are given at the back of the book. Section and objective references for each question are included with the answers.

A Cumulative Review after every chapter starting with Chapter 2 revisits skills and concepts from all preceding chapters to help students recall previously learned material and prepare for exams. Answers to all Cumulative Review exercises are coded by section and objective at the back of the book to help students identify areas where additional practice is needed.

A new design enhances the Bittinger guided-learning approach. Margin exercises are now located next to examples for easier navigation, and answers for those exercises are given at the bottom of the page for immediate feedback.

Hallmark Features

Revised! The **Bittinger Student Organizer** card at the front of the text helps students keep track of important contacts and dates and provides a weekly planner to help schedule time for classes, studying, and homework. A helpful list of study tips found in each chapter is also included.

New! **Chapter Openers** feature motivating real-world applications that are revisited later in the chapters. This feature engages students and prepares them for the upcoming chapter material.

New! **Real-Data Applications** encourage students to see and interpret the mathematics that appears every day in the world around them. Many applications are drawn from the fields of business and economics, life and physical sciences, social sciences, medicine, and areas of general interest such as sports and daily life.

Study Tips appear throughout the text to give students pointers on how to develop good study habits as they progress through the course, encouraging them to get involved in the learning process. For easy reference, a list of Study Tips by chapter, section, and page number is included in the Bittinger Student Organizer.

Algebraic– Graphical Connections To provide a visual understanding of algebra, algebraic–graphical connections are included in each chapter beginning with Chapter 3. This feature gives the algebra more meaning by connecting it to a graphical interpretation.

Caution Boxes are found at relevant points throughout the text. The heading *"Caution!"* alerts students to coverage of a common misconception or an error often made in performing a particular mathematics operation or skill.

Revised! Optional **Calculator Corners** are located where appropriate throughout the text. These streamlined Calculator Corners are written to be accessible to students and to represent current calculators. A calculator icon indicates exercises suitable for calculator use.

Immediate Practice and Assessment in Each Section

OBJECTIVES → SKILL TO REVIEW → EXPOSITION → EXAMPLES WITH DETAILED ANNOTATIONS AND VISUAL ART PIECES → MARGIN EXERCISES → EXERCISE SETS

Objective Boxes begin each section. A boxed list of objectives is keyed by letter not only to section subheadings, but also to the section exercise sets and the Mid-Chapter Review and the Summary and Review exercises, as well as to the answers to the questions in the Chapter Tests and Cumulative Reviews. This correlation enables students to easily find appropriate review material if they need help with a particular exercise or skill at the objective level.

New! **Skill to Review** exercises, found at the beginning of most sections, link to a section objective and offer students a just-in-time review of a previously presented skill that relates to new material in the section. For convenient studying, objective references are followed by two practice exercises for immediate review and reinforcement. Answers to these exercises are given at the bottom of the page for immediate feedback.

Revised! **Annotated Examples** provide annotations and color highlighting to lead students through the structured steps of the examples. The level of detail in these annotations is a significant reason for students' success with this book. This edition contains over 130 new examples.

Revised! The **art and photo program** is designed to help students visualize mathematical concepts and real-data applications. Many applications include source lines and feature graphs and drawings similar to those students see in the media. The use of color is carried out in a methodical and precise manner so that it conveys a consistent meaning, which enhances the readability of the text. For example, the use of both red and blue in mathematical art increases understanding of the concepts. When two lines are graphed using the same set of axes, one is usually red and the other blue. Note that equation labels are the same color as the corresponding line to aid in understanding.

Revised! **Margin Exercises**, now located next to examples for easier navigation, accompany examples throughout the text and give students the opportunity to work similar problems for immediate practice and reinforcement of the concept just learned. Answers are now available at the bottom of the page.

Exercise Sets

To give students ample opportunity to practice what they have learned, each section is followed by an extensive exercise set *keyed by letter to the section objectives* for easy review and remediation. In addition, students also have the opportunity to synthesize the objectives from the current section with those from preceding sections. **For Extra Help** icons, shown at the beginning of each exercise set, indicate supplementary learning resources that students may need. This edition contains over 1130 new exercises.

- **Skill Maintenance Exercises**, found in each exercise set, review concepts from other sections in the text to prepare students for their final examination. Section and objective codes appear next to each Skill Maintenance exercise for easy reference. All Skill Maintenance answers are included in the text.
- **Vocabulary Reinforcement Exercises** provide an integrated review of key terms that students must know to communicate effectively in the language of mathematics. These appear once per chapter in the Skill Maintenance portion of an exercise set.
- **Synthesis Exercises** help build critical-thinking skills by requiring students to use what they know to synthesize, or combine, learning objectives from the current section with those from previous sections. These are available in most exercise sets.

Mid-Chapter Review

New! A **Mid-Chapter Review** gives students the opportunity to reinforce their understanding of the mathematical skills and concepts just covered before they move on to new material. Section and objective references are included for convenient studying, and answers to all the Mid-Chapter Review exercises are included in the text. The types of exercises are as follows:

- **Concept Reinforcement** are true/false questions that enhance students' understanding of mathematical concepts. These are also available in the Summary and Review at the end of the chapter.
- **Guided Solutions** present worked-out problems with blanks for students to fill in the correct expressions to complete the solution.
- **Mixed Review** provides free-response exercises, similar to those in the preceding sections in the chapter, reinforcing mastery of skills and concepts.
- **Understanding Through Discussion and Writing** lets students demonstrate their understanding of mathematical concepts by expressing their thoughts in spoken and written form. This type of exercise is also found in each Chapter Summary and Review.

Matching Feature

Translating for Success problem sets give extra practice with the important "Translate" step of the process for solving word problems. After translating each of ten problems into its appropriate equation or inequality, students are asked to choose from fifteen possible translations, encouraging them to comprehend the problem before matching.

Visualizing for Success problem sets ask students to match an equation or inequality with its graph by focusing on characteristics of the equation or inequality and the corresponding attributes of the graph. This feature appears at least once in each chapter that contains graphing instruction and reviews graphing skills and concepts with exercises from all preceding chapters.

End-of-Chapter Material

Revised! The **Chapter Summary and Review** at the end of each chapter is expanded to provide more comprehensive in-text practice and review. Section and objective references and answers to all the Chapter Summary and Review exercises are included in the text.

- **Key Terms, Properties, and Formulas** are highlighted, with page references for convenient review.
- **Concept Reinforcement** offers true/false questions to enhance student understanding of mathematical concepts.
- New! **Important Concepts** are listed by section objectives, followed by *a worked-out example* for reference and review and *a similar practice exercise* for students to solve.
- **Review Exercises**, including Synthesis exercises and two new multiple-choice exercises, covering the whole chapter are organized by objective.
- **Understanding Through Discussion and Writing** exercises strengthen understanding by giving students a chance to express their thoughts in spoken or written form.

Chapter Tests, including Synthesis questions and a new multiple-choice question, allow students to review and test their comprehension of chapter skills prior to taking an instructor's exam. Answers to all questions in the Chapter Test are given at the back of the book. Section and objective references for each question are included with the answers.

New! **A Cumulative Review** now follows every chapter starting with Chapter 2; this review revisits skills and concepts from all preceding chapters to help students recall previously learned material and prepare for exams. Answers to all Cumulative Review exercises are coded by section and objective at the back of the book to help students identify areas where additional practice is needed.

For Extra Help

Student Supplements

New! Worksheets for Classroom or Lab Practice
(ISBN: 978-0-321-64073-4)

These classroom- and lab-friendly workbooks offer the following resources for every section of the text: a list of learning objectives, vocabulary practice problems, and extra practice exercises with ample work space.

Student's Solutions Manual (ISBN: 978-0-321-64070-3)
By Judith Penna

Contains completely worked-out annotated solutions for all the odd-numbered exercises in the text. Also includes fully worked-out annotated solutions for all the exercises (odd- and even-numbered) in the Mid-Chapter Reviews, the Summary and Reviews, the Chapter Tests, and the Cumulative Reviews.

Chapter Test Prep Videos

Chapter Tests can serve as practice tests to help you study. Watch instructors work through step-by-step solutions to all the Chapter Test exercises from the textbook. Chapter Test Prep videos are available on YouTube (search using BittingerIntroAlg) and in MyMathLab. They are also included on the Video Resources on DVD described below and available for purchase at www.MyPearsonStore.com.

Video Resources on DVD Featuring Chapter Test Prep Videos
(ISBN: 978-0-321-64075-8)

- Complete set of lectures covering every objective of every section in the textbook
- Complete set of Chapter Test Prep videos (see above)
- All videos include optional English and Spanish subtitles.
- Ideal for distance learning or supplemental instruction
- DVD-ROM format for student use at home or on campus

InterAct Math Tutorial Website (www.interactmath.com)

Get practice and tutorial help online! This interactive tutorial website provides algorithmically generated practice exercises that correlate directly to the exercises in the textbook. Students can retry an exercise as many times as they like with new values each time for unlimited practice and mastery. Every exercise is accompanied by an interactive guided solution that provides helpful feedback for incorrect answers, and students can also view a worked-out sample problem that steps them through an exercise similar to the one they're working on.

MathXL® Tutorials on CD (ISBN: 978-0-321-64064-2)

This interactive tutorial CD-ROM provides algorithmically generated practice exercises that are correlated at the objective level to the exercises in the textbook. Every practice exercise is accompanied by an example and a guided solution designed to involve students in the solution process. Selected exercises may also include a video clip to help students visualize concepts. The software provides helpful feedback for incorrect answers and can generate printed summaries of students' progress.

Instructor Supplements

Annotated Instructor's Edition (ISBN: 978-0-321-62897-8)

Includes answers to all exercises printed in blue on the same page as the exercises. Also includes the student answer section, for easy reference.

Instructor's Solutions Manual (ISBN: 978-0-321-64068-0)
By Judith Penna

Contains brief solutions to the even-numbered exercises in the exercise sets. Also includes fully worked-out annotated solutions for all the exercises (odd- and even-numbered) in the Mid-Chapter Reviews, the Summary and Reviews, the Chapter Tests, and the Cumulative Reviews.

Printed Test Forms (ISBN: 978-0-321-64067-3)
By Laurie Hurley

- Contains one diagnostic test and one pretest for each chapter.
- New! Includes two versions of a short mid-chapter quiz.
- Provides eight test forms for every chapter and eight test forms for the final exam.
- For the chapter tests, four free-response tests are modeled after the chapter tests in the main text, two tests are designed for 50-minute class periods and organized so that each objective in the chapter is covered on one of the tests, and two tests consist of multiple-choice questions. Chapter tests also include more challenging Synthesis questions.
- For the final exam, three test forms are organized by chapter, three forms are organized by question type, and two forms are multiple-choice tests.

Instructor's Resource Manual
(ISBN: 978-0-321-64071-0)

- Features resources and teaching tips designed to help both new and adjunct faculty with course preparation and classroom management.
- New! Includes a mini-lecture for each section of the text with objectives, key examples, and teaching tips.
- Additional resources include general first-time advice, sample syllabi, teaching tips, collaborative learning activities, correlation guide, video index, and transparency masters.

Additional Media Supplements

MyMathLab® Online Course (access code required)

MyMathLab is a series of text-specific, easily customizable online courses for Pearson Education's textbooks in mathematics and statistics. Powered by CourseCompass™ (our online teaching and learning environment) and MathXL® (our online homework, tutorial, and assessment system), MyMathLab gives instructors the tools they need to deliver all or a portion of their course online, whether their students are in a lab setting or working from home. MyMathLab provides a rich and flexible set of course materials, featuring free-response exercises that are algorithmically generated for unlimited practice and mastery. Students can also use online tools, such as video lectures, animations, interactive math games, and a multimedia textbook, to independently improve their understanding and performance. Instructors can use MyMathLab's homework and test managers to select and assign online exercises correlated directly to the textbook, and they can also create and assign their own online exercises and import TestGen tests for added flexibility. MyMathLab's online gradebook—designed specifically for mathematics and statistics—automatically tracks students' homework and test results and gives the instructor control over how to calculate final grades. Instructors can also add offline (paper-and-pencil) grades to the gradebook. MyMathLab also includes access to the **Pearson Tutor Center** (www.pearsontutorservices.com). The Tutor Center is staffed by qualified mathematics instructors who provide textbook-specific tutoring for students via toll-free phone, fax, email, and interactive Web sessions. MyMathLab is available to qualified adopters. For more information, visit our website at www.mymathlab.com or contact your sales representative.

MathXL® Online Course (access code required)

MathXL® is a powerful online homework, tutorial, and assessment system that accompanies Pearson Education's textbooks in mathematics or statistics.

With MathXL, instructors can

- create, edit, and assign online homework and tests using algorithmically generated exercises correlated at the objective level to the textbook.
- create and assign their own online exercises and import TestGen tests for added flexibility.
- maintain records of all student work tracked in MathXL's online gradebook.

With MathXL, students can

- take chapter tests in MathXL and receive personalized study plans based on their test results.
- use the study plan to link directly to tutorial exercises for the objectives they need to study and retest.
- access supplemental animations and video clips directly from selected exercises.

MathXL is available to qualified adopters. For more information, visit our website at www.mathxl.com, or contact your Pearson sales representative.

TestGen® (www.pearsoned.com/testgen) enables instructors to build, edit, and print tests using a computerized bank of questions developed to cover all the objectives of the text. TestGen is algorithmically based, allowing instructors to create multiple but equivalent versions of the same question or test with the click of a button. Instructors can also modify test bank questions or add new questions. The software and test bank are available for download from Pearson Education's online catalog.

PowerPoint® Lecture Slides present key concepts and definitions from the text. Slides are available to download from within MyMathLab and from Pearson Education's online catalog.

Pearson Math Adjunct Support Center (http://www.pearsontutorservices.com/math-adjunct.html) is staffed by qualified instructors with more than 100 years of combined experience at both the community college and university levels. Assistance is provided for faculty in the following areas: suggested syllabus consultation, tips on using materials packed with your book, book-specific content assistance, and teaching suggestions, including advice on classroom strategies.

Acknowledgments

Our deepest appreciation to all of you who helped to shape this edition by reviewing and spending time with us on your campuses. In particular, we would like to thank the following reviewers of *Introductory Algebra* and *Introductory and Intermediate Algebra*:

Gus Brar, *Delaware County Community College*
Carol Curtis, *Fresno City College*
Shreyas Desai, *Atlanta Metropolitan College*
Hope Essien, *Malcolm X College*
Kimberly J. Fara, *Des Moines Area Community College–Carroll Campus*
Dianne Hendrickson, *Becker College*
Susan Meshulam, *Indiana University Purdue University Indianapolis*
Marcia Venzon, *Texas A&M University–Corpus Christi*

The endless hours of hard work by Martha Morong, Geri Davis, and Judy Beecher have led to products of which we are immensely proud. We also want to thank Judy Penna for writing the Student's and Instructor's Solutions Manuals and for her strong leadership in the preparation of the printed supplements and video lectures with Barbara Johnson. Other strong support has come from Laurie Hurley for the Printed Test Forms and for accuracy checking, along with checkers Holly Martinez and Barbara Johnson and proofreader Patty LaGree. Michelle Lanosga assisted with applications research. We also wish to recognize Tom Atwater, Margaret Donlan, and Patty Schwarzkopf, who wrote video scripts.

In addition, a number of people at Pearson have contributed in special ways to the development and production of this textbook including the Developmental Math team: Vice President, Executive Director of Development Carol Trueheart, Senior Development Editor Dawn Nuttall, Production Manager Ron Hampton, Senior Designer Beth Paquin, Associate Editors Joanna Doxey and Christine Whitlock, Editorial Assistant Jonathan Wooding, Associate Media Producer Nathaniel Koven, and Media Producer Ceci Fleming. Executive Editor Cathy Cantin and Executive Marketing Manager Michelle Renda encouraged our vision and provided marketing insight. Kari Heen, Executive Project Manager, deserves special recognition for overseeing every phase of the project and keeping it moving.

CHAPTER

R

Prealgebra Review

Real-World Application

Find the area of a large irrigated farming circle with a diameter of 1834 ft. Use $\frac{22}{7}$ for π.

R.1 Factoring and LCMs

OBJECTIVES

a Find all the factors of numbers and find prime factorizations of numbers.

b Find the LCM of two or more numbers using prime factorizations.

To the student:

At the front of the text, you will find a Student Organizer card. This pullout card will help you keep track of important dates and useful contact information. You can also use it to plan time for class, study, work, and relaxation. By managing your time wisely, you will provide yourself the best possible opportunity to be successful in this course.

Find all the factors of each number.

1. 9 **2.** 16

3. 24 **4.** 180

Answers

1. 1, 3, 9 **2.** 1, 2, 4, 8, 16 **3.** 1, 2, 3, 4, 6, 8, 12, 24 **4.** 1, 2, 3, 4, 5, 6, 9, 10, 12, 15, 18, 20, 30, 36, 45, 60, 90, 180

a Factors and Prime Factorizations

We begin our review with *factoring*, a necessary skill for addition and subtraction with fraction notation. Factoring is also an important skill in algebra.

The numbers we will be factoring are **natural numbers**:

1, 2, 3, 4, 5, and so on.

To **factor** a number means to express the number as a product. Consider the product $12 = 3 \cdot 4$. We say that 3 and 4 are **factors** of 12 and that $3 \cdot 4$ is a **factorization** of 12. Since $12 = 12 \cdot 1$, we also know that 12 and 1 are factors of 12 and that $12 \cdot 1$ is a factorization of 12.

EXAMPLE 1 Find all the factors of 12.

We first find all two-factor products:

$12 = 1 \cdot 12, \quad 12 = 2 \cdot 6, \quad 12 = 3 \cdot 4.$

The factors of 12 are 1, 2, 3, 4, 6, and 12.

EXAMPLE 2 Find all the factors of 150.

We first find some factorizations:

$150 = 1 \cdot 150, \quad 150 = 2 \cdot 75, \quad 150 = 3 \cdot 50,$
$150 = 5 \cdot 30, \quad 150 = 6 \cdot 25, \quad 150 = 10 \cdot 15.$

The factors of 150 are 1, 2, 3, 5, 6, 10, 15, 25, 30, 50, 75, and 150.

Note that the word "factor" is used both as a noun and as a verb. You **factor** when you express a number as a product. The numbers you multiply together to get the product are **factors**.

Do Margin Exercises 1–4.

PRIME NUMBER

A natural number that has *exactly two different factors*, itself and 1, is called a **prime number**.

EXAMPLE 3 Which of these numbers are prime? 7, 4, 11, 18, 1

7 is prime. It has exactly two different factors, 1 and 7.
4 is *not* prime. It has three different factors, 1, 2, and 4.
11 is prime. It has exactly two different factors, 1 and 11.
18 is *not* prime. It has factors 1, 2, 3, 6, 9, and 18.
1 is *not* prime. It does not have two *different* factors.

In the margin at right is a table of the prime numbers from 2 to 157. There are more extensive tables, but these prime numbers will be the most helpful to you in this text.

Do Exercise 5.

If a natural number, other than 1, is not prime, we call it **composite**. Every composite number can be factored into a product of prime numbers. Such a factorization is called a **prime factorization**.

EXAMPLE 4 Find the prime factorization of 36.

We begin by factoring 36 any way we can. One way is like this:

$$36 = 4 \cdot 9.$$

The factors 4 and 9 are not prime, so we factor them:

$$\begin{aligned} 36 &= \;\; 4 \quad \cdot \quad 9 \\ &\quad\;\; \downarrow \qquad\;\; \downarrow \\ &= 2 \cdot 2 \cdot 3 \cdot 3. \end{aligned}$$

The factors in the last factorization are all prime, so we now have the *prime factorization* of 36. Note that 1 is *not* part of this factorization because it is not prime.

Another way to find the prime factorization of 36 is like this:

$$36 = 2 \cdot 18 = 2 \cdot 3 \cdot 6 = 2 \cdot 3 \cdot 2 \cdot 3.$$

In effect, we begin factoring any way we can think of and keep factoring until all factors are prime. Using a **factor tree** might also be helpful.

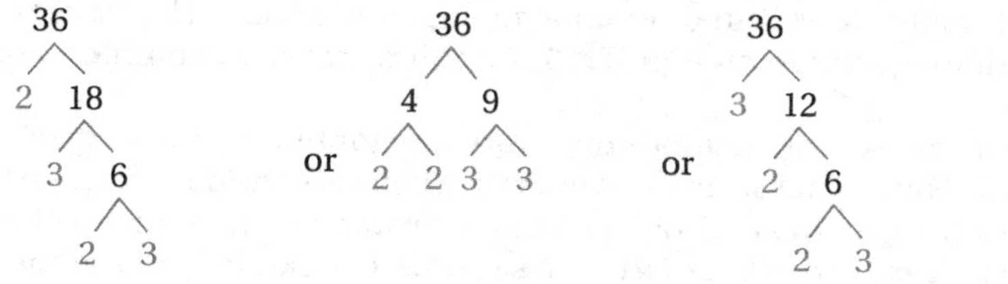

$36 = 2 \cdot 3 \cdot 2 \cdot 3$ $\quad$ $36 = 2 \cdot 2 \cdot 3 \cdot 3$ $\quad$ $36 = 3 \cdot 2 \cdot 2 \cdot 3$

No matter which way we begin, the result is the same: The prime factorization of 36 contains two factors of 2 and two factors of 3. Every composite number has a *unique* prime factorization.

EXAMPLE 5 Find the prime factorization of 60.

This time, we use the list of primes from the table. We go through the table until we find a prime that is a factor of 60. The first such prime is 2.

$$60 = 2 \cdot 30$$

We keep dividing by 2 until it is not possible to do so.

$$60 = 2 \cdot 2 \cdot 15$$

Now we go to the next prime in the table that is a factor of 60. It is 3.

$$60 = 2 \cdot 2 \cdot 3 \cdot 5$$

Each factor in $2 \cdot 2 \cdot 3 \cdot 5$ is a prime. Thus this is the prime factorization.

Do Exercises 6–9.

A TABLE OF PRIMES

2, 3, 5, 7, 11, 13, 17, 19, 23, 29, 31, 37, 41, 43, 47, 53, 59, 61, 67, 71, 73, 79, 83, 89, 97, 101, 103, 107, 109, 113, 127, 131, 137, 139, 149, 151, 157

5. Which of these numbers are prime?

8, 6, 13, 14, 1

Find the prime factorization.

6. 48 **7.** 50

8. 770 **9.** 2340

Answers

5. 13 **6.** $2 \cdot 2 \cdot 2 \cdot 2 \cdot 3$
7. $2 \cdot 5 \cdot 5$ **8.** $2 \cdot 5 \cdot 7 \cdot 11$
9. $2 \cdot 2 \cdot 3 \cdot 3 \cdot 5 \cdot 13$

(b) Least Common Multiples

Least common multiples are used to add and subtract with fraction notation.

The **multiples** of a number all have that number as a factor. For example, the multiples of 2 are

2, 4, 6, 8, 10, 12, 14, 16, ...

We could name each of them in such a way as to show 2 as a factor. For example, $14 = 2 \cdot 7$.

The multiples of 3 all have 3 as a factor:

3, 6, 9, 12, 15, 18, ...

Two or more numbers always have many multiples in common. From lists of multiples, we can find common multiples.

EXAMPLE 6 Find the common multiples of 2 and 3.

We make lists of their multiples and circle the multiples that appear in both lists.

2, 4, (6), 8, 10, (12), 14, 16, (18), 20, 22, (24), 26, 28, (30), 32, 34, (36), . . . ;
3, (6), 9, (12), 15, (18), 21, (24), 27, (30), 33, (36), ...

The common multiples of 2 and 3 are

6, 12, 18, 24, 30, 36, ...

Do Exercises 10 and 11.

10. Find the common multiples of 3 and 5 by making lists of multiples.

11. Find the common multiples of 9 and 15 by making lists of multiples.

In Example 6, we found common multiples of 2 and 3. The *least*, or smallest, of those common multiples is 6. We abbreviate **least common multiple** as **LCM**.

There are several methods that work well for finding the LCM of several numbers. Some of these do not work well when we consider expressions with variables such as $4ab$ and $12abc$. We now review a method that will work in arithmetic *and in algebra as well.* To see how it works, let's look at the prime factorizations of 9 and 15 in order to find the LCM:

$$9 = 3 \cdot 3, \qquad 15 = 3 \cdot 5.$$

Any multiple of 9 must have *two* 3's as factors. Any multiple of 15 must have *one* 3 and *one* 5 as factors. The smallest multiple of 9 and 15 is

$$3 \cdot 3 \cdot 5 = 45.$$

Two 3's; 9 is a factor

One 3, one 5; 15 is a factor

The LCM must have all the factors of 9 and all the factors of 15, *but the factors are not repeated when they are common to both numbers.*

To find the LCM of several numbers using prime factorizations:

a) Write the prime factorization of each number.

b) Form the LCM by writing the product of the different factors from step (a), using each factor the greatest number of times that it occurs in any *one* of the factorizations.

Answers

10. 15, 30, 45, 60, . . .
11. 45, 90, 135, 180, . . .

EXAMPLE 7 Find the LCM of 40 and 100.

a) We find the prime factorizations:

$$40 = 2 \cdot 2 \cdot 2 \cdot 5,$$
$$100 = 2 \cdot 2 \cdot 5 \cdot 5.$$

b) The different prime factors are 2 and 5. We write 2 as a factor three times (the greatest number of times that it occurs in any *one* factorization). We write 5 as a factor two times (the greatest number of times that it occurs in any *one* factorization).

The LCM is $2 \cdot 2 \cdot 2 \cdot 5 \cdot 5$, or 200.

Do Exercises 12 and 13.

Find each LCM by factoring.

12. 8 and 10 **13.** 18 and 27

EXAMPLE 8 Find the LCM of 27, 90, and 84.

a) We factor:

$$27 = 3 \cdot 3 \cdot 3,$$
$$90 = 2 \cdot 3 \cdot 3 \cdot 5,$$
$$84 = 2 \cdot 2 \cdot 3 \cdot 7.$$

b) We write 2 as a factor two times, 3 three times, 5 one time, and 7 one time.

The LCM is $2 \cdot 2 \cdot 3 \cdot 3 \cdot 3 \cdot 5 \cdot 7$, or 3780.

Do Exercise 14.

14. Find the LCM of 18, 24, and 30.

EXAMPLE 9 Find the LCM of 7 and 21.

Since 7 is prime, it has no prime factorization. It still, however, must be a factor of the LCM:

$$7 = 7,$$
$$21 = 3 \cdot 7.$$

The LCM is $7 \cdot 3$, or 21.

If one number is a factor of another, then the LCM is the larger of the two numbers.

Do Exercises 15 and 16.

Find each LCM.

15. 3, 18 **16.** 12, 24

EXAMPLE 10 Find the LCM of 8 and 9.

We have

$$8 = 2 \cdot 2 \cdot 2,$$
$$9 = 3 \cdot 3.$$

The LCM is $2 \cdot 2 \cdot 2 \cdot 3 \cdot 3$, or 72.

If two or more numbers have no common prime factor, then the LCM is the product of the numbers.

Do Exercises 17 and 18.

Find each LCM.

17. 4, 9 **18.** 5, 6, 7

Answers

12. 40 **13.** 54 **14.** 360 **15.** 18
16. 24 **17.** 36 **18.** 210

R.1 Exercise Set

For Extra Help
MyMathLab | MathXL PRACTICE | WATCH | DOWNLOAD | READ | REVIEW

Always review the objectives before doing an exercise set. See page 2. Note how the objectives are keyed to the exercises.

a Find all the factors of each number.

1. 20 **2.** 36 **3.** 72 **4.** 81

Find the prime factorization of each number.

5. 15 **6.** 14 **7.** 22 **8.** 33 **9.** 9

10. 25 **11.** 49 **12.** 121 **13.** 18 **14.** 24

15. 40 **16.** 56 **17.** 90 **18.** 120 **19.** 210

20. 330 **21.** 91 **22.** 143 **23.** 119 **24.** 221

b Find the prime factorization of the numbers. Then find the LCM.

25. 4, 5 **26.** 18, 40 **27.** 24, 36 **28.** 24, 27 **29.** 3, 15

30. 20, 40 **31.** 30, 40 **32.** 50, 60 **33.** 13, 23 **34.** 17, 29

35. 18, 30 **36.** 45, 72 **37.** 30, 36 **38.** 30, 50 **39.** 24, 30

40. 60, 70 **41.** 12, 18 **42.** 18, 24 **43.** 12, 28 **44.** 35, 45

45. 2, 3, 5 **46.** 3, 5, 7 **47.** 24, 36, 12 **48.** 8, 16, 22

49. 5, 12, 15 **50.** 12, 18, 40 **51.** 6, 12, 18 **52.** 24, 35, 45

Planet Orbits. The earth, Jupiter, Saturn, and Uranus all revolve around the sun. The earth takes 1 yr, Jupiter 12 yr, Saturn 30 yr, and Uranus 84 yr to make a complete revolution. On a certain night, you look at those three distant planets and wonder how many years it will be before they have the same position. (*Hint*: To find out, determine the LCM of 12, 30, and 84. It will be that number of years.)

Source: *The Handy Science Answer Book*

53. How often will Jupiter and Saturn have the same position in the night sky as seen from the earth?

54. How often will Jupiter and Uranus have the same position in the night sky as seen from the earth?

55. How often will Saturn and Uranus have the same position in the night sky as seen from the earth?

56. How often will Jupiter, Saturn, and Uranus have the same position in the night sky as seen from the earth?

African Artistry. In Africa, the design of every woven handbag, or *gipatsi* (plural, *sipatsi*), is created by repeating two or more geometric patterns. Each pattern encircles the bag, sharing the strands of fabric with any pattern above or below. The length, or period, of each pattern is the number of strands required to construct the pattern. For a gipatsi to be considered beautiful, each individual pattern must fit a whole number of times around the bag.

Source: Gerdes, Paulus. *Women, Art and Geometry in Southern Africa.* Asmara, Eritrea: Africa World Press, Inc., p. 5.

57. A weaver is using two patterns to create a gipatsi. Pattern A is 10 strands long, and pattern B is 3 strands long. What is the smallest number of strands that can be used to complete the gipatsi?

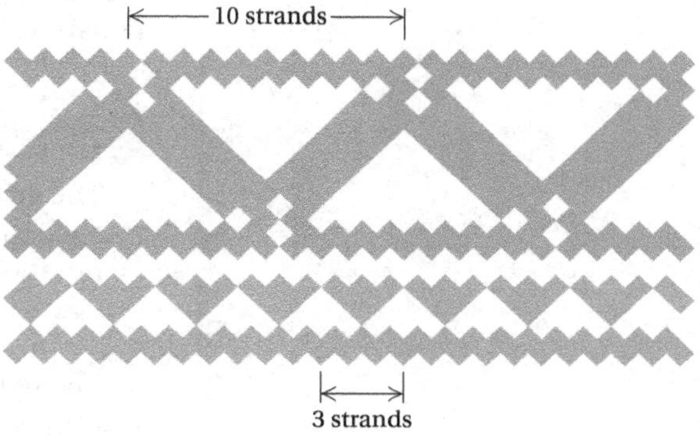

58. A weaver is using a four-strand pattern, a six-strand pattern, and an eight-strand pattern. What is the smallest number of strands that can be used to complete the gipatsi?

Synthesis

To the student and the instructor: The Synthesis exercises found at the end of every exercise set challenge students to combine concepts or skills studied in that section or in preceding parts of the text. Exercises marked with a 🖩 symbol are meant to be solved using a calculator.

59. Consider the numbers 8 and 12. Determine whether each of the following is the LCM of 8 and 12. Tell why or why not.

a) $2 \cdot 2 \cdot 3 \cdot 3$ **b)** $2 \cdot 2 \cdot 2 \cdot 3 \cdot 5$ **c)** $2 \cdot 3 \cdot 3$ **d)** $2 \cdot 2 \cdot 2 \cdot 3$

🖩 Use a calculator to find the LCM of the numbers.

60. 288, 324

61. 2700, 7800

R.2 Fraction Notation

OBJECTIVES

a) Find equivalent fraction expressions by multiplying by 1.

b) Simplify fraction notation.

c) Add, subtract, multiply, and divide using fraction notation.

We now review fraction notation and its use with addition, subtraction, multiplication, and division of *arithmetic numbers.*

a Equivalent Expressions and Fraction Notation

An example of **fraction notation** for a number is

$$\frac{2}{3}\begin{matrix}\leftarrow \text{Numerator}\\ \leftarrow \text{Denominator}\end{matrix}$$

The top number is called the **numerator**, and the bottom number is called the **denominator**.

The **whole numbers** consist of the natural numbers and 0:

$$0, \; 1, \; 2, \; 3, \; 4, \; 5, \ldots.$$

The **arithmetic numbers**, also called the **nonnegative rational numbers**, consist of the whole numbers and the fractions, such as $\frac{2}{3}$ and $\frac{9}{5}$.

ARITHMETIC NUMBERS

The **arithmetic numbers** are the whole numbers and the fractions, such as $8, \frac{3}{4}$, and $\frac{6}{5}$. All these numbers can be named with fraction notation $\frac{a}{b}$, where a and b are whole numbers and $b \neq 0$.

Note that all whole numbers can be named with fraction notation. For example, we can name the whole number 8 as $\frac{8}{1}$. We call 8 and $\frac{8}{1}$ **equivalent expressions.**

Being able to find an equivalent expression is critical to a study of algebra. Two simple but powerful properties of numbers that allow us to find equivalent expressions are the identity properties of 0 and 1.

THE IDENTITY PROPERTY OF 0 (ADDITIVE IDENTITY)

For any number a,

$$a + 0 = a.$$

(Adding 0 to any number gives that same number—for example, $12 + 0 = 12$.)

THE IDENTITY PROPERTY OF 1 (MULTIPLICATIVE IDENTITY)

For any number a,

$$a \cdot 1 = a.$$

$\left(\text{Multiplying any number by 1 gives that same number—for example, } \frac{3}{5} \cdot 1 = \frac{3}{5}.\right)$

Here are some ways to name the number 1:

$$\frac{5}{5}, \quad \frac{3}{3}, \quad \text{and} \quad \frac{26}{26}.$$

The following property allows us to find equivalent fraction expressions.

EQUIVALENT EXPRESSIONS FOR 1

For any number a, $a \neq 0$,

$$\frac{a}{a} = 1.$$

We can use the identity property of 1 and the preceding result to find equivalent fraction expressions.

EXAMPLE 1 Write a fraction expression equivalent to $\frac{2}{3}$ with a denominator of 15.

Note that $15 = 3 \cdot 5$. We want fraction notation for $\frac{2}{3}$ that has a denominator of 15, but the denominator 3 is missing a factor of 5. We multiply by 1, using $\frac{5}{5}$ as an equivalent expression for 1. Recall from arithmetic that to multiply with fraction notation, we multiply numerators and we multiply denominators:

$$\frac{2}{3} = \frac{2}{3} \cdot 1 \qquad \text{Using the identity property of 1}$$

$$= \frac{2}{3} \cdot \frac{5}{5} \qquad \text{Using } \frac{5}{5} \text{ for 1}$$

$$= \frac{10}{15}. \qquad \text{Multiplying numerators and denominators}$$

Do Exercises 1–3.

1. Write a fraction expression equivalent to $\frac{2}{3}$ with a denominator of 12.

2. Write a fraction expression equivalent to $\frac{3}{4}$ with a denominator of 28.

3. Multiply by 1 to find three different fraction expressions for $\frac{7}{8}$.

b Simplifying Expressions

We know that $\frac{1}{2}, \frac{2}{4}, \frac{4}{8}$, and so on, all name the same number. Any arithmetic number can be named in many ways. The **simplest fraction notation** is the notation that has the smallest numerator and denominator. We call the process of finding the simplest fraction notation **simplifying**. We reverse the process of Example 1 by first factoring the numerator and the denominator. Then we factor the fraction expression and remove a factor of 1 using the identity property of 1.

EXAMPLE 2 Simplify: $\frac{10}{15}$.

$$\frac{10}{15} = \frac{2 \cdot 5}{3 \cdot 5} \qquad \text{Factoring the numerator and the denominator. In this case, each is the prime factorization.}$$

$$= \frac{2}{3} \cdot \frac{5}{5} \qquad \text{Factoring the fraction expression}$$

$$= \frac{2}{3} \cdot 1$$

$$= \frac{2}{3} \qquad \text{Using the identity property of 1 (removing a factor of 1)}$$

Answers

1. $\frac{8}{12}$ 2. $\frac{21}{28}$ 3. $\frac{14}{16}, \frac{21}{24}, \frac{28}{32}$; answers may vary

EXAMPLE 3 Simplify: $\dfrac{36}{24}$.

$$\begin{aligned} \frac{36}{24} &= \frac{2 \cdot 3 \cdot 2 \cdot 3}{2 \cdot 2 \cdot 3 \cdot 2} && \text{Factoring the numerator and the denominator} \\ &= \frac{2 \cdot 3 \cdot 2}{2 \cdot 3 \cdot 2} \cdot \frac{3}{2} && \text{Factoring the fraction expression} \\ &= 1 \cdot \frac{3}{2} \\ &= \frac{3}{2} && \text{Removing a factor of 1} \end{aligned}$$

It is always a good idea to check at the end to see if you have indeed factored out all the common factors of the numerator and the denominator.

Canceling

Canceling is a shortcut that you may have used to remove a factor of 1 when working with fraction notation. With *great* concern, we mention it as a possible way to speed up your work. You should use canceling only when removing common factors in numerators and denominators. Each common factor allows us to remove a factor of 1 in a product. **Canceling *cannot* be done when adding.** Our concern is that "canceling" be performed with care and understanding. Example 3 might have been done faster as follows:

$$\frac{36}{24} = \frac{\cancel{2} \cdot \cancel{3} \cdot \cancel{2} \cdot 3}{\cancel{2} \cdot \cancel{2} \cdot \cancel{3} \cdot 2} = \frac{3}{2}, \quad \text{or} \quad \frac{36}{24} = \frac{3 \cdot \cancel{12}}{2 \cdot \cancel{12}} = \frac{3}{2}, \quad \text{or} \quad \frac{\overset{\overset{3}{\cancel{18}}}{\cancel{36}}}{\underset{\underset{2}{\cancel{12}}}{\cancel{24}}} = \frac{3}{2}.$$

Caution!

The difficulty with canceling is that it is often applied incorrectly in situations like the following:

$$\frac{2 + 3}{\cancel{2}} = 3; \qquad \frac{\cancel{4} + 1}{\cancel{4} + 2} = \frac{1}{2}; \qquad \frac{1\cancel{5}}{\cancel{5}4} = \frac{1}{4}.$$

Wrong! Wrong! Wrong!

The correct answers are

$$\frac{2 + 3}{2} = \frac{5}{2}; \qquad \frac{4 + 1}{4 + 2} = \frac{5}{6};$$

$$\frac{15}{54} = \frac{3 \cdot 5}{3 \cdot 18} = \frac{3}{3} \cdot \frac{5}{18} = \frac{5}{18}.$$

In each situation, the number canceled was not a factor of 1. Factors are parts of products. For example, in $2 \cdot 3$, 2 and 3 are factors, but in $2 + 3$, 2 and 3 are *not* factors.

Do Exercises 4–7.

Simplify.

4. $\dfrac{18}{45}$

5. $\dfrac{38}{18}$

6. $\dfrac{72}{27}$

7. $\dfrac{32}{56}$

Answers

4. $\frac{2}{5}$ 5. $\frac{19}{9}$ 6. $\frac{8}{3}$ 7. $\frac{4}{7}$

We can always insert the number 1 as a factor. The identity property of 1 allows us to do that.

EXAMPLE 4 Simplify: $\frac{18}{72}$.

$$\frac{18}{72} = \frac{2 \cdot \cancel{9}}{8 \cdot \cancel{9}} = \frac{2}{8} = \frac{\cancel{2} \cdot 1}{\cancel{2} \cdot 4} = \frac{1}{4}, \quad \text{or} \quad \frac{18}{72} = \frac{1 \cdot \cancel{18}}{4 \cdot \cancel{18}} = \frac{1}{4}$$

EXAMPLE 5 Simplify: $\frac{72}{9}$.

$\frac{72}{9} = \frac{8 \cdot 9}{1 \cdot 9}$ Factoring and inserting a factor of 1 in the denominator

$= \frac{8 \cdot \cancel{9}}{1 \cdot \cancel{9}}$ Removing a factor of 1: $\frac{9}{9} = 1$

$= \frac{8}{1} = 8$ Simplifying

Do Exercises 8 and 9.

Simplify.

8. $\frac{27}{54}$ **9.** $\frac{48}{12}$

C Multiplication, Addition, Subtraction, and Division

After we have performed an operation of multiplication, addition, subtraction, or division, the answer may not be in simplified form. We simplify, if at all possible.

Multiplication

To multiply using fraction notation, we multiply the numerators to get the new numerator, and we multiply the denominators to get the new denominator.

MULTIPLYING FRACTIONS

To multiply fractions, multiply the numerators and multiply the denominators:

$$\frac{a}{b} \cdot \frac{c}{d} = \frac{a \cdot c}{b \cdot d}.$$

EXAMPLE 6 Multiply and simplify: $\frac{5}{6} \cdot \frac{9}{25}$.

$\frac{5}{6} \cdot \frac{9}{25} = \frac{5 \cdot 9}{6 \cdot 25}$ Multiplying numerators and denominators

$= \frac{5 \cdot 3 \cdot 3}{2 \cdot 3 \cdot 5 \cdot 5}$ Factoring the numerator and the denominator

$= \frac{\cancel{5} \cdot \cancel{3} \cdot 3}{2 \cdot \cancel{3} \cdot \cancel{5} \cdot 5}$ Removing a factor of 1: $\frac{3 \cdot 5}{3 \cdot 5} = 1$

$= \frac{3}{10}$ Simplifying

Do Exercises 10 and 11.

Multiply and simplify.

10. $\frac{6}{5} \cdot \frac{25}{12}$ **11.** $\frac{3}{8} \cdot \frac{5}{3} \cdot \frac{7}{2}$

Answers

8. $\frac{1}{2}$ **9.** 4 **10.** $\frac{5}{2}$ **11.** $\frac{35}{16}$

Addition

When denominators are the same, we can add by adding the numerators and keeping the same denominator.

> **ADDING FRACTIONS WITH LIKE DENOMINATORS**
>
> To add fractions when denominators are the same, add the numerators and keep the same denominator:
>
> $$\frac{a}{c} + \frac{b}{c} = \frac{a + b}{c}.$$

EXAMPLE 7 Add: $\frac{4}{8} + \frac{5}{8}$.

The common denominator is 8. We add the numerators and keep the common denominator:

$$\frac{4}{8} + \frac{5}{8} = \frac{4 + 5}{8} = \frac{9}{8}.$$

> To convert from a mixed numeral to fraction notation:
>
> $$3\frac{5}{8} = \frac{29}{8}$$
>
> ⓐ Multiply the whole number by the denominator:
>
> $3 \cdot 8 = 24.$
>
> ⓑ Add the result to the numerator:
>
> $24 + 5 = 29.$
>
> ⓒ Keep the denominator.

In arithmetic, we generally write $\frac{9}{8}$ as $1\frac{1}{8}$. (See a review of converting from a mixed numeral to fraction notation at left.) In algebra, you will find that *improper fraction* symbols such as $\frac{9}{8}$ are more useful and are quite *proper* for our purposes.

What do we do when denominators are different? We find a common denominator. We can do this by multiplying by 1. Consider adding $\frac{1}{6}$ and $\frac{3}{4}$. There are several common denominators that can be obtained. Let's look at two possibilities.

A.
$$\begin{aligned}\frac{1}{6} + \frac{3}{4} &= \frac{1}{6} \cdot 1 + \frac{3}{4} \cdot 1\\ &= \frac{1}{6} \cdot \frac{4}{4} + \frac{3}{4} \cdot \frac{6}{6}\\ &= \frac{4}{24} + \frac{18}{24}\\ &= \frac{22}{24}\\ &= \frac{11}{12} \qquad \text{Simplifying}\end{aligned}$$

B.
$$\begin{aligned}\frac{1}{6} + \frac{3}{4} &= \frac{1}{6} \cdot 1 + \frac{3}{4} \cdot 1\\ &= \frac{1}{6} \cdot \frac{2}{2} + \frac{3}{4} \cdot \frac{3}{3}\\ &= \frac{2}{12} + \frac{9}{12}\\ &= \frac{11}{12}\end{aligned}$$

We had to simplify in **A**. We didn't have to simplify in **B**. In **B**, we used the least common multiple of the denominators, 12. That number is called the **least common denominator**, or **LCD**. Using the LCD allows us to add fractions using the smallest numbers possible.

> **ADDING FRACTIONS WITH DIFFERENT DENOMINATORS**
>
> To add fractions when denominators are different:
>
> **a)** Find the least common multiple of the denominators. That number is the least common denominator, LCD.
>
> **b)** Multiply by 1, using the appropriate notation n/n for each fraction to express fractions in terms of the LCD.
>
> **c)** Add the numerators, keeping the same denominator.
>
> **d)** Simplify, if possible.

EXAMPLE 8 Add and simplify: $\frac{3}{8} + \frac{5}{12}$.

The LCM of the denominators, 8 and 12, is 24. Thus the LCD is 24. We multiply each fraction by 1 to obtain the LCD:

$$\frac{3}{8} + \frac{5}{12} = \frac{3}{8} \cdot \frac{3}{3} + \frac{5}{12} \cdot \frac{2}{2}$$ Multiplying by 1. Since $3 \cdot 8 = 24$, we multiply the first number by $\frac{3}{3}$. Since $2 \cdot 12 = 24$, we multiply the second number by $\frac{2}{2}$.

$$= \frac{9}{24} + \frac{10}{24}$$

$$= \frac{9 + 10}{24}$$ Adding the numerators and keeping the same denominator

$$= \frac{19}{24}.$$

EXAMPLE 9 Add and simplify: $\frac{11}{30} + \frac{5}{18}$.

We first look for the LCM of 30 and 18. That number is then the LCD. We find the prime factorization of each denominator:

$$\frac{11}{30} + \frac{5}{18} = \frac{11}{5 \cdot 2 \cdot 3} + \frac{5}{2 \cdot 3 \cdot 3}.$$

The LCD is $5 \cdot 2 \cdot 3 \cdot 3$, or 90. To get the LCD in the first denominator, we need a factor of 3. To get the LCD in the second denominator, we need a factor of 5. We get these numbers by multiplying by 1:

$$\frac{11}{30} + \frac{5}{18} = \frac{11}{5 \cdot 2 \cdot 3} \cdot \frac{3}{3} + \frac{5}{2 \cdot 3 \cdot 3} \cdot \frac{5}{5}$$ Multiplying by 1

$$= \frac{33}{5 \cdot 2 \cdot 3 \cdot 3} + \frac{25}{2 \cdot 3 \cdot 3 \cdot 5}$$ The denominators are now the LCD.

$$= \frac{58}{5 \cdot 2 \cdot 3 \cdot 3}$$ Adding the numerators and keeping the LCD

$$= \frac{\cancel{2} \cdot 29}{5 \cdot \cancel{2} \cdot 3 \cdot 3}$$ Factoring the numerator and removing a factor of 1

$$= \frac{29}{45}.$$ Simplifying

Do Exercises 12–15.

Add and simplify.

12. $\frac{4}{5} + \frac{3}{5}$

13. $\frac{5}{6} + \frac{7}{6}$

14. $\frac{5}{6} + \frac{7}{10}$

15. $\frac{13}{24} + \frac{7}{40}$

Subtraction

When subtracting, we also multiply by 1 to obtain the LCD. After we have made the denominators the same, we can subtract by subtracting the numerators and keeping the same denominator.

EXAMPLE 10 Subtract and simplify: $\frac{9}{8} - \frac{4}{5}$.

$$\frac{9}{8} - \frac{4}{5} = \frac{9}{8} \cdot \frac{5}{5} - \frac{4}{5} \cdot \frac{8}{8}$$ The LCD is 40.

$$= \frac{45}{40} - \frac{32}{40}$$

$$= \frac{45 - 32}{40} = \frac{13}{40}$$ Subtracting the numerators and keeping the same denominator

Answers

12. $\frac{7}{5}$ 13. 2 14. $\frac{23}{15}$ 15. $\frac{43}{60}$

EXAMPLE 11 Subtract and simplify: $\frac{7}{10} - \frac{1}{5}$.

$$\frac{7}{10} - \frac{1}{5} = \frac{7}{10} - \frac{1}{5} \cdot \frac{2}{2} \quad \text{The LCD is 10; } \frac{7}{10} \text{ already has the LCD.}$$
$$= \frac{7}{10} - \frac{2}{10} = \frac{7-2}{10}$$
$$= \frac{5}{10}$$
$$= \frac{1 \cdot \cancel{5}}{2 \cdot \cancel{5}} = \frac{1}{2} \quad \text{Removing a factor of 1: } \frac{5}{5} = 1$$

Do Exercises 16 and 17.

Subtract and simplify.

16. $\frac{7}{8} - \frac{2}{5}$

17. $\frac{5}{12} - \frac{2}{9}$

Reciprocals

Two numbers whose product is 1 are called **reciprocals**, or **multiplicative inverses**, of each other. All the arithmetic numbers, except zero, have reciprocals.

EXAMPLES

12. The reciprocal of $\frac{2}{3}$ is $\frac{3}{2}$ because $\frac{2}{3} \cdot \frac{3}{2} = \frac{6}{6} = 1$.

13. The reciprocal of 9 is $\frac{1}{9}$ because $9 \cdot \frac{1}{9} = \frac{9}{9} = 1$.

14. The reciprocal of $\frac{1}{4}$ is 4 because $\frac{1}{4} \cdot 4 = \frac{4}{4} = 1$.

Do Exercises 18–21.

Find each reciprocal.

18. $\frac{4}{11}$

19. $\frac{15}{7}$

20. 5

21. $\frac{1}{3}$

Reciprocals and Division

Reciprocals and the number 1 can be used to justify a fast way to divide arithmetic numbers. We multiply by 1, carefully choosing the expression for 1.

EXAMPLE 15 Divide $\frac{2}{3}$ by $\frac{7}{5}$.

This is a symbol for 1.

$$\frac{2}{3} \div \frac{7}{5} = \frac{\frac{2}{3}}{\frac{7}{5}} = \frac{\frac{2}{3}}{\frac{7}{5}} \cdot \frac{\frac{5}{7}}{\frac{5}{7}} \quad \text{Multiplying by } \frac{\frac{5}{7}}{\frac{5}{7}}. \text{ We use } \tfrac{5}{7} \text{ because it is the reciprocal of } \tfrac{7}{5}.$$
$$= \frac{\frac{2}{3} \cdot \frac{5}{7}}{\frac{7}{5} \cdot \frac{5}{7}} \quad \text{Multiplying numerators and denominators}$$
$$= \frac{\frac{10}{21}}{\frac{35}{35}} = \frac{\frac{10}{21}}{1} \quad \tfrac{35}{35} = 1$$
$$= \frac{10}{21} \quad \text{Simplifying}$$

After multiplying in Example 15, we had a denominator of $\frac{35}{35}$, or 1. That was because we used $\frac{5}{7}$, the reciprocal of the divisor, for both the numerator and the denominator of the symbol for 1.

Do Exercise 22.

22. Divide by multiplying by 1:

$$\frac{\frac{3}{5}}{\frac{4}{7}}.$$

Answers

16. $\frac{19}{40}$ 17. $\frac{7}{36}$ 18. $\frac{11}{4}$ 19. $\frac{7}{15}$
20. $\frac{1}{5}$ 21. 3 22. $\frac{21}{20}$

When multiplying by 1 to divide, we get a denominator of 1. What do we get in the numerator? In Example 15, we got $\frac{2}{3} \cdot \frac{5}{7}$. This is the product of $\frac{2}{3}$, the dividend, and $\frac{5}{7}$, the reciprocal of the divisor. This gives us a procedure for dividing fractions.

DIVIDING FRACTIONS

To divide fractions, multiply by the reciprocal of the divisor:

$$\frac{a}{b} \div \frac{c}{d} = \frac{a}{b} \cdot \frac{d}{c}.$$

EXAMPLE 16 Divide by multiplying by the reciprocal of the divisor: $\frac{1}{2} \div \frac{3}{5}$.

$\frac{1}{2} \div \frac{3}{5} = \frac{1}{2} \cdot \frac{5}{3}$ — $\frac{5}{3}$ is the reciprocal of $\frac{3}{5}$

$= \frac{5}{6}$ — Multiplying

After dividing, always simplify if possible.

EXAMPLE 17 Divide and simplify: $\frac{2}{3} \div \frac{4}{9}$.

$\frac{2}{3} \div \frac{4}{9} = \frac{2}{3} \cdot \frac{9}{4}$ — $\frac{9}{4}$ is the reciprocal of $\frac{4}{9}$

$= \frac{2 \cdot 9}{3 \cdot 4}$ — Multiplying numerators and denominators

$= \frac{\cancel{2} \cdot \cancel{3} \cdot 3}{\cancel{3} \cdot \cancel{2} \cdot 2}$ — Removing a factor of 1: $\frac{2 \cdot 3}{2 \cdot 3} = 1$

$= \frac{3}{2}$

Do Exercises 23–26.

EXAMPLE 18 Divide and simplify: $\frac{5}{6} \div 30$.

$$\frac{5}{6} \div 30 = \frac{5}{6} \div \frac{30}{1} = \frac{5}{6} \cdot \frac{1}{30} = \frac{5 \cdot 1}{6 \cdot 30} = \frac{\cancel{5} \cdot 1}{6 \cdot \cancel{5} \cdot 6} = \frac{1}{6 \cdot 6} = \frac{1}{36}$$

Removing a factor of 1: $\frac{5}{5} = 1$

EXAMPLE 19 Divide and simplify: $24 \div \frac{3}{8}$.

$$24 \div \frac{3}{8} = \frac{24}{1} \div \frac{3}{8} = \frac{24}{1} \cdot \frac{8}{3} = \frac{24 \cdot 8}{1 \cdot 3} = \frac{\cancel{3} \cdot 8 \cdot 8}{1 \cdot \cancel{3}} = \frac{8 \cdot 8}{1} = 64$$

Removing a factor of 1: $\frac{3}{3} = 1$

Do Exercises 27 and 28.

Calculator Corner

Operations on Fractions We can perform operations on fractions on a graphing calculator. To find $\frac{3}{4} + \frac{1}{2}$ and express the result as a fraction, we press 3 ÷ 4 + 1 ÷ 2 MATH 1 ENTER. The keystrokes MATH 1 select the ▷FRAC option from the MATH menu, causing the result to be expressed in fraction form. The calculator display is shown below.

```
3/4+1/2▶Frac
                 5/4
```

Exercises: Perform each calculation. Give the answer in fraction notation.

1. $\frac{5}{6} + \frac{7}{8}$
2. $\frac{13}{16} - \frac{4}{7}$
3. $\frac{15}{4} \cdot \frac{7}{12}$
4. $\frac{4}{5} \cdot \frac{3}{8}$

Divide by multiplying by the reciprocal of the divisor. Then simplify.

23. $\frac{4}{3} \div \frac{7}{2}$
24. $\frac{5}{4} \div \frac{3}{2}$
25. $\frac{\frac{2}{9}}{\frac{5}{12}}$
26. $\frac{\frac{5}{6}}{\frac{45}{22}}$

Divide and simplify.

27. $\frac{7}{8} \div 56$
28. $36 \div \frac{4}{9}$

Answers

23. $\frac{8}{21}$ 24. $\frac{5}{6}$ 25. $\frac{8}{15}$
26. $\frac{11}{27}$ 27. $\frac{1}{64}$ 28. 81

R.2 Exercise Set

For Extra Help MyMathLab MathXL PRACTICE WATCH DOWNLOAD READ REVIEW

a Write an equivalent expression for each of the following. Use the indicated name for 1.

1. $\frac{3}{4}\left(\text{Use } \frac{3}{3} \text{ for } 1.\right)$

2. $\frac{5}{6}\left(\text{Use } \frac{10}{10} \text{ for } 1.\right)$

3. $\frac{3}{5}\left(\text{Use } \frac{20}{20} \text{ for } 1.\right)$

4. $\frac{8}{9}\left(\text{Use } \frac{4}{4} \text{ for } 1.\right)$

5. $\frac{13}{20}\left(\text{Use } \frac{8}{8} \text{ for } 1.\right)$

6. $\frac{13}{32}\left(\text{Use } \frac{40}{40} \text{ for } 1.\right)$

Write an equivalent expression with the given denominator.

7. $\frac{7}{8}$ (Denominator: 24)

8. $\frac{5}{6}$ (Denominator: 48)

9. $\frac{5}{4}$ (Denominator: 16)

10. $\frac{2}{9}$ (Denominator: 54)

11. $\frac{17}{19}$ (Denominator: 437)

12. $\frac{15}{23}$ (Denominator: 437)

b Simplify.

13. $\frac{18}{27}$

14. $\frac{49}{56}$

15. $\frac{56}{14}$

16. $\frac{48}{27}$

17. $\frac{6}{42}$

18. $\frac{13}{104}$

19. $\frac{56}{7}$

20. $\frac{132}{11}$

21. $\frac{19}{76}$

22. $\frac{17}{51}$

23. $\frac{100}{20}$

24. $\frac{150}{25}$

25. $\frac{425}{525}$

26. $\frac{625}{325}$

27. $\frac{2600}{1400}$

28. $\frac{4800}{1600}$

29. $\frac{8 \cdot x}{6 \cdot x}$

30. $\frac{13 \cdot v}{39 \cdot v}$

c Compute and simplify.

31. $\frac{1}{3} \cdot \frac{1}{4}$

32. $\frac{15}{16} \cdot \frac{8}{5}$

33. $\frac{15}{4} \cdot \frac{3}{4}$

34. $\frac{10}{11} \cdot \frac{11}{10}$

35. $\frac{1}{3} + \frac{1}{3}$

36. $\frac{1}{4} + \frac{1}{3}$

37. $\frac{4}{9} + \frac{13}{18}$

38. $\frac{4}{5} + \frac{8}{15}$

39. $\frac{3}{10} + \frac{8}{15}$

40. $\frac{9}{8} + \frac{7}{12}$

41. $\frac{7}{30} + \frac{5}{12}$

42. $\frac{3}{16} - \frac{1}{18}$

43. $\frac{5}{4} - \frac{3}{4}$

44. $\frac{12}{5} - \frac{2}{5}$

45. $\frac{11}{12} - \frac{3}{8}$

46. $\frac{15}{16} - \frac{5}{12}$

47. $\frac{11}{12} - \frac{2}{5}$

48. $\frac{15}{16} - \frac{2}{3}$

49. $\frac{7}{6} \div \frac{3}{5}$

50. $\frac{7}{5} \div \frac{3}{4}$

51. $\frac{8}{9} \div \frac{4}{15}$

52. $\frac{3}{4} \div \frac{3}{7}$

53. $\frac{1}{8} \div \frac{1}{4}$

54. $\frac{1}{20} \div \frac{1}{5}$

55. $\frac{\frac{13}{12}}{\frac{39}{5}}$

56. $\frac{\frac{17}{6}}{\frac{3}{8}}$

57. $100 \div \frac{1}{5}$

58. $78 \div \frac{1}{6}$

59. $\frac{3}{4} \div 10$

60. $\frac{5}{6} \div 15$

61. $1000 - \frac{1}{100}$

62. $\frac{147}{50} - 2$

63. $30 \div \frac{1}{30}$

64. $\frac{1}{30} \div 30$

Skill Maintenance

This heading indicates that the exercises that follow are *Skill Maintenance exercises,* which review any skill previously studied in the text. You can expect such exercises in every exercise set. Answers to *all* skill maintenance exercises are found at the back of the book. If you miss an exercise, restudy the objective shown in red.

Find the prime factorization. [R.1a]

65. 28 **66.** 56 **67.** 1000 **68.** 192 **69.** 2001

Find each LCM. [R.1b]

70. 18, 63 **71.** 16, 24 **72.** 28, 49, 56 **73.** 48, 64, 96 **74.** 25, 75, 150

Synthesis

Simplify.

75. $\frac{192}{256}$

76. $\frac{p \cdot q}{r \cdot q}$

77. $\frac{64 \cdot a \cdot b}{16 \cdot a \cdot b}$

78. $\frac{4 \cdot 9 \cdot 24}{2 \cdot 8 \cdot 15}$

79. $\frac{36 \cdot (2 \cdot h)}{8 \cdot (9 \cdot h)}$

80. $\frac{256 \cdot a \cdot b \cdot c \cdot d}{192 \cdot b \cdot c \cdot d}$

R.3 Decimal Notation

OBJECTIVES

a Convert from decimal notation to fraction notation.

b Add, subtract, multiply, and divide using decimal notation.

c Round numbers to a specified decimal place.

Let's say that the cost of a sound system is

$1768.95.

This amount is given in **decimal notation**. The following place-value chart shows the place value of each digit in 1768.95.

PLACE-VALUE CHART

Ten Thousands	Thousands	Hundreds	Tens	Ones	Tenths	Hundredths	Thousandths	Ten-Thousandths
10,000	1000	100	10	1	$\frac{1}{10}$	$\frac{1}{100}$	$\frac{1}{1000}$	$\frac{1}{10,000}$
	1	7	6	8 .	9	5		

a Converting from Decimal Notation to Fraction Notation

When we multiply by 1, a number is not changed. If we choose the notation $\frac{10}{10}, \frac{100}{100}, \frac{1000}{1000}$, and so on for 1, we can move a decimal point in a numerator to the right to convert from decimal notation to fraction notation.

Look for a pattern in the following products:

$$0.1 = 0.1 \times 1 = 0.1 \times \frac{10}{10} = \frac{0.1 \times 10}{10} = \frac{1}{10};$$

$$0.6875 = 0.6875 \times 1 = 0.6875 \times \frac{10,000}{10,000} = \frac{0.6875 \times 10,000}{10,000} = \frac{6875}{10,000};$$

$$53.47 = 53.47 \times 1 = 53.47 \times \frac{100}{100} = \frac{53.47 \times 100}{100} = \frac{5347}{100}.$$

To convert from decimal notation to fraction notation:

a) Count the number of decimal places. — 4.98 (2 places)

b) Move the decimal point that many places to the right. — 4.98. (Move 2 places.)

c) Write the result over a denominator with that number of zeros. — $\frac{498}{100}$ (2 zeros)

EXAMPLE 1 Convert 0.876 to fraction notation. Do not simplify.

0.876 (3 places) 0.876. (3 places) $0.876 = \frac{876}{1000}$ (3 zeros)

EXAMPLE 2 Convert 1.5018 to fraction notation. Do not simplify.

1.5018   1.5018. (4 places) $1.5018 = \frac{15,018}{10,000}$ (4 zeros)

Do Exercises 1–4.

Convert to fraction notation. Do not simplify.

1. 0.568
2. 2.3
3. 89.04
4. 0.009

To convert from fraction notation to decimal notation when the denominator is a number like 10, 100, or 1000:

a) Count the number of zeros. $\frac{8679}{1000}$ 3 zeros

b) Move the decimal point that number of places to the left. Leave off the denominator. 8.679. Move 3 places.

EXAMPLE 3 Convert to decimal notation: $\frac{123,067}{10,000}$.

$\frac{123,067}{10,000}$ (4 zeros)   12.3067. (4 places) $\frac{123,067}{10,000} = 12.3067$

Do Exercises 5–8.

Convert to decimal notation.

5. $\frac{4131}{1000}$
6. $\frac{4131}{10,000}$
7. $\frac{573}{100}$
8. $\frac{49}{10}$

b Addition, Subtraction, Multiplication, and Division

ADDITION WITH DECIMAL NOTATION

Adding with decimal notation is similar to adding whole numbers. First, line up the decimal points. Then add the thousandths, then the hundredths, and so on, carrying if necessary.

EXAMPLE 4 Add: 74 + 26.46 + 0.998.

```
   1 1 1
   7 4.
   2 6.4 6
+      0.9 9 8
--------------
 1 0 1.4 5 8
```

You can place extra zeros to the right of any decimal point so that there are the same number of decimal places in all the addends, but this is not necessary. If you did so, the preceding problem would look like this:

```
   1 1 1
   7 4.0 0 0     Adding zeros to 74
   2 6.4 6 0     Adding zeros to 26.46
+    0.9 9 8
--------------
 1 0 1.4 5 8
```

Do Exercises 9 and 10.

Add.

9. 69 + 1.785 + 213.67

10. 17.95 + 14.68 + 236

Answers

1. $\frac{568}{1000}$ 2. $\frac{23}{10}$ 3. $\frac{8904}{100}$ 4. $\frac{9}{1000}$
5. 4.131 6. 0.4131 7. 5.73 8. 4.9
9. 284.455 10. 268.63

SUBTRACTION WITH DECIMAL NOTATION

Subtracting with decimal notation is similar to subtracting whole numbers. First, line up the decimal points. Then subtract the thousandths, then the hundredths, the tenths, and so on, borrowing if necessary. Extra zeros can be added if needed.

EXAMPLES

Subtract.

11. 29.35 − 1.674

12. 92.375 − 27.692

13. 100 − 0.41

14. 240 − 0.117

5. Subtract: 76.14 − 18.953.

$$\begin{array}{r} {\scriptstyle 15\ 10\ 13} \\ {\scriptstyle 6\ \ \not{5}\ \ \not{0}\ \ \not{3}\ 10} \\ \not{7}\ \not{6}.\not{1}\ \not{4}\ \not{0} \\ -\ 1\ 8.9\ 5\ 3 \\ \hline 5\ 7.1\ 8\ 7 \end{array}$$

6. Subtract: 200 − 0.68.

$$\begin{array}{r} {\scriptstyle 1\ \ 9\ \ 9\ \ 9\ 10} \\ \not{2}\ \not{0}\ \not{0}.\not{0}\ \not{0} \\ -\quad 0.6\ 8 \\ \hline 1\ 9\ 9.3\ 2 \end{array}$$

Do Exercises 11–14.

Look at this product.

$$\underbrace{5.14}_{\text{2 places}} \times \underbrace{0.8}_{\text{1 place}} = \frac{514}{100} \times \frac{8}{10} = \frac{514 \times 8}{100 \times 10} = \frac{4112}{1000} = 4.\underbrace{112}_{\text{3 places}}$$

We can also do this calculation more quickly by multiplying the whole numbers 8 and 514 and then determining the position of the decimal point.

MULTIPLICATION WITH DECIMAL NOTATION

a) Ignore the decimal points and multiply as whole numbers.

b) Place the decimal point in the result of step (a) by adding the number of decimal places in the original factors.

EXAMPLE 7 Multiply: 5.14 × 0.8.

a) We ignore the decimal points and multiply as whole numbers.

$$\begin{array}{r} {\scriptstyle 1\ 3\ \ } \\ 5.1\ 4 \\ \times\quad 0.8 \\ \hline 4\ 1\ 1\ 2 \end{array}$$

b) We then place the decimal point in the result of step (a) by adding the number of decimal places in the original factors.

$$\begin{array}{rl} 5.1\ 4 & \leftarrow \text{2 decimal places} \\ \times\quad 0.8 & \leftarrow \text{1 decimal place} \\ \hline 4.\underbrace{1\ 1\ 2} & \leftarrow \text{3 decimal places} \end{array}$$

Multiply.

15. $\begin{array}{r} 6.5\ 2 \\ \times\ \ 0.9 \\ \hline \end{array}$

16. $\begin{array}{r} 6.5\ 2 \\ \times\ 0.0\ 9 \\ \hline \end{array}$

17. $\begin{array}{r} 5\ 6.7\ 6 \\ \times\ 0.9\ 0\ 8 \\ \hline \end{array}$

18. $\begin{array}{r} 0.0\ 3 \\ \times\ 0.0\ 0\ 1 \\ \hline \end{array}$

Do Exercises 15–18.

Answers

11. 27.676 **12.** 64.683 **13.** 99.59 **14.** 239.883 **15.** 5.868 **16.** 0.5868 **17.** 51.53808 **18.** 0.00003

Note that $37.6 \div 8 = 4.7$ because $8 \times 4.7 = 37.6$. If we write this as shown at right, we see how the following method can be used to divide by a whole number.

```
     4.7
8 ) 37.6
    32
     5 6
     5 6
       0
```

DIVIDING WHEN THE DIVISOR IS A WHOLE NUMBER

a) Place the decimal point in the quotient directly above the decimal point in the dividend.

b) Divide as whole numbers.

EXAMPLE 8 Divide: $216.75 \div 25$.

a)

```
         .
25 ) 216.75
        ↑
```

Place the decimal point.

b)

```
         8.67
25 ) 216.75
     200
      16 7
      15 0
       1 75
       1 75
          0
```

Divide as though dividing whole numbers.

Do Exercises 19 and 20.

Sometimes it is helpful to write extra zeros to the right of the decimal point. Doing so does not change the answer. Remember that the decimal point for a whole number, though not normally written, is to the right of the number.

EXAMPLE 9 Divide: $54 \div 8$.

a)

```
      .
8 ) 54.
```

b)

```
     6.75
8 ) 54.00
    48
     6 0
     5 6
       40
       40
        0
```

Extra zeros are written to the right of the decimal point as needed.

Do Exercises 21 and 22.

DIVIDING WHEN THE DIVISOR IS NOT A WHOLE NUMBER

a) Move the decimal point in the divisor as many places to the right as it takes to make it a whole number. Move the decimal point in the dividend the same number of places to the right and place the decimal point in the quotient.

b) Divide as whole numbers, inserting zeros if necessary.

Calculator Corner

Operations with Decimal Notation To find $62.043 - 48.915$, for example, we press 6 2 . 0 4 3 − 4 8 . 9 1 5 ENTER. Note that the subtraction operation key − must be used rather than the opposite key (−) to perform this computation. We will discuss the use of the (−) key in Chapter 1.

To find 6.73×2.18, we press 6 . 7 3 × 2 . 1 8 ENTER. The results of these computations are shown below.

```
62.043−48.915
              13.128
6.73*2.18
             14.6714
```

Exercises: Use a calculator to perform each operation.

1. $26 + 13.47 + 0.95$
2. $9.03 - 5.7$
3. 0.159×4.36
4. $135.66 \div 57$

Divide.

19. $7\,\overline{)\,342.3}$

20. $16\,\overline{)\,253.12}$

Divide.

21. $25\,\overline{)\,32}$

22. $38\,\overline{)\,682.1}$

Answers

19. 48.9 **20.** 15.82
21. 1.28 **22.** 17.95

EXAMPLE 10 Divide: $83.79 \div 0.098$.

a)

$$0.0\,9\,8_{\wedge}\overline{)\,8\,3.7\,9\,0_{\wedge}}$$

b)

$$\begin{array}{r}
8\,5\,5. \\
0.0\,9\,8_{\wedge}\overline{)\,8\,3.7\,9\,0_{\wedge}} \\
\underline{7\,8\,4} \\
5\,3\,9 \\
\underline{4\,9\,0} \\
4\,9\,0 \\
\underline{4\,9\,0} \\
0
\end{array}$$

Divide.

23. $0.0\,2\,4\,\overline{)\,2\,0.5\,4\,4}$

24. $4.6\,\overline{)\,3.9\,1}$

Do Exercises 23 and 24.

Converting from Fraction Notation to Decimal Notation

To convert from fraction notation to decimal notation when the denominator is not a number like 10, 100, or 1000, we divide the numerator by the denominator.

EXAMPLE 11 Convert to decimal notation: $\frac{5}{16}$.

$$\begin{array}{r}
0.3\,1\,2\,5 \\
1\,6\,\overline{)\,5.0\,0\,0\,0} \\
\underline{4\,8} \\
2\,0 \\
\underline{1\,6} \\
4\,0 \\
\underline{3\,2} \\
8\,0 \\
\underline{8\,0} \\
0
\end{array}$$

If we get a remainder of 0, the decimal *terminates.* Thus, $\frac{5}{16} = 0.3125$.

EXAMPLE 12 Convert to decimal notation: $\frac{7}{12}$.

$$\begin{array}{r}
0.5\,8\,3\,3 \\
1\,2\,\overline{)\,7.0\,0\,0\,0} \\
\underline{6\,0} \\
1\,0\,0 \\
\underline{9\,6} \\
4\,0 \\
\underline{3\,6} \\
4\,0 \\
\underline{3\,6} \\
4
\end{array}$$

The number 4 repeats as a remainder, so the digit 3 will repeat in the quotient. Therefore,

$$\frac{7}{12} = 0.583333\ldots.$$

Instead of dots, we often put a bar over the repeating part—in this case, only the 3. Thus,

$$\frac{7}{12} = 0.58\overline{3}.$$

Convert to decimal notation.

25. $\frac{5}{8}$

26. $\frac{2}{3}$

27. $\frac{84}{11}$

28. $\frac{7}{40}$

Do Exercises 25–28.

Answers

23. 856 24. 0.85 25. 0.625
26. $0.\overline{6}$ 27. $7.\overline{63}$ 28. 0.175

C Rounding

When working with decimal notation in real-life situations, we often shorten notation by **rounding**. Although there are many rules for rounding, we will use the following.

> **ROUNDING DECIMAL NOTATION**
>
> To round to a certain place:
>
> **a)** Locate the digit in that place.
>
> **b)** Consider the digit to its right.
>
> **c)** If the digit to the right is 5 or higher, round up. If the digit to the right is less than 5, round down.

EXAMPLE 13 Round 3872.2459 to the nearest tenth.

a) We locate the digit in the tenths place, 2.

3 8 7 2.2 4 5 9
↑ (under 2)

b) Then we consider the next digit to the right, 4.

3 8 7 2.2 4 5 9
↑ (under 4)

c) Since that digit, 4, is less than 5, we round down.

3 8 7 2.2 ⟵ This is the answer.

EXAMPLE 14 Round 3872.2459 to the nearest thousandth, hundredth, tenth, one, ten, hundred, and thousand.

thousandth:	3872.246
hundredth:	3872.25
tenth:	3872.2
one:	3872
ten:	3870
hundred:	3900
thousand:	4000

Caution!

Each time you round, use the original number.

Do Exercises 29–45.

In rounding, we sometimes use the symbol $\approx$, which means "is approximately equal to." Thus,

$$46.124 \approx 46.1.$$

Round to the nearest tenth.

29. 2.76 **30.** 13.85

31. 7.009 **32.** 272.3446

Round to the nearest hundredth.

33. 7.834 **34.** 34.675

35. 0.025 **36.** 100.9748

Round to the nearest thousandth.

37. 0.9434 **38.** 8.0038

39. 43.1119 **40.** 37.4005

Round 7459.8549 to the nearest:

41. Thousandth.

42. Hundredth.

43. Tenth.

44. One.

45. Ten.

Answers

29. 2.8 **30.** 13.9 **31.** 7.0 **32.** 272.3 **33.** 7.83 **34.** 34.68 **35.** 0.03 **36.** 100.97 **37.** 0.943 **38.** 8.004 **39.** 43.112 **40.** 37.401 **41.** 7459.855 **42.** 7459.85 **43.** 7459.9 **44.** 7460 **45.** 7460

R.3 Exercise Set

For Extra Help MyMathLab — Math XL PRACTICE, WATCH, DOWNLOAD, READ, REVIEW

a Convert to fraction notation. Do not simplify.

1. 5.3

2. 2.7

3. 0.67

4. 0.93

5. 2.0007

6. 4.0008

7. 7889.8

8. 1122.3

Convert to decimal notation.

9. $\frac{1}{10}$

10. $\frac{1}{100}$

11. $\frac{1}{10,000}$

12. $\frac{1}{1000}$

13. $\frac{9999}{1000}$

14. $\frac{39}{10,000}$

15. $\frac{4578}{10,000}$

16. $\frac{94}{100,000}$

b Add.

17. $\begin{array}{r} 415.78 \\ +\ 29.16 \\ \hline \end{array}$

18. $\begin{array}{r} 708.99 \\ +\ 75.48 \\ \hline \end{array}$

19. $\begin{array}{r} 234.000 \\ +\ 156.617 \\ \hline \end{array}$

20. $\begin{array}{r} 1345.12 \\ +\ 566.98 \\ \hline \end{array}$

21. 85 + 67.95 + 2.774

22. 119 + 43.74 + 18.876

23. 17.95 + 16.99 + 28.85

24. 14.59 + 16.79 + 19.95

Subtract.

25. $\begin{array}{r} 78.110 \\ -\ 45.876 \\ \hline \end{array}$

26. $\begin{array}{r} 14.080 \\ -\ 9.199 \\ \hline \end{array}$

27. $\begin{array}{r} 38.7 \\ -\ 11.865 \\ \hline \end{array}$

28. $\begin{array}{r} 300. \\ -\ 24.677 \\ \hline \end{array}$

29. 57.86 − 9.95

30. 2.6 − 1.08

31. 3 − 1.0807

32. 5 − 3.4051

Multiply.

33. $\begin{array}{r} 7.34 \\ \times\ 1.8 \\ \hline \end{array}$

34. $\begin{array}{r} 6.55 \\ \times\ 3.2 \\ \hline \end{array}$

35. $\begin{array}{r} 0.86 \\ \times\ 0.93 \\ \hline \end{array}$

36. $\begin{array}{r} 0.028 \\ \times\ 7.409 \\ \hline \end{array}$

37. $\begin{array}{r} 17.95 \\ \times\ 10 \\ \hline \end{array}$

38. $\begin{array}{r} 18.94 \\ \times\ 0.1 \\ \hline \end{array}$

39. $\begin{array}{r} 0.457 \\ \times\ 3.08 \\ \hline \end{array}$

40. $\begin{array}{r} 0.0024 \\ \times\ 0.015 \\ \hline \end{array}$

41. $\begin{array}{r} 3.642 \\ \times\ 0.99 \\ \hline \end{array}$

42. $\begin{array}{r} 287.4 \\ \times\ 1.08 \\ \hline \end{array}$

Divide.

43. $72\overline{)165.6}$

44. $5.2\overline{)44.2}$

45. $8.5\overline{)44.2}$

46. $7.8\overline{)72.54}$

47. $9.9\overline{)0.2277}$

48. $100\overline{)95}$

49. $0.64\overline{)12}$

50. $1.6\overline{)75}$

51. $1.05\overline{)693}$

52. $25\overline{)4}$

53. $8.6\overline{)5.848}$

54. $0.47\overline{)0.1222}$

Convert to decimal notation.

55. $\frac{11}{32}$

56. $\frac{17}{32}$

57. $\frac{13}{11}$

58. $\frac{17}{12}$

59. $\frac{5}{9}$

60. $\frac{5}{6}$

61. $\frac{19}{9}$

62. $\frac{9}{11}$

c Round to the nearest hundredth, tenth, one, ten, and hundred.

63. 745.06534

64. 317.18565

65. 6780.50568

66. 840.15493

Round to the nearest cent (nearest hundredth) and to the nearest dollar (nearest one).

67. $17.988

68. $20.492

69. $346.075

70. $4.718

Round to the nearest dollar.

71. $16.95

72. $17.50

73. $189.50

74. $567.24

Divide and round to the nearest ten-thousandth, thousandth, hundredth, tenth, and one.

75. $\frac{2}{7}$

76. $\frac{23}{17}$

77. $\frac{23}{39}$

78. $\frac{1000}{81}$

Skill Maintenance

Calculate. [R.2c]

79. $\frac{7}{8} + \frac{5}{32}$

80. $\frac{15}{16} - \frac{11}{12}$

81. $\frac{15}{16} \cdot \frac{11}{12}$

82. $\frac{15}{32} \div \frac{3}{8}$

83. $\frac{9}{70} + \frac{8}{15}$

84. $\frac{11}{21} + \frac{13}{16}$

85. $\frac{9}{10} + \frac{1}{100} + \frac{113}{1000}$

86. $\frac{1}{7} + \frac{4}{21} + \frac{9}{10}$

Find the prime factorization. [R.1a]

87. 208

88. 128

89. 1250

90. 2560

Synthesis

Convert to decimal notation.

91. $\frac{5}{7}$

92. $\frac{8}{13}$

93. $\frac{9}{14}$

94. $\frac{6}{17}$

R.4 Percent Notation

OBJECTIVES

a) Convert from percent notation to decimal notation.

b) Convert from percent notation to fraction notation.

c) Convert from decimal notation to percent notation.

d) Convert from fraction notation to percent notation.

a) Converting to Decimal Notation

Of all retail drug prescriptions, 13.9% are filled in supermarkets. What does this mean? It means that of every 100 prescriptions, 13.9 are filled in supermarkets. Thus, 13.9% is a ratio of 13.9 to 100.

Retail Prescription Drug Sales

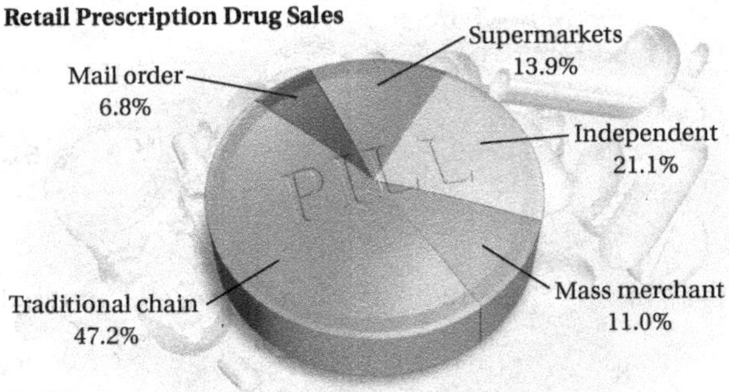

SOURCE: National Association of Chain Drug Stores, Alexandria, VA; *NACDS Foundation Chain Pharmacy Industry Profile*, 2006

The percent symbol % means "per hundred." We can regard the percent symbol as a part of a name for a number. For example,

$$28\% \quad \text{is defined to mean} \quad 28 \times 0.01, \quad \text{or} \quad 28 \times \frac{1}{100}, \quad \text{or} \quad \frac{28}{100}.$$

NOTATION FOR $n\%$

$$n\% \quad \text{means} \quad n \times 0.01, \quad \text{or} \quad n \times \frac{1}{100}, \quad \text{or} \quad \frac{n}{100}.$$

EXAMPLE 1 *Retail Drug Prescriptions.* Of all retail drug prescriptions, 6.8% are filled by mail order. Convert 6.8% to decimal notation.

$6.8\% = 6.8 \times 0.01$ Replacing % with $\times$ 0.01

$= 0.068$

FROM PERCENT NOTATION TO DECIMAL NOTATION

To convert from percent notation to decimal notation, move the decimal point *two* places to the *left* and drop the percent symbol.

EXAMPLE 2 Convert 43.67% to decimal notation.

43.67% 0.43.67 43.67% = 0.4367

Move the decimal point two places to the left.

Do Exercises 1–3.

1. **Food Prices.** Inflation in food prices averaged only 2.1% per year from 1996 to 2006. From June 2007 to June 2008, this inflation was 6.1%. Convert 2.1% and 6.1% to decimal notation.
Source: *AARP Bulletin*, September 2008, "Going Hungry in America," by Peter Jaret

Convert to decimal notation.

2. 100%
3. 66.67%

Answers

1. 0.021; 0.061 2. 1 3. 0.6667

b Converting to Fraction Notation

EXAMPLE 3 Convert 88% to fraction notation.

$$88\% = 88 \times \frac{1}{100} \qquad \text{Replacing \% with } \times \frac{1}{100}$$
$$= \frac{88}{100} \qquad \text{Multiplying. You need not simplify.}$$

EXAMPLE 4 Convert 34.8% to fraction notation.

$$34.8\% = 34.8 \times \frac{1}{100} \qquad \text{Replacing \% with } \times \frac{1}{100}$$
$$= \frac{34.8}{100}$$
$$= \frac{34.8}{100} \cdot \frac{10}{10} \qquad \text{Multiplying by 1 to get a whole number in the numerator}$$
$$= \frac{348}{1000} \qquad \text{You need not simplify.}$$

Do Exercises 4–8.

4. Number of Bedrooms. In 2007, 35% of new single-family homes had 4 or more bedrooms. Convert 35% to fraction notation.
Source: U.S. Census Bureau

Convert to fraction notation.

5. 53% **6.** 45.9%

7. 0.23% **8.** 4.375%

c Converting from Decimal Notation

By applying the definition of percent in reverse, we can convert from decimal notation to percent notation. We multiply by 1, expressing it as 100 × 0.01 and replacing × 0.01 with %.

EXAMPLE 5 *Foreign-Born Residents.* In 2007, 0.349 of the residents of Los Angeles were foreign-born. Convert 0.349 to percent notation.
Sources: U.S. Census Bureau; *USA TODAY*

$$0.349 = 0.349 \times 1 \qquad \text{Identity property of 1}$$
$$= 0.349 \times (100 \times 0.01) \qquad \text{Expressing 1 as } 100 \times 0.01$$
$$= (0.349 \times 100) \times 0.01$$
$$= 34.9 \times 0.01$$
$$= 34.9\% \qquad \text{Replacing } \times 0.01 \text{ with \%}$$

FROM DECIMAL NOTATION TO PERCENT NOTATION

To convert from decimal notation to percent notation, move the decimal point *two* places to the *right* and write the percent symbol.

EXAMPLE 6 Convert 0.082 to percent notation.

0.082 0.08.2 0.082 = 8.2%

Move the decimal point two places to the right.

Do Exercises 9–11.

9. Foreign-Born Residents. In 2007, 0.087 of the residents of Detroit were foreign-born. Convert 0.087 to percent notation.
Sources: U.S. Census Bureau; *USA TODAY*

Convert to percent notation.

10. 6.77 **11.** 0.9944

d Converting from Fraction Notation

We can convert from fraction notation to percent notation by converting first to decimal notation. Then we move the decimal point two places to the *right* and write a percent symbol.

Answers

4. $\frac{35}{100}$ **5.** $\frac{53}{100}$ **6.** $\frac{459}{1000}$ **7.** $\frac{23}{10{,}000}$
8. $\frac{4375}{100{,}000}$ **9.** 8.7% **10.** 677%
11. 99.44%

EXAMPLE 7 Convert $\frac{5}{8}$ to percent notation.

a) We first find decimal notation for $\frac{5}{8}$ using long division.

$$\begin{array}{r} 0.6\,2\,5 \\ 8\,\overline{)\,5.0\,0\,0} \\ \underline{4\,8} \\ 2\,0 \\ \underline{1\,6} \\ 4\,0 \\ \underline{4\,0} \\ 0 \end{array}$$

Thus, $\frac{5}{8} = 0.625$.

b) We then convert the decimal notation to percent notation by moving the decimal point two places to the right and writing the percent symbol.

$$0.62.5 \qquad \frac{5}{8} = 62.5\%, \text{ or } 62\frac{1}{2}\% \qquad 0.5 = \frac{5}{10} = \frac{1}{2}$$

EXAMPLE 8 Convert $\frac{227}{150}$ to percent notation.

a) We first find decimal notation for $\frac{227}{150}$ using long division.

$$\begin{array}{r} 1.5\,1\,3\,3\,\ldots \\ 150\,\overline{)\,2\,2\,7.0\,0\,0\,0\,0} \\ \underline{1\,5\,0} \\ 7\,7\,0 \\ \underline{7\,5\,0} \\ 2\,0\,0 \\ \underline{1\,5\,0} \\ 5\,0\,0 \\ \underline{4\,5\,0} \\ 5\,0\,0 \\ \underline{4\,5\,0} \\ 5\,0 \end{array}$$

We get a repeating decimal: $1.51\overline{3}$.

b) Next, we convert the decimal notation to percent notation by moving the decimal point two places to the right and writing the percent symbol.

$$1.51.\overline{3} \qquad \frac{227}{150} = 151.\overline{3}\%, \text{ or } 151\frac{1}{3}\% \qquad 0.\overline{3} = \frac{1}{3}$$

Do Exercises 12–15.

EXAMPLE 9 *Pet Food.* Of the \$38.5 billion spent on pets in 2006, approximately $\frac{6}{25}$ was spent on food. Convert $\frac{6}{25}$ to percent notation.

Source: American Pet Products Manufacturers Association

We can use long division. Or, since $4 \cdot 25 = 100$, we can multiply by a form of 1 to obtain 100 in the denominator:

$$\frac{6}{25} = \frac{6}{25} \cdot \frac{4}{4} = \frac{24}{100} = 24 \times \frac{1}{100} = 24\%.$$

Do Exercise 16.

Convert to percent notation.

12. $\frac{1}{8}$ **13.** $\frac{436}{75}$

14. $\frac{7}{16}$ **15.** $\frac{5}{12}$

16. Passports. In 2007, $\frac{3}{10}$ of all Americans had passports. Convert $\frac{3}{10}$ to percent notation.
Sources: Associated Press; *Time*, January 14, 2008

Answers

12. 12.5%, or $12\frac{1}{2}\%$ **13.** $581.\overline{3}\%$, or $581\frac{1}{3}\%$
14. 43.75%, or $43\frac{3}{4}\%$ **15.** $41.\overline{6}\%$, or $41\frac{2}{3}\%$
16. 30%

R.4 Exercise Set

For Extra Help

MyMathLab | Math XL PRACTICE | WATCH | DOWNLOAD | READ | REVIEW

a Convert the percent notation in each sentence to decimal notation.

1. *Walking to Work.* In Boston, 13% of commuters walk to work.
Source: SustainLane

2. *Hospital Patients.* The average age of hospital patients in the United States is 52.5 years old. Those 75 and older make up 24% of the patient population.
Source: U.S. Centers for Disease Control and Prevention

3. *Under 15 Years Old.* It is projected that by 2010, 35.1% of the population in Pakistan will be under 15 years old. In the United States, 20.0% will be under 15 years old.
Source: U.S. Census Bureau

4. *65 Years and Older.* It is projected that by 2010, 4.4% of the population of Pakistan will be 65 years and older. In the United States, 13.0% will be 65 years and older.
Source: U.S. Census Bureau

Convert to decimal notation.

5. 63%

6. 64%

7. 94.1%

8. 34.6%

9. 1%

10. 100%

11. 0.61%

12. 125%

13. 240%

14. 0.73%

15. 3.25%

16. 2.3%

b Convert the percent notation in each sentence to fraction notation.

17. *Lunch Break.* Of all corporate executives, 39% have 30 min or less for a lunch break.
Source: OfficeTeam Survey

18. *College Applications.* About 71% of high school graduates who apply to colleges submit three or more college applications.
Source: Higher Education Research Institute, UCLA

19. *Women in Space.* As of March 2008, the number of women who had flown in space was about 10.5% of all astronauts who had flown in space.
Source: *Time*, March 24, 2008

20. *Army.* Approximately 36.5% of the U.S. Armed Forces are enlisted in the Army.
Source: U.S. Department of Defense Personnel, 2006

21. *Fluent in English.* Of all second-generation Latinos in the United States, 88% are fluent in English.
Source: Pew Research Center

22. *Melanoma.* The number of melanoma cancer cases rose 31% from 2000 to 2008.
Source: American Cancer Society

Convert to fraction notation.

23. 60%

24. 40%

25. 28.9%

26. 37.5%

27. 110%

28. 120%

29. 0.042%

30. 0.68%

31. 250%

32. 3.2%

33. 3.47%

34. 12.557%

c Convert the decimal notation in each sentence to percent notation.

35. *Realtor Income.* From 2006 to 2007, the median income for realtors fell 0.107.

Source: National Association of Realtors

36. *Level of Education.* In Utah, 0.912 of the population 25 years and older are high school graduates, and 0.27 have a bachelor's degree or more.

Source: U.S. Census Bureau

37. *Private Schools.* In the United States, 0.14 of school-age children attend private schools.

Source: National Center for Education Statistics

38. *Eating and Drinking in Vehicles.* In a recent survey, 0.21 of adult drivers said that they prohibit eating and drinking in their vehicles.

Source: Kelton Research for YES Essentials

Convert to percent notation.

39. 0.99

40. 0.83

41. 1

42. 8.56

43. 0.0047

44. 2

45. 0.072

46. 1.34

47. 9.2

48. 0.013

49. 0.0068

50. 0.675

d Convert to percent notation.

51. $\frac{1}{6}$

52. $\frac{1}{5}$

53. $\frac{13}{20}$

54. $\frac{14}{25}$

55. $\frac{29}{100}$

56. $\frac{123}{100}$

57. $\frac{8}{10}$

58. $\frac{7}{10}$

59. $\frac{3}{5}$

60. $\frac{17}{50}$

61. $\frac{2}{3}$

62. $\frac{7}{8}$

63. $\frac{7}{4}$

64. $\frac{3}{8}$

65. $\frac{3}{4}$

66. $\frac{99.4}{100}$

Convert the fraction notation in each sentence to percent notation.

67. *Checking e-Mail.* The longest that approximately $\frac{2}{5}$ of workers with personal digital assistants (PDAs) go without checking their e-mail is less than 30 min.
Source: Studylogic for Starwood Hotels and Resorts/Sheraton

68. *Truck Drivers.* Of all truck drivers, $\frac{11}{50}$ spend 40 or more weeks per year on the road.
Source: Atlas Van Lines Survey

a, b, c, d *Women at Work.* The table below lists the percentages of people in various professions who are women. Fill in the blanks in the table.

WOMEN IN THE WORKPLACE

	PROFESSION	DECIMAL NOTATION	FRACTION NOTATION	PERCENT NOTATION
69.	Firefighter			4%
70.	Computer programmer			25%
71.	Insurance underwriter	0.69		
72.	Dietician/nutritionist	0.91		
73.	Pharmacist		$\frac{49}{100}$	
74.	Clergy		$\frac{13}{100}$	
75.	Postal-service mail carrier			36%
76.	Physician/surgeon			32%

SOURCE: *Statistical Abstract of the United States*, 2008

Skill Maintenance

Convert to decimal notation. [R.3b]

77. $\frac{9}{4}$

78. $\frac{17}{11}$

Calculate. [R.3b]

79. 23.458×7.03

80. $7.8\overline{)440.154}$

Synthesis

Simplify. Express the answer in percent notation.

81. $18\% + 14\%$

82. $84\% - 12\%$

83. $1 - 30\%$

84. $50\% - 0.5\%$

85. $1 + 5\%$

86. $42\% - (1 - 58\%)$

87. $3(1 + 15\%)$

88. $7(1\% + 13\%)$

89. $\frac{100\%}{40}$

90. $\frac{3}{4} + 20\%$

R.5 Exponential Notation and Order of Operations

OBJECTIVES

a) Write exponential notation for a product.

b) Evaluate exponential expressions.

c) Simplify expressions using the rules for order of operations.

a) Exponential Notation

Exponents provide a shorter way of writing products. An abbreviation for a product in which the factors are the same is called a **power**. An expression for a power is called **exponential notation**. For

$$\underbrace{10 \cdot 10 \cdot 10}_{3 \text{ factors}}, \quad \text{we write} \quad 10^3.$$

This is read "ten to the third power." We call the number 3 an **exponent** and we say that 10 is the **base**. For example,

$$a \cdot a \cdot a \cdot a = a^4.$$

This is the exponent. (4)
This is the base. (a)

An exponent of 2 or greater tells how many times the base is used as a factor.

EXPONENTIAL NOTATION

For any natural number n greater than or equal to 2,

$$b^n = \overbrace{b \cdot b \cdot b \cdot b \cdots b}^{n \text{ factors}}.$$

Write exponential notation.

1. $4 \cdot 4 \cdot 4$
2. $6 \cdot 6 \cdot 6 \cdot 6 \cdot 6$
3. 1.08×1.08

EXAMPLE 1 Write exponential notation for $10 \cdot 10 \cdot 10 \cdot 10 \cdot 10$.

$$10 \cdot 10 \cdot 10 \cdot 10 \cdot 10 = 10^5$$

Do Exercises 1–3.

b) Evaluating Exponential Expressions

Evaluate.

4. 10^4
5. 8^3
6. $(1.1)^3$
7. $\left(\frac{2}{9}\right)^2$

EXAMPLE 2 Evaluate: 3^4.

We have

$$3^4 = 3 \cdot 3 \cdot 3 \cdot 3 = 9 \cdot 9 = 81.$$

Do Exercises 4–7.

c) Order of Operations

What does $4 + 5 \times 2$ mean? If we add 4 and 5 and multiply the result by 2, we get 18. If we multiply 5 and 2 and add 4 to the result, we get 14. Since the results are different, we see that the order in which we carry out operations is important. To indicate which operation is to be done first, we use grouping symbols such as parentheses ( ), or brackets [ ], or braces { }. For example, $(3 \times 5) + 6 = 15 + 6 = 21$, but $3 \times (5 + 6) = 3 \times 11 = 33$.

Answers

1. 4^3 2. 6^5 3. 1.08^2 4. 10,000 5. 512 6. 1.331 7. $\frac{4}{81}$

Grouping symbols tell us what to do first. If there are no grouping symbols, there is a set of rules for the order in which operations should be done.

RULES FOR ORDER OF OPERATIONS

1. Do all calculations within grouping symbols before operations outside.
2. Evaluate all exponential expressions.
3. Do all multiplications and divisions in order from left to right.
4. Do all additions and subtractions in order from left to right.

EXAMPLE 3 Calculate: $15 - 2 \times 5 + 3$.

$15 - 2 \times 5 + 3 = 15 - 10 + 3$		Multiplying
	$= 5 + 3$	Subtracting
	$= 8$	Adding

Do Exercises 8 and 9.

Always calculate within parentheses first. When there are exponents and no parentheses, simplify powers first.

EXAMPLE 4 Calculate: $(3 \times 4)^2$.

$(3 \times 4)^2 = (12)^2$		Working within parentheses first
	$= 144$	Evaluating the exponential expression

EXAMPLE 5 Calculate: 3×4^2.

$3 \times 4^2 = 3 \times 16$		Evaluating the exponential expression
	$= 48$	Multiplying

Note that Examples 4 and 5 show that $(3 \times 4)^2 \neq 3 \times 4^2$.

EXAMPLE 6 Calculate: $7 + 3 \times 29 - 4^2$.

$7 + 3 \times 29 - 4^2 = 7 + 3 \times 29 - 16$		There are no parentheses, so we find 4^2 first.
	$= 7 + 87 - 16$	Multiplying
	$= 94 - 16$	Adding
	$= 78$	Subtracting

Do Exercises 10–13.

EXAMPLE 7 Calculate: $100 \div 20 \div 2$.

$100 \div 20 \div 2 = 5 \div 2$		Doing the divisions in order from left to right
	$= \frac{5}{2}$, or 2.5	Doing the second division

Calculator Corner

Exponents and Powers We use the [^] key to evaluate exponential notation on a graphing calculator. To find 3^5, for example, we press [3] [^] [5] [ENTER]. To find $\left(\frac{5}{8}\right)^3$ and express the result in fraction notation, we press [(] [5] [÷] [8] [)] [^] [3] [MATH] [1] [ENTER]. Note that the parentheses are necessary in this calculation.

The calculator has a special [x^2] key that can be used to raise a number to the second power. To find 2.4^2, for example, we press [2] [.] [4] [x^2] [ENTER].

```
3^5
                 243
(5/8)^3►Frac
             125/512
2.4²
                5.76
2.4^2
                5.76
```

Exercises: Evaluate.

1. 7^9
2. 1.8^4
3. 23.4^3
4. $\left(\frac{2}{3}\right)^6$

Calculate.

8. $16 - 3 \times 5 + 4$
9. $4 + 5 \times 2$

Calculate.

10. $18 - 4 \times 3 + 7$
11. $(2 \times 5)^3$
12. 2×5^3
13. $8 + 2 \times 5^3 - 4 \cdot 20$

Answers

8. 5 **9.** 14 **10.** 13
11. 1000 **12.** 250 **13.** 178

EXAMPLE 8 Calculate: $1000 \div \frac{1}{10} \cdot \frac{4}{5}$.

$$1000 \div \frac{1}{10} \cdot \frac{4}{5} = (1000 \cdot 10) \cdot \frac{4}{5} \quad \text{Doing the division first}$$
$$= 10{,}000 \cdot \frac{4}{5} \quad \text{Multiplying inside the parentheses}$$
$$= 8000 \quad \text{Multiplying}$$

Do Exercises 14 and 15.

Calculate.

14. $51.2 \div 0.64 \div 40$

15. $1000 \cdot \frac{1}{10} \div \frac{4}{5}$

Sometimes combinations of grouping symbols are used. The rules still apply. We begin with the innermost grouping symbols and work to the outside.

EXAMPLE 9 Calculate: $5[4 + (8 - 2)]$.

$$5[4 + (8 - 2)] = 5[4 + 6] \quad \text{Subtracting within the parentheses first}$$
$$= 5[10] \quad \text{Adding inside the brackets}$$
$$= 50 \quad \text{Multiplying}$$

A fraction bar can play the role of a grouping symbol.

EXAMPLE 10 Calculate: $\frac{12(9 - 7) + 4 \cdot 5}{3^3 - 2^4}$.

We do the calculations separately in the numerator and in the denominator, and then divide the results:

$$\frac{12(9 - 7) + 4 \cdot 5}{3^3 - 2^4} = \frac{12(2) + 4 \cdot 5}{27 - 16} = \frac{24 + 20}{11} = \frac{44}{11} = 4.$$

Do Exercises 16 and 17.

Calculate.

16. $4[(8 - 3) + 7]$

17. $\frac{13(10 - 6) + 4 \cdot 9}{5^2 - 3^2}$

Calculator Corner

Order of Operations Computations are generally entered on a graphing calculator as they are written. To calculate $3 + 4 \cdot 2$, for example, we press 3 + 4 × 2 ENTER. The result is 11.

We enter grouping symbols (parentheses, brackets, and braces) using the (and) keys. To calculate $7(13 - 2) - 40$, we press 7 (1 3 − 2) − 4 0 ENTER. The result is 37.

We indicate that a fraction bar acts as a grouping symbol by enclosing both the numerator and the denominator in parentheses. To calculate $\frac{38 + 142}{47 - 2}$, for example, we rewrite it with grouping symbols as $(38 + 142) \div (47 - 2)$. We press (3 8 + 1 4 2) ÷ (4 7 − 2) ENTER. The result is 4.

3+4*2	
	11
7(13−2)−40	
	37
(38+142)/(47−2)	
	4

Exercises: Calculate.

1. $68 - 8 \div 4 + 3 \cdot 5$

2. $\frac{311 - 17^2}{13 - 2}$

3. $(15 + 3)^3 + 4(12 - 7)^2$

4. $3.2 + 4.7[159.3 - 2.1(60.3 - 59.4)]$

5. $785 - \frac{5^4 - 285}{17 + 3 \cdot 51}$

6. $12^5 - 12^4 + 11^5 \div 11^3 - 10.2^2$

Answers

14. 2 **15.** 125 **16.** 48 **17.** $\frac{11}{2}$

R.5 Exercise Set

For Extra Help MyMathLab: MathXL PRACTICE, WATCH, DOWNLOAD, READ, REVIEW

a Write exponential notation.

1. $5 \times 5 \times 5 \times 5$

2. $3 \times 3 \times 3 \times 3 \times 3$

3. $10 \cdot 10 \cdot 10$

4. $1 \cdot 1 \cdot 1$

5. $10 \times 10 \times 10 \times 10 \times 10 \times 10$

6. $18 \cdot 18$

b Evaluate.

7. 7^2

8. 4^3

9. 9^5

10. 12^4

11. 10^2

12. 1^5

13. 1^4

14. $(1.8)^2$

15. $(2.3)^2$

16. $(0.1)^3$

17. $(0.2)^3$

18. $(14.8)^2$

19. $(20.4)^2$

20. $\left(\frac{4}{5}\right)^2$

21. $\left(\frac{3}{8}\right)^2$

22. 2^4

23. 5^3

24. $(1.4)^3$

25. $1000 \times (1.02)^3$

26. $2000 \times (1.06)^2$

c Calculate.

27. $9 + 2 \times 8$

28. $14 + 6 \times 6$

29. $9(8) + 7(6)$

30. $30(5) + 2(2)$

31. $39 - 4 \times 2 + 2$

32. $14 - 2 \times 6 + 7$

33. $9 \div 3 + 16 \div 8$

34. $32 - 8 \div 4 - 2$

35. $7 + 10 - 10 \div 2$

36. $(5 \cdot 4)^2$

37. $(6 \cdot 3)^2$

38. $3 \cdot 2^3$

39. $4 \cdot 5^2$

40. $(7 + 3)^2$

41. $(8 + 2)^3$

42. $7 + 2^2$

43. $6 + 4^2$

44. $(5 - 2)^2$

45. $(3 - 2)^2$

46. $10 - 3^2$

47. $4^3 \div 8 - 4$

48. $20 + 4^3 \div 8 - 4$

49. $120 - 3^3 \cdot 4 \div 6$

50. $7 \times 3^4 + 18$

51. $6[9 + (3 + 4)]$

52. $8[(13 + 6) - 11]$

53. $8 + (7 + 9)$

54. $(8 + 7) + 9$

55. $15(4 + 2)$

56. $15 \cdot 4 + 15 \cdot 2$

57. $12 - (8 - 4)$

58. $(12 - 8) - 4$

59. $1000 \div 100 \div 10$

60. $256 \div 32 \div 4$

61. $2000 \div \frac{3}{50} \cdot \frac{3}{2}$

62. $400 \times 0.64 \div 3.2$

63. $75 \div 15 \cdot 4 \cdot 8 \div 32$

64. $84 \div 12 \cdot 10 \div 35 \cdot 8 \cdot 2 \div 16$

65. $16 \cdot 5 \div 80 \div 12 \cdot 36 \cdot 9$

66. $20 \cdot 45 \div 15 \div 15 \cdot 60 \div 12$

67. $\frac{80 - 6^2}{9^2 + 3^2}$

68. $\frac{5^2 + 4^3 - 3}{9^2 - 2^2 + 1^5}$

69. $\frac{3(6 + 7) - 5 \cdot 4}{6 \cdot 7 + 8(4 - 1)}$

70. $\frac{20(8 - 3) - 4(10 - 3)}{10(6 + 2) + 2(5 + 2)}$

71. $8 \cdot 2 - (12 - 0) \div 3 - (5 - 2)$

72. $95 - 2^3 \cdot 5 \div (24 - 4)$

Skill Maintenance

Find percent notation. [R.4d]

73. $\frac{5}{16}$

74. $\frac{11}{6}$

Simplify. [R.2b]

75. $\frac{9}{2001}$

76. $\frac{2005}{3640}$

77. Find the prime factorization of 48. [R.1a]

78. Find the LCM of 12, 24, and 56. [R.1b]

Synthesis

Write each of the following with a single exponent.

79. $\frac{10^5}{10^3}$

80. $\frac{10^7}{10^2}$

81. $5^4 \cdot 5^2$

82. $\frac{2^8}{8^2}$

83. *Five 5's.* We can use five 5's and grouping symbols to represent the numbers 0 through 10. For example,

$$0 = 5 \cdot 5 \cdot 5(5 - 5), \quad 1 = \frac{5 + 5}{5} - \frac{5}{5}, \quad 2 = \frac{5 \cdot 5 - 5}{5 + 5}.$$

Often more than one representation is possible. Use five 5's to represent the numbers 3 through 10.

CHAPTER R

Summary and Review

Key Terms, Properties, and Formulas

natural numbers, p. 2
factor (verb), p. 2
factor (noun), p. 2
factorization, p. 2
prime number, p. 2
composite number, p. 3
prime factorization, p. 3
multiples, p. 4
least common multiple (LCM), p. 4
fraction notation, p. 8
numerator, p. 8
denominator, p. 8
whole numbers, p. 8
arithmetic numbers, p. 8
nonnegative rational numbers, p. 8
equivalent expressions, p. 8
least common denominator, p. 12
reciprocals, p. 14
multiplicative inverses, p. 14
decimal notation, p. 18
percent notation, $n\%$, p. 26
power, p. 32
exponent, p. 32
base, p. 32
exponential notation, p. 32

Identity Property of 0: $a + 0 = a$

Identity Property of 1: $a \cdot 1 = a$

Equivalent Expressions for 1: $\frac{a}{a} = 1,\ a \neq 0$

$n\% = n \times 0.01 = n \times \frac{1}{100} = \frac{n}{100}$

Exponential Notation: $a^n = \underbrace{a \cdot a \cdot a \cdots a}_{n \text{ factors}}$

Perimeter of a Rectangle: $P = 2 \cdot (l + w)$, or $P = 2 \cdot l + 2 \cdot w$

Perimeter of a Square: $P = 4 \cdot s$

Area of a Rectangle: $A = l \cdot w$

Area of a Square: $A = s \cdot s$, or $A = s^2$

Area of a Parallelogram: $A = b \cdot h$

Area of a Triangle: $A = \frac{1}{2} \cdot b \cdot h$

Radius and Diameter of a Circle: $d = 2 \cdot r$, or $r = \frac{d}{2}$

Circumference of a Circle: $C = \pi \cdot d$, or $C = 2 \cdot \pi \cdot r$

Area of a Circle: $A = \pi \cdot r \cdot r$, or $A = \pi \cdot r^2$

Volume of a Rectangular Solid: $V = l \cdot w \cdot h$

Concept Reinforcement

Determine whether each statement is true or false.

________ **1.** The least common multiple of two numbers is always larger than or equal to the larger number. [R.1b]

________ **2.** To convert from decimal notation to percent notation, move the decimal point two places to the left and write the percent symbol. [R.4c]

________ **3.** The number 1 is not prime. [R.1a]

Review Exercises

The review exercises that follow are for practice. Answers are at the back of the book. If you miss an exercise, restudy the objective indicated in red next to the exercise or direction line that precedes it.

Find the prime factorization. [R.1a]

1. 92

2. 1400

Find the LCM. [R.1b]

3. 13, 32

4. 5, 18, 45

Write an equivalent expression using the indicated number for 1. [R.2a]

5. $\frac{2}{5}$ $\left(\text{Use } \frac{6}{6} \text{ for } 1.\right)$

6. $\frac{12}{23}$ $\left(\text{Use } \frac{8}{8} \text{ for } 1.\right)$

Write an equivalent expression with the given denominator. [R.2a]

7. $\frac{5}{8}$ (Denominator: 64)

8. $\frac{13}{12}$ (Denominator: 84)

Simplify. [R.2b]

9. $\frac{20}{48}$

10. $\frac{1020}{1820}$

Compute and simplify. [R.2c]

11. $\frac{4}{9} + \frac{5}{12}$

12. $\frac{3}{4} \div 3$

13. $\frac{2}{3} - \frac{1}{15}$

14. $\frac{9}{10} \cdot \frac{16}{5}$

15. $\frac{11}{18} + \frac{13}{16}$

16. $\frac{35}{36} + \frac{23}{24}$

17. $\frac{25}{27} + \frac{17}{18}$

18. $\frac{29}{42} + \frac{17}{28}$

19. $\frac{35}{36} - \frac{19}{24}$

20. $\frac{13}{16} - \frac{11}{18}$

21. $\frac{29}{42} - \frac{17}{28}$

22. $\frac{11}{36} - \frac{1}{20}$

23. Convert to fraction notation: 17.97. [R.3a]

24. Convert to decimal notation: $\frac{2337}{10{,}000}$. [R.3a]

Add. [R.3b]

25. $\begin{array}{r} 2344.56 \\ +\ \ \ 98.345 \\ \hline \end{array}$

26. 6.04 + 78 + 1.9898

Subtract. [R.3b]

27. 20.4 − 11.058

28. $\begin{array}{r} 789.032 \\ -\ 655.768 \\ \hline \end{array}$

Multiply. [R.3b]

29. $\begin{array}{r} 17.95 \\ \times\ \ \ \ 24 \\ \hline \end{array}$

30. $\begin{array}{r} 56.95 \\ \times\ \ 1.94 \\ \hline \end{array}$

Divide. [R.3b]

31. $2.8 \overline{)\,155.68}$

32. $52 \overline{)\,23.4}$

33. Convert to decimal notation: $\frac{19}{12}$. [R.3b]

34. Round to the nearest tenth: 34.067. [R.3c]

35. *Population of Africa.* In 2008, the population of the world was 6,835,000,000. About 14.2% of the world population is in Africa. Convert 14.2% to decimal notation. [R.4a]

Source: U.S. Census Bureau

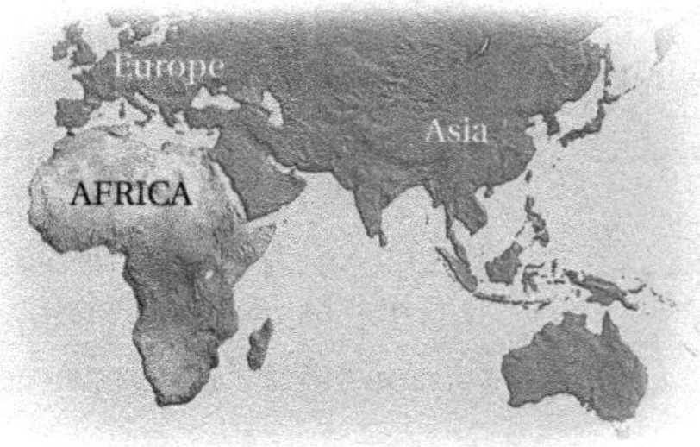

36. *Farms in Missouri.* Of all the farms in the United States, 0.0502 of them are in Missouri. Convert 0.0502 to percent notation. [R.4c]

Source: U.S. Department of Agriculture, National Agricultural Statistics Service

37. *Blood Type.* In the United States, 35.7% of the population has blood type A, Rh positive. Convert 35.7% to fraction notation. [R.4b]

Source: Stanford School of Medicine, Blood Center

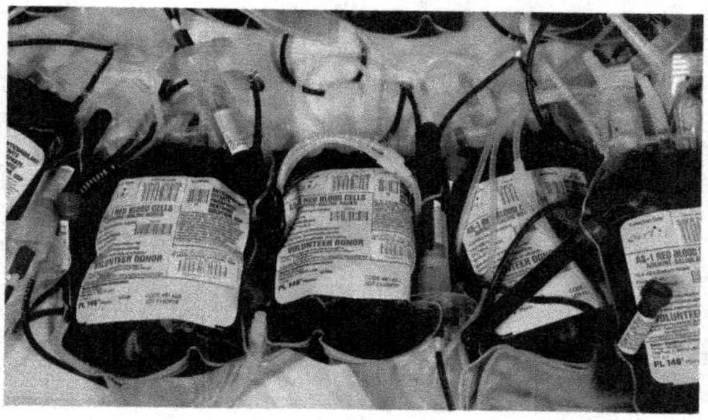

38. *Soccer.* Of Americans 12 to 17 years old, 396 of every 1000 have played soccer. Convert $\frac{396}{1000}$ to percent notation. [R.4d]

Source: ESPN Sports Poll, a service of TNS Sport

Convert to percent notation. [R.4d]

39. $\frac{5}{8}$

40. $\frac{29}{25}$

41. Write exponential notation: $6 \cdot 6 \cdot 6$. [R.5a]

42. Evaluate: $(1.06)^2$. [R.5b]

Calculate. [R.5c]

43. $120 - 6^2 \div 4 + 8$

44. $64 \div 16 \cdot 32 \div 48 \div 12 \cdot 18$

45. $(120 - 6^2) \div 4 + 8$

46. $64 \cdot 16 \div 32 \div 48 \div 12 \cdot 18$

47. $(120 - 6^2) \div (4 + 8)$

48. $8^2 \cdot 2^4 \div 2^2 \cdot 8 \div 48 \div 12 \cdot 18$

49. Calculate: $\frac{4(18 - 8) + 7 \cdot 9}{9^2 - 8^2}$. [R.5c]

CHAPTER

R Test

For Extra Help

CHAPTER Test Prep VIDEOS

Step-by-step test solutions are found on the Chapter Test Prep Videos available via the Video Resources on DVD, in MyMathLab, and on YouTube (search "BittingerIntroAlg" and click on "Channels").

1. Find the prime factorization of 300.

2. Find the LCM of 15, 24, and 60.

3. Write an expression equivalent to $\frac{3}{7}$ using $\frac{7}{7}$ as a name for 1.

4. Write an expression equivalent to $\frac{11}{16}$ with a denominator of 48.

Simplify.

5. $\dfrac{16}{24}$

6. $\dfrac{925}{1525}$

Compute and simplify.

7. $\dfrac{10}{27} \div \dfrac{8}{3}$

8. $\dfrac{9}{10} - \dfrac{5}{8}$

9. $\dfrac{11}{12} + \dfrac{17}{18}$

10. $\dfrac{10}{27} \cdot \dfrac{3}{8}$

11. Convert to fraction notation (do not simplify): 6.78.

12. Convert to decimal notation: $\dfrac{1895}{1000}$.

13. Add: $7.14 + 89 + 2.8787$.

14. Subtract: $1800 - 3.42$.

15. Multiply: $\begin{array}{r} 123.6 \\ \times \quad 3.52 \\ \hline \end{array}$

16. Divide: $7.2 \overline{)\,11.52}$

17. Convert to decimal notation: $\dfrac{23}{11}$.

18. Round 234.7284 to the nearest tenth.

19. Round 234.7284 to the nearest thousandth.

20. Convert to decimal notation: 0.7%.

21. Convert to fraction notation: 91%.

22. Convert to percent notation: $\dfrac{11}{25}$.

23. Evaluate: 5^4.

24. Evaluate: $(1.2)^2$.

25. Calculate: $200 - 2^3 + 5 \times 10$.

26. Calculate: $8000 \div 0.16 \div 2.5$.

27. *Home Equity Loan Rate.* A recent bank promotion offered a home equity loan at a low interest rate of 5.4%. Convert 5.4% to decimal notation.

28. *Dermatologists.* Of the 902,100 doctors in the United States, 12 of every 1000 are dermatologists. Convert $\frac{12}{1000}$ to percent notation.

Source: American Medical Association

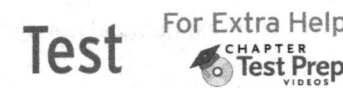

Introduction to Real Numbers and Algebraic Expressions

CHAPTER

1

Real-World Application

The tallest mountain in the world, when measured from base to peak, is Mauna Kea (White Mountain) in Hawaii. From its base 19,684 ft below sea level in the Hawaiian Trough, it rises 33,480 ft. What is the elevation of the peak above sea level?

Source: The Guinness Book of Records

This problem appears as Exercise 71 in Exercise Set 1.3.

1.1 Introduction to Algebra

OBJECTIVES

a Evaluate algebraic expressions by substitution.

b Translate phrases to algebraic expressions.

The study of algebra involves the use of equations to solve problems. Equations are constructed from algebraic expressions. The purpose of this section is to introduce you to the types of expressions encountered in algebra.

a Evaluating Algebraic Expressions

In arithmetic, you have worked with expressions such as

$$49 + 75, \quad 8 \times 6.07, \quad 29 - 14, \quad \text{and} \quad \frac{5}{6}.$$

In algebra, we can use letters to represent numbers and work with *algebraic expressions* such as

$$x + 75, \quad 8 \times y, \quad 29 - t, \quad \text{and} \quad \frac{a}{b}.$$

Mountain Peaks in the United States

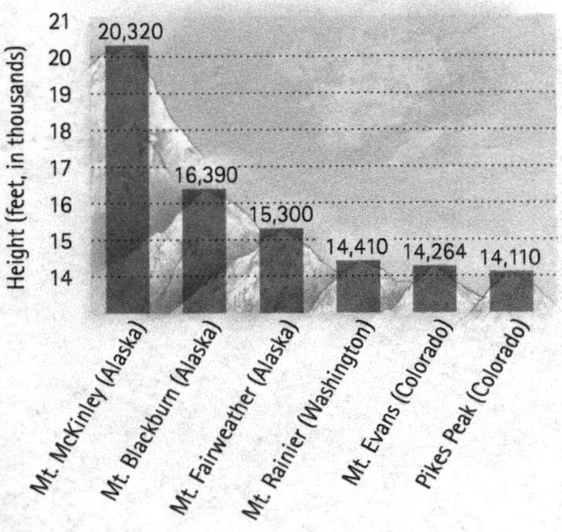

SOURCE: U.S. Department of the Interior, Geological Survey

Sometimes a letter can represent various numbers. In that case, we call the letter a **variable**. Let a = your age. Then a is a variable since a changes from year to year. Sometimes a letter can stand for just one number. In that case, we call the letter a **constant**. Let b = your date of birth. Then b is a constant.

Where do algebraic expressions occur? Most often we encounter them when we are solving applied problems. For example, consider the bar graph shown at left, one that we might find in a book or a magazine. Suppose we want to know how much higher Mt. McKinley is than Mt. Evans. Using arithmetic, we might simply subtract. But let's see how we can determine this using algebra. We translate the problem into a statement of equality, an equation. It could be done as follows:

Height of Mt. Evans	plus	How much more	is	Height of Mt. McKinley
↓	↓	↓	↓	↓
14,264	+	x	=	20,320.

Note that we have an algebraic expression, $14{,}264 + x$, on the left of the equals sign. To find the number x, we can subtract 14,264 on both sides of the equation:

$$14{,}264 + x = 20{,}320$$
$$14{,}264 + x - 14{,}264 = 20{,}320 - 14{,}264$$
$$x = 6056.$$

This value of x gives the answer, 6056 ft.

We call $14{,}264 + x$ an *algebraic expression* and $14{,}264 + x = 20{,}320$ an *algebraic equation*. Note that there is no equals sign, =, in an algebraic expression.

In arithmetic, you probably would do this subtraction without ever considering an equation. *In algebra, more complex problems are difficult to solve without first writing an equation.*

Do Exercise 1.

1. Translate this problem to an equation. Then solve the equation.

Mountain Peaks. There are 92 mountain peaks in the United States that are higher than 14,000 ft. The bar graph above shows data for six of these. How much higher is Mt. Fairweather than Mt. Rainier?

Answer

1. $14{,}410 + x = 15{,}300$; 890 ft

An **algebraic expression** consists of variables, constants, numerals, operation signs, and/or grouping symbols. When we replace a variable with a number, we say that we are **substituting** for the variable. When we replace all of the variables in an expression with numbers and carry out the operations in the expression, we are **evaluating the expression.**

EXAMPLE 1 Evaluate $x + y$ when $x = 37$ and $y = 29$.

We substitute 37 for x and 29 for y and carry out the addition:

$$x + y = 37 + 29 = 66.$$

The number 66 is called the **value** of the expression when $x = 37$ and $y = 29$.

Algebraic expressions involving multiplication can be written in several ways. For example, "8 times a" can be written as

$$8 \times a, \quad 8 \cdot a, \quad 8(a), \quad \text{or simply} \quad 8a.$$

Two letters written together without an operation symbol, such as ab, also indicate a multiplication.

EXAMPLE 2 Evaluate $3y$ when $y = 14$.

$$3y = 3(14) = 42$$

Do Exercises 2–4.

2. Evaluate $a + b$ when $a = 38$ and $b = 26$.

3. Evaluate $x - y$ when $x = 57$ and $y = 29$.

4. Evaluate $4t$ when $t = 15$.

EXAMPLE 3 *Area of a Rectangle.* The area A of a rectangle of length l and width w is given by the formula $A = lw$. Find the area when l is 24.5 in. and w is 16 in.

We substitute 24.5 in. for l and 16 in. for w and carry out the multiplication:

$$\begin{aligned} A = lw &= (24.5 \text{ in.})(16 \text{ in.}) \\ &= (24.5)(16)(\text{in.})(\text{in.}) \\ &= 392 \text{ in}^2, \text{ or } 392 \text{ square inches.} \end{aligned}$$

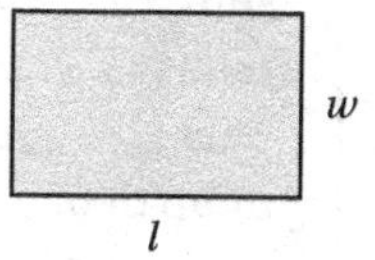

Do Exercise 5.

5. Find the area of a rectangle when l is 24 ft and w is 8 ft.

Algebraic expressions involving division can also be written in several ways. For example, "8 divided by t" can be written as

$$8 \div t, \quad \frac{8}{t}, \quad 8/t, \quad \text{or} \quad 8 \cdot \frac{1}{t},$$

where the fraction bar is a division symbol.

EXAMPLE 4 Evaluate $\frac{a}{b}$ when $a = 63$ and $b = 9$.

We substitute 63 for a and 9 for b and carry out the division:

$$\frac{a}{b} = \frac{63}{9} = 7.$$

EXAMPLE 5 Evaluate $\frac{12m}{n}$ when $m = 8$ and $n = 16$.

$$\frac{12m}{n} = \frac{12 \cdot 8}{16} = \frac{96}{16} = 6$$

Answers

2. 64 3. 28 4. 60 5. 192 ft^2

6. Evaluate a/b when $a = 200$ and $b = 8$.

7. Evaluate $10p/q$ when $p = 40$ and $q = 25$.

8. **Motorcycle Travel.** Find the time it takes to travel 660 mi if the speed is 55 mph.

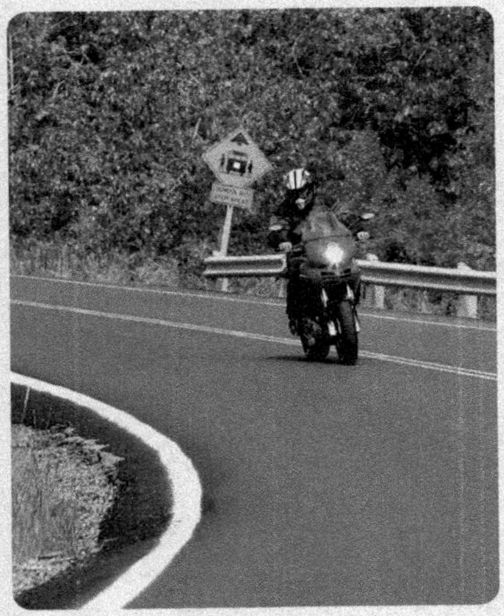

Do Exercises 6 and 7.

EXAMPLE 6 *Motorcycle Travel.* Ed wants to travel 660 mi on his motorcycle on a particular day. The time t, in hours, that it takes to travel 660 mi is given by

$$t = \frac{660}{r},$$

where r is the speed of Ed's motorcycle. Find the time of travel if the speed r is 60 mph.

We substitute 60 for r and carry out the division:

$$t = \frac{660}{r} = \frac{660}{60} = 11 \text{ hr.}$$

Do Exercise 8.

b Translating to Algebraic Expressions

In algebra, we translate problems to equations. The different parts of an equation are translations of word phrases to algebraic expressions. It is easier to translate if we know that certain words often translate to certain operation symbols.

KEY WORDS, PHRASES, AND CONCEPTS

ADDITION (+)	SUBTRACTION (−)	MULTIPLICATION (·)	DIVISION (÷)
add	subtract	multiply	divide
added to	subtracted from	multiplied by	divided by
sum	difference	product	quotient
total	minus	times	
plus	less than	of	
more than	decreased by		
increased by	take away		

To the student: At the front of the text, you will find a Student Organizer card. This pullout card will help you keep track of important dates and useful contact information. You can also use it to plan time for class, study, work, and relaxation. By managing your time wisely, you will provide yourself the best possible opportunity to be successful in this course.

EXAMPLE 7 Translate to an algebraic expression:

Twice (or two times) some number.

Think of some number, say, 8. We can write 2 times 8 as 2×8, or $2 \cdot 8$. We multiplied by 2. Do the same thing using a variable. We can use any variable we wish, such as x, y, m, or n. Let's use y to stand for some number. If we multiply by 2, we get an expression

$$y \times 2, \quad 2 \times y, \quad 2 \cdot y, \quad \text{or} \quad 2y.$$

In algebra, $2y$ is the expression generally used.

EXAMPLE 8 Translate to an algebraic expression:

Thirty-eight percent of some number.

Let $n =$ the number. The word "of" translates to a multiplication symbol, so we could write any of the following expressions as a translation:

$$38\% \cdot n, \quad 0.38 \times n, \quad \text{or} \quad 0.38n.$$

Answers

6. 25 **7.** 16 **8.** 12 hr

EXAMPLE 9 Translate to an algebraic expression:

Seven less than some number.

We let x represent the number. If the number were 10, then 7 less than 10 is $10 - 7$, or 3. If we knew the number to be 34, then 7 less than the number would be $34 - 7$. Thus if the number is x, then the translation is

$x - 7$.

Caution!

Note that $7 - x$ is *not* a correct translation of the expression in Example 9. The expression $7 - x$ is a translation of "seven minus some number" or "some number less than seven."

EXAMPLE 10 Translate to an algebraic expression:

Eighteen more than a number.

We let $t =$ the number. Now if the number were 6, then the translation would be $6 + 18$, or $18 + 6$. If we knew the number to be 17, then the translation would be $17 + 18$, or $18 + 17$. If the number is t, then the translation is

$t + 18$, or $18 + t$.

EXAMPLE 11 Translate to an algebraic expression:

A number divided by 5.

We let $m =$ the number. Now if the number were 7, then the translation would be $7 \div 5$, or $7/5$, or $\frac{7}{5}$. If the number were 21, then the translation would be $21 \div 5$, or $21/5$, or $\frac{21}{5}$. If the number is m, then the translation is

$m \div 5$, $m/5$, or $\frac{m}{5}$.

EXAMPLE 12 Translate each phrase to an algebraic expression.

PHRASE	ALGEBRAIC EXPRESSION
Five more than some number	$n + 5$, or $5 + n$
Half of a number	$\frac{1}{2}t$, $\frac{t}{2}$, or $t/2$
Five more than three times some number	$3p + 5$, or $5 + 3p$
The difference of two numbers	$x - y$
Six less than the product of two numbers	$mn - 6$
Seventy-six percent of some number	$76\%z$, or $0.76z$
Four less than twice some number	$2x - 4$

Do Exercises 9–17.

Translate each phrase to an algebraic expression.

9. Eight less than some number

10. Eight more than some number

11. Four less than some number

12. Half of some number

13. Six more than eight times some number

14. The difference of two numbers

15. Fifty-nine percent of some number

16. Two hundred less than the product of two numbers

17. The sum of two numbers

Answers

9. $x - 8$ 10. $y + 8$, or $8 + y$
11. $m - 4$ 12. $\frac{1}{2} \cdot p$, or $\frac{p}{2}$
13. $8x + 6$, or $6 + 8x$ 14. $a - b$
15. $59\%x$, or $0.59x$ 16. $xy - 200$
17. $p + q$

For Extra Help

MyMathLab | MathXL PRACTICE | WATCH | DOWNLOAD | READ | REVIEW

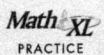

a Substitute to find values of the expressions in each of the following applied problems.

1. *Commuting Time.* It takes Erin 24 min less time to commute to work than it does George. Suppose that the variable x stands for the time it takes George to get to work. Then $x - 24$ stands for the time it takes Erin to get to work. How long does it take Erin to get to work if it takes George 56 min? 93 min? 105 min?

2. *Enrollment Costs.* At Emmett Community College, it costs \$600 to enroll in the 8 A.M. section of Elementary Algebra. Suppose that the variable n stands for the number of students who enroll. Then $600n$ stands for the total amount of money collected for this course. How much is collected if 34 students enroll? 78 students? 250 students?

3. *Area of a Triangle.* The area A of a triangle with base b and height h is given by $A = \frac{1}{2}bh$. Find the area when $b = 45$ m (meters) and $h = 86$ m.

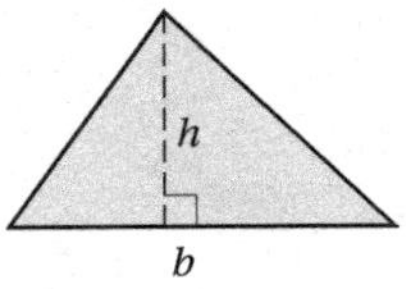

4. *Area of a Parallelogram.* The area A of a parallelogram with base b and height h is given by $A = bh$. Find the area of the parallelogram when the height is 15.4 cm (centimeters) and the base is 6.5 cm.

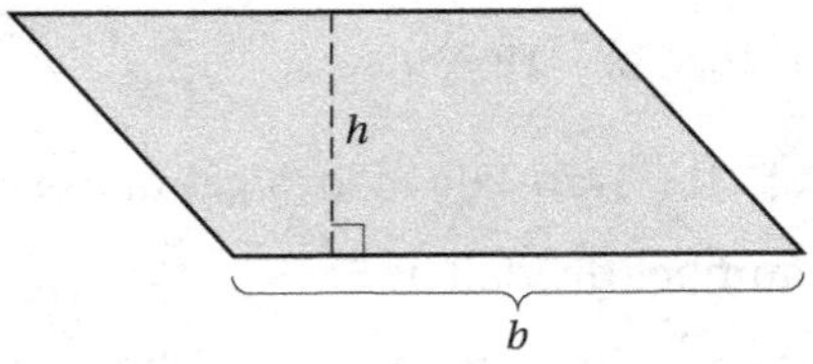

5. *Distance Traveled.* A driver who drives at a constant speed of r miles per hour for t hours will travel a distance of d miles given by $d = rt$ miles. How far will a driver travel at a speed of 65 mph for 4 hr?

6. *Simple Interest.* The simple interest I on a principal of P dollars at interest rate r for time t, in years, is given by $I = Prt$. Find the simple interest on a principal of \$4800 at 9% for 2 years. (*Hint*: 9% = 0.09.)

7. *Hockey Goal.* The front of a regulation hockey goal is a rectangle that is 6 ft wide and 4 ft high. Find its area.
Source: National Hockey League

8. *Zoology.* A great white shark has triangular teeth. Each tooth measures about 5 cm across the base and has a height of 6 cm. Find the surface area of one side of one tooth. (See Exercise 3.)

Evaluate.

9. $8x$, when $x = 7$

10. $6y$, when $y = 7$

11. $\frac{c}{d}$, when $c = 24$ and $d = 3$

12. $\frac{p}{q}$, when $p = 16$ and $q = 2$

13. $\frac{3p}{q}$, when $p = 2$ and $q = 6$

14. $\frac{5y}{z}$, when $y = 15$ and $z = 25$

15. $\frac{x + y}{5}$, when $x = 10$ and $y = 20$

16. $\frac{p + q}{2}$, when $p = 2$ and $q = 16$

17. $\frac{x - y}{8}$, when $x = 20$ and $y = 4$

18. $\frac{m - n}{5}$, when $m = 16$ and $n = 6$

b Translate each phrase to an algebraic expression. Use any letter for the variable(s) unless directed otherwise.

19. Seven more than some number

20. Nine more than some number

21. Twelve less than some number

22. Fourteen less than some number

23. Some number increased by four

24. Some number increased by thirteen

25. b more than a

26. c more than d

27. x divided by y

28. c divided by h

29. x plus w

30. s added to t

31. m subtracted from n

32. p subtracted from q

33. The sum of two numbers

34. The sum of nine and some number

35. Twice some number

36. Three times some number

37. Three multiplied by some number

38. The product of eight and some number

39. Six more than four times some number

40. Two more than six times some number

41. Eight less than the product of two numbers

42. The product of two numbers minus seven

43. Five less than twice some number

44. Six less than seven times some number

45. Three times some number plus eleven

46. Some number times 8 plus 5

47. The sum of four times a number plus three times another number

48. Five times a number minus eight times another number

49. The product of 89% and your salary

50. 67% of the women attending

51. Your salary after a 5% salary increase if your salary before the increase was s

52. The price of a blouse after a 30% reduction if the price before the reduction was P

53. Danielle drove at a speed of 65 mph for t hours. How far did Danielle travel? (See Exercise 5.)

54. Dino drove his pickup truck at 55 mph for t hours. How far did he travel? (See Exercise 5.)

55. Lisa had $50 before spending x dollars on pizza. How much money remains?

56. Juan has d dollars before spending $29.95 on a DVD of the movie *Chicago*. How much did Juan have after the purchase?

57. Robert's part-time job pays $8.50 per hour. How much does he earn for working n hours?

58. Meredith pays her babysitter $10 per hour. What does it cost her to hire the sitter for m hours?

Skill Maintenance

This heading indicates that the exercises that follow are Skill Maintenance exercises, which review any skill previously studied in the text. You can expect such exercises in every exercise set. Answers to *all* skill maintenance exercises are found at the back of the book. If you miss an exercise, restudy the objective shown in red.

Find the prime factorization. [R.1a]

59. 54 **60.** 32 **61.** 108 **62.** 192 **63.** 1023

Find the LCM. [R.1b]

64. 6, 18 **65.** 6, 24, 32 **66.** 10, 20, 30 **67.** 16, 24, 32 **68.** 18, 36, 44

Synthesis

To the student and the instructor: The Synthesis exercises found at the end of most exercise sets challenge students to combine concepts or skills studied in that section or in preceding parts of the text.

Evaluate.

69. $\dfrac{a - 2b + c}{4b - a}$, when $a = 20$, $b = 10$, and $c = 5$

70. $\dfrac{x}{y} - \dfrac{5}{x} + \dfrac{2}{y}$, when $x = 30$ and $y = 6$

71. $\dfrac{12 - c}{c + 12b}$, when $b = 1$ and $c = 12$

72. $\dfrac{2w - 3z}{7y}$, when $w = 5$, $y = 6$, and $z = 1$

1.2 The Real Numbers

A **set** is a collection of objects. (See Appendix D for more on sets.) For our purposes, we will most often be considering sets of numbers. One way to name a set uses what is called **roster notation**. For example, roster notation for the set containing the numbers 0, 2, and 5 is $\{0, 2, 5\}$.

Sets that are part of other sets are called **subsets**. In this section, we become acquainted with the set of *real numbers* and its various subsets.

Two important subsets of the real numbers are listed below using roster notation.

OBJECTIVES

- **a** State the integer that corresponds to a real-world situation.
- **b** Graph rational numbers on the number line.
- **c** Convert from fraction notation for a rational number to decimal notation.
- **d** Determine which of two real numbers is greater and indicate which, using < or >. Given an inequality like $a > b$, write another inequality with the same meaning. Determine whether an inequality like $-3 \leq 5$ is true or false.
- **e** Find the absolute value of a real number.

NATURAL NUMBERS

The set of **natural numbers** $= \{1, 2, 3, \ldots\}$. These are the numbers used for counting.

WHOLE NUMBERS

The set of **whole numbers** $= \{0, 1, 2, 3, \ldots\}$. This is the set of natural numbers and 0.

We can represent these sets on the number line. The natural numbers are to the right of zero. The whole numbers are the natural numbers and zero.

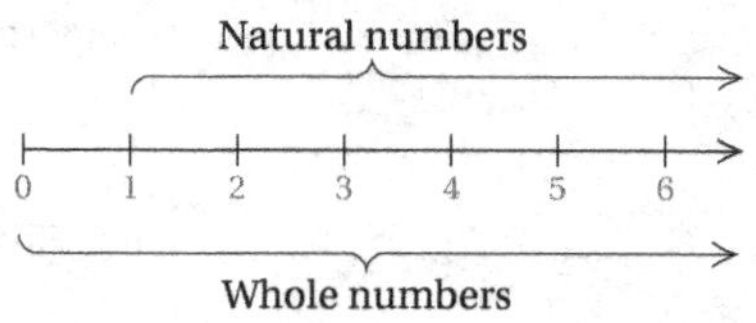

We create a new set, called the *integers*, by starting with the whole numbers, 0, 1, 2, 3, and so on. For each natural number 1, 2, 3, and so on, we obtain a new number to the left of zero on the number line:

For the number 1, there will be an *opposite* number -1 (negative 1).

For the number 2, there will be an *opposite* number -2 (negative 2).

For the number 3, there will be an *opposite* number -3 (negative 3), and so on.

The **integers** consist of the whole numbers and these new numbers.

INTEGERS

The set of **integers** $= \{\ldots, -5, -4, -3, -2, -1, 0, 1, 2, 3, 4, 5, \ldots\}$.

We picture the integers on the number line as follows.

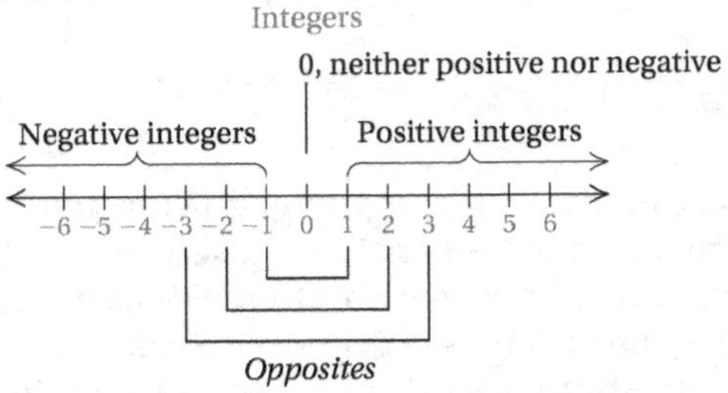

We call the integers to the left of zero **negative integers.** The natural numbers are also called **positive integers**. Zero is neither positive nor negative. We call −1 and 1 **opposites** of each other. Similarly, −2 and 2 are opposites, −3 and 3 are opposites, −100 and 100 are opposites, and 0 is its own opposite. Pairs of opposite numbers like −3 and 3 are the same distance from zero. The integers extend infinitely on the number line to the left and right of zero.

a Integers and the Real World

Integers correspond to many real-world problems and situations. The following examples will help you get ready to translate problem situations that involve integers to mathematical language.

EXAMPLE 1 Tell which integer corresponds to this situation: The temperature is 4 degrees below zero.

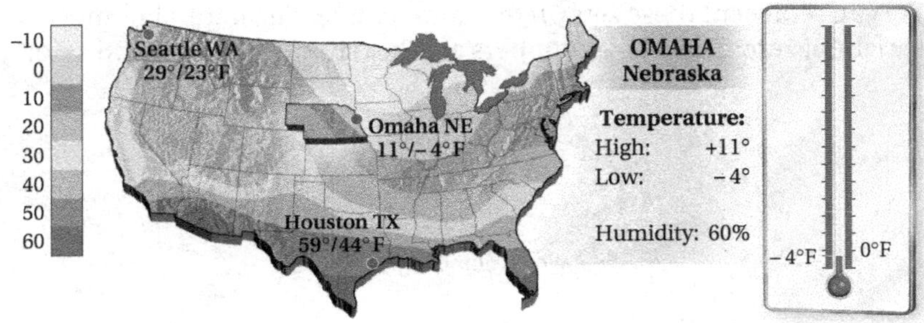

The integer −4 corresponds to the situation. The temperature is −4°.

EXAMPLE 2 *"Jeopardy."* Tell which integer corresponds to this situation: A contestant missed a $600 question on the television game show "Jeopardy."

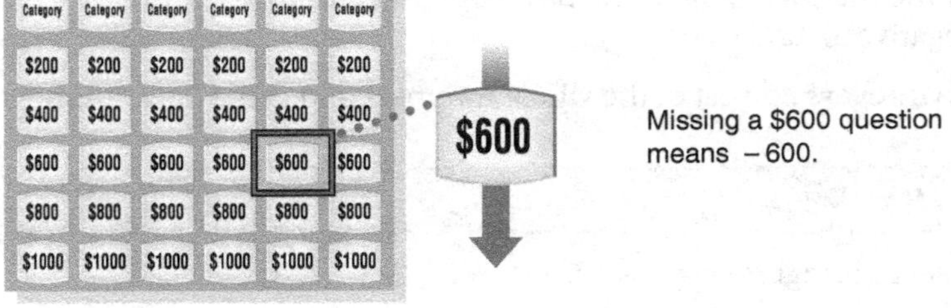

Missing a $600 question causes a $600 loss on the score—that is, the contestant earns −600 dollars.

EXAMPLE 3 *Elevation.* Tell which integer corresponds to this situation: The shores of California's largest lake, the Salton Sea, are 227 ft below sea level.
Source: Salton Sea Authority

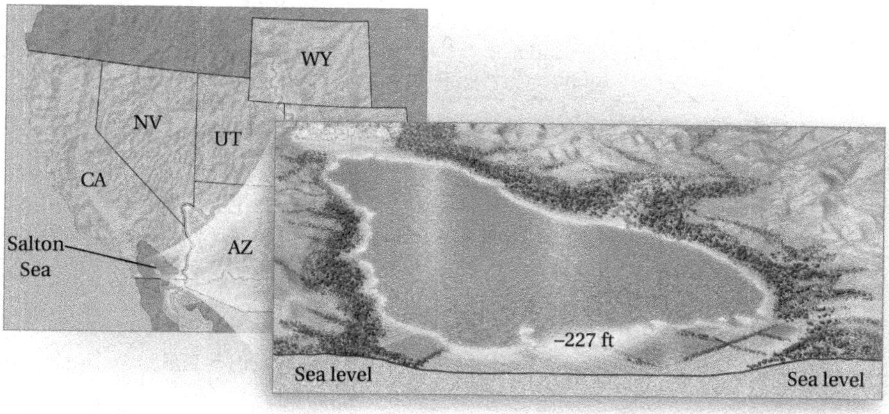

The integer −227 corresponds to the situation. The elevation is −227 ft.

EXAMPLE 4 *Stock Price Change.* Tell which integers correspond to this situation: Hal owns a stock whose price decreased $16 per share over a recent period. He owns another stock whose price increased $2 per share over the same period.

The integer −16 corresponds to the decrease in the value of the first stock. The integer 2 represents the increase in the value of the second stock.

Do Exercises 1–5.

Tell which integers correspond to each situation.

1. **Temperature High and Low.** The highest recorded temperature in Nevada is 125°F on June 29, 1994, in Laughlin. The lowest recorded temperature in Nevada is 50°F below zero on January 8, 1937, in San Jacinto.
Source: National Climatic Data Center, Asheville, NC, and Storm Phillips, STORMFAX, INC.

2. **Stock Decrease.** The price of a stock decreased $3 per share over a recent period.

3. At 10 sec before liftoff, ignition occurs. At 148 sec after liftoff, the first stage is detached from the rocket.

4. The halfback gained 8 yd on first down. The quarterback was sacked for a 5-yd loss on second down.

5. A submarine dove 120 ft, rose 50 ft, and then dove 80 ft.

b The Rational Numbers

We created the set of integers by obtaining a negative number for each natural number and also including 0. To create a larger number system, called the set of **rational numbers**, we consider quotients of integers with nonzero divisors. The following are some examples of rational numbers:

$$\frac{2}{3},\quad -\frac{2}{3},\quad \frac{7}{1},\quad 4,\quad -3,\quad 0,\quad \frac{23}{-8},\quad 2.4,\quad -0.17,\quad 10\frac{1}{2}.$$

The number $-\frac{2}{3}$ (read "negative two-thirds") can also be named $\frac{-2}{3}$ or $\frac{2}{-3}$; that is,

$$-\frac{a}{b} = \frac{-a}{b} = \frac{a}{-b}.$$

The number 2.4 can be named $\frac{24}{10}$ or $\frac{12}{5}$, and −0.17 can be named $-\frac{17}{100}$. We can describe the set of rational numbers as follows.

RATIONAL NUMBERS

The set of **rational numbers** = the set of numbers $\frac{a}{b}$, where a and b are integers and b is not equal to 0 ($b \neq 0$).

Answers

1. 125; −50 2. The integer −3 corresponds to the decrease in the stock's value.
3. −10; 148 4. 8; −5 5. −120; 50; −80

Note that this new set of numbers, the rational numbers, contains the whole numbers, the integers, the arithmetic numbers (also called the non-negative rational numbers), and the negative rational numbers.

We picture the rational numbers on the number line as follows.

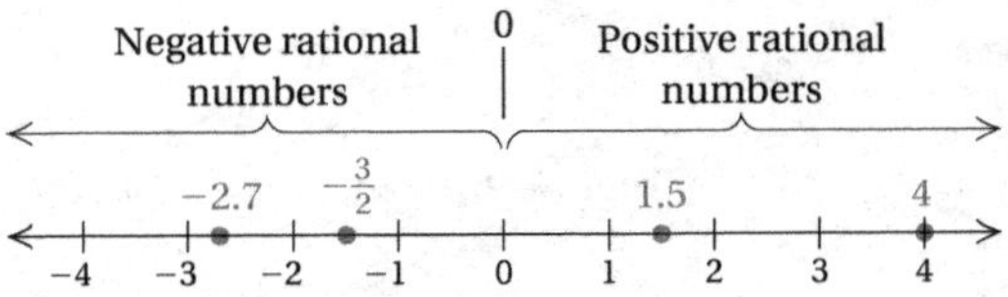

To **graph** a number means to find and mark its point on the number line. Some rational numbers are graphed in the preceding figure.

EXAMPLE 5 Graph: $\frac{5}{2}$.

The number $\frac{5}{2}$ can also be named $2\frac{1}{2}$, or 2.5. Its graph is halfway between 2 and 3.

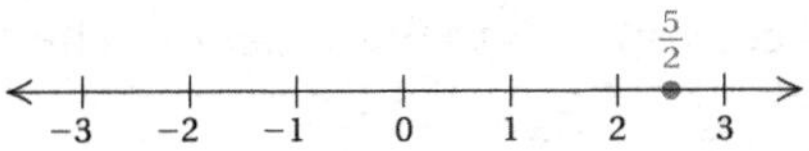

Graph on the number line.

6. $-\frac{7}{2}$

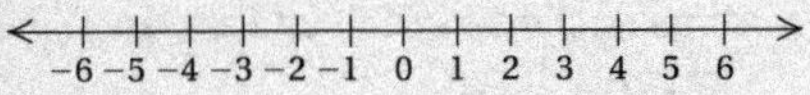

7. 1.4

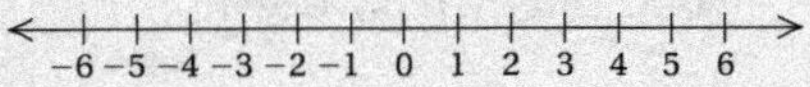

8. $-\frac{11}{4}$

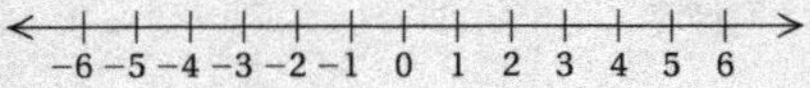

EXAMPLE 6 Graph: −3.2.

The graph of −3.2 is $\frac{2}{10}$ of the way from −3 to −4.

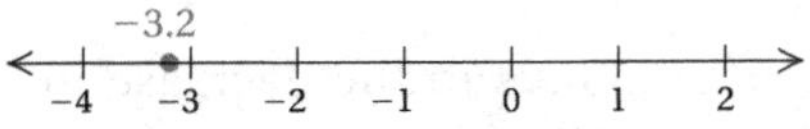

EXAMPLE 7 Graph: $\frac{13}{8}$.

The number $\frac{13}{8}$ can also be named $1\frac{5}{8}$, or 1.625. The graph is $\frac{5}{8}$ of the way from 1 to 2.

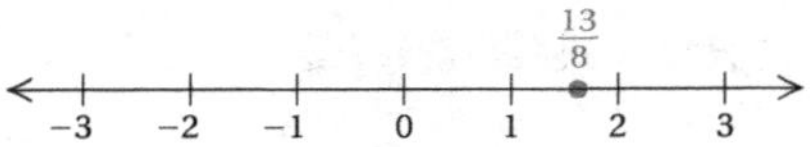

Do Exercises 6–8.

C Notation for Rational Numbers

Each rational number can be named using fraction notation or decimal notation.

EXAMPLE 8 Convert to decimal notation: $-\frac{5}{8}$.

We first find decimal notation for $\frac{5}{8}$. Since $\frac{5}{8}$ means 5 ÷ 8, we divide.

```
     0.6 2 5
8 ) 5.0 0 0
    4 8
    ---
      2 0
      1 6
      ---
        4 0
        4 0
        ---
          0
```

Thus, $\frac{5}{8} = 0.625$, so $-\frac{5}{8} = -0.625$.

Answers

6.

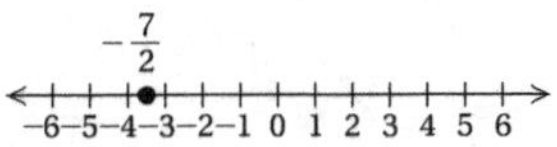

7.

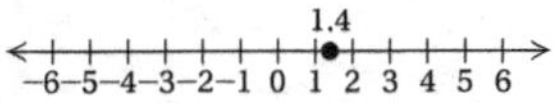

8.

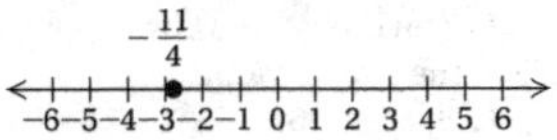

Decimal notation for $-\frac{5}{8}$ is -0.625. We consider -0.625 to be a **terminating decimal**. Decimal notation for some numbers repeats.

EXAMPLE 9 Convert to decimal notation: $\frac{7}{11}$.

$$\begin{array}{r} 0.6\,3\,6\,3\ldots \\ 11\overline{)\,7.0\,0\,0\,0} \\ \underline{6\,6} \\ 4\,0 \\ \underline{3\,3} \\ 7\,0 \\ \underline{6\,6} \\ 4\,0 \\ \underline{3\,3} \\ 7 \end{array} \qquad \text{Dividing}$$

We can abbreviate **repeating decimal** notation by writing a bar over the repeating part—in this case, we write $0.\overline{63}$. Thus, $\frac{7}{11} = 0.\overline{63}$.

Each rational number can be expressed in either terminating or repeating decimal notation.

The following are other examples showing how rational numbers can be named using fraction notation or decimal notation:

$$0 = \frac{0}{8}, \quad \frac{27}{100} = 0.27, \quad -8\frac{3}{4} = -8.75, \quad -\frac{13}{6} = -2.1\overline{6}.$$

Do Exercises 9–11.

d The Real Numbers and Order

Every rational number has a point on the number line. However, there are some points on the line for which there is no rational number. These points correspond to what are called **irrational numbers**.

What kinds of numbers are irrational? One example is the number π, which is used in finding the area and the circumference of a circle: $A = \pi r^2$ and $C = 2\pi r$.

Another example of an irrational number is the square root of 2, named $\sqrt{2}$. It is the length of the diagonal of a square with sides of length 1. It is also the number that when multiplied by itself gives 2—that is, $\sqrt{2} \cdot \sqrt{2} = 2$. There is no rational number that can be multiplied by itself to get 2. But the following are rational *approximations*:

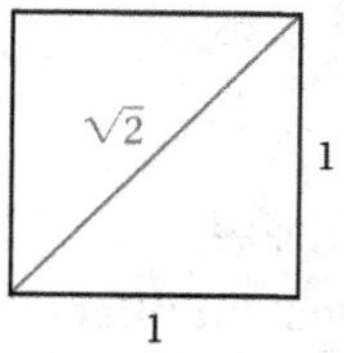

1.4 is an approximation of $\sqrt{2}$ because $(1.4)^2 = 1.96$;

1.41 is a better approximation because $(1.41)^2 = 1.9881$;

1.4142 is an even better approximation because $(1.4142)^2 = 1.99996164$.

We can find rational approximations for square roots using a calculator.

Find decimal notation.

9. $-\frac{3}{8}$

10. $-\frac{6}{11}$

11. $\frac{4}{3}$

Calculator Corner

Approximating Square Roots and π Square roots are found by pressing 2ND $\sqrt{\ }$. ($\sqrt{\ }$ is the second operation associated with the x^2 key.)

To find an approximation for $\sqrt{48}$, we press 2ND $\sqrt{\ }$ 4 8 ENTER. The approximation 6.92820323 is displayed.

To find $8 \cdot \sqrt{13}$, we press 8 2ND $\sqrt{\ }$ 1 3 ENTER. The approximation 28.8444102 is displayed. The number π is used widely enough to have its own key. (π is the second operation associated with the ^ key.)

To approximate π, we press 2ND π ENTER. The approximation 3.141592654 is displayed.

Exercises: Approximate.

1. $\sqrt{76}$

2. $\sqrt{317}$

3. $15 \cdot \sqrt{20}$

4. $29 + \sqrt{42}$

5. π

6. $29 \cdot \pi$

7. $\pi \cdot 13^2$

8. $5 \cdot \pi + 8 \cdot \sqrt{237}$

Answers

9. -0.375 **10.** $-0.\overline{54}$ **11.** $1.\overline{3}$

Decimal notation for rational numbers *either* terminates *or* repeats.
Decimal notation for irrational numbers *neither* terminates *nor* repeats.

Some other examples of irrational numbers are $\sqrt{3}$, $-\sqrt{8}$, $\sqrt{11}$, and 0.121221222122221.... Whenever we take the square root of a number that is not a perfect square, we will get an irrational number.

The rational numbers and the irrational numbers together correspond to all the points on the number line and make up what is called the **real-number system**.

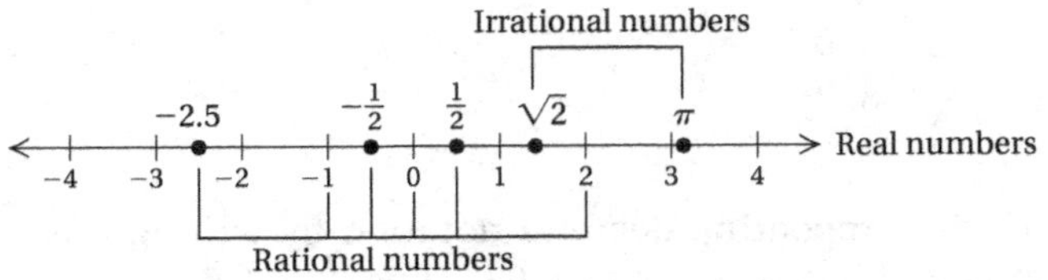

REAL NUMBERS

The set of **real numbers** = The set of all numbers corresponding to points on the number line.

The real numbers consist of the rational numbers and the irrational numbers. The following figure shows the relationships among various kinds of numbers.

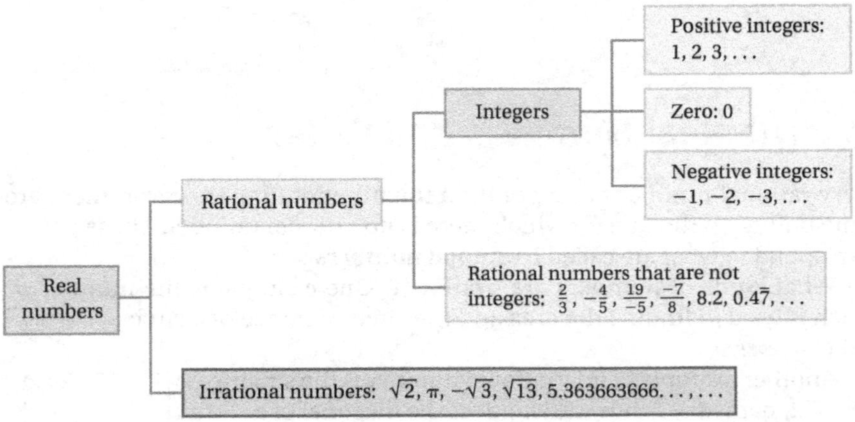

Order

Real numbers are named in order on the number line, increasing as we move from left to right. For any two numbers on the line, the one on the left is less than the one on the right.

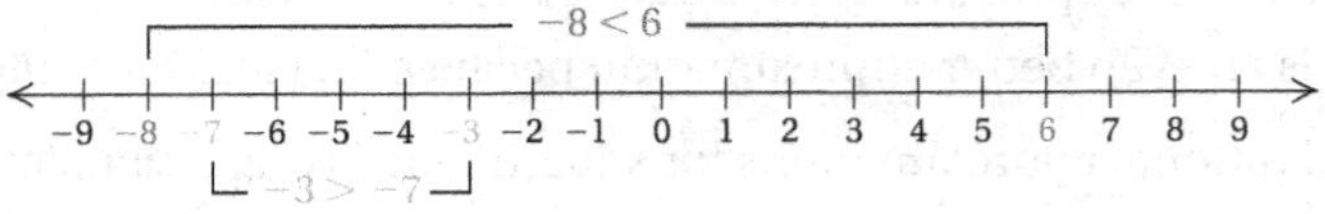

We use the symbol **<** to mean "**is less than.**" The sentence $-8 < 6$ means "−8 is less than 6." The symbol **>** means "**is greater than.**" The sentence $-3 > -7$ means "−3 is greater than −7." The sentences $-8 < 6$ and $-3 > -7$ are **inequalities**.

Calculator Corner

Negative Numbers on a Calculator; Converting to Decimal Notation We use the opposite key (−) to enter negative numbers on a graphing calculator. Note that this is different from the − key, which is used for the operation of subtraction. To convert $-\frac{5}{8}$ to decimal notation, as in Example 8, we press (−) 5 ÷ 8 ENTER. The result is −0.625.

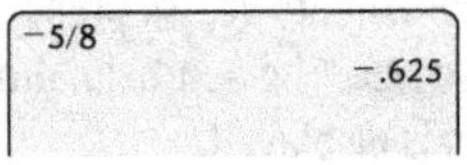

Exercises: Convert each of the following negative numbers to decimal notation.

1. $-\frac{3}{4}$ **2.** $-\frac{9}{20}$

3. $-\frac{1}{8}$ **4.** $-\frac{9}{5}$

5. $-\frac{27}{40}$ **6.** $-\frac{11}{16}$

7. $-\frac{7}{2}$ **8.** $-\frac{19}{25}$

EXAMPLES Use either $<$ or $>$ for $\square$ to write a true sentence.

10. $2 \square 9$ — Since 2 is to the left of 9, 2 is less than 9, so $2 < 9$.

11. $-7 \square 3$ — Since -7 is to the left of 3, we have $-7 < 3$.

12. $6 \square -12$ — Since 6 is to the right of -12, then $6 > -12$.

13. $-18 \square -5$ — Since -18 is to the left of -5, we have $-18 < -5$.

14. $-2.7 \square -\frac{3}{2}$ — The answer is $-2.7 < -\frac{3}{2}$.

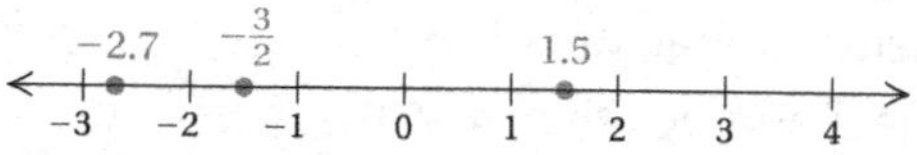

15. $1.5 \square -2.7$ — The answer is $1.5 > -2.7$.

16. $1.38 \square 1.83$ — The answer is $1.38 < 1.83$.

17. $-3.45 \square 1.32$ — The answer is $-3.45 < 1.32$.

18. $-4 \square 0$ — The answer is $-4 < 0$.

19. $5.8 \square 0$ — The answer is $5.8 > 0$.

20. $\frac{5}{8} \square \frac{7}{11}$ — We convert to decimal notation: $\frac{5}{8} = 0.625$ and $\frac{7}{11} = 0.6363\ldots$. Thus, $\frac{5}{8} < \frac{7}{11}$.

21. $-\frac{1}{2} \square -\frac{1}{3}$ — The answer is $-\frac{1}{2} < -\frac{1}{3}$.

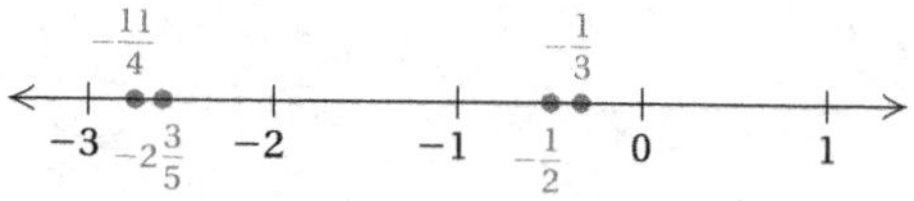

22. $-2\frac{3}{5} \square -\frac{11}{4}$ — The answer is $-2\frac{3}{5} > -\frac{11}{4}$.

Do Exercises 12–19.

Note that both $-8 < 6$ and $6 > -8$ are true. Every true inequality yields another true inequality when we interchange the numbers or variables and reverse the direction of the inequality sign.

ORDER; $>$, $<$

$a < b$ also has the meaning $b > a$.

EXAMPLES Write another inequality with the same meaning.

23. $-3 > -8$ — The inequality $-8 < -3$ has the same meaning.

24. $a < -5$ — The inequality $-5 > a$ has the same meaning.

A helpful mental device is to think of an inequality sign as an "arrow" with the arrowhead pointing to the smaller number.

Do Exercises 20 and 21.

Use either $<$ or $>$ for $\square$ to write a true sentence.

12. $-3 \square 7$

13. $-8 \square -5$

14. $7 \square -10$

15. $3.1 \square -9.5$

16. $-4.78 \square -5.01$

17. $-\frac{2}{3} \square -\frac{5}{9}$

18. $-\frac{11}{8} \square \frac{23}{15}$

19. $0 \square -9.9$

Write another inequality with the same meaning.

20. $-5 < 7$

21. $x > 4$

Answers

12. $<$ 13. $<$ 14. $>$ 15. $>$ 16. $>$ 17. $<$ 18. $<$ 19. $>$ 20. $7 > -5$ 21. $4 < x$

Note that all positive real numbers are greater than zero and all negative real numbers are less than zero.

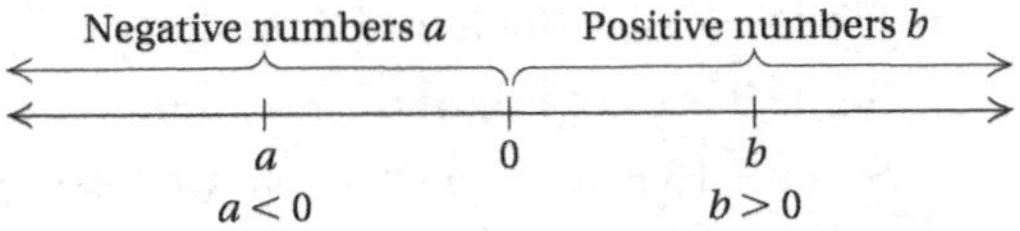

If b is a positive real number, then $b > 0$.
If a is a negative real number, then $a < 0$.

Expressions like $a \leq b$ and $b \geq a$ are also inequalities. We read $\boldsymbol{a \leq b}$ as "**a is less than or equal to b**." We read $\boldsymbol{a \geq b}$ as "**a is greater than or equal to b**."

EXAMPLES Write true or false for each statement.

25. $-3 \leq 5.4$ True since $-3 < 5.4$ is true

26. $-3 \leq -3$ True since $-3 = -3$ is true

27. $-5 \geq 1\frac{2}{3}$ False since neither $-5 > 1\frac{2}{3}$ nor $-5 = 1\frac{2}{3}$ is true

Do Exercises 22–24.

e Absolute Value

From the number line, we see that numbers like 4 and -4 are the same distance from zero. Distance is always a nonnegative number. We call the distance of a number from zero on the number line the **absolute value** of the number.

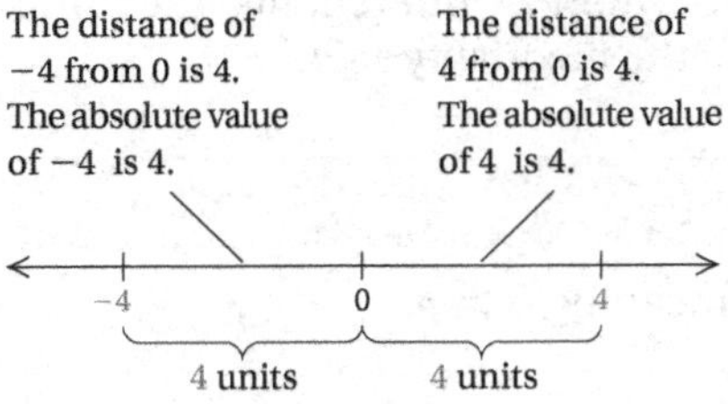

ABSOLUTE VALUE

The **absolute value** of a number is its distance from zero on the number line. We use the symbol $|x|$ to represent the absolute value of a number x.

Write true or false.

22. $-4 \leq -6$

23. $7.8 \geq 7.8$

24. $-2 \leq \frac{3}{8}$

Calculator Corner

Absolute Value The absolute-value operation is the first item in the Catalog on the TI-84 Plus graphing calculator. To find $|-7|$, as in Example 28 on the following page, we first press 2ND CATALOG ENTER to copy "abs(" to the home screen. (CATALOG is the second operation associated with the 0 numeric key.) Then we press (−) 7) ENTER. The result is 7. To find $|-\frac{1}{2}|$ and express the result as a fraction, we press 2ND CATALOG ENTER (−) 1 ÷ 2) MATH 1 ENTER. The result is $\frac{1}{2}$.

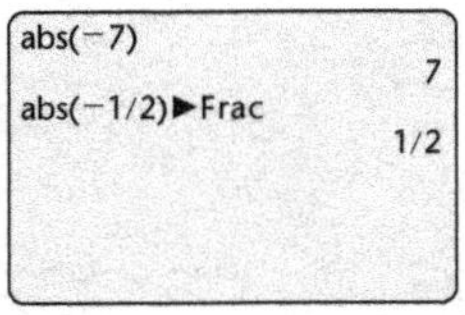

Exercises: Find the absolute value.

1. $|-5|$ **2.** $|17|$

3. $|0|$ **4.** $|6.48|$

5. $|-12.7|$ **6.** $|-0.9|$

7. $\left|-\frac{5}{7}\right|$ **8.** $\left|\frac{4}{3}\right|$

Answers

22. False **23.** True **24.** True

FINDING ABSOLUTE VALUE

a) If a number is negative, its absolute value is its opposite.

b) If a number is positive or zero, its absolute value is the same as the number.

EXAMPLES Find the absolute value.

28. $|-7|$ The distance of -7 from 0 is 7, so $|-7| = 7$.

29. $|12|$ The distance of 12 from 0 is 12, so $|12| = 12$.

30. $|0|$ The distance of 0 from 0 is 0, so $|0| = 0$.

31. $\left|\frac{3}{2}\right| = \frac{3}{2}$

32. $|-2.73| = 2.73$

Do Exercises 25–28.

Find the absolute value.

25. $|8|$

26. $|-9|$

27. $\left|-\frac{2}{3}\right|$

28. $|5.6|$

STUDY TIPS

USING THIS TEXTBOOK

You will find many Study Tips throughout the book. An index of all Study Tips can be found on the Bittinger Student Organizer at the front of the book. One of the most important ways to improve your math study skills is to learn the proper use of the textbook. Here we highlight a few points that we consider most helpful.

- **Be sure to note the special symbols (a), (b), (c), and so on, that correspond to the objectives you are to be able to master.** The first time you see them is in the margin at the beginning of each section; the second time is in the subheadings of each section; and the third time is in the exercise set for the section. You will also find them referred to in the skill maintenance exercises in each exercise set, in the mid-chapter review, and in the review exercises at the end of the chapter, as well as in the answers to the chapter tests and the cumulative reviews. These objective symbols allow you to refer to the appropriate place in the text whenever you need to review a topic.
- **Read and study each step of each example.** The examples include important side comments that explain each step. These carefully chosen examples and notes prepare you for success in the exercise set.
- **Stop and do the margin exercises as you study a section.** Doing the margin exercises is one of the most effective ways to enhance your ability to learn mathematics from this text. Don't deprive yourself of its benefits!
- **Note the icons listed at the top of each exercise set.** These refer to the many distinctive multimedia study aids that accompany the book.
- **Odd-numbered exercises.** Usually an instructor assigns some odd-numbered exercises. When you complete these, you can check your answers at the back of the book. If you miss any, check your work in the *Student's Solutions Manual* or ask your instructor for guidance.
- **Even-numbered exercises.** Whether or not your instructor assigns the even-numbered exercises, always do some on your own. Remember, there are no answers given for the class tests, so you need to practice doing exercises without answers. Check your answers later with a friend or your instructor.

Answers

25. 8 **26.** 9 **27.** $\frac{2}{3}$ **28.** 5.6

1.2 Exercise Set

For Extra Help
MyMathLab | Math XL PRACTICE | WATCH | DOWNLOAD | READ | REVIEW

a State the integers that correspond to the situation.

1. *Death Valley.* With an elevation of 282 ft below sea level, Badwater Basin in California's Death Valley has the lowest elevation in the United States.
Source: Desert USA

2. *Pollution Fine.* The Massey Energy Company, the nation's fourth largest coal producer, was fined $20 million for water pollution in 2008.
Source: Environmental Protection Agency

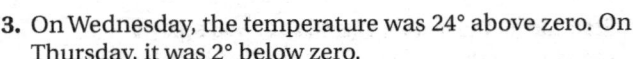

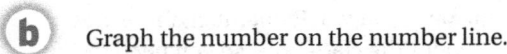

3. On Wednesday, the temperature was 24° above zero. On Thursday, it was 2° below zero.

4. A student deposited her tax refund of $750 in a savings account. Two weeks later, she withdrew $125 to pay technology fees.

5. *Temperature Extremes.* The highest temperature ever created in a lab is 3,600,000,000°F. The lowest temperature ever created is approximately 460°F below zero.
Sources: *Live Science; Guinness Book of World Records*

6. *Extreme Climate.* Verkhoyansk, a river port in northeast Siberia, has the most extreme climate on the planet. Its average monthly winter temperature is 58.5°F below zero, and its average monthly summer temperature is 56.5°F.
Source: *Guinness Book of World Records*

7. In bowling, the Alley Cats are 34 pins behind the Strikers going into the last frame. Describe the situation of each team.

8. During a video game, Maggie intercepted a missile worth 20 points, lost a starship worth 150 points, and captured a landing base worth 300 points.

b Graph the number on the number line.

9. $\frac{10}{3}$ −6 −5 −4 −3 −2 −1 0 1 2 3 4 5 6

10. $-\frac{17}{4}$ −6 −5 −4 −3 −2 −1 0 1 2 3 4 5 6

11. -5.2 −6 −5 −4 −3 −2 −1 0 1 2 3 4 5 6

12. 4.78 −6 −5 −4 −3 −2 −1 0 1 2 3 4 5 6

13. $-4\frac{2}{5}$ −6 −5 −4 −3 −2 −1 0 1 2 3 4 5 6

14. $2\frac{6}{11}$ −6 −5 −4 −3 −2 −1 0 1 2 3 4 5 6

c Convert to decimal notation.

15. $-\frac{7}{8}$

16. $-\frac{3}{16}$

17. $\frac{5}{6}$

18. $\frac{5}{3}$

19. $-\frac{7}{6}$

20. $-\frac{5}{12}$

21. $\frac{2}{3}$

22. $-\frac{11}{9}$

23. $\frac{1}{10}$

24. $\frac{1}{4}$

25. $-\frac{1}{2}$

26. $\frac{9}{8}$

27. $\frac{4}{25}$

28. $-\frac{7}{20}$

d Use either $<$ or $>$ for $\square$ to write a true sentence.

29. $8 \square 0$

30. $3 \square 0$

31. $-8 \square 3$

32. $6 \square -6$

33. $-8 \square 8$

34. $0 \square -9$

35. $-8 \square -5$

36. $-4 \square -3$

37. $-5 \square -11$

38. $-3 \square -4$

39. $-6 \square -5$

40. $-10 \square -14$

41. $2.14 \square 1.24$

42. $-3.3 \square -2.2$

43. $-14.5 \square 0.011$

44. $17.2 \square -1.67$

45. $-12.88 \square -6.45$

46. $-14.34 \square -17.88$

47. $-\frac{1}{2} \square -\frac{2}{3}$

48. $-\frac{5}{4} \square -\frac{3}{4}$

49. $-\frac{2}{3} \square \frac{1}{3}$

50. $\frac{3}{4} \square -\frac{5}{4}$

51. $\frac{5}{12} \square \frac{11}{25}$

52. $-\frac{13}{16} \square -\frac{5}{9}$

Write an inequality with the same meaning.

53. $-6 > x$

54. $x < 8$

55. $-10 \le y$

56. $12 \ge t$

Write true or false.

57. $-5 \le -6$

58. $-7 \ge -10$

59. $4 \ge 4$

60. $7 \le 7$

61. $-3 \ge -11$

62. $-1 \le -5$

63. $0 \ge 8$

64. $-5 \le 7$

e Find the absolute value.

65. $|-3|$

66. $|-6|$

67. $|10|$

68. $|11|$

69. $|0|$

70. $|-2.7|$

71. $|-30.4|$

72. $|325|$

73. $\left|-\frac{2}{3}\right|$

74. $\left|-\frac{10}{7}\right|$

75. $\left|\frac{0}{4}\right|$

76. $|14.8|$

77. $|-2.65|$

78. $\left|-3\frac{5}{8}\right|$

79. $\left|-7\frac{4}{5}\right|$

Skill Maintenance

Convert to decimal notation. [R.4a]

80. $23\frac{4}{5}\%$

81. 63%

82. 22.76%

83. 110%

Convert to percent notation. [R.4d]

84. $\frac{5}{4}$

85. $\frac{13}{25}$

86. $\frac{19}{32}$

87. $\frac{5}{6}$

Synthesis

List in order from the least to the greatest.

88. $-\frac{2}{3}, \frac{1}{2}, -\frac{3}{4}, -\frac{5}{6}, \frac{3}{8}, \frac{1}{6}$

89. $\frac{2}{3}, -\frac{1}{7}, \frac{1}{3}, -\frac{2}{7}, -\frac{2}{3}, \frac{2}{5}, -\frac{1}{3}, -\frac{2}{5}, \frac{9}{8}$

90. $-5.16, -4.24, -8.76, 5.23, 1.85, -2.13$

91. $-8\frac{7}{8}, 7^1, -5, |-6|, 4, |3|, -8\frac{5}{8}, -100, 0, 1^7, \frac{14}{4}, -\frac{67}{8}$

Given that $0.\overline{3} = \frac{1}{3}$ and $0.\overline{6} = \frac{2}{3}$, express each of the following as a quotient or a ratio of two integers.

92. $0.\overline{1}$

93. $0.\overline{9}$

94. $5.\overline{5}$

1.3 Addition of Real Numbers

In this section, we consider addition of real numbers. First, to gain an understanding, we add using the number line. Then we consider rules for addition.

OBJECTIVES

a Add real numbers without using the number line.

b Find the opposite, or additive inverse, of a real number.

c Solve applied problems involving addition of real numbers.

ADDITION ON THE NUMBER LINE

To do the addition $a + b$ on the number line, start at 0, move to a, and then move according to b.

a) If b is positive, move from a to the right.

b) If b is negative, move from a to the left.

c) If b is 0, stay at a.

EXAMPLE 1 Add: $3 + (-5)$.

We start at 0 and move to 3. Then we move 5 units left since -5 is negative.

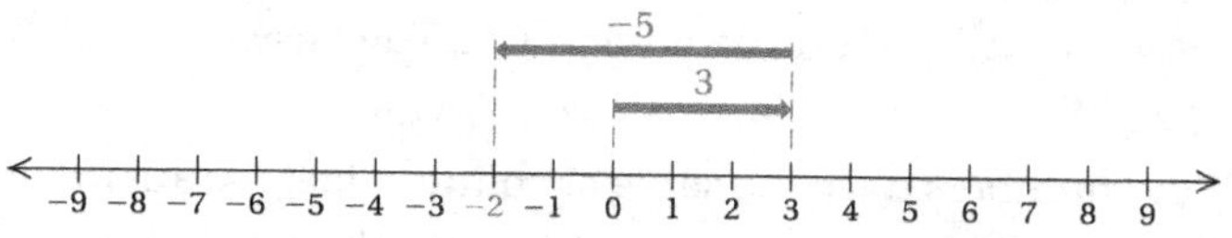

$3 + (-5) = -2$

EXAMPLE 2 Add: $-4 + (-3)$.

We start at 0 and move to -4. Then we move 3 units left since -3 is negative.

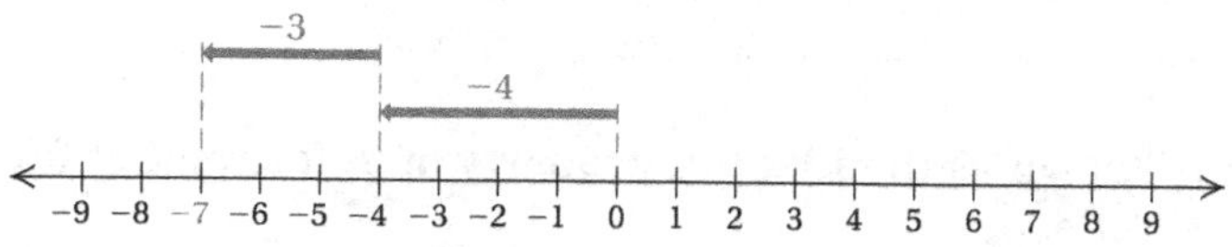

$-4 + (-3) = -7$

EXAMPLE 3 Add: $-4 + 9$.

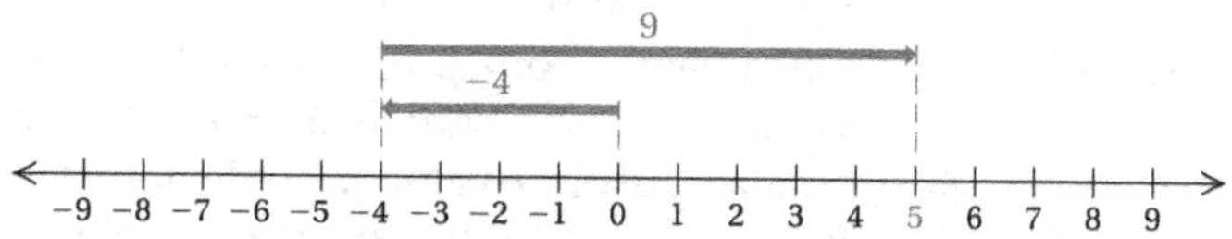

$-4 + 9 = 5$

STUDY TIPS

SMALL STEPS LEAD TO GREAT SUCCESS

What is your long-term goal for getting an education? How does math help you to attain that goal? As you begin this course, approach each short-term task, such as going to class, asking questions, using your time wisely, and doing your homework, as part of the framework of your long-term goal.

Add using the number line.

1. $0 + (-3)$

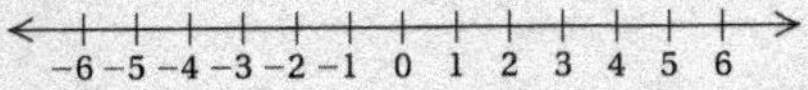

2. $1 + (-4)$

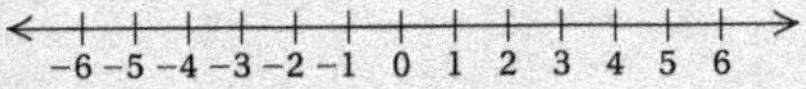

3. $-3 + (-2)$

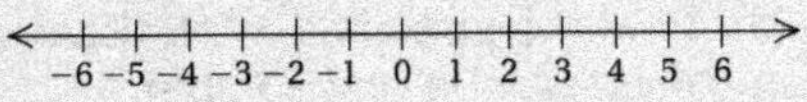

4. $-3 + 7$

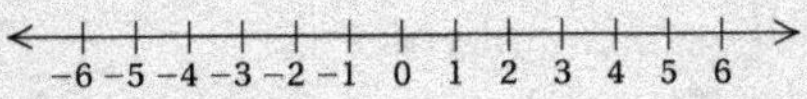

5. $-2.4 + 2.4$

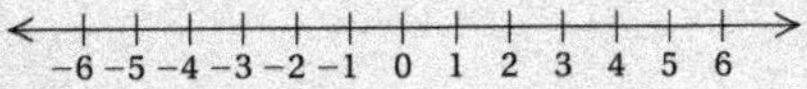

6. $-\frac{5}{2} + \frac{1}{2}$

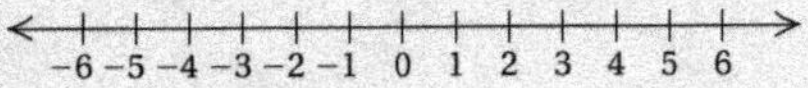

Answers

1. −3 **2.** −3 **3.** −5
4. 4 **5.** 0 **6.** −2

EXAMPLE 4 Add: $-5.2 + 0$.

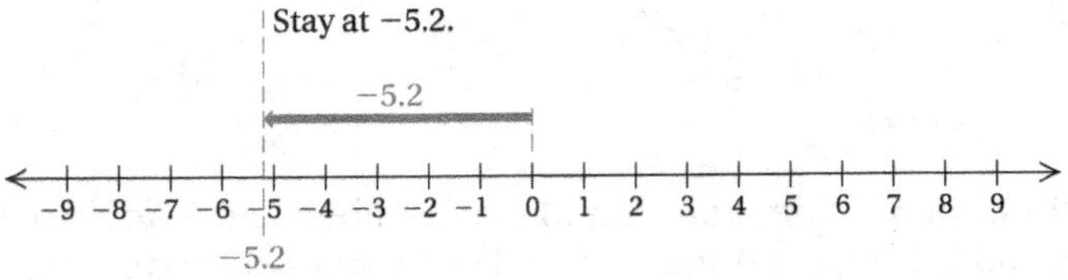

$-5.2 + 0 = -5.2$

Do Exercises 1–6.

a Adding Without the Number Line

You may have noticed some patterns in the preceding examples. These lead us to rules for adding without using the number line that are more efficient for adding larger numbers.

RULES FOR ADDITION OF REAL NUMBERS

1. *Positive numbers*: Add the same as arithmetic numbers. The answer is positive.
2. *Negative numbers*: Add absolute values. The answer is negative.
3. *A positive number and a negative number*:
   - If the numbers have the same absolute value, the answer is 0.
   - If the numbers have different absolute values, subtract the smaller absolute value from the larger. Then:
     - **a)** If the positive number has the greater absolute value, the answer is positive.
     - **b)** If the negative number has the greater absolute value, the answer is negative.
4. *One number is zero*: The sum is the other number.

Rule 4 is known as the **identity property of 0.** It says that for any real number a, $a + 0 = a$.

EXAMPLES Add without using the number line.

5. $-12 + (-7) = -19$ Two negatives. Add the absolute values: $|-12| + |-7| = 12 + 7 = 19$. Make the answer *negative*: -19.

6. $-1.4 + 8.5 = 7.1$ One negative, one positive. Find the absolute values: $|-1.4| = 1.4$; $|8.5| = 8.5$. Subtract the smaller absolute value from the larger: $8.5 - 1.4 = 7.1$. The *positive* number, 8.5, has the larger absolute value, so the answer is *positive*: 7.1.

7. $-36 + 21 = -15$ One negative, one positive. Find the absolute values: $|-36| = 36$; $|21| = 21$. Subtract the smaller absolute value from the larger: $36 - 21 = 15$. The *negative* number, -36, has the larger absolute value, so the answer is *negative*: -15.

8. $1.5 + (-1.5) = 0$ — The numbers have the same absolute value. The sum is 0.

9. $-\frac{7}{8} + 0 = -\frac{7}{8}$ — One number is zero. The sum is $-\frac{7}{8}$.

10. $-9.2 + 3.1 = -6.1$

11. $-\frac{3}{2} + \frac{9}{2} = \frac{6}{2} = 3$

12. $-\frac{2}{3} + \frac{5}{8} = -\frac{16}{24} + \frac{15}{24} = -\frac{1}{24}$

Do Exercises 7–20.

Suppose we want to add several numbers, some positive and some negative, as follows. How can we proceed?

$$15 + (-2) + 7 + 14 + (-5) + (-12)$$

We can change grouping and order as we please when adding. For instance, we can group the positive numbers together and the negative numbers together and add them separately. Then we add the two results.

EXAMPLE 13 Add: $15 + (-2) + 7 + 14 + (-5) + (-12)$.

a) $15 + 7 + 14 = 36$ — Adding the positive numbers

b) $-2 + (-5) + (-12) = -19$ — Adding the negative numbers

$36 + (-19) = 17$ — Adding the results in (a) and (b)

We can also add the numbers in any other order we wish, say, from left to right as follows:

$$\begin{aligned} 15 + (-2) + 7 + 14 + (-5) + (-12) &= 13 + 7 + 14 + (-5) + (-12) \\ &= 20 + 14 + (-5) + (-12) \\ &= 34 + (-5) + (-12) \\ &= 29 + (-12) \\ &= 17 \end{aligned}$$

Do Exercises 21–24.

b Opposites, or Additive Inverses

Suppose we add two numbers that are **opposites**, such as 6 and -6. The result is 0. When opposities are added, the result is always 0. Opposites are also called **additive inverses**. Every real number has an opposite, or additive inverse.

OPPOSITES, OR ADDITIVE INVERSES

Two numbers whose sum is 0 are called **opposites**, or **additive inverses**, of each other.

Add without using the number line.

7. $-5 + (-6)$
8. $-9 + (-3)$
9. $-4 + 6$
10. $-7 + 3$
11. $5 + (-7)$
12. $-20 + 20$
13. $-11 + (-11)$
14. $10 + (-7)$
15. $-0.17 + 0.7$
16. $-6.4 + 8.7$
17. $-4.5 + (-3.2)$
18. $-8.6 + 2.4$
19. $\frac{5}{9} + \left(-\frac{7}{9}\right)$
20. $-\frac{1}{5} + \left(-\frac{3}{4}\right)$

Add.

21. $(-15) + (-37) + 25 + 42 + (-59) + (-14)$
22. $42 + (-81) + (-28) + 24 + 18 + (-31)$
23. $-2.5 + (-10) + 6 + (-7.5)$
24. $-35 + 17 + 14 + (-27) + 31 + (-12)$

Answers

7. -11 8. -12 9. 2 10. -4 11. -2 12. 0 13. -22 14. 3 15. 0.53 16. 2.3 17. -7.7 18. -6.2 19. $-\frac{2}{9}$ 20. $-\frac{19}{20}$ 21. -58 22. -56 23. -14 24. -12

Find the opposite, or additive inverse, of each number.

25. -4 **26.** 8.7

27. -7.74 **28.** $-\frac{8}{9}$

29. 0 **30.** 12

Evaluate $-x$ and $-(-x)$ when:

31. $x = 14$. **32.** $x = 1$.

33. $x = -19$. **34.** $x = -1.6$.

35. $x = \frac{2}{3}$. **36.** $x = -\frac{9}{8}$.

Answers

25. 4 **26.** -8.7 **27.** 7.74 **28.** $\frac{8}{9}$
29. 0 **30.** -12 **31.** -14; 14
32. -1; 1 **33.** 19; -19 **34.** 1.6; -1.6
35. $-\frac{2}{3}; \frac{2}{3}$ **36.** $\frac{9}{8}; -\frac{9}{8}$

EXAMPLES Find the opposite, or additive inverse, of each number.

14. 34 The opposite of 34 is -34 because $34 + (-34) = 0$.

15. -8 The opposite of -8 is 8 because $-8 + 8 = 0$.

16. 0 The opposite of 0 is 0 because $0 + 0 = 0$.

17. $-\frac{7}{8}$ The opposite of $-\frac{7}{8}$ is $\frac{7}{8}$ because $-\frac{7}{8} + \frac{7}{8} = 0$.

Do Exercises 25–30.

To name the opposite, we use the symbol $-$, as follows.

SYMBOLIZING OPPOSITES

The opposite, or additive inverse, of a number a can be named $-a$ (read "the opposite of a," or "the additive inverse of a").

Note that if we take a number, say, 8, and find its opposite, -8, and then find the opposite of the result, we will have the original number, 8, again.

THE OPPOSITE OF AN OPPOSITE

The **opposite of the opposite** of a number is the number itself. (The additive inverse of the additive inverse of a number is the number itself.) That is, for any number a,

$$-(-a) = a.$$

EXAMPLE 18 Evaluate $-x$ and $-(-x)$ when $x = 16$.

If $x = 16$, then $-x = -16$. The opposite of 16 is -16.

If $x = 16$, then $-(-x) = -(-16) = 16$. The opposite of the opposite of 16 is 16.

EXAMPLE 19 Evaluate $-x$ and $-(-x)$ when $x = -3$.

If $x = -3$, then $-x = -(-3) = 3$.

If $x = -3$, then $-(-x) = -(-(-3)) = -(3) = -3$.

Note that in Example 19 we used a second set of parentheses to show that we are substituting the negative number -3 for x. Symbolism like $--x$ is not considered meaningful.

Do Exercises 31–36.

A symbol such as -8 is usually read "negative 8." It could be read "the additive inverse of 8," because the additive inverse of 8 is negative 8. It could also be read "the opposite of 8," because the opposite of 8 is -8. Thus a symbol like -8 can be read in more than one way. It is never correct to read -8 as "minus 8."

Caution!

A symbol like $-x$, which has a variable, should be read "the opposite of x" or "the additive inverse of x" and *not* "negative x," because we do not know whether x represents a positive number, a negative number, or 0. You can check this in Examples 18 and 19.

We can use the symbolism $-a$ to restate the definition of opposite, or additive inverse.

OPPOSITES, OR ADDITIVE INVERSES

For any real number a, the **opposite**, or **additive inverse**, of a, denoted $-a$, is such that

$$a + (-a) = (-a) + a = 0.$$

Signs of Numbers

A negative number is sometimes said to have a "negative sign." A positive number is said to have a "positive sign." When we replace a number with its opposite, we can say that we have "changed its sign."

EXAMPLES Find the opposite. (Change the sign.)

20. -3 $\quad -(-3) = 3$

21. $-\frac{2}{13}$ $\quad -\left(-\frac{2}{13}\right) = \frac{2}{13}$

22. 0 $\quad -(0) = 0$

23. 14 $\quad -(14) = -14$

Do Exercises 37–40.

Find the opposite. (Change the sign.)

37. -4

38. -13.4

39. 0

40. $\frac{1}{4}$

c Applications and Problem Solving

Addition of real numbers occurs in many real-world situations.

EXAMPLE 24 *Lake Level.* In the course of one four-month period, the water level of Lake Clearwater went down 2 ft, up 1 ft, down 5 ft, and up 3 ft. By how much had the lake level changed at the end of the four months?

We let $T =$ the total change in the level of the lake. Then the problem translates to a sum:

Total change	is	1st change	plus	2nd change	plus	3rd change	plus	4th change
↓	↓	↓	↓	↓	↓	↓	↓	↓
T	$=$	-2	$+$	1	$+$	(-5)	$+$	$3.$

Adding from left to right, we have

$$T = -2 + 1 + (-5) + 3 = -1 + (-5) + 3$$
$$= -6 + 3$$
$$= -3.$$

The lake level had dropped 3 ft at the end of the four-month period.

Do Exercise 41.

41. Change in Class Size. During the first two weeks of the semester in Jim's algebra class, 4 students withdrew, 8 students enrolled late, and 6 students were dropped as "no shows." By how many students had the class size changed at the end of the first two weeks?

Answers

37. 4 **38.** 13.4 **39.** 0
40. $-\frac{1}{4}$ **41.** -2 students

1.3 Exercise Set

For Extra Help

MyMathLab | MathXL PRACTICE | WATCH | DOWNLOAD | READ | REVIEW

a Add. Do not use the number line except as a check.

1. $2 + (-9)$ **2.** $-5 + 2$ **3.** $-11 + 5$ **4.** $4 + (-3)$ **5.** $-6 + 6$

6. $8 + (-8)$ **7.** $-3 + (-5)$ **8.** $-4 + (-6)$ **9.** $-7 + 0$ **10.** $-13 + 0$

11. $0 + (-27)$ **12.** $0 + (-35)$ **13.** $17 + (-17)$ **14.** $-15 + 15$ **15.** $-17 + (-25)$

16. $-24 + (-17)$ **17.** $18 + (-18)$ **18.** $-13 + 13$ **19.** $-28 + 28$ **20.** $11 + (-11)$

21. $8 + (-5)$ **22.** $-7 + 8$ **23.** $-4 + (-5)$ **24.** $10 + (-12)$ **25.** $13 + (-6)$

26. $-3 + 14$ **27.** $-25 + 25$ **28.** $50 + (-50)$ **29.** $53 + (-18)$ **30.** $75 + (-45)$

31. $-8.5 + 4.7$ **32.** $-4.6 + 1.9$ **33.** $-2.8 + (-5.3)$ **34.** $-7.9 + (-6.5)$ **35.** $-\frac{3}{5} + \frac{2}{5}$

36. $-\frac{4}{3} + \frac{2}{3}$ **37.** $-\frac{2}{9} + \left(-\frac{5}{9}\right)$ **38.** $-\frac{4}{7} + \left(-\frac{6}{7}\right)$ **39.** $-\frac{5}{8} + \frac{1}{4}$ **40.** $-\frac{5}{6} + \frac{2}{3}$

41. $-\frac{5}{8} + \left(-\frac{1}{6}\right)$ **42.** $-\frac{5}{6} + \left(-\frac{2}{9}\right)$ **43.** $-\frac{3}{8} + \frac{5}{12}$ **44.** $-\frac{7}{16} + \frac{7}{8}$

45. $-\frac{1}{6} + \frac{7}{10}$ **46.** $-\frac{11}{18} + \left(-\frac{3}{4}\right)$ **47.** $\frac{7}{15} + \left(-\frac{1}{9}\right)$ **48.** $-\frac{4}{21} + \frac{3}{14}$

49. $76 + (-15) + (-18) + (-6)$

50. $29 + (-45) + 18 + 32 + (-96)$

51. $-44 + \left(-\frac{3}{8}\right) + 95 + \left(-\frac{5}{8}\right)$

52. $24 + 3.1 + (-44) + (-8.2) + 63$

53. $98 + (-54) + 113 + (-998) + 44 + (-612)$

54. $-458 + (-124) + 1025 + (-917) + 218$

b Find the opposite, or additive inverse.

55. 24

56. -64

57. -26.9

58. 48.2

Evaluate $-x$ when:

59. $x = 8$.

60. $x = -27$.

61. $x = -\frac{13}{8}$.

62. $x = \frac{1}{236}$.

Evaluate $-(-x)$ when:

63. $x = -43$.

64. $x = 39$.

65. $x = \frac{4}{3}$.

66. $x = -7.1$.

Find the opposite. (Change the sign.)

67. -24

68. -12.3

69. $-\frac{3}{8}$

70. 10

c Solve.

71. *Tallest Mountain.* The tallest mountain in the world, when measured from base to peak, is Mauna Kea (White Mountain) in Hawaii. From its base 19,684 ft below sea level in the Hawaiian Trough, it rises 33,480 ft. What is the elevation of the peak above sea level?
Source: *The Guinness Book of Records*

72. *Telephone Bills.* Erika's cell-phone bill for July was \$82. She sent a check for \$50 and then made \$37 worth of calls in August. How much did she then owe on her cell-phone bill?

73. *Temperature Changes.* One day the temperature in Lawrence, Kansas, is 32°F at 6:00 A.M. It rises 15° by noon, but falls 50° by midnight when a cold front moves in. What is the final temperature?

74. *Stock Changes.* On a recent day, the price of a stock opened at a value of \$61.38. During the day, it rose \$4.75, dropped \$7.38, and rose \$5.13. Find the value of the stock at the end of the day.

75. *Profits and Losses.* The profit of a business is expressed as a positive number and referred to as operating "in the black." A loss is expressed as a negative number and is referred to as operating "in the red." The profits and losses of Xponent Corporation over various years are shown in the bar graph below. Find the sum of the profits and losses.

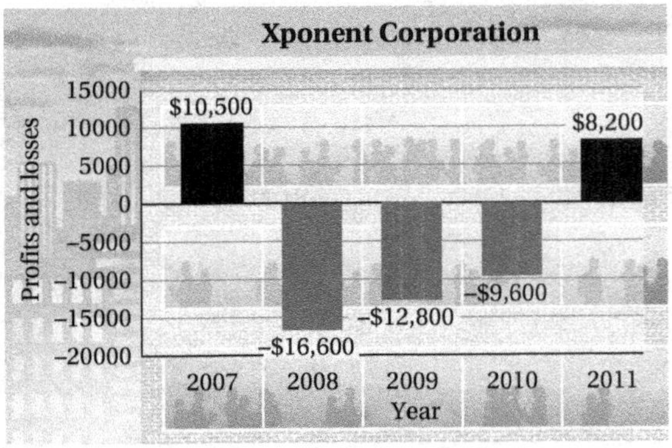

76. *Football Yardage.* In a college football game, the quarterback attempted passes with the following results. Find the total gain or loss.

TRY	GAIN OR LOSS
1st	13-yd gain
2nd	12-yd loss
3rd	21-yd gain

77. *Credit-Card Bills.* On August 1, Lyle's credit-card bill shows that he owes $470. During the month of August, Lyle sends a check for $45 to the credit-card company, charges another $160 in merchandise, and then pays off another $500 of his bill. What is the new amount that Lyle owes at the end of August?

78. *Account Balance.* Leah has $460 in a checking account. She writes a check for $530, makes a deposit of $75, and then writes a check for $90. What is the balance in her account?

Skill Maintenance

Convert to decimal notation. [R.4a]

79. 71.3%

80. $92\frac{7}{8}\%$

Convert to percent notation. [R.4d]

81. $\frac{1}{8}$

82. $\frac{13}{32}$

83. Divide and simplify: $\frac{2}{3} \div \frac{5}{12}$. [R.2c]

84. Subtract and simplify: $\frac{2}{3} - \frac{5}{12}$. [R.2c]

Synthesis

85. For what numbers x is $-x$ negative?

86. For what numbers x is $-x$ positive?

87. If a is positive and b is negative, then $-a + b$ is:

A. Positive.
B. Negative.
C. 0.
D. Cannot be determined without more information

88. If $a = b$ and a and b are negative, then $-a + (-b)$ is:

A. Positive.
B. Negative.
C. 0.
D. Cannot be determined without more information

1.4 Subtraction of Real Numbers

(a) Subtraction

We now consider subtraction of real numbers.

SUBTRACTION

The difference $a - b$ is the number c for which $a = b + c$.

Consider, for example, $45 - 17$. *Think*: What number can we add to 17 to get 45? Since $45 = 17 + 28$, we know that $45 - 17 = 28$. Let's consider an example whose answer is a negative number.

EXAMPLE 1 Subtract: $3 - 7$.

Think: What number can we add to 7 to get 3? The number must be negative. Since $7 + (-4) = 3$, we know the number is -4: $3 - 7 = -4$. That is, $3 - 7 = -4$ because $7 + (-4) = 3$.

Do Exercises 1–3.

The definition above does not provide the most efficient way to do subtraction. We can develop a faster way to subtract. As a rationale for the faster way, let's compare $3 + 7$ and $3 - 7$ on the number line.

To find $3 + 7$ on the number line, we start at 0, move to 3, and then move 7 units farther to the right since 7 is positive.

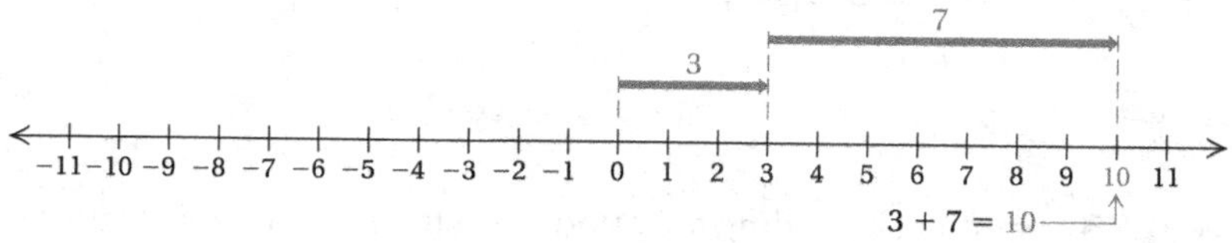

To find $3 - 7$, we do the "opposite" of adding 7: We move 7 units to the *left* to do the subtracting. This is the same as *adding* the opposite of 7, -7, to 3.

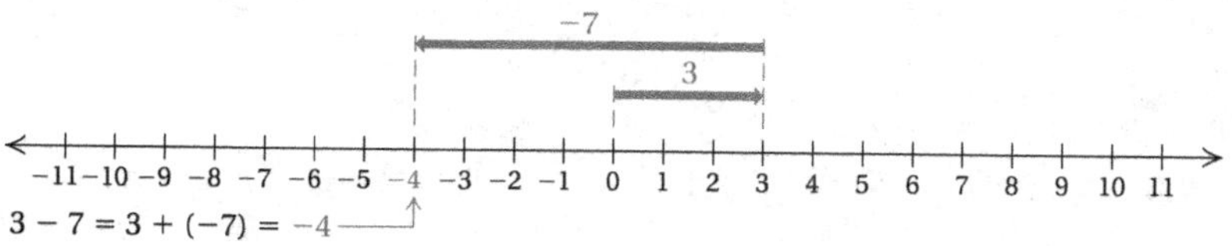

Do Exercises 4–6.

Look for a pattern in the examples shown at right.

SUBTRACTING	ADDING AN OPPOSITE
$5 - 8 = -3$	$5 + (-8) = -3$
$-6 - 4 = -10$	$-6 + (-4) = -10$
$-7 - (-2) = -5$	$-7 + 2 = -5$

OBJECTIVES

(a) Subtract real numbers and simplify combinations of additions and subtractions.

(b) Solve applied problems involving subtraction of real numbers.

Subtract.

1. $-6 - 4$

Think: What number can be added to 4 to get -6:

$\square + 4 = -6?$

2. $-7 - (-10)$

Think: What number can be added to -10 to get -7:

$\square + (-10) = -7?$

3. $-7 - (-2)$

Think: What number can be added to -2 to get -7:

$\square + (-2) = -7?$

Subtract. Use the number line, doing the "opposite" of addition.

4. $5 - 9$

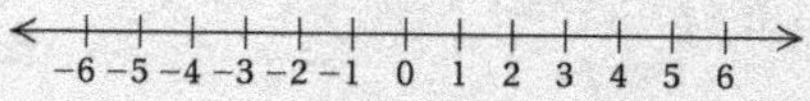

5. $-3 - 2$

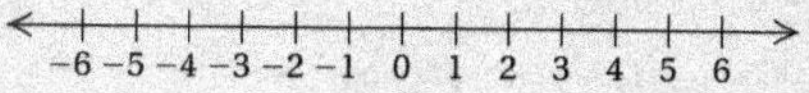

6. $-4 - (-3)$

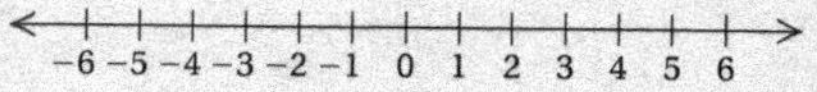

Answers

1. −10 2. 3 3. −5 4. −4
5. −5 6. −1

Complete the addition and compare with the subtraction.

7. $4 - 6 = -2;$
$4 + (-6) =$ ______

8. $-3 - 8 = -11;$
$-3 + (-8) =$ ______

9. $-5 - (-9) = 4;$
$-5 + 9 =$ ______

10. $-5 - (-3) = -2;$
$-5 + 3 =$ ______

Do Exercises 7–10.

Perhaps you have noticed that we can subtract by adding the opposite of the number being subtracted. This can always be done.

SUBTRACTING BY ADDING THE OPPOSITE

For any real numbers a and b,

$$a - b = a + (-b).$$

(To subtract, add the opposite, or additive inverse, of the number being subtracted.)

This is the method generally used for quick subtraction of real numbers.

EXAMPLES Subtract.

2. $2 - 6 = 2 + (-6) = -4$ — The opposite of 6 is -6. We change the subtraction to addition and add the opposite. *Check*: $-4 + 6 = 2$.

3. $4 - (-9) = 4 + 9 = 13$ — The opposite of -9 is 9. We change the subtraction to addition and add the opposite. *Check*: $13 + (-9) = 4$.

4. $-4.2 - (-3.6) = -4.2 + 3.6 = -0.6$ — Adding the opposite. *Check*: $-0.6 + (-3.6) = -4.2$.

5. $-\frac{1}{2} - \left(-\frac{3}{4}\right) = -\frac{1}{2} + \frac{3}{4}$ — Adding the opposite.

$= -\frac{2}{4} + \frac{3}{4} = \frac{1}{4}$ — *Check*: $\frac{1}{4} + \left(-\frac{3}{4}\right) = -\frac{1}{2}$.

Subtract.

11. $2 - 8$

12. $-6 - 10$

13. $12.4 - 5.3$

14. $-8 - (-11)$

15. $-8 - (-8)$

16. $\frac{2}{3} - \left(-\frac{5}{6}\right)$

Do Exercises 11–16.

EXAMPLES Subtract by adding the opposite of the number being subtracted.

6. $3 - 5$ — *Think*: "Three minus five is three plus the opposite of five"

$3 - 5 = 3 + (-5) = -2$

7. $\frac{1}{8} - \frac{7}{8}$ — *Think*: "One-eighth minus seven-eighths is one-eighth plus the opposite of seven-eighths"

$\frac{1}{8} - \frac{7}{8} = \frac{1}{8} + \left(-\frac{7}{8}\right) = -\frac{6}{8}$, or $-\frac{3}{4}$

8. $-4.6 - (-9.8)$ — *Think*: "Negative four point six minus negative nine point eight is negative four point six plus the opposite of negative nine point eight"

$-4.6 - (-9.8) = -4.6 + 9.8 = 5.2$

9. $-\frac{3}{4} - \frac{7}{5}$ — *Think*: "Negative three-fourths minus seven-fifths is negative three-fourths plus the opposite of seven-fifths"

$-\frac{3}{4} - \frac{7}{5} = -\frac{3}{4} + \left(-\frac{7}{5}\right) = -\frac{15}{20} + \left(-\frac{28}{20}\right) = -\frac{43}{20}$

Subtract by adding the opposite of the number being subtracted.

17. $3 - 11$

18. $12 - 5$

19. $-12 - (-9)$

20. $-12.4 - 10.9$

21. $-\frac{4}{5} - \left(-\frac{4}{5}\right)$

Do Exercises 17–21.

Answers

7. -2 8. -11 9. 4 10. -2 11. -6
12. -16 13. 7.1 14. 3 15. 0 16. $\frac{3}{2}$
17. -8 18. 7 19. -3 20. -23.3
21. 0

When several additions and subtractions occur together, we can make them all additions.

EXAMPLES Simplify.

10. $8 - (-4) - 2 - (-4) + 2 = 8 + 4 + (-2) + 4 + 2$ Adding the opposite

$= 16$

11. $8.2 - (-6.1) + 2.3 - (-4) = 8.2 + 6.1 + 2.3 + 4 = 20.6$

12. $\frac{3}{4} - \left(-\frac{1}{12}\right) - \frac{5}{6} - \frac{2}{3} = \frac{9}{12} + \frac{1}{12} + \left(-\frac{10}{12}\right) + \left(-\frac{8}{12}\right)$

$= \frac{9 + 1 + (-10) + (-8)}{12}$

$= \frac{-8}{12} = -\frac{8}{12} = -\frac{2}{3}$

Do Exercises 22–24.

Simplify.

22. $-6 - (-2) - (-4) - 12 + 3$

23. $\frac{2}{3} - \frac{4}{5} - \left(-\frac{11}{15}\right) + \frac{7}{10} - \frac{5}{2}$

24. $-9.6 + 7.4 - (-3.9) - (-11)$

b Applications and Problem Solving

Let's now see how we can use subtraction of real numbers to solve applied problems.

EXAMPLE 13 *Surface Temperatures on Mars.* Surface temperatures on Mars vary from $-128°C$ during polar night to 27°C at the equator during midday at the closest point in orbit to the sun. Find the difference between the highest value and the lowest value in this temperature range.

Source: Mars Institute

We let $D =$ the difference in the temperatures. Then the problem translates to the following subtraction:

Difference in temperature	is	Highest temperature	minus	Lowest temperature
↓	↓	↓	↓	↓
D	$=$	27	$-$	(-128)
D	$= 27 + 128 = 155.$			

The difference in the temperatures is 155°C.

Do Exercise 25.

25. Temperature Extremes. The highest temperature ever recorded in the United States is 134°F in Greenland Ranch, California, on July 10, 1913. The lowest temperature ever recorded is $-80°F$ in Prospect Creek, Alaska, on January 23, 1971. How much higher was the temperature in Greenland Ranch than the temperature in Prospect Creek?

Source: National Oceanographic and Atmospheric Administration

Answers

22. -9 **23.** $-\frac{6}{5}$ **24.** 12.7 **25.** 214°F

1.4 Exercise Set

For Extra Help
MyMathLab
Math XL PRACTICE · WATCH · DOWNLOAD · READ · REVIEW

a Subtract.

1. $2 - 9$

2. $3 - 8$

3. $-8 - (-2)$

4. $-6 - (-8)$

5. $-11 - (-11)$

6. $-6 - (-6)$

7. $12 - 16$

8. $14 - 19$

9. $20 - 27$

10. $30 - 4$

11. $-9 - (-3)$

12. $-7 - (-9)$

13. $-40 - (-40)$

14. $-9 - (-9)$

15. $7 - (-7)$

16. $4 - (-4)$

17. $8 - (-3)$

18. $-7 - 4$

19. $-6 - 8$

20. $6 - (-10)$

21. $-4 - (-9)$

22. $-14 - 2$

23. $-6 - (-5)$

24. $-4 - (-3)$

25. $8 - (-10)$

26. $5 - (-6)$

27. $-5 - (-2)$

28. $-3 - (-1)$

29. $-7 - 14$

30. $-9 - 16$

31. $0 - (-5)$

32. $0 - (-1)$

33. $-8 - 0$

34. $-9 - 0$

35. $7 - (-5)$

36. $7 - (-4)$

37. $2 - 25$

38. $18 - 63$

39. $-42 - 26$

40. $-18 - 63$

41. $-71 - 2$

42. $-49 - 3$

43. $24 - (-92)$

44. $48 - (-73)$

45. $-50 - (-50)$

46. $-70 - (-70)$

47. $-\frac{3}{8} - \frac{5}{8}$

48. $\frac{3}{9} - \frac{9}{9}$

49. $\frac{3}{4} - \frac{2}{3}$

50. $\frac{5}{8} - \frac{3}{4}$

51. $-\frac{3}{4} - \frac{2}{3}$

52. $-\frac{5}{8} - \frac{3}{4}$

53. $-\frac{5}{8} - \left(-\frac{3}{4}\right)$

54. $-\frac{3}{4} - \left(-\frac{2}{3}\right)$

55. $6.1 - (-13.8)$

56. $1.5 - (-3.5)$

57. $-2.7 - 5.9$

58. $-3.2 - 5.8$

59. $0.99 - 1$

60. $0.87 - 1$

61. $-79 - 114$

62. $-197 - 216$

63. $0 - (-500)$

64. $500 - (-1000)$

65. $-2.8 - 0$

66. $6.04 - 1.1$

67. $7 - 10.53$

68. $8 - (-9.3)$

69. $\frac{1}{6} - \frac{2}{3}$

70. $-\frac{3}{8} - \left(-\frac{1}{2}\right)$

71. $-\frac{4}{7} - \left(-\frac{10}{7}\right)$

72. $\frac{12}{5} - \frac{12}{5}$

73. $-\frac{7}{10} - \frac{10}{15}$

74. $-\frac{4}{18} - \left(-\frac{2}{9}\right)$

75. $\frac{1}{5} - \frac{1}{3}$

76. $-\frac{1}{7} - \left(-\frac{1}{6}\right)$

77. $\frac{5}{12} - \frac{7}{16}$

78. $-\frac{1}{35} - \left(-\frac{9}{40}\right)$

79. $-\frac{2}{15} - \frac{7}{12}$

80. $\frac{2}{21} - \frac{9}{14}$

Simplify.

81. $18 - (-15) - 3 - (-5) + 2$

82. $22 - (-18) + 7 + (-42) - 27$

83. $-31 + (-28) - (-14) - 17$

84. $-43 - (-19) - (-21) + 25$

85. $-34 - 28 + (-33) - 44$

86. $39 + (-88) - 29 - (-83)$

87. $-93 - (-84) - 41 - (-56)$

88. $84 + (-99) + 44 - (-18) - 43$

89. $-5.4 - (-30.9) + 30.8 + 40.2 - (-12)$

90. $14.9 - (-50.7) + 20 - (-32.8)$

91. $-\frac{7}{12} + \frac{3}{4} - \left(-\frac{5}{8}\right) - \frac{13}{24}$

92. $-\frac{11}{16} + \frac{5}{32} - \left(-\frac{1}{4}\right) + \frac{7}{8}$

b Solve.

93. *Ocean Depth.* The deepest point in the Pacific Ocean is the Marianas Trench, with a depth of 10,924 m. The deepest point in the Atlantic Ocean is the Puerto Rico Trench, with a depth of 8605 m. What is the difference in the elevation of the two trenches?

Source: *The World Almanac and Book of Facts*

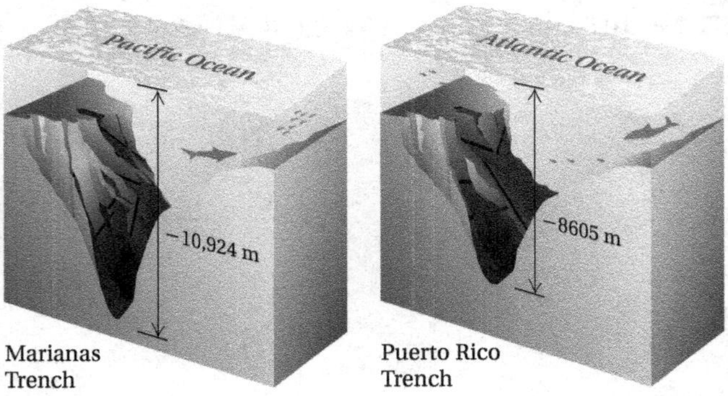

94. *Elevations in Africa.* The elevation of the highest point in Africa, Mt. Kilimanjaro, Tanzania, is 19,340 ft. The lowest elevation, at Lake Assal, Djibouti, is −512 ft. What is the difference in the elevations of the two locations?

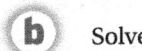

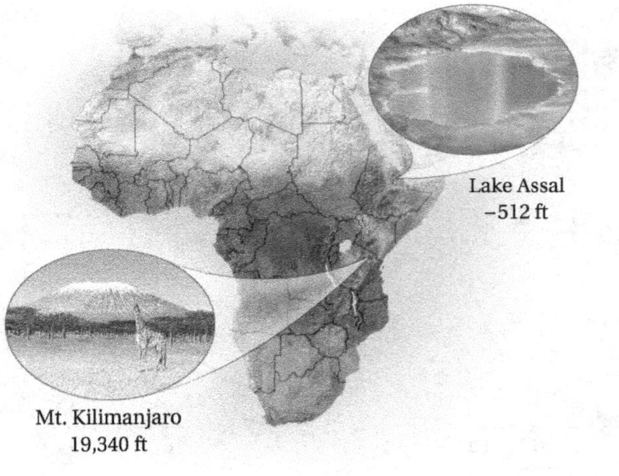

95. Claire has a charge of \$476.89 on her credit card, but she then returns a sweater that cost \$128.95. How much does she now owe on her credit card?

96. Chris has \$720 in a checking account. He writes a check for \$970 to pay for a sound system. What is the balance in his checking account?

97. *Difference in Elevation.* At its highest point, the elevation of Denver, Colorado, is 5672 ft above sea level. At its lowest point, the elevation of New Orleans, Louisiana, is 4 ft below sea level. Find the difference in the elevations.

Source: *Information Please Almanac*

98. *Difference in Elevation.* The lowest elevation in North America, Death Valley, California, is 282 ft below sea level. The highest elevation in North America, Mount McKinley, Alaska, is 20,320 ft. Find the difference in elevation between the highest point and the lowest point.

Source: National Geographic Society

99. *Low Points on Continents.* The lowest point in Africa is Lake Assal, which is 512 ft below sea level. The lowest point in South America is the Valdes Peninsula, which is 131 ft below sea level. How much lower is Lake Assal than the Valdes Peninsula?

Source: National Geographic Society

100. *Temperature Records.* The greatest recorded temperature change in one 24-hr period occurred between January 23 and January 24, 1916, in Browning, Montana, where the temperature fell from to 44°F to −56°F. By how much did the temperature drop?

Source: *The Guinness Book of Records*

101. *Surface Temperature on Mercury.* Surface temperatures on Mercury vary from 840°F on the equator when the planet is closest to the sun to −290°F at night. Find the difference between these two temperatures.

102. *Run Differential.* In baseball, the difference between the number of runs that a team scores and the number of runs that it allows its opponents to score is called the *run differential.* That is,

$$\text{Run differential} = \begin{matrix}\text{Number of}\\ \text{runs scored}\end{matrix} - \begin{matrix}\text{Number of}\\ \text{runs allowed.}\end{matrix}$$

Teams strive for a positive run differential.

Source: Major League Baseball

a) In a recent season, the Chicago White Sox scored 810 runs and allowed 729 runs to be scored on them. Find the run differential.

b) In a recent season, the Pittsburgh Pirates scored 735 runs and allowed 884 runs to be scored on them. Find the run differential.

Skill Maintenance

Simplify. [R.5c]

103. $256 \div 64 \div 2^3 + 100$

104. $5 \cdot 6 + (7 \cdot 2)^2$

105. $2^5 \div 4 + 20 \div 2^2$

106. $65 - 5^2 \div 5 - 5 \cdot 2$

107. Add and simplify: $\frac{1}{8} + \frac{7}{12} + \frac{5}{24}$. [R.2c]

108. Simplify: $\frac{164}{256}$. [R.2b]

Synthesis

Determine whether each statement is true or false for all integers a and b. If false, give an example to show why. Examples may vary.

109. $a - 0 = 0 - a$

110. $0 - a = a$

111. If $a \neq b$, then $a - b \neq 0$.

112. If $a = -b$, then $a + b = 0$.

113. If $a + b = 0$, then a and b are opposites.

114. If $a - b = 0$, then $a = -b$.

Mid-Chapter Review

Concept Reinforcement

Determine whether each statement is true or false.

______ **1.** All rational numbers can be named using fraction notation. [1.2c]

______ **2.** If $a > b$, then a lies to the left of b on the number line. [1.2d]

______ **3.** The absolute value of a number is always nonnegative. [1.2e]

______ **4.** We can translate "7 less than y" as $7 - y$. [1.1b]

Guided Solutions

Fill in each blank with the number that creates a correct statement or solution.

5. Evaluate $-x$ and $-(-x)$ when $x = -4$. [1.3b]

$-x = -(\square) = \square$;

$-(-x) = -(-(\square)) = -(\square) = \square$

Subtract. [1.4a]

6. $5 - 13 = 5 + (\square) = \square$

7. $-6 - 7 = -6 + (\square) = \square$

Mixed Review

Evaluate. [1.1a]

8. $\dfrac{3m}{n}$, when $m = 8$ and $n = 6$

9. $\dfrac{a + b}{2}$, when $a = 5$ and $b = 17$

Translate each phrase to an algebraic expression. Use any letter for the variable. [1.1b]

10. Three times some number

11. Five less than some number

12. State the integers that correspond to this situation: Jerilyn deposited $450 in her checking account. Later that week, she wrote a check for $79. [1.2a]

13. Graph -3.5 on the number line. [1.2b]

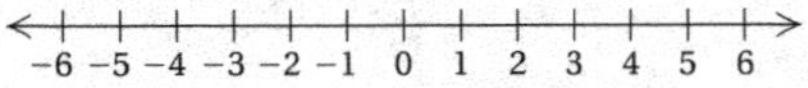

Convert to decimal notation. [1.2c]

14. $-\dfrac{4}{5}$

15. $\dfrac{7}{3}$

Use either $<$ or $>$ for $\square$ to write a true sentence. [1.2d]

16. $-5 \;\square\; -3$

17. $-9.9 \;\square\; -10.1$

Write true or false. [1.2d]

18. $-8 \geq -5$

19. $-4 \leq -4$

Write an inequality with the same meaning. [1.2d]

20. $y < 5$

21. $-3 \geq t$

Find the absolute value. [1.2e]

22. $|15.6|$

23. $|-18|$

24. $|0|$

25. $\left|-\frac{12}{5}\right|$

Find the opposite, or additive inverse, of the number. [1.3b]

26. -5.6

27. $\frac{7}{4}$

28. 0

29. -49

30. Evaluate $-x$ when x is -19. [1.3b]

31. Evaluate $-(-x)$ when x is 2.3. [1.3b]

Compute and simplify. [1.3a], [1.4a]

32. $7 + (-9)$

33. $-\frac{3}{8} + \frac{1}{4}$

34. $3.6 + (-3.6)$

35. $-8 + (-9)$

36. $\frac{2}{3} + \left(-\frac{9}{8}\right)$

37. $-4.2 + (-3.9)$

38. $-14 + 5$

39. $19 + (-21)$

40. $-4.1 - 6.3$

41. $5 - (-11)$

42. $-\frac{1}{4} - \left(-\frac{3}{5}\right)$

43. $12 - 24$

44. $-8 - (-4)$

45. $-\frac{1}{2} - \frac{5}{6}$

46. $12.3 - 14.1$

47. $6 - (-7)$

48. $16 - (-9) - 20 - (-4)$

49. $-4 + (-10) - (-3) - 12$

50. $17 - (-25) + 15 - (-18)$

51. $-9 + (-3) + 16 - (-10)$

Solve. [1.3c], [1.4b]

52. *Temperature Change.* In chemistry lab, Ben works with a substance whose initial temperature is 25°C. During an experiment, the temperature falls to −8°C. Find the difference between the two temperatures.

53. *Stock Price Change.* The price of a stock opened at $56.12. During the day, it dropped $1.18, then rose $1.22, and then dropped $1.36. Find the value of the stock at the end of the day.

Understanding Through Discussion and Writing

54. Give three examples of rational numbers that are not integers. Explain. [1.2b]

55. Give three examples of irrational numbers. Explain the difference between an irrational number and a rational number. [1.2b, d]

56. Explain in your own words why the sum of two negative numbers is always negative. [1.3a]

57. If a negative number is subtracted from a positive number, will the result always be positive? Why or why not? [1.4a]

1.5 Multiplication of Real Numbers

OBJECTIVES

a. Multiply real numbers.

b. Solve applied problems involving multiplication of real numbers.

a Multiplication

Multiplication of real numbers is very much like multiplication of arithmetic numbers. The only difference is that we must determine whether the answer is positive or negative.

Multiplication of a Positive Number and a Negative Number

To see how to multiply a positive number and a negative number, consider the pattern of the following.

This number decreases by 1 each time.

$$\begin{aligned} 4 \cdot 5 &= 20 \\ 3 \cdot 5 &= 15 \\ 2 \cdot 5 &= 10 \\ 1 \cdot 5 &= 5 \\ 0 \cdot 5 &= 0 \\ -1 \cdot 5 &= -5 \\ -2 \cdot 5 &= -10 \\ -3 \cdot 5 &= -15 \end{aligned}$$

This number decreases by 5 each time.

1. Complete, as in the example.

$$\begin{aligned} 4 \cdot 10 &= 40 \\ 3 \cdot 10 &= 30 \\ 2 \cdot 10 &= \\ 1 \cdot 10 &= \\ 0 \cdot 10 &= \\ -1 \cdot 10 &= \\ -2 \cdot 10 &= \\ -3 \cdot 10 &= \end{aligned}$$

Do Exercise 1.

According to this pattern, it looks as though the product of a negative number and a positive number is negative. That is the case, and we have the first part of the rule for multiplying real numbers.

THE PRODUCT OF A POSITIVE NUMBER AND A NEGATIVE NUMBER

To multiply a positive number and a negative number, multiply their absolute values. The answer is negative.

EXAMPLES Multiply.

1. $8(-5) = -40$

2. $-\frac{1}{3} \cdot \frac{5}{7} = -\frac{5}{21}$

3. $(-7.2)5 = -36$

Do Exercises 2–7.

Multiply.

2. $-3 \cdot 6$

3. $20 \cdot (-5)$

4. $4 \cdot (-20)$

5. $-\frac{2}{3} \cdot \frac{5}{6}$

6. $-4.23(7.1)$

7. $\frac{7}{8}\left(-\frac{4}{5}\right)$

Answers

1. 20; 10; 0; −10; −20; −30 2. −18
3. −100 4. −80 5. $-\frac{5}{9}$
6. −30.033 7. $-\frac{7}{10}$

Multiplication of Two Negative Numbers

How do we multiply two negative numbers? Again, we look for a pattern.

This number decreases by 1 each time. This number increases by 5 each time.

$$\begin{aligned} 4 \cdot (-5) &= -20 \\ 3 \cdot (-5) &= -15 \\ 2 \cdot (-5) &= -10 \\ 1 \cdot (-5) &= -5 \\ 0 \cdot (-5) &= 0 \\ -1 \cdot (-5) &= 5 \\ -2 \cdot (-5) &= 10 \\ -3 \cdot (-5) &= 15 \end{aligned}$$

Do Exercise 8.

According to the pattern, it appears that the product of two negative numbers is positive. That is actually so, and we have the second part of the rule for multiplying real numbers.

THE PRODUCT OF TWO NEGATIVE NUMBERS

To multiply two negative numbers, multiply their absolute values. The answer is positive.

Do Exercises 9–14.

The following is another way to consider the rules we have for multiplication.

To multiply two nonzero real numbers:

a) Multiply the absolute values.

b) If the signs are the same, the answer is positive.

c) If the signs are different, the answer is negative.

Multiplication by Zero

The only case that we have not considered is multiplying by zero. As with nonnegative numbers, the product of any real number and 0 is 0.

THE MULTIPLICATION PROPERTY OF ZERO

For any real number a,

$$a \cdot 0 = 0 \cdot a = 0.$$

(The product of 0 and any real number is 0.)

EXAMPLES Multiply.

4. $(-3)(-4) = 12$

5. $-1.6(2) = -3.2$

6. $-19 \cdot 0 = 0$

7. $\left(-\frac{5}{6}\right)\left(-\frac{1}{9}\right) = \frac{5}{54}$

8. $0 \cdot (-452) = 0$

9. $23 \cdot 0 \cdot \left(-8\frac{2}{3}\right) = 0$

Do Exercises 15–20.

8. Complete, as in the example.

$$\begin{aligned} 3 \cdot (-10) &= -30 \\ 2 \cdot (-10) &= -20 \\ 1 \cdot (-10) &= \\ 0 \cdot (-10) &= \\ -1 \cdot (-10) &= \\ -2 \cdot (-10) &= \\ -3 \cdot (-10) &= \end{aligned}$$

Multiply.

9. $-9 \cdot (-3)$

10. $-16 \cdot (-2)$

11. $-7 \cdot (-5)$

12. $-\frac{4}{7}\left(-\frac{5}{9}\right)$

13. $-\frac{3}{2}\left(-\frac{4}{9}\right)$

14. $-3.25(-4.14)$

Multiply.

15. $5(-6)$

16. $(-5)(-6)$

17. $(-3.2) \cdot 10$

18. $\left(-\frac{4}{5}\right)\left(\frac{10}{3}\right)$

19. $0 \cdot (-34.2)$

20. $-\frac{5}{7} \cdot 0 \cdot \left(-4\frac{2}{3}\right)$

Answers

8. -10; 0; 10; 20; 30 **9.** 27 **10.** 32 **11.** 35 **12.** $\frac{20}{63}$ **13.** $\frac{2}{3}$ **14.** 13.455 **15.** -30 **16.** 30 **17.** -32 **18.** $-\frac{8}{3}$ **19.** 0 **20.** 0

Multiplying More Than Two Numbers

When multiplying more than two real numbers, we can choose order and grouping as we please.

EXAMPLES Multiply.

10. $-8 \cdot 2(-3) = -16(-3)$ Multiplying the first two numbers

$= 48$

11. $-8 \cdot 2(-3) = 24 \cdot 2$ Multiplying the negatives. Every pair of negative numbers gives a positive product.

$= 48$

12. $-3(-2)(-5)(4) = 6(-5)(4)$ Multiplying the first two numbers

$= (-30)4$

$= -120$

13. $\left(-\frac{1}{2}\right)(8)\left(-\frac{2}{3}\right)(-6) = (-4)4$ Multiplying the first two numbers and the last two numbers

$= -16$

14. $-5 \cdot (-2) \cdot (-3) \cdot (-6) = 10 \cdot 18 = 180$

15. $(-3)(-5)(-2)(-3)(-6) = (-30)(18) = -540$

Considering that the product of a pair of negative numbers is positive, we see the following pattern.

> The product of an even number of negative numbers is positive.
> The product of an odd number of negative numbers is negative.

Do Exercises 21–26.

EXAMPLE 16 Evaluate $2x^2$ when $x = 3$ and when $x = -3$.

$2x^2 = 2(3)^2 = 2(9) = 18;$

$2x^2 = 2(-3)^2 = 2(9) = 18$

Let's compare the expressions $(-x)^2$ and $-x^2$.

EXAMPLE 17 Evaluate $(-x)^2$ and $-x^2$ when $x = 5$.

$(-x)^2 = (-5)^2 = (-5)(-5) = 25;$ Substitute 5 for x. Then evaluate the power.

$-x^2 = -(5)^2 = -(25) = -25$ Substitute 5 for x. Evaluate the power. Then find the opposite.

In Example 17, we see that the expressions $(-x)^2$ and $-x^2$ are *not* equivalent. That is, they do not have the same value for every allowable replacement of the variable by a real number. To find $(-x)^2$, we take the opposite and then square. To find $-x^2$, we find the square and then take the opposite.

Multiply.

21. $5 \cdot (-3) \cdot 2$

22. $-3 \times (-4.1) \times (-2.5)$

23. $-\frac{1}{2} \cdot \left(-\frac{4}{3}\right) \cdot \left(-\frac{5}{2}\right)$

24. $-2 \cdot (-5) \cdot (-4) \cdot (-3)$

25. $(-4)(-5)(-2)(-3)(-1)$

26. $(-1)(-1)(-2)(-3)(-1)(-1)$

Answers

21. -30 **22.** -30.75 **23.** $-\frac{5}{3}$
24. 120 **25.** -120 **26.** 6

EXAMPLE 18 Evaluate $(-a)^2$ and $-a^2$ when $a = -4$.

To make sense of the substitutions and computations, we introduce extra grouping symbols into the expressions.

$$(-a)^2 = [-(-4)]^2 = [4]^2 = 16;$$
$$-a^2 = -(-4)^2 = -(16) = -16$$

Do Exercises 27–29.

27. Evaluate $3x^2$ when $x = 4$ and when $x = -4$.

28. Evaluate $(-x)^2$ and $-x^2$ when $x = 2$.

29. Evaluate $(-x)^2$ and $-x^2$ when $x = -3$.

b Applications and Problem Solving

We now consider multiplication of real numbers in real-world applications.

EXAMPLE 19 *Chemical Reaction.* During a chemical reaction, the temperature in a beaker decreased by 2°C every minute until 10:23 A.M. If the temperature was 17°C at 10:00 A.M., when the reaction began, what was the temperature at 10:23 A.M.?

This is a multistep problem. We first find the total number of degrees that the temperature dropped, using −2° for each minute. Since it dropped 2° for each of the 23 minutes, we know that the total drop d is given by

$$d = 23 \cdot (-2) = -46.$$

To determine the temperature after this time period, we find the sum of 17 and −46, or

$$T = 17 + (-46) = -29.$$

Thus the temperature at 10:23 A.M. was −29°C.

Do Exercise 30.

30. Chemical Reaction. During a chemical reaction, the temperature in a beaker increased by 3°C every minute until 1:34 P.M. If the temperature was −17°C at 1:10 P.M., when the reaction began, what was the temperature at 1:34 P.M.?

STUDY TIPS

MAKING POSITIVE CHOICES

Making the right choices can give you the power to succeed in learning mathematics.

You can choose to improve your attitude and raise the academic goals that you have set for yourself. Projecting a positive attitude toward your study of mathematics and expecting a positive outcome can make it easier for you to learn and to perform well in this course.

Here are some positive choices you can make:

- Choose to make a strong commitment to learning.
- Choose to allocate the proper amount of time to learn.
- Choose to place the primary responsibility for learning on yourself.

Well-known American psychologist William James once said, "The one thing that will guarantee the successful conclusion of a doubtful undertaking is faith in the beginning that you can do it."

Answers

27. 48; 48 **28.** 4; −4
29. 9; −9 **30.** 55°C

1.5 Exercise Set

For Extra Help
MyMathLab
MathXL PRACTICE | WATCH | DOWNLOAD | READ | REVIEW

a Multiply.

1. $-4 \cdot 2$

2. $-3 \cdot 5$

3. $-8 \cdot 6$

4. $-5 \cdot 2$

5. $8 \cdot (-3)$

6. $9 \cdot (-5)$

7. $-9 \cdot 8$

8. $-10 \cdot 3$

9. $-8 \cdot (-2)$

10. $-2 \cdot (-5)$

11. $-7 \cdot (-6)$

12. $-9 \cdot (-2)$

13. $15 \cdot (-8)$

14. $-12 \cdot (-10)$

15. $-14 \cdot 17$

16. $-13 \cdot (-15)$

17. $-25 \cdot (-48)$

18. $39 \cdot (-43)$

19. $-3.5 \cdot (-28)$

20. $97 \cdot (-2.1)$

21. $9 \cdot (-8)$

22. $7 \cdot (-9)$

23. $4 \cdot (-3.1)$

24. $3 \cdot (-2.2)$

25. $-5 \cdot (-6)$

26. $-6 \cdot (-4)$

27. $-7 \cdot (-3.1)$

28. $-4 \cdot (-3.2)$

29. $\frac{2}{3} \cdot \left(-\frac{3}{5}\right)$

30. $\frac{5}{7} \cdot \left(-\frac{2}{3}\right)$

31. $-\frac{3}{8} \cdot \left(-\frac{2}{9}\right)$

32. $-\frac{5}{8} \cdot \left(-\frac{2}{5}\right)$

33. -6.3×2.7

34. -4.1×9.5

35. $-\frac{5}{9} \cdot \frac{3}{4}$

36. $-\frac{8}{3} \cdot \frac{9}{4}$

37. $7 \cdot (-4) \cdot (-3) \cdot 5$

38. $9 \cdot (-2) \cdot (-6) \cdot 7$

39. $-\frac{2}{3} \cdot \frac{1}{2} \cdot \left(-\frac{6}{7}\right)$

40. $-\frac{1}{8} \cdot \left(-\frac{1}{4}\right) \cdot \left(-\frac{3}{5}\right)$

41. $-3 \cdot (-4) \cdot (-5)$

42. $-2 \cdot (-5) \cdot (-7)$

43. $-2 \cdot (-5) \cdot (-3) \cdot (-5)$

44. $-3 \cdot (-5) \cdot (-2) \cdot (-1)$

45. $\frac{1}{5}\left(-\frac{2}{9}\right)$

46. $-\frac{3}{5}\left(-\frac{2}{7}\right)$

47. $-7 \cdot (-21) \cdot 13$

48. $-14 \cdot (34) \cdot 12$

49. $-4 \cdot (-1.8) \cdot 7$

50. $-8 \cdot (-1.3) \cdot (-5)$

51. $-\frac{1}{9}\left(-\frac{2}{3}\right)\left(\frac{5}{7}\right)$

52. $-\frac{7}{2}\left(-\frac{5}{7}\right)\left(-\frac{2}{5}\right)$

53. $4 \cdot (-4) \cdot (-5) \cdot (-12)$

54. $-2 \cdot (-3) \cdot (-4) \cdot (-5)$

55. $0.07 \cdot (-7) \cdot 6 \cdot (-6)$

56. $80 \cdot (-0.8) \cdot (-90) \cdot (-0.09)$

57. $\left(-\frac{5}{6}\right)\left(\frac{1}{8}\right)\left(-\frac{3}{7}\right)\left(-\frac{1}{7}\right)$

58. $\left(\frac{4}{5}\right)\left(-\frac{2}{3}\right)\left(-\frac{15}{7}\right)\left(\frac{1}{2}\right)$

59. $(-14) \cdot (-27) \cdot 0$

60. $7 \cdot (-6) \cdot 5 \cdot (-4) \cdot 3 \cdot (-2) \cdot 1 \cdot 0$

61. $(-8)(-9)(-10)$

62. $(-7)(-8)(-9)(-10)$

63. $(-6)(-7)(-8)(-9)(-10)$

64. $(-5)(-6)(-7)(-8)(-9)(-10)$

65. $(-1)^{12}$

66. $(-1)^9$

67. Evaluate $(-x)^2$ and $-x^2$ when $x = 4$ and when $x = -4$.

68. Evaluate $(-x)^2$ and $-x^2$ when $x = 10$ and when $x = -10$.

69. Evaluate $(-3x)^2$ and $-3x^2$ when $x = 7$.

70. Evaluate $(-2x)^2$ and $-2x^2$ when $x = 3$.

71. Evaluate $5x^2$ when $x = 2$ and when $x = -2$.

72. Evaluate $2x^2$ when $x = 5$ and when $x = -5$.

73. Evaluate $-2x^3$ when $x = 1$ and when $x = -1$.

74. Evaluate $-3x^3$ when $x = 2$ and when $x = -2$.

b Solve.

75. *Weight Loss.* Dave lost 2 lb each week for a period of 10 weeks. Express his total weight change as an integer.

76. *Stock Loss.* Emma lost \$3 each day for a period of 5 days in the value of a stock she owned. Express her total loss as an integer.

77. *Chemical Reaction.* The temperature of a chemical compound was 0°C at 11:00 A.M. During a reaction, it dropped 3°C per minute until 11:18 A.M. What was the temperature at 11:18 A.M.?

78. *Chemical Reaction.* The temperature of a chemical compound was −5°C at 3:20 P.M. During a reaction, it increased 2°C per minute until 3:52 P.M. What was the temperature at 3:52 P.M.?

79. *Stock Price.* The price of a stock began the day at \$23.75 per share and dropped \$1.38 per hour for 8 hr. What was the price of the stock after 8 hr?

80. *Population Decrease.* The population of Bloomtown was 12,500. It decreased 380 each year for 4 yr. What was the population of the town after 4 yr?

81. *Diver's Position.* After diving 95 m below the sea level, a diver rises at a rate of 7 m/min for 9 min. Where is the diver in relation to the surface at the end of the 9-min period?

82. *Checking Account Balance.* Karen had \$68 in her checking account. After she had written checks to make seven purchases at \$13 each, what was the balance in her checking account?

83. *Drop in Temperature.* The temperature in Osgood was 62°F at 2:00 P.M. It dropped 6°F per hour for the next 4 hr. What was the temperature at the end of the 4-hr period?

84. *Juice Consumption.* Eliza bought a 64-oz container of cranberry juice and drank 8 oz per day for a week. How much juice was left in the container at the end of the week?

Skill Maintenance

85. Find the LCM of 36 and 60. [R.1b]

86. Find the prime factorization of 4608. [R.1a]

Simplify. [R.2b]

87. $\frac{26}{39}$

88. $\frac{48}{54}$

89. $\frac{264}{484}$

90. $\frac{1025}{6625}$

91. $\frac{275}{800}$

92. $\frac{111}{201}$

93. $\frac{11}{264}$

94. $\frac{78}{13}$

Synthesis

95. If a is positive and b is negative, then $-ab$ is:

A. Positive.
B. Negative.
C. 0.
D. Cannot be determined without more information

96. If a is positive and b is negative, then $(-a)(-b)$ is:

A. Positive.
B. Negative.
C. 0.
D. Cannot be determined without more information

97. Below is a number line showing 0 and two positive numbers x and y. Use a compass or ruler to locate the following as best you can:

$2x,\ 3x,\ 2y,\ -x,\ -y,\ x+y,\ x-y,\ x-2y.$

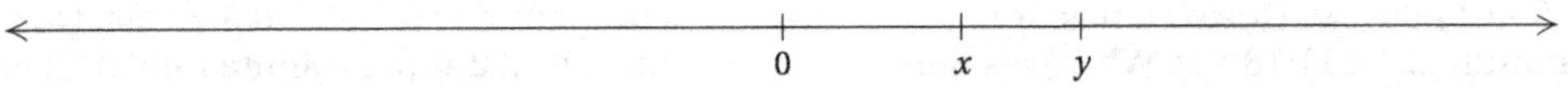

98. Of all possible quotients of the numbers 10, $-\frac{1}{2}$, -5, and $\frac{1}{5}$, which two produce the largest quotient? Which two produce the smallest quotient?

1.6 Division of Real Numbers

We now consider division of real numbers. The definition of division results in rules for division that are the same as those for multiplication.

a Division of Integers

DIVISION

The quotient $a \div b$, or $\frac{a}{b}$, where $b \neq 0$, is that unique real number c for which $a = b \cdot c$.

Let's use the definition to divide integers.

EXAMPLES Divide, if possible. Check your answer.

1. $14 \div (-7) = -2$ — *Think*: What number multiplied by -7 gives 14? That number is -2. *Check*: $(-2)(-7) = 14$.

2. $\frac{-32}{-4} = 8$ — *Think*: What number multiplied by -4 gives -32? That number is 8. *Check*: $8(-4) = -32$.

3. $\frac{-10}{7} = -\frac{10}{7}$ — *Think*: What number multiplied by 7 gives -10? That number is $-\frac{10}{7}$. *Check*: $-\frac{10}{7} \cdot 7 = -10$.

4. $\frac{-17}{0}$ **is not defined.** — *Think*: What number multiplied by 0 gives -17? There is no such number because the product of 0 and *any* number is 0.

The rules for division are the same as those for multiplication.

To multiply or divide two real numbers (where the divisor is nonzero):

a) Multiply or divide the absolute values.
b) If the signs are the same, the answer is positive.
c) If the signs are different, the answer is negative.

Do Margin Exercises 1–6.

Excluding Division by 0

Example 4 shows why we cannot divide -17 by 0. We can use the same argument to show why we cannot divide any nonzero number b by 0. Consider $b \div 0$. We look for a number that when multiplied by 0 gives b. There is no such number because the product of 0 and any number is 0. Thus we cannot divide a nonzero number b by 0.

On the other hand, if we divide 0 by 0, we look for a number c such that $0 \cdot c = 0$. But $0 \cdot c = 0$ for any number c. Thus it appears that $0 \div 0$ could be any number we choose. Getting any answer we want when we divide 0 by 0 would be very confusing. Thus we agree that division by 0 is not defined.

OBJECTIVES

a Divide integers.

b Find the reciprocal of a real number.

c Divide real numbers.

d Solve applied problems involving division of real numbers.

SKILL TO REVIEW
Objective R.2c: Divide and simplify using fraction notation.

Divide and simplify.

1. $\frac{6}{5} \div \frac{9}{2}$
2. $30 \div \frac{5}{6}$

Divide.

1. $6 \div (-3)$
   Think: What number multiplied by -3 gives 6?

2. $\frac{-15}{-3}$
   Think: What number multiplied by -3 gives -15?

3. $-24 \div 8$
   Think: What number multiplied by 8 gives -24?

4. $\frac{-48}{-6}$
5. $\frac{30}{-5}$
6. $\frac{30}{-7}$

Answers

Skill to Review:
1. $\frac{4}{15}$ 2. 36

Margin Exercises:
1. -2 2. 5 3. -3 4. 8
5. -6 6. $-\frac{30}{7}$

EXCLUDING DIVISION BY 0

Division by 0 is not defined.

$$a \div 0, \text{ or } \frac{a}{0}, \text{ is not defined for all real numbers } a.$$

Dividing 0 by Other Numbers

Note that

$$0 \div 8 = 0 \text{ because } 0 = 0 \cdot 8; \qquad \frac{0}{-5} = 0 \text{ because } 0 = 0 \cdot (-5).$$

DIVIDENDS OF 0

Zero divided by any nonzero real number is 0:

$$\frac{0}{a} = 0; \qquad a \neq 0.$$

EXAMPLES Divide.

5. $0 \div (-6) = 0$ **6.** $\frac{0}{12} = 0$ **7.** $\frac{-3}{0}$ is not defined.

Divide, if possible.

7. $\frac{-5}{0}$ **8.** $\frac{0}{-3}$

Do Exercises 7 and 8.

b Reciprocals

When two numbers like $\frac{1}{2}$ and 2 are multiplied, the result is 1. Such numbers are called **reciprocals** of each other. Every nonzero real number has a reciprocal, also called a **multiplicative inverse**.

RECIPROCALS

Two numbers whose product is 1 are called **reciprocals**, or **multiplicative inverses**, of each other.

EXAMPLES Find the reciprocal.

8. $\frac{7}{8}$ The reciprocal of $\frac{7}{8}$ is $\frac{8}{7}$ because $\frac{7}{8} \cdot \frac{8}{7} = 1$.

9. -5 The reciprocal of -5 is $-\frac{1}{5}$ because $-5\left(-\frac{1}{5}\right) = 1$.

10. 3.9 The reciprocal of 3.9 is $\frac{1}{3.9}$ because $3.9\left(\frac{1}{3.9}\right) = 1$.

11. $-\frac{1}{2}$ The reciprocal of $-\frac{1}{2}$ is -2 because $\left(-\frac{1}{2}\right)(-2) = 1$.

12. $-\frac{2}{3}$ The reciprocal of $-\frac{2}{3}$ is $-\frac{3}{2}$ because $\left(-\frac{2}{3}\right)\left(-\frac{3}{2}\right) = 1$.

13. $\frac{3y}{8x}$ The reciprocal of $\frac{3y}{8x}$ is $\frac{8x}{3y}$ because $\left(\frac{3y}{8x}\right)\left(\frac{8x}{3y}\right) = 1$.

Answers

7. Not defined 8. 0

RECIPROCAL PROPERTIES

For $a \neq 0$, the reciprocal of a can be named $\frac{1}{a}$ and the reciprocal of $\frac{1}{a}$ is a.

The reciprocal of a nonzero number $\frac{a}{b}$ can be named $\frac{b}{a}$.

The number 0 has no reciprocal.

Find the reciprocal.

9. $\frac{2}{3}$

10. $-\frac{5}{4}$

11. -3

12. $-\frac{1}{5}$

13. 1.3

14. $\frac{a}{6b}$

Do Exercises 9–14.

The reciprocal of a positive number is also a positive number, because the product of the two numbers must be the positive number 1. The reciprocal of a negative number is also a negative number, because the product of the two numbers must be the positive number 1.

THE SIGN OF A RECIPROCAL

The reciprocal of a number has the same sign as the number itself.

Caution!

It is important *not* to confuse *opposite* with *reciprocal*. Keep in mind that the opposite, or additive inverse, of a number is what we add to the number to get 0. The reciprocal, or multiplicative inverse, is what we multiply the number by to get 1.

Compare the following.

NUMBER	OPPOSITE (Change the sign.)	RECIPROCAL (Invert but do not change the sign.)
$-\frac{3}{8}$	$\frac{3}{8}$	$-\frac{8}{3}$
19	-19	$\frac{1}{19}$
$\frac{18}{7}$	$-\frac{18}{7}$	$\frac{7}{18}$
-7.9	7.9	$-\frac{1}{7.9}$, or $-\frac{10}{79}$
0	0	Not defined

$\left(-\frac{3}{8}\right)\left(-\frac{8}{3}\right) = 1$

$-\frac{3}{8} + \frac{3}{8} = 0$

15. Complete the following table.

NUMBER	OPPOSITE	RECIPROCAL
$\frac{2}{3}$		
$-\frac{5}{4}$		
0		
1		
-8		
-4.7		

Do Exercise 15.

Answers

9. $\frac{3}{2}$ **10.** $-\frac{4}{5}$ **11.** $-\frac{1}{3}$ **12.** -5 **13.** $\frac{1}{1.3}$, or $\frac{10}{13}$ **14.** $\frac{6b}{a}$ **15.** $-\frac{2}{3}$ and $\frac{3}{2}$; $\frac{5}{4}$ and $-\frac{4}{5}$; 0 and not defined; -1 and 1; 8 and $-\frac{1}{8}$; 4.7 and $-\frac{1}{4.7}$, or $-\frac{10}{47}$

c Division of Real Numbers

We know that we can subtract by adding an opposite. Similarly, we can divide by multiplying by a reciprocal.

RECIPROCALS AND DIVISION

For any real numbers a and b, $b \neq 0$,

$$a \div b = \frac{a}{b} = a \cdot \frac{1}{b}.$$

(To divide, multiply by the reciprocal of the divisor.)

EXAMPLES Rewrite each division as a multiplication.

14. $-4 \div 3$ $\quad$ $-4 \div 3$ is the same as $-4 \cdot \frac{1}{3}$

15. $\frac{6}{-7}$ $\quad$ $\frac{6}{-7} = 6\left(-\frac{1}{7}\right)$

16. $\frac{3}{5} \div \left(-\frac{9}{7}\right)$ $\quad$ $\frac{3}{5} \div \left(-\frac{9}{7}\right) = \frac{3}{5}\left(-\frac{7}{9}\right)$

17. $\frac{x+2}{5}$ $\quad$ $\frac{x+2}{5} = (x+2)\frac{1}{5}$ $\quad$ Parentheses are necessary here.

18. $\frac{-17}{1/b}$ $\quad$ $\frac{-17}{1/b} = -17 \cdot b$

Do Exercises 16–20.

When actually doing division calculations, we sometimes multiply by a reciprocal and we sometimes divide directly. With fraction notation, it is usually better to multiply by a reciprocal. With decimal notation, it is usually better to divide directly.

EXAMPLES Divide by multiplying by the reciprocal of the divisor.

19. $\frac{2}{3} \div \left(-\frac{5}{4}\right) = \frac{2}{3} \cdot \left(-\frac{4}{5}\right) = -\frac{8}{15}$

20. $-\frac{5}{6} \div \left(-\frac{3}{4}\right) = -\frac{5}{6} \cdot \left(-\frac{4}{3}\right) = \frac{20}{18} = \frac{10 \cdot 2}{9 \cdot 2} = \frac{10}{9} \cdot \frac{2}{2} = \frac{10}{9}$

Caution!

Be careful *not* to change the sign when taking a reciprocal!

21. $-\frac{3}{4} \div \frac{3}{10} = -\frac{3}{4} \cdot \left(\frac{10}{3}\right) = -\frac{30}{12} = -\frac{5 \cdot 6}{2 \cdot 6} = -\frac{5}{2} \cdot \frac{6}{6} = -\frac{5}{2}$

Do Exercises 21 and 22.

Rewrite each division as a multiplication.

16. $\frac{4}{7} \div \left(-\frac{3}{5}\right)$

17. $\frac{5}{-8}$

18. $\frac{a-b}{7}$

19. $\frac{-23}{1/a}$

20. $-5 \div 7$

Divide by multiplying by the reciprocal of the divisor.

21. $\frac{4}{7} \div \left(-\frac{3}{5}\right)$

22. $-\frac{12}{7} \div \left(-\frac{3}{4}\right)$

Answers

16. $\frac{4}{7} \cdot \left(-\frac{5}{3}\right)$ **17.** $5 \cdot \left(-\frac{1}{8}\right)$

18. $(a-b) \cdot \frac{1}{7}$ **19.** $-23 \cdot a$

20. $-5 \cdot \left(\frac{1}{7}\right)$ **21.** $-\frac{20}{21}$ **22.** $\frac{16}{7}$

With decimal notation, it is easier to carry out long division than to multiply by the reciprocal.

EXAMPLES Divide.

22. $-27.9 \div (-3) = \frac{-27.9}{-3} = 9.3$ Do the long division $3\overline{)27.9}$ (quotient 9.3). The answer is positive.

23. $-6.3 \div 2.1 = -3$ Do the long division $2.1\overline{)6.3}$ (quotient 3.). The answer is negative.

Do Exercises 23 and 24.

Divide.

23. $21.7 \div (-3.1)$

24. $-20.4 \div (-4)$

Consider the following:

1. $\frac{2}{3} = \frac{2}{3} \cdot 1 = \frac{2}{3} \cdot \frac{-1}{-1} = \frac{2(-1)}{3(-1)} = \frac{-2}{-3}$. Thus, $\frac{2}{3} = \frac{-2}{-3}$.

(A negative number divided by a negative number is positive.)

2. $-\frac{2}{3} = -1 \cdot \frac{2}{3} = \frac{-1}{1} \cdot \frac{2}{3} = \frac{-1 \cdot 2}{1 \cdot 3} = \frac{-2}{3}$. Thus, $-\frac{2}{3} = \frac{-2}{3}$.

(A negative number divided by a positive number is negative.)

3. $\frac{-2}{3} = \frac{-2}{3} \cdot 1 = \frac{-2}{3} \cdot \frac{-1}{-1} = \frac{-2(-1)}{3(-1)} = \frac{2}{-3}$. Thus, $-\frac{2}{3} = \frac{2}{-3}$.

(A positive number divided by a negative number is negative.)

We can use the following properties to make sign changes in fraction notation.

SIGN CHANGES IN FRACTION NOTATION

For any numbers a and b, $b \neq 0$:

1. $\frac{-a}{-b} = \frac{a}{b}$

(The opposite of a number a divided by the opposite of another number b is the same as the quotient of the two numbers a and b.)

2. $\frac{-a}{b} = \frac{a}{-b} = -\frac{a}{b}$

(The opposite of a number a divided by another number b is the same as the number a divided by the opposite of the number b, and both are the same as the opposite of *a divided by b*.)

Do Exercises 25–27.

Find two equal expressions for each number with negative signs in different places.

25. $\frac{-5}{6}$

26. $-\frac{8}{7}$

27. $\frac{10}{-3}$

Answers

23. -7 **24.** 5.1 **25.** $\frac{5}{-6}; -\frac{5}{6}$ **26.** $\frac{8}{-7}; \frac{-8}{7}$ **27.** $\frac{-10}{3}; -\frac{10}{3}$

d Applications and Problem Solving

EXAMPLE 24 *Chemical Reaction.* During a chemical reaction, the temperature in a beaker decreased every minute by the same number of degrees. The temperature was 56°F at 10:10 A.M. By 10:42 A.M., the temperature had dropped to −12°F. By how many degrees did it change each minute?

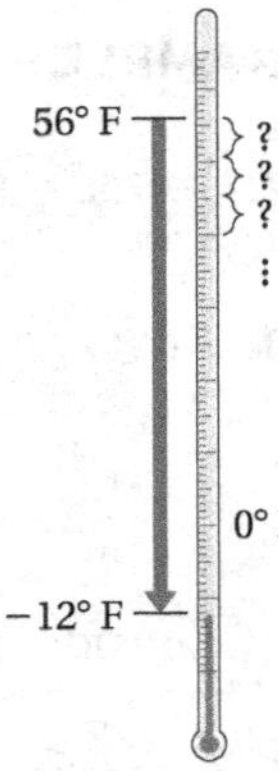

We first determine by how many degrees d the temperature changed altogether. We subtract −12 from 56:

$$d = 56 - (-12) = 56 + 12 = 68.$$

The temperature changed a total of 68°. We can express this as −68° since the temperature dropped.

The amount of time t that passed was 42 − 10, or 32 min. Thus the number of degrees T that the temperature dropped each minute is given by

$$T = \frac{d}{t} = \frac{-68}{32} = -2.125.$$

The change was −2.125°F per minute.

Do Exercise 28.

28. Chemical Reaction. During a chemical reaction, the temperature in a beaker decreased every minute by the same number of degrees. The temperature was 71°F at 2:12 P.M. By 2:37 P.M., the temperature had changed to −14°F. By how many degrees did it change each minute?

Calculator Corner

Operations on the Real Numbers We can perform operations on the real numbers on a graphing calculator. Recall that negative numbers are entered using the opposite key, (−), rather than the subtraction operation key, −. Consider the sum −5 + (−3.8). We use parentheses when we write this sum in order to separate the addition symbol and the "opposite of" symbol and thus make the expression more easily read. When we enter this calculation on a graphing calculator, however, the parentheses are not necessary. We can press (−) 5 + (−) 3 . 8 ENTER. The result is −8.8. Note that it is not incorrect to enter the parentheses. The result will be the same if this is done.

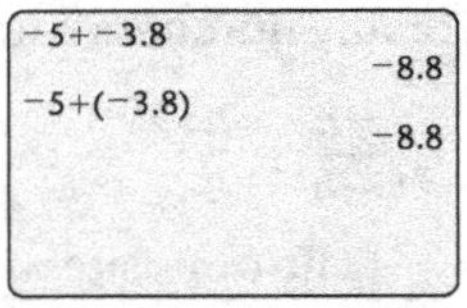

To find the difference 10 − (−17), we press 1 0 − (−) 1 7 ENTER. The result is 27. We can also multiply and divide real numbers. To find −5 · (−7), we press (−) 5 × (−) 7 ENTER, and to find 45 ÷ (−9), we press 4 5 ÷ (−) 9 ENTER. Note that it is not necessary to use parentheses in any of these calculations.

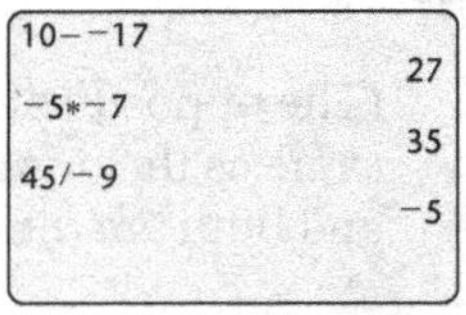

Exercises: Use a calculator to perform each operation.

1. −8 + 4	**2.** 1.2 + (−1.5)	**3.** −7 + (−5)	**4.** −7.6 + (−1.9)
5. −8 − 4	**6.** 1.2 − (−1.5)	**7.** −7 − (−5)	**8.** −7.6 − (−1.9)
9. −8 · 4	**10.** 1.2 · (−1.5)	**11.** −7 · (−5)	**12.** −7.6 · (−1.9)
13. −8 ÷ 4	**14.** 1.2 ÷ (−1.5)	**15.** −7 ÷ (−5)	**16.** −7.6 ÷ (−1.9)

Answer

28. −3.4°F per minute

1.6 Exercise Set

For Extra Help

MyMathLab MathXL PRACTICE WATCH DOWNLOAD READ REVIEW

a Divide, if possible. Check each answer.

1. $48 \div (-6)$

2. $\frac{42}{-7}$

3. $\frac{28}{-2}$

4. $24 \div (-12)$

5. $\frac{-24}{8}$

6. $-18 \div (-2)$

7. $\frac{-36}{-12}$

8. $-72 \div (-9)$

9. $\frac{-72}{9}$

10. $\frac{-50}{25}$

11. $-100 \div (-50)$

12. $\frac{-200}{8}$

13. $-108 \div 9$

14. $\frac{-63}{-7}$

15. $\frac{200}{-25}$

16. $-300 \div (-16)$

17. $\frac{75}{0}$

18. $\frac{0}{-5}$

19. $\frac{0}{-2.6}$

20. $\frac{-23}{0}$

b Find the reciprocal.

21. $\frac{15}{7}$

22. $\frac{3}{8}$

23. $-\frac{47}{13}$

24. $-\frac{31}{12}$

25. 13

26. -10

27. -32

28. 15

29. $\frac{1}{-7.1}$

30. $\frac{1}{-4.9}$

31. $\frac{1}{9}$

32. $\frac{1}{16}$

33. $\frac{1}{4y}$

34. $\frac{-1}{8a}$

35. $\frac{2a}{3b}$

36. $\frac{-4y}{3x}$

C Rewrite each division as a multiplication.

37. $4 \div 17$

38. $5 \div (-8)$

39. $\frac{8}{-13}$

40. $-\frac{13}{47}$

41. $\frac{13.9}{-1.5}$

42. $-\frac{47.3}{21.4}$

43. $\frac{2}{3} \div \left(-\frac{4}{5}\right)$

44. $\frac{3}{4} \div \left(-\frac{7}{10}\right)$

45. $\frac{x}{\frac{1}{y}}$

46. $\frac{13}{\frac{1}{x}}$

47. $\frac{3x + 4}{5}$

48. $\frac{4y - 8}{-7}$

Divide.

49. $\frac{3}{4} \div \left(-\frac{2}{3}\right)$

50. $\frac{7}{8} \div \left(-\frac{1}{2}\right)$

51. $-\frac{5}{4} \div \left(-\frac{3}{4}\right)$

52. $-\frac{5}{9} \div \left(-\frac{5}{6}\right)$

53. $-\frac{2}{7} \div \left(-\frac{4}{9}\right)$

54. $-\frac{3}{5} \div \left(-\frac{5}{8}\right)$

55. $-\frac{3}{8} \div \left(-\frac{8}{3}\right)$

56. $-\frac{5}{8} \div \left(-\frac{6}{5}\right)$

57. $-\frac{5}{6} \div \frac{2}{3}$

58. $-\frac{7}{16} \div \frac{3}{8}$

59. $-\frac{9}{4} \div \frac{5}{12}$

60. $-\frac{3}{5} \div \frac{7}{10}$

61. $\frac{-11}{-13}$

62. $\frac{-21}{-25}$

63. $-6.6 \div 3.3$

64. $-44.1 \div (-6.3)$

65. $\dfrac{48.6}{-3}$

66. $\dfrac{-1.9}{20}$

67. $\dfrac{-12.5}{5}$

68. $\dfrac{-17.8}{3.2}$

69. $11.25 \div (-9)$

70. $-9.6 \div (-6.4)$

71. $\dfrac{-9}{17 - 17}$

72. $\dfrac{-8}{-5 + 5}$

d *Percent of Increase or Decrease in Employment.* A percent of increase is generally positive and a percent of decrease is generally negative. The table below lists estimates of the number of job opportunities for various occupations in 2006 and 2016. In Exercises 73–76, find the missing numbers.

	OCCUPATION	NUMBER OF JOBS IN 2006 (in thousands)	NUMBER OF JOBS IN 2016 (in thousands)	CHANGE	PERCENT OF INCREASE OR DECREASE
	Electrician	705	757	52	7.4%
	File clerk	234	137	−97	−41.5%
73.	Athletic trainer	17	21	4	
74.	Child-care worker	1388	1636	248	
75.	Cashier	3527	3411	−116	
76.	Fisherman	38	32	−6	

SOURCE: U.S. Bureau of Labor Statistics *Occupational Outlook Handbook*

Skill Maintenance

Simplify. [R.5c]

77. $2^3 - 5 \cdot 3 + 8 \cdot 10 \div 2$

78. $16 \cdot 2^3 - 5 \cdot 3 + 80 \div 10 \cdot 2$

79. $1000 \div 100 \div 10$

80. $216 \cdot 6^3 \div 6^2$

81. Simplify: $\dfrac{264}{468}$. [R.2b]

82. Convert to decimal notation: 47.7%. [R.4a]

83. Convert to percent notation: $\dfrac{7}{8}$. [R.4d]

84. Simplify: $\dfrac{40}{60}$. [R.2b]

85. Divide and simplify: $\dfrac{12}{25} \div \dfrac{32}{75}$. [R.2c]

86. Multiply and simplify: $\dfrac{12}{25} \cdot \dfrac{32}{75}$. [R.2c]

Synthesis

87. Find the reciprocal of −10.5. What happens if you take the reciprocal of the result?

88. Determine those real numbers a for which the opposite of a is the same as the reciprocal of a.

Determine whether each expression represents a positive number or a negative number when a and b are negative.

89. $\dfrac{-a}{b}$

90. $\dfrac{-a}{-b}$

91. $-\left(\dfrac{a}{-b}\right)$

92. $-\left(\dfrac{-a}{b}\right)$

93. $-\left(\dfrac{-a}{-b}\right)$

1.7 Properties of Real Numbers

OBJECTIVES

a Find equivalent fraction expressions and simplify fraction expressions.

b Use the commutative and associative laws to find equivalent expressions.

c Use the distributive laws to multiply expressions like 8 and $x - y$.

d Use the distributive laws to factor expressions like $4x - 12 + 24y$.

e Collect like terms.

a Equivalent Expressions

In solving equations and doing other kinds of work in algebra, we manipulate expressions in various ways. For example, instead of $x + x$, we might write $2x$, knowing that the two expressions represent the same number for any allowable replacement of x. In that sense, the expressions $x + x$ and $2x$ are **equivalent**, as are $\frac{3}{x}$ and $\frac{3x}{x^2}$, even though 0 is not an allowable replacement because division by 0 is not defined.

EQUIVALENT EXPRESSIONS

Two expressions that have the same value for all allowable replacements are called **equivalent**.

The expressions $x + 3x$ and $5x$ are *not* equivalent, as we see in Margin Exercise 2.

Do Exercises 1 and 2.

In this section, we will consider several laws of real numbers that will allow us to find equivalent expressions. The first two laws are the *identity properties of 0 and 1.*

THE IDENTITY PROPERTY OF 0

For any real number a,

$$a + 0 = 0 + a = a.$$

(The number 0 is the *additive identity.*)

THE IDENTITY PROPERTY OF 1

For any real number a,

$$a \cdot 1 = 1 \cdot a = a.$$

(The number 1 is the *multiplicative identity.*)

We often refer to the use of the identity property of 1 as "multiplying by 1." We can use this method to find equivalent fraction expressions. Recall from arithmetic that to multiply with fraction notation, we multiply the numerators and multiply the denominators. (See also Section R.2.)

EXAMPLE 1 Write a fraction expression equivalent to $\frac{2}{3}$ with a denominator of $3x$:

$$\frac{2}{3} = \frac{\square}{3x}.$$

Complete the table by evaluating each expression for the given values.

1.

Value	$x + x$	$2x$
$x = 3$		
$x = -6$		
$x = 4.8$		

2.

Value	$x + 3x$	$5x$
$x = 2$		
$x = -6$		
$x = 4.8$		

Answers

1. 6, 6; −12, −12; 9.6, 9.6 **2.** 8, 10; −24, −30; 19.2, 24

Note that $3x = 3 \cdot x$. We want fraction notation for $\frac{2}{3}$ that has a denominator of $3x$, but the denominator 3 is missing a factor of x. Thus we multiply by 1, using x/x as an equivalent expression for 1:

$$\frac{2}{3} = \frac{2}{3} \cdot 1 = \frac{2}{3} \cdot \frac{x}{x} = \frac{2x}{3x}.$$

The expressions $2/3$ and $2x/(3x)$ are equivalent. They have the same value for any allowable replacement. Note that $2x/3x$ is not defined for a replacement of 0, but for all nonzero real numbers, the expressions $2/3$ and $2x/(3x)$ have the same value.

Do Exercises 3 and 4.

3. Write a fraction expression equivalent to $\frac{3}{4}$ with a denominator of 8:

$$\frac{3}{4} = \frac{\square}{8}.$$

4. Write a fraction expression equivalent to $\frac{3}{4}$ with a denominator of $4t$:

$$\frac{3}{4} = \frac{\square}{4t}.$$

In algebra, we consider an expression like $2/3$ to be "simplified" from $2x/(3x)$. To find such simplified expressions, we use the identity property of 1 to remove a factor of 1. (See also Section R.2.)

EXAMPLE 2 Simplify: $-\dfrac{20x}{12x}$.

$$-\frac{20x}{12x} = -\frac{5 \cdot 4x}{3 \cdot 4x}$$ We look for the largest factor common to both the numerator and the denominator and factor each.

$$= -\frac{5}{3} \cdot \frac{4x}{4x}$$ Factoring the fraction expression

$$= -\frac{5}{3} \cdot 1$$ $\frac{4x}{4x} = 1$

$$= -\frac{5}{3}$$ Removing a factor of 1 using the identity property of 1

EXAMPLE 3 Simplify: $\dfrac{14ab}{56a}$.

$$\frac{14ab}{56a} = \frac{14a \cdot b}{14a \cdot 4} = \frac{14a}{14a} \cdot \frac{b}{4} = 1 \cdot \frac{b}{4} = \frac{b}{4}$$

Do Exercises 5–8.

Simplify.

5. $\dfrac{3y}{4y}$

6. $-\dfrac{16m}{12m}$

7. $\dfrac{5xy}{40y}$

8. $\dfrac{18p}{24pq}$

b The Commutative and Associative Laws

The Commutative Laws

Let's examine the expressions $x + y$ and $y + x$, as well as xy and yx.

EXAMPLE 4 Evaluate $x + y$ and $y + x$ when $x = 4$ and $y = 3$.

We substitute 4 for x and 3 for y in both expressions:

$$x + y = 4 + 3 = 7; \qquad y + x = 3 + 4 = 7.$$

EXAMPLE 5 Evaluate xy and yx when $x = 3$ and $y = -12$.

We substitute 3 for x and -12 for y in both expressions:

$$xy = 3 \cdot (-12) = -36; \qquad yx = (-12) \cdot 3 = -36.$$

Do Exercises 9 and 10.

9. Evaluate $x + y$ and $y + x$ when $x = -2$ and $y = 3$.

10. Evaluate xy and yx when $x = -2$ and $y = 5$.

Answers

3. $\frac{6}{8}$ **4.** $\frac{3t}{4t}$ **5.** $\frac{3}{4}$ **6.** $-\frac{4}{3}$
7. $\frac{x}{8}$ **8.** $\frac{3}{4q}$ **9.** 1; 1 **10.** -10; -10

STUDY TIPS

VIDEO RESOURCES

Developed and produced especially for this text, and now available on DVD-ROM with Chapter Test Prep Videos that walk you through step-by-step solutions to all the Chapter Test exercises, these videos feature an engaging team of instructors who present material and concepts using examples and exercises from every section of the text. The complete digitized video set, both affordable and portable, makes it easy and convenient for you to watch video segments at home or on campus. (ISBN: 978-0-321-64075-8, available for purchase at www.MyPearsonStore.com)

The expressions $x + y$ and $y + x$ have the same values no matter what the variables stand for. Thus they are equivalent. Therefore, when we add two numbers, the order in which we add does not matter. Similarly, the expressions xy and yx are equivalent. They also have the same values, no matter what the variables stand for. Therefore, when we multiply two numbers, the order in which we multiply does not matter.

The following are examples of general patterns or laws.

THE COMMUTATIVE LAWS

Addition. For any numbers a and b,

$$a + b = b + a.$$

(We can change the order when adding without affecting the answer.)

Multiplication. For any numbers a and b,

$$ab = ba.$$

(We can change the order when multiplying without affecting the answer.)

Using a commutative law, we know that $x + 2$ and $2 + x$ are equivalent. Similarly, $3x$ and $x(3)$ are equivalent. Thus, in an algebraic expression, we can replace one with the other and the result will be equivalent to the original expression.

EXAMPLE 6 Use the commutative laws to write an equivalent expression: **(a)** $y + 5$; **(b)** mn; **(c)** $7 + xy$.

a) An expression equivalent to $y + 5$ is $5 + y$ by the commutative law of addition.

b) An expression equivalent to mn is nm by the commutative law of multiplication.

c) An expression equivalent to $7 + xy$ is $xy + 7$ by the commutative law of addition. Another expression equivalent to $7 + xy$ is $7 + yx$ by the commutative law of multiplication. Another equivalent expression is $yx + 7$.

Use a commutative law to write an equivalent expression.

11. $x + 9$

12. pq

13. $xy + t$

Do Exercises 11-13.

The Associative Laws

Now let's examine the expressions $a + (b + c)$ and $(a + b) + c$. Note that these expressions involve the use of parentheses as *grouping* symbols, and they also involve three numbers. Calculations within parentheses are to be done first.

EXAMPLE 7 Calculate and compare: $3 + (8 + 5)$ and $(3 + 8) + 5$.

$3 + (8 + 5) = 3 + 13$ Calculating within parentheses first; adding the 8 and the 5

$= 16$;

$(3 + 8) + 5 = 11 + 5$ Calculating within parentheses first; adding the 3 and the 8

$= 16$

Answers

11. $9 + x$ **12.** qp
13. $t + xy$, or $yx + t$, or $t + yx$

The two expressions in Example 7 name the same number. Moving the parentheses to group the additions differently does not affect the value of the expression.

EXAMPLE 8 Calculate and compare: $3 \cdot (4 \cdot 2)$ and $(3 \cdot 4) \cdot 2$.

$$3 \cdot (4 \cdot 2) = 3 \cdot 8 = 24; \qquad (3 \cdot 4) \cdot 2 = 12 \cdot 2 = 24$$

Do Exercises 14 and 15.

14. Calculate and compare:
$8 + (9 + 2)$ and $(8 + 9) + 2$.

15. Calculate and compare:
$10 \cdot (5 \cdot 3)$ and $(10 \cdot 5) \cdot 3$.

You may have noted that when only addition is involved, numbers can be grouped any way we please without affecting the answer. When only multiplication is involved, numbers can also be grouped any way we please without affecting the answer.

THE ASSOCIATIVE LAWS

Addition. For any numbers a, b, and c,

$$a + (b + c) = (a + b) + c.$$

(Numbers can be grouped in any manner for addition.)

Multiplication. For any numbers a, b, and c,

$$a \cdot (b \cdot c) = (a \cdot b) \cdot c.$$

(Numbers can be grouped in any manner for multiplication.)

EXAMPLE 9 Use an associative law to write an equivalent expression: **(a)** $(y + z) + 3$; **(b)** $8(xy)$.

a) An expression equivalent to $(y + z) + 3$ is $y + (z + 3)$ by the associative law of addition.

b) An expression equivalent to $8(xy)$ is $(8x)y$ by the associative law of multiplication.

Do Exercises 16 and 17.

Use an associative law to write an equivalent expression.

16. $r + (s + 7)$

17. $9(ab)$

The associative laws say that numbers can be grouped any way we please when only additions or only multiplications are involved. Thus we often omit the parentheses. For example,

$$x + (y + 2) \text{ means } x + y + 2, \quad \text{and} \quad (lw)h \text{ means } lwh.$$

Using the Commutative and Associative Laws Together

EXAMPLE 10 Use the commutative and associative laws to write at least three expressions equivalent to $(x + 5) + y$.

a) $(x + 5) + y = x + (5 + y)$ Using the associative law first and then using the commutative law
$= x + (y + 5)$

b) $(x + 5) + y = y + (x + 5)$ Using the commutative law twice
$= y + (5 + x)$

c) $(x + 5) + y = (5 + x) + y$ Using the commutative law first and then the associative law
$= 5 + (x + y)$

Answers

14. 19; 19 **15.** 150; 150 **16.** $(r + s) + 7$
17. $(9a)b$

EXAMPLE 11 Use the commutative and associative laws to write at least three expressions equivalent to $(3x)y$.

a) $(3x)y = 3(xy)$
$= 3(yx)$ Using the associative law first and then using the commutative law

b) $(3x)y = y(3x)$
$= y(x \cdot 3)$ Using the commutative law twice

c) $(3x)y = (x \cdot 3)y$
$= x(3y)$
$= x(y \cdot 3)$ Using the commutative law, and then the associative law, and then the commutative law again

Do Exercises 18 and 19.

Use the commutative and associative laws to write at least three equivalent expressions.

18. $4(tu)$

19. $r + (2 + s)$

c The Distributive Laws

The *distributive laws* are the basis of many procedures in both arithmetic and algebra. They are probably the most important laws that we use to manipulate algebraic expressions. The distributive law of multiplication over addition involves two operations: addition and multiplication.

Let's begin by considering a multiplication problem from arithmetic:

```
    4 5
      7
    3 5  ← This is 7 · 5.
  2 8 0  ← This is 7 · 40.
  3 1 5  ← This is the sum 7 · 5 + 7 · 40.
```

To carry out the multiplication, we actually added two products. That is,

$$7 \cdot 45 = 7(5 + 40) = 7 \cdot 5 + 7 \cdot 40.$$

Let's examine this further. If we wish to multiply a sum of several numbers by a factor, we can either add and then multiply, or multiply and then add.

EXAMPLE 12 Compute in two ways: $5 \cdot (4 + 8)$.

a) $5 \cdot (4 + 8)$ Adding within parentheses first, and then multiplying
$= 5 \cdot 12$
$= 60$

b) $5 \cdot (4 + 8) = (5 \cdot 4) + (5 \cdot 8)$ Distributing the multiplication to terms within parentheses first and then adding
$= 20 + 40$
$= 60$

Do Exercises 20–22.

Compute.

20. a) $7 \cdot (3 + 6)$

b) $(7 \cdot 3) + (7 \cdot 6)$

21. a) $2 \cdot (10 + 30)$

b) $(2 \cdot 10) + (2 \cdot 30)$

22. a) $(2 + 5) \cdot 4$

b) $(2 \cdot 4) + (5 \cdot 4)$

THE DISTRIBUTIVE LAW OF MULTIPLICATION OVER ADDITION

For any numbers a, b, and c,

$$a(b + c) = ab + ac.$$

Answers

18. $(4t)u$, $(tu)4$, $t(4u)$; answers may vary **19.** $(2 + r) + s$, $(r + s) + 2$, $s + (r + 2)$; answers may vary **20.** (a) $7 \cdot 9 = 63$; (b) $21 + 42 = 63$ **21.** (a) $2 \cdot 40 = 80$; (b) $20 + 60 = 80$ **22.** (a) $7 \cdot 4 = 28$; (b) $8 + 20 = 28$

In the statement of the distributive law, we know that in an expression such as $ab + ac$, the multiplications are to be done first according to the rules for order of operations. (See Section R.5.) So, instead of writing $(4 \cdot 5) + (4 \cdot 7)$, we can write $4 \cdot 5 + 4 \cdot 7$. However, in $a(b + c)$, we cannot omit the parentheses. If we did, we would have $ab + c$, which means $(ab) + c$. For example, $3(4 + 2) = 3(6) = 18$, but $3 \cdot 4 + 2 = 12 + 2 = 14$.

There is another distributive law that relates multiplication and subtraction. This law says that to multiply by a difference, we can either subtract and then multiply, or multiply and then subtract.

THE DISTRIBUTIVE LAW OF MULTIPLICATION OVER SUBTRACTION

For any numbers a, b, and c,

$$a(b - c) = ab - ac.$$

We often refer to "*the* distributive law" when we mean *either* or *both* of these laws.

Do Exercises 23–25.

Calculate.

23. **a)** $4(5 - 3)$
b) $4 \cdot 5 - 4 \cdot 3$

24. **a)** $-2 \cdot (5 - 3)$
b) $-2 \cdot 5 - (-2) \cdot 3$

25. **a)** $5 \cdot (2 - 7)$
b) $5 \cdot 2 - 5 \cdot 7$

What do we mean by the *terms* of an expression? **Terms** are separated by addition signs. If there are subtraction signs, we can find an equivalent expression that uses addition signs.

EXAMPLE 13 What are the terms of $3x - 4y + 2z$?

We have

$$3x - 4y + 2z = 3x + (-4y) + 2z. \quad \text{Separating parts with + signs}$$

The terms are $3x$, $-4y$, and $2z$.

Do Exercises 26 and 27.

What are the terms of each expression?

26. $5x - 8y + 3$

27. $-4y - 2x + 3z$

The distributive laws are a basis for a procedure in algebra called **multiplying**. In an expression like $8(a + 2b - 7)$, we multiply each term inside the parentheses by 8:

$$8(a + 2b - 7) = 8 \cdot a + 8 \cdot 2b - 8 \cdot 7 = 8a + 16b - 56.$$

EXAMPLES Multiply.

14. $9(x - 5) = 9 \cdot x - 9 \cdot 5$ Using the distributive law of multiplication over subtraction

$= 9x - 45$

15. $\frac{2}{3}(w + 1) = \frac{2}{3} \cdot w + \frac{2}{3} \cdot 1$ Using the distributive law of multiplication over addition

$= \frac{2}{3}w + \frac{2}{3}$

16. $\frac{4}{3}(s - t + w) = \frac{4}{3}s - \frac{4}{3}t + \frac{4}{3}w$ Using both distributive laws

Do Exercises 28–30.

Multiply.

28. $3(x - 5)$

29. $5(x + 1)$

30. $\frac{3}{5}(p + q - t)$

Answers

23. (a) $4 \cdot 2 = 8$; (b) $20 - 12 = 8$
24. (a) $-2 \cdot 2 = -4$; (b) $-10 + 6 = -4$
25. (a) $5(-5) = -25$; (b) $10 - 35 = -25$
26. $5x, -8y, 3$ **27.** $-4y, -2x, 3z$
28. $3x - 15$ **29.** $5x + 5$
30. $\frac{3}{5}p + \frac{3}{5}q - \frac{3}{5}t$

EXAMPLE 17 Multiply: $-4(x - 2y + 3z)$.

$$-4(x - 2y + 3z) = -4 \cdot x - (-4)(2y) + (-4)(3z)$$ Using both distributive laws

$$= -4x - (-8y) + (-12z)$$ Multiplying

$$= -4x + 8y - 12z$$

We can also do this problem by first finding an equivalent expression with all plus signs and then multiplying:

$$-4(x - 2y + 3z) = -4[x + (-2y) + 3z]$$
$$= -4 \cdot x + (-4)(-2y) + (-4)(3z)$$
$$= -4x + 8y - 12z.$$

Do Exercises 31–33.

Multiply.

31. $-2(x - 3)$

32. $5(x - 2y + 4z)$

33. $-5(x - 2y + 4z)$

EXAMPLES Name the property or law illustrated by each equation.

	Equation	*Property*
18.	$5x = x(5)$	Commutative law of multiplication
19.	$a + (8.5 + b) = (a + 8.5) + b$	Associative law of addition
20.	$0 + 11 = 11$	Identity property of 0
21.	$(-5s)t = -5(st)$	Associative law of multiplication
22.	$\frac{3}{4} \cdot 1 = \frac{3}{4}$	Identity property of 1
23.	$12.5(w - 3) = 12.5w - 12.5(3)$	Distributive law of multiplication over subtraction
24.	$y + \frac{1}{2} = \frac{1}{2} + y$	Commutative law of addition

Do Exercises 34–40.

Name the property or law illustrated by each equation.

34. $(-8a)b = -8(ab)$

35. $p \cdot 1 = p$

36. $m + 34 = 34 + m$

37. $2(t + 5) = 2t + 2(5)$

38. $0 + k = k$

39. $-8x = x(-8)$

40. $x + (4.3 + b) = (x + 4.3) + b$

d Factoring

Factoring is the reverse of multiplying. To factor, we can use the distributive laws in reverse:

$$ab + ac = a(b + c) \quad \text{and} \quad ab - ac = a(b - c).$$

FACTORING

To **factor** an expression is to find an equivalent expression that is a product.

To factor $9x - 45$, for example, we find an equivalent expression that is a product: $9(x - 5)$. This reverses the multiplication that we did in Example 14. When all the terms of an expression have a factor in common, we can "factor it out" using the distributive laws. Note the following.

$9x$ has the factors $9, -9, 3, -3, 1, -1, x, -x, 3x, -3x, 9x, -9x$;

-45 has the factors $1, -1, 3, -3, 5, -5, 9, -9, 15, -15, 45, -45$

Answers

31. $-2x + 6$ **32.** $5x - 10y + 20z$ **33.** $-5x + 10y - 20z$ **34.** Associative law of multiplication **35.** Identity property of 1 **36.** Commutative law of addition **37.** Distributive law of multiplication over addition **38.** Identity property of 0 **39.** Commutative law of multiplication **40.** Associative law of addition

We generally remove the largest common factor. In this case, that factor is 9. Thus,

$$9x - 45 = 9 \cdot x - 9 \cdot 5$$
$$= 9(x - 5).$$

Remember that an expression has been factored when we have found an equivalent expression that is a product. Above, we note that $9x - 45$ and $9(x - 5)$ are equivalent expressions. The expression $9x - 45$ is the difference of $9x$ and 45; the expression $9(x - 5)$ is the product of 9 and $(x - 5)$.

EXAMPLES Factor.

25. $5x - 10 = 5 \cdot x - 5 \cdot 2$ Try to do this step mentally.
$= 5(x - 2)$ You can check by multiplying.

26. $ax - ay + az = a(x - y + z)$

27. $9x + 27y - 9 = 9 \cdot x + 9 \cdot 3y - 9 \cdot 1 = 9(x + 3y - 1)$

Note in Example 27 that you might, at first, just factor out a 3, as follows:

$$9x + 27y - 9 = 3 \cdot 3x + 3 \cdot 9y - 3 \cdot 3$$
$$= 3(3x + 9y - 3).$$

At this point, the mathematics is correct, but the answer is not because there is another factor of 3 that can be factored out, as follows:

$$3 \cdot 3x + 3 \cdot 9y - 3 \cdot 3 = 3(3x + 9y - 3)$$
$$= 3(3 \cdot x + 3 \cdot 3y - 3 \cdot 1)$$
$$= 3 \cdot 3(x + 3y - 1)$$
$$= 9(x + 3y - 1).$$

We now have a correct answer, but it took more work than we did in Example 27. Thus it is better to look for the *greatest common factor* at the outset.

EXAMPLES Factor. Try to write just the answer, if you can.

28. $5x - 5y = 5(x - y)$

29. $-3x + 6y - 9z = -3(x - 2y + 3z)$

We usually factor out a negative factor when the first term is negative. The way we factor can depend on the situation in which we are working. We might also factor the expression in Example 29 as follows:

$$-3x + 6y - 9z = 3(-x + 2y - 3z).$$

30. $18z - 12x - 24 = 6(3z - 2x - 4)$

31. $\frac{1}{2}x + \frac{3}{2}y - \frac{1}{2} = \frac{1}{2}(x + 3y - 1)$

Remember that you can always check factoring by multiplying. Keep in mind that an expression is factored when it is written as a product.

Do Exercises 41–46.

Factor.

41. $6x - 12$

42. $3x - 6y + 9$

43. $bx + by - bz$

44. $16a - 36b + 42$

45. $\frac{3}{8}x - \frac{5}{8}y + \frac{7}{8}$

46. $-12x + 32y - 16z$

Answers

41. $6(x - 2)$ **42.** $3(x - 2y + 3)$
43. $b(x + y - z)$ **44.** $2(8a - 18b + 21)$
45. $\frac{1}{8}(3x - 5y + 7)$ **46.** $-4(3x - 8y + 4z)$, or $4(-3x + 8y - 4z)$

e Collecting Like Terms

Terms such as $5x$ and $-4x$, whose variable factors are exactly the same, are called **like terms.** Similarly, numbers, such as -7 and 13, are like terms. Also, $3y^2$ and $9y^2$ are like terms because the variables are raised to the same power. Terms such as $4y$ and $5y^2$ are not like terms, and $7x$ and $2y$ are not like terms.

The process of **collecting like terms** is also based on the distributive laws. We can apply a distributive law when a factor is on the right because of the commutative law of multiplication.

Later in this text, terminology like "collecting like terms" and "combining like terms" will also be referred to as "simplifying."

EXAMPLES Collect like terms. Try to write just the answer, if you can.

32. $4x + 2x = (4 + 2)x = 6x$ Factoring out the x using a distributive law

33. $2x + 3y - 5x - 2y = 2x - 5x + 3y - 2y$
$= (2 - 5)x + (3 - 2)y = -3x + 1y = -3x + y$

34. $3x - x = 3x - 1x = (3 - 1)x = 2x$

35. $x - 0.24x = 1 \cdot x - 0.24x = (1 - 0.24)x = 0.76x$

36. $x - 6x = 1 \cdot x - 6 \cdot x = (1 - 6)x = -5x$

37. $4x - 7y + 9x - 5 + 3y - 8 = 13x - 4y - 13$

38. $\frac{2}{3}a - b + \frac{4}{5}a + \frac{1}{4}b - 10 = \frac{2}{3}a - 1 \cdot b + \frac{4}{5}a + \frac{1}{4}b - 10$
$= \left(\frac{2}{3} + \frac{4}{5}\right)a + \left(-1 + \frac{1}{4}\right)b - 10$
$= \left(\frac{10}{15} + \frac{12}{15}\right)a + \left(-\frac{4}{4} + \frac{1}{4}\right)b - 10$
$= \frac{22}{15}a - \frac{3}{4}b - 10$

Do Exercises 47–53.

Collect like terms.

47. $6x - 3x$

48. $7x - x$

49. $x - 9x$

50. $x - 0.41x$

51. $5x + 4y - 2x - y$

52. $3x - 7x - 11 + 8y + 4 - 13y$

53. $-\frac{2}{3} - \frac{3}{5}x + y + \frac{7}{10}x - \frac{2}{9}y$

STUDY TIPS

LEARNING RESOURCES

Please see the preface for more information on these resources and others. To order any of our products, call (800) 824-7799 in the United States or (201) 767-5021 outside the United States, or visit your campus bookstore.

- The *Student's Solutions Manual* contains fully worked-out solutions to the odd-numbered exercises in the exercise sets, as well as solutions to all exercises in the Mid-Chapter Reviews, end-of-chapter Review Exercises, Chapter Tests, and Cumulative Reviews. (ISBN: 978-0-321-64070-3)
- *Worksheets for Classroom or Lab Practice* provide a list of learning objectives, vocabulary and practice problems, and extra practice problems with ample work space. (ISBN: 978-0-321-64073-4)
- As described on p. 96 and in the Preface, Video Resources on DVD Featuring Chapter Test Prep Videos provide section-level lectures for every objective and step-by-step solutions to all the Chapter Test exercises in this textbook. The Chapter Test videos are also available on YouTube (search using BittingerIntroAlg) and in MyMathLab.
- InterAct Math Tutorial Website (www.interactmath.com) provides algorithmically generated practice exercises that correlate directly to the exercises in the textbook.
- MathXL® Tutorials on CD provide practice exercises correlated at the objective level to the exercises in the textbook. Every practice exercise is accompanied by an example and a guided solution, and selected exercises may also include a video clip to help illustrate a concept.

Answers

47. $3x$ **48.** $6x$ **49.** $-8x$ **50.** $0.59x$
51. $3x + 3y$ **52.** $-4x - 5y - 7$
53. $\frac{1}{10}x + \frac{7}{9}y - \frac{2}{3}$

1.7 Exercise Set

For Extra Help MyMathLab — MathXL PRACTICE | WATCH | DOWNLOAD | READ | REVIEW

a Find an equivalent expression with the given denominator.

1. $\frac{3}{5} = \frac{\square}{5y}$ **2.** $\frac{5}{8} = \frac{\square}{8t}$ **3.** $\frac{2}{3} = \frac{\square}{15x}$ **4.** $\frac{6}{7} = \frac{\square}{14y}$ **5.** $\frac{2}{x} = \frac{\square}{x^2}$ **6.** $\frac{4}{9x} = \frac{\square}{9xy}$

Simplify.

7. $-\frac{24a}{16a}$ **8.** $-\frac{42t}{18t}$ **9.** $-\frac{42ab}{36ab}$ **10.** $-\frac{64pq}{48pq}$ **11.** $\frac{20st}{15t}$ **12.** $\frac{21w}{7wz}$

b Write an equivalent expression. Use a commutative law.

13. $y + 8$ **14.** $x + 3$ **15.** mn **16.** yz

17. $9 + xy$ **18.** $11 + ab$ **19.** $ab + c$ **20.** $rs + t$

Write an equivalent expression. Use an associative law.

21. $a + (b + 2)$ **22.** $3(vw)$ **23.** $(8x)y$ **24.** $(y + z) + 7$

25. $(a + b) + 3$ **26.** $(5 + x) + y$ **27.** $3(ab)$ **28.** $(6x)y$

Use the commutative and associative laws to write three equivalent expressions.

29. $(a + b) + 2$ **30.** $(3 + x) + y$ **31.** $5 + (v + w)$ **32.** $6 + (x + y)$

33. $(xy)3$ **34.** $(ab)5$ **35.** $7(ab)$ **36.** $5(xy)$

c Multiply.

37. $2(b + 5)$ **38.** $4(x + 3)$ **39.** $7(1 + t)$ **40.** $4(1 + y)$

41. $6(5x + 2)$ **42.** $9(6m + 7)$ **43.** $7(x + 4 + 6y)$ **44.** $4(5x + 8 + 3p)$

45. $7(x - 3)$

46. $15(y - 6)$

47. $-3(x - 7)$

48. $1.2(x - 2.1)$

49. $\frac{2}{3}(b - 6)$

50. $\frac{5}{8}(y + 16)$

51. $7.3(x - 2)$

52. $5.6(x - 8)$

53. $-\frac{3}{5}(x - y + 10)$

54. $-\frac{2}{3}(a + b - 12)$

55. $-9(-5x - 6y + 8)$

56. $-7(-2x - 5y + 9)$

57. $-4(x - 3y - 2z)$

58. $8(2x - 5y - 8z)$

59. $3.1(-1.2x + 3.2y - 1.1)$

60. $-2.1(-4.2x - 4.3y - 2.2)$

List the terms of each expression.

61. $4x + 3z$

62. $8x - 1.4y$

63. $7x + 8y - 9z$

64. $8a + 10b - 18c$

d Factor. Check by multiplying.

65. $2x + 4$

66. $5y + 20$

67. $30 + 5y$

68. $7x + 28$

69. $14x + 21y$

70. $18a + 24b$

71. $14t - 7$

72. $25m - 5$

73. $8x - 24$

74. $10x - 50$

75. $18a - 24b$

76. $32x - 20y$

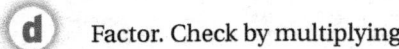

77. $-4y + 32$

78. $-6m + 24$

79. $5x + 10 + 15y$

80. $9a + 27b + 81$

81. $16m - 32n + 8$

82. $6x + 10y - 2$

83. $12a + 4b - 24$

84. $8m - 4n + 12$

85. $8x + 10y - 22$

86. $9a + 6b - 15$

87. $ax - a$

88. $by - 9b$

89. $ax - ay - az$

90. $cx + cy - cz$

91. $-18x + 12y + 6$

92. $-14x + 21y + 7$

93. $\frac{2}{3}x - \frac{5}{3}y + \frac{1}{3}$

94. $\frac{3}{5}a + \frac{4}{5}b - \frac{1}{5}$

95. $36x - 6y + 18z$

96. $8a - 4b + 20c$

e Collect like terms.

97. $9a + 10a$

98. $12x + 2x$

99. $10a - a$

100. $-16x + x$

101. $2x + 9z + 6x$

102. $3a - 5b + 7a$

103. $7x + 6y^2 + 9y^2$

104. $12m^2 + 6q + 9m^2$

105. $41a + 90 - 60a - 2$

106. $42x - 6 - 4x + 2$

107. $23 + 5t + 7y - t - y - 27$

108. $45 - 90d - 87 - 9d + 3 + 7d$

109. $\frac{1}{2}b + \frac{1}{2}b$

110. $\frac{2}{3}x + \frac{1}{3}x$

111. $2y + \frac{1}{4}y + y$

112. $\frac{1}{2}a + a + 5a$

113. $11x - 3x$

114. $9t - 17t$

115. $6n - n$

116. $100t - t$

117. $y - 17y$

118. $3m - 9m + 4$

119. $-8 + 11a - 5b + 6a - 7b + 7$

120. $8x - 5x + 6 + 3y - 2y - 4$

121. $9x + 2y - 5x$

122. $8y - 3z + 4y$

123. $11x + 2y - 4x - y$

124. $13a + 9b - 2a - 4b$

125. $2.7x + 2.3y - 1.9x - 1.8y$

126. $6.7a + 4.3b - 4.1a - 2.9b$

127. $\frac{13}{2}a + \frac{9}{5}b - \frac{2}{3}a - \frac{3}{10}b - 42$

128. $\frac{11}{4}x + \frac{2}{3}y - \frac{4}{5}x - \frac{1}{6}y + 12$

Skill Maintenance

Find the LCM. [R.1b]

129. 16, 18

130. 18, 24

131. 16, 18, 24

132. 12, 15, 20

133. 16, 32

134. 24, 72

135. 15, 45, 90

136. 18, 54, 108

137. Add and simplify: $\frac{11}{12} + \frac{15}{16}$. [R.2c]

138. Subtract and simplify: $\frac{7}{8} - \frac{2}{3}$. [R.2c]

139. Subtract and simplify: $\frac{1}{8} - \frac{1}{3}$. [R.2c], [1.4a]

140. Convert to percent notation: $\frac{3}{10}$. [R.4d]

Synthesis

Determine whether the expressions are equivalent. Explain why if they are. Give an example if they are not. Examples may vary.

141. $3t + 5$ and $3 \cdot 5 + t$

142. $4x$ and $x + 4$

143. $5m + 6$ and $6 + 5m$

144. $(x + y) + z$ and $z + (x + y)$

145. Factor: $q + qr + qrs + qrst$.

146. Collect like terms:
$21x + 44xy + 15y - 16x - 8y - 38xy + 2y + xy$.

1.8 Simplifying Expressions; Order of Operations

We now expand our ability to manipulate expressions by first considering opposites of sums and differences. Then we simplify expressions involving parentheses.

OBJECTIVES

a Find an equivalent expression for an opposite without parentheses, where an expression has several terms.

b Simplify expressions by removing parentheses and collecting like terms.

c Simplify expressions with parentheses inside parentheses.

d Simplify expressions using the rules for order of operations.

a Opposites of Sums

What happens when we multiply a real number by -1? Consider the following products:

$$-1(7) = -7, \qquad -1(-5) = 5, \qquad -1(0) = 0.$$

From these examples, it appears that when we multiply a number by -1, we get the opposite, or additive inverse, of that number.

THE PROPERTY OF −1

For any real number a,

$$-1 \cdot a = -a.$$

(Negative one times a is the opposite, or additive inverse, of a.)

The property of -1 enables us to find expressions equivalent to opposites of sums.

EXAMPLES Find an equivalent expression without parentheses.

1. $-(3 + x) = -1(3 + x)$ Using the property of -1

$= -1 \cdot 3 + (-1)x$ Using a distributive law, multiplying each term by -1

$= -3 + (-x)$ Using the property of -1

$= -3 - x$

2. $-(3x + 2y + 4) = -1(3x + 2y + 4)$ Using the property of -1

$= -1(3x) + (-1)(2y) + (-1)4$ Using a distributive law

$= -3x - 2y - 4$ Using the property of -1

Do Exercises 1 and 2.

Find an equivalent expression without parentheses.

1. $-(x + 2)$

2. $-(5x + 2y + 8)$

Suppose we want to remove parentheses in an expression like

$$-(x - 2y + 5).$$

We can first rewrite any subtractions inside the parentheses as additions. Then we take the opposite of each term:

$$-(x - 2y + 5) = -[x + (-2y) + 5]$$
$$= -x + 2y + (-5) = -x + 2y - 5.$$

The most efficient method for removing parentheses is to replace each term in the parentheses with its opposite ("change the sign of every term"). Doing so for $-(x - 2y + 5)$, we obtain $-x + 2y - 5$ as an equivalent expression.

Answers

1. $-x - 2$ **2.** $-5x - 2y - 8$

Find an equivalent expression without parentheses. Try to do this in one step.

3. $-(6 - t)$

4. $-(x - y)$

5. $-(-4a + 3t - 10)$

6. $-(18 - m - 2n + 4z)$

EXAMPLES Find an equivalent expression without parentheses.

3. $-(5 - y) = -5 + y$ Changing the sign of each term

4. $-(2a - 7b - 6) = -2a + 7b + 6$

5. $-(-3x + 4y + z - 7w - 23) = 3x - 4y - z + 7w + 23$

Do Exercises 3–6.

b Removing Parentheses and Simplifying

When a sum is added to another expression, as in $5x + (2x + 3)$, we can simply remove, or drop, the parentheses and collect like terms because of the associative law of addition:

$$5x + (2x + 3) = 5x + 2x + 3 = 7x + 3.$$

On the other hand, when a sum is subtracted from another expression, as in $3x - (4x + 2)$, we cannot simply drop the parentheses. However, we can subtract by adding an opposite. We then remove parentheses by changing the sign of each term inside the parentheses and collecting like terms.

EXAMPLE 6 Remove parentheses and simplify.

$3x - (4x + 2) = 3x + [-(4x + 2)]$ Adding the opposite of $(4x + 2)$

$= 3x + (-4x - 2)$ Changing the sign of each term inside the parentheses

$= 3x - 4x - 2$

$= -x - 2$ Collecting like terms

Caution!

Note that $3x - (4x + 2) \neq 3x - 4x + 2$. You cannot simply drop the parentheses.

Remove parentheses and simplify.

7. $5x - (3x + 9)$

8. $5y - 2 - (2y - 4)$

Do Exercises 7 and 8.

In practice, the first three steps of Example 6 are usually combined by changing the sign of each term in parentheses and then collecting like terms.

EXAMPLES Remove parentheses and simplify.

7. $5y - (3y + 4) = 5y - 3y - 4$ Removing parentheses by changing the sign of every term inside the parentheses

$= 2y - 4$ Collecting like terms

8. $3x - 2 - (5x - 8) = 3x - 2 - 5x + 8$

$= -2x + 6$

9. $(3a + 4b - 5) - (2a - 7b + 4c - 8)$

$= 3a + 4b - 5 - 2a + 7b - 4c + 8$

$= a + 11b - 4c + 3$

Remove parentheses and simplify.

9. $6x - (4x + 7)$

10. $8y - 3 - (5y - 6)$

11. $(2a + 3b - c) - (4a - 5b + 2c)$

Do Exercises 9–11.

Answers

3. $-6 + t$ **4.** $-x + y$ **5.** $4a - 3t + 10$
6. $-18 + m + 2n - 4z$ **7.** $2x - 9$
8. $3y + 2$ **9.** $2x - 7$ **10.** $3y + 3$
11. $-2a + 8b - 3c$

Next, consider subtracting an expression consisting of several terms multiplied by a number other than 1 or -1.

EXAMPLE 10 Remove parentheses and simplify.

$$\begin{aligned} x - 3(x + y) &= x + [-3(x + y)] && \text{Adding the opposite of } 3(x+y) \\ &= x + [-3x - 3y] && \text{Multiplying } x + y \text{ by } -3 \\ &= x - 3x - 3y \\ &= -2x - 3y && \text{Collecting like terms} \end{aligned}$$

EXAMPLES Remove parentheses and simplify

11. $3y - 2(4y - 5) = 3y - 8y + 10$ Multiplying each term in the parentheses by -2

$= -5y + 10$

12. $(2a + 3b - 7) - 4(-5a - 6b + 12)$

$= 2a + 3b - 7 + 20a + 24b - 48 = 22a + 27b - 55$

13. $2y - \frac{1}{3}(9y - 12) = 2y - 3y + 4 = -y + 4$

14. $6(5x - 3y) - 2(8x + y) = 30x - 18y - 16x - 2y = 14x - 20y$

Do Exercises 12–16.

Remove parentheses and simplify.

12. $y - 9(x + y)$

13. $5a - 3(7a - 6)$

14. $4a - b - 6(5a - 7b + 8c)$

15. $5x - \frac{1}{4}(8x + 28)$

16. $4.6(5x - 3y) - 5.2(8x + y)$

C Parentheses Within Parentheses

In addition to parentheses, some expressions contain other grouping symbols such as brackets [ ] and braces { }.

When more than one kind of grouping symbol occurs, do the computations in the innermost ones first. Then work from the inside out.

EXAMPLES Simplify.

15. $[3 - (7 + 3)] = [3 - 10] = -7$

16. $\{8 - [9 - (12 + 5)]\} = \{8 - [9 - 17]\}$ Computing $12 + 5$

$= \{8 - [-8]\}$ Computing $9 - 17$

$= 8 + 8 = 16$

17. $\left[(-4) \div \left(-\frac{1}{4}\right)\right] \div \frac{1}{4} = [(-4) \cdot (-4)] \div \frac{1}{4}$ Working within the brackets; computing $(-4) \div \left(-\frac{1}{4}\right)$

$= 16 \div \frac{1}{4}$

$= 16 \cdot 4 = 64$

18. $4(2 + 3) - \{7 - [4 - (8 + 5)]\}$

$= 4 \cdot 5 - \{7 - [4 - 13]\}$ Working with the innermost parentheses first

$= 20 - \{7 - [-9]\}$ Computing $4 \cdot 5$ and $4 - 13$

$= 20 - 16$ Computing $7 - [-9]$

$= 4$

Do Exercises 17–20.

Simplify.

17. $12 - (8 + 2)$

18. $9 - [10 - (13 + 6)]$

19. $[24 \div (-2)] \div (-2)$

20. $5(3 + 4) - \{8 - [5 - (9 + 6)]\}$

Answers

12. $-9x - 8y$ **13.** $-16a + 18$
14. $-26a + 41b - 48c$ **15.** $3x - 7$
16. $-18.6x - 19y$ **17.** 2 **18.** 18
19. 6 **20.** 17

EXAMPLE 19 Simplify.

$$[5(x + 2) - 3x] - [3(y + 2) - 7(y - 3)]$$

$= [5x + 10 - 3x] - [3y + 6 - 7y + 21]$ Working with the innermost parentheses first

$= [2x + 10] - [-4y + 27]$ Collecting like terms within brackets

$= 2x + 10 + 4y - 27$ Removing brackets

$= 2x + 4y - 17$ Collecting like terms

Do Exercise 21.

21. Simplify:
$[3(x + 2) + 2x] - [4(y + 2) - 3(y - 2)]$.

d Order of Operations

When several operations are to be done in a calculation or a problem, we apply the same rules that we did in Section R.5. We repeat them here for review. (If you did not study that section earlier, you may wish to do so now.)

RULES FOR ORDER OF OPERATIONS

1. Do all calculations within grouping symbols before operations outside.
2. Evaluate all exponential expressions.
3. Do all multiplications and divisions in order from left to right.
4. Do all additions and subtractions in order from left to right.

These rules are consistent with the way in which most computers and scientific calculators perform calculations.

EXAMPLE 20 Simplify: $-34 \cdot 56 - 17$.

There are no parentheses or powers, so we start with the third step.

$-34 \cdot 56 - 17 = -1904 - 17$ Doing all multiplications and divisions in order from left to right

$= -1921$ Doing all additions and subtractions in order from left to right

EXAMPLE 21 Simplify: $25 \div (-5) + 50 \div (-2)$.

There are no calculations inside parentheses and no powers. The parentheses with (-5) and (-2) are used only to represent the negative numbers. We begin by doing all multiplications and divisions.

$$\underbrace{25 \div (-5)} + \underbrace{50 \div (-2)}$$

$= -5 + (-25)$ Doing all multiplications and divisions in order from left to right

$= -30$ Doing all additions and subtractions in order from left to right

Do Exercises 22–24.

Simplify.

22. $23 - 42 \cdot 30$

23. $32 \div 8 \cdot 2$

24. $-24 \div 3 - 48 \div (-4)$

Answers

21. $5x - y - 8$ **22.** -1237 **23.** 8 **24.** 4

EXAMPLE 22 Simplify: $-2^4 + 51 \cdot 4 - (37 + 23 \cdot 2)$.

$$-2^4 + 51 \cdot 4 - (37 + 23 \cdot 2)$$

$= -2^4 + 51 \cdot 4 - (37 + 46)$ — Following the rules for order of operations within the parentheses first

$= -2^4 + 51 \cdot 4 - 83$ — Completing the addition inside parentheses

$= -16 + 51 \cdot 4 - 83$ — Evaluating exponential expressions. Note that $-2^4 \neq (-2)^4$.

$= -16 + 204 - 83$ — Doing all multiplications

$= 188 - 83$ — Doing all additions and subtractions in order from left to right

$= 105$

A fraction bar can play the role of a grouping symbol, although such a symbol is not as evident as the others.

EXAMPLE 23 Simplify: $\dfrac{-64 \div (-16) \div (-2)}{2^3 - 3^2}$.

An equivalent expression with brackets as grouping symbols is

$$[-64 \div (-16) \div (-2)] \div [2^3 - 3^2].$$

This shows, in effect, that we do the calculations in the numerator and then in the denominator, and divide the results:

$$\frac{-64 \div (-16) \div (-2)}{2^3 - 3^2} = \frac{4 \div (-2)}{8 - 9} = \frac{-2}{-1} = 2.$$

Do Exercises 25 and 26.

Simplify.

25. $-4^3 + 52 \cdot 5 + 5^3 - (4^2 - 48 \div 4)$

26. $\dfrac{5 - 10 - 5 \cdot 23}{2^3 + 3^2 - 7}$

STUDY TIPS

PREPARING FOR AND TAKING A TEST

- **Do a thorough review of the chapter, focusing on the objectives and the examples.** Study the notes that you have taken in class also, as well as any hand-outs that your instructor has prepared for you.
- **Do the review exercises in the Summary and Review at the end of the chapter.** Check your answers using the answers at the back of the book. If you have trouble with an exercise, return to the objective indicated by the objective symbol given with the exercise and study that material further.
- **Do the Chapter Test at the end of the chapter.** Check your answers using the answers at the back of the book. Use the objective symbols in the answer section to direct yourself to material that requires further study.
- **When taking a test, read each question carefully. Try to answer all the questions the first time through, but be sure to pace yourself.** Don't allow yourself to spend a disproportionate amount of time on any one question. As you answer the questions, mark those to recheck if you have time.
- **Write your test in a neat and orderly manner.** This will make it easier for you to recheck your work and will also allow your instructor to follow your work when grading your test.

Answers

25. 317 **26.** −12

Calculator Corner

Order of Operations and Grouping Symbols Parentheses are necessary in some calculations in order to ensure that operations are performed in the desired order. To simplify $-5(3 - 6) - 12$, we press [(-)] [5] [(] [3] [−] [6] [)] [−] [1] [2] [ENTER]. The result is 3. Without parentheses, the computation is $-5 \cdot 3 - 6 - 12$, and the result is -33.

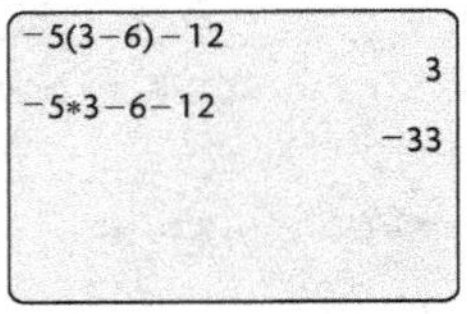

When a negative number is raised to an even power, parentheses must also be used. To find $(-3)^4$, we press [(] [(-)] [3] [)] [^] [4] [ENTER]. The result is 81. Without parentheses, the computation is $-3^4 = -1 \cdot 3^4 = -1 \cdot 81 = -81$.

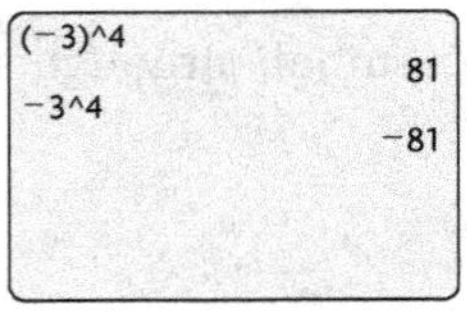

To simplify an expression like $\dfrac{49 - 104}{7 + 4}$, we must enter it as $(49 - 104) \div (7 + 4)$. We press [(] [4] [9] [−] [1] [0] [4] [)] [÷] [(] [7] [+] [4] [)] [ENTER]. The result is -5.

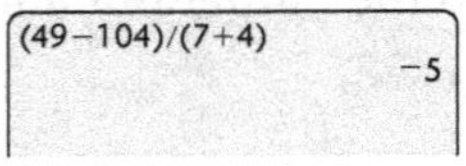

Exercises: Calculate.

1. $-8 + 4(7 - 9) + 5$

2. $-3[2 + (-5)]$

3. $7[4 - (-3)] + 5[3^2 - (-4)]$

4. $(-7)^6$

5. $(-17)^5$

6. $(-104)^3$

7. -7^6

8. -17^5

9. -104^3

10. $\dfrac{38 - 178}{5 + 30}$

11. $\dfrac{311 - 17^2}{2 - 13}$

12. $785 - \dfrac{285 - 5^4}{17 + 3 \cdot 51}$

1.8 Exercise Set

For Extra Help
MyMathLab
Math XL PRACTICE | WATCH | DOWNLOAD | READ | REVIEW

a Find an equivalent expression without parentheses.

1. $-(2x + 7)$

2. $-(8x + 4)$

3. $-(8 - x)$

4. $-(a - b)$

5. $-(4a - 3b + 7c)$

6. $-(x - 4y - 3z)$

7. $-(6x - 8y + 5)$

8. $-(4x + 9y + 7)$

9. $-(3x - 5y - 6)$

10. $-(6a - 4b - 7)$

11. $-(-8x - 6y - 43)$

12. $-(-2a + 9b - 5c)$

b Remove parentheses and simplify.

13. $9x - (4x + 3)$

14. $4y - (2y + 5)$

15. $2a - (5a - 9)$

16. $12m - (4m - 6)$

17. $2x + 7x - (4x + 6)$

18. $3a + 2a - (4a + 7)$

19. $2x - 4y - 3(7x - 2y)$

20. $3a - 9b - 1(4a - 8b)$

21. $15x - y - 5(3x - 2y + 5z)$

22. $4a - b - 4(5a - 7b + 8c)$

23. $(3x + 2y) - 2(5x - 4y)$

24. $(-6a - b) - 5(2b + a)$

25. $(12a - 3b + 5c) - 5(-5a + 4b - 6c)$

26. $(-8x + 5y - 12) - 6(2x - 4y - 10)$

c Simplify.

27. $9 - 2(5 - 4)$

28. $6 - 5(8 - 4)$

29. $8[7 - 6(4 - 2)]$

30. $10[7 - 4(7 - 5)]$

31. $[4(9 - 6) + 11] - [14 - (6 + 4)]$

32. $[7(8 - 4) + 16] - [15 - (7 + 8)]$

33. $[10(x + 3) - 4] + [2(x - 1) + 6]$

34. $[9(x + 5) - 7] + [4(x - 12) + 9]$

35. $[7(x + 5) - 19] - [4(x - 6) + 10]$

36. $[6(x + 4) - 12] - [5(x - 8) + 14]$

37. $3\{[7(x - 2) + 4] - [2(2x - 5) + 6]\}$

38. $4\{[8(x - 3) + 9] - [4(3x - 2) + 6]\}$

39. $4\{[5(x - 3) + 2] - 3[2(x + 5) - 9]\}$

40. $3\{[6(x - 4) + 5] - 2[5(x + 8) - 3]\}$

d Simplify.

41. $8 - 2 \cdot 3 - 9$

42. $8 - (2 \cdot 3 - 9)$

43. $(8 - 2 \cdot 3) - 9$

44. $(8 - 2)(3 - 9)$

45. $[(-24) \div (-3)] \div \left(-\frac{1}{2}\right)$

46. $[32 \div (-2)] \div \left(-\frac{1}{4}\right)$

47. $16 \cdot (-24) + 50$

48. $10 \cdot 20 - 15 \cdot 24$

49. $2^4 + 2^3 - 10$

50. $40 - 3^2 - 2^3$

51. $5^3 + 26 \cdot 71 - (16 + 25 \cdot 3)$

52. $4^3 + 10 \cdot 20 + 8^2 - 23$

53. $4 \cdot 5 - 2 \cdot 6 + 4$

54. $4 \cdot (6 + 8)/(4 + 3)$

55. $4^3/8$

56. $5^3 - 7^2$

57. $8(-7) + 6(-5)$

58. $10(-5) + 1(-1)$

59. $19 - 5(-3) + 3$

60. $14 - 2(-6) + 7$

61. $9 \div (-3) + 16 \div 8$

62. $-32 - 8 \div 4 - (-2)$

63. $-4^2 + 6$

64. $-5^2 + 7$

65. $-8^2 - 3$

66. $-9^2 - 11$

67. $12 - 20^3$

68. $20 + 4^3 \div (-8)$

69. $2 \cdot 10^3 - 5000$

70. $-7(3^4) + 18$

71. $6[9 - (3 - 4)]$

72. $8[(6 - 13) - 11]$

73. $-1000 \div (-100) \div 10$

74. $256 \div (-32) \div (-4)$

75. $8 - (7 - 9)$

76. $(8 - 7) - 9$

77. $\dfrac{10 - 6^2}{9^2 + 3^2}$

78. $\dfrac{5^2 - 4^3 - 3}{9^2 - 2^2 - 1^5}$

79. $\dfrac{3(6 - 7) - 5 \cdot 4}{6 \cdot 7 - 8(4 - 1)}$

80. $\dfrac{20(8 - 3) - 4(10 - 3)}{10(2 - 6) - 2(5 + 2)}$

81. $\dfrac{|2^3 - 3^2| + |12 \cdot 5|}{-32 \div (-16) \div (-4)}$

82. $\dfrac{|3 - 5|^2 - |7 - 13|}{|12 - 9| + |11 - 14|}$

Skill Maintenance

In each of Exercises 83–90, fill in the blank with the correct term from the given list. Some of the choices may not be used and some may be used more than once.

83. The set of ________________ is $\{\ldots, -5, -4, -3, -2, -1, 0, 1, 2, 3, \ldots\}$. [1.2a]

84. Two numbers whose sum is 0 are called ________________ of each other. [1.3b]

85. The ________________ of addition says that $a + b = b + a$ for any real numbers a and b. [1.7b]

86. The ________________ states that for any real number a, $a \cdot 1 = 1 \cdot a = a$. [1.7a]

87. The ________________ of addition says that $a + (b + c) = (a + b) + c$ for any real numbers a, b, and c. [1.7b]

88. The ________________ of multiplication says that $a(bc) = (ab)c$ for any real numbers a, b, and c. [1.7b]

89. Two numbers whose product is 1 are called ________________ of each other. [1.6b]

90. The equation $y + 0 = y$ illustrates the ________________. [1.7a]

natural numbers
whole numbers
integers
real numbers
multiplicative inverses
additive inverses
commutative law
associative law
distributive law
identity property of 0
identity property of 1
property of -1

Synthesis

Find an equivalent expression by enclosing the last three terms in parentheses preceded by a minus sign.

91. $6y + 2x - 3a + c$

92. $x - y - a - b$

93. $6m + 3n - 5m + 4b$

Simplify.

94. $z - \{2z - [3z - (4z - 5z) - 6z] - 7z\} - 8z$

95. $\{x - [f - (f - x)] + [x - f]\} - 3x$

96. $x - \{x - 1 - [x - 2 - (x - 3 - \{x - 4 - [x - 5 - (x - 6)]\})]\}$

97. Use your calculator to do the following.

a) Evaluate $x^2 + 3$ when $x = 7$, when $x = -7$, and when $x = -5.013$.

b) Evaluate $1 - x^2$ when $x = 5$, when $x = -5$, and when $x = -10.455$.

98. Express $3^3 + 3^3 + 3^3$ as a power of 3.

Find the average.

99. $-15, 20, 50, -82, -7, -2$

100. $-1, 1, 2, -2, 3, -8, -10$

CHAPTER 1

Summary and Review

Key Terms and Properties

variable, p. 42
constant, p. 42
algebraic expression, p. 43
substitute, p. 43
evaluate, p. 43
natural numbers, p. 49
whole numbers, p. 49
integers, p. 49
opposites, p. 50
rational numbers, p. 51
terminating decimal, p. 53
repeating decimal, p. 53
irrational numbers, p. 53
real numbers, p. 54
absolute value, p. 56
additive inverse, p. 63
reciprocals, p. 86
multiplicative inverse, p. 86
equivalent expressions, p. 94
factor, p. 100
like terms, p. 102
collect like terms, p. 102

Properties of the Real-Number System

The Commutative Laws: $a + b = b + a, \quad ab = ba$

The Associative Laws: $a + (b + c) = (a + b) + c, \quad a(bc) = (ab)c$

The Identity Properties: $a + 0 = 0 + a = a, \quad a \cdot 1 = 1 \cdot a = a$

The Inverse Properties: For any real number a, there is an opposite $-a$ such that $a + (-a) = (-a) + a = 0$.
For any nonzero real number a, there is a reciprocal $\frac{1}{a}$ such that $a \cdot \frac{1}{a} = \frac{1}{a} \cdot a = 1$.

The Distributive Laws: $a(b + c) = ab + ac, \quad a(b - c) = ab - ac$

The Property of -1: $-1 \cdot a = -a$

Concept Reinforcement

Determine whether each statement is true or false.

_______ **1.** Every whole number is also an integer. [1.2d]

_______ **2.** The product of an even number of negative numbers is positive. [1.5a]

_______ **3.** The product of a number and its multiplicative inverse is -1. [1.6b]

_______ **4.** $a < b$ also has the meaning $b \geq a$. [1.2d]

Important Concepts

Objective 1.1a Evaluate algebraic expressions by substitution.

Example Evaluate $y - z$ when $y = 5$ and $z = -7$.

$y - z = 5 - (-7) = 5 + 7 = 12$

Practice Exercise

1. Evaluate $2a + b$ when $a = -1$ and $b = 16$.

Objective 1.2d Determine which of two real numbers is greater and indicate which, using $<$ or $>$.

Example Use $<$ or $>$ for $\square$ to write a true sentence: $-5 \square -12$.

Since -5 is to the right of -12 on the number line, we have $-5 > -12$.

Practice Exercise

2. Use $<$ or $>$ for $\square$ to write a true sentence: $-6 \square -3$.

Objective 1.2e Find the absolute value of a real number.

Example Find the absolute value: **(a)** $|21|$; **(b)** $|-3.2|$; **(c)** $|0|$.

a) The number is positive, so the absolute value is the same as the number.

$|21| = 21$

b) The number is negative, so we make it positive.

$|-3.2| = 3.2$

c) The number is 0, so the absolute value is the same as the number.

$|0| = 0$

Practice Exercise

3. Find: $\left|-\frac{5}{4}\right|$.

Objective 1.3a Add real numbers without using the number line.

Example Add without using the number line: **(a)** $-13 + 4$; **(b)** $-2 + (-3)$.

a) We have a negative number and a positive number. The absolute values are 13 and 4. The difference is 9. The negative number has the larger absolute value, so the answer is negative.

$-13 + 4 = -9$

b) We have two negative numbers. The sum of the absolute values is $2 + 3$, or 5. The answer is negative.

$-2 + (-3) = -5$

Practice Exercise

4. Add without using the number line: $-5.6 + (-2.9)$.

Objective 1.4a Subtract real numbers.

Example Subtract: $-4 - (-6)$.

$-4 - (-6) = -4 + 6 = 2$

Practice Exercise

5. Subtract: $7 - 9$.

Objective 1.5a Multiply real numbers.

Example Multiply: **(a)** $-1.9(4)$; **(b)** $-7(-6)$.

a) The signs are different, so the answer is negative.

$-1.9(4) = -7.6$

b) The signs are the same, so the answer is positive.

$-7(-6) = 42$

Practice Exercise

6. Multiply: $-8(-7)$.

Objective 1.6a Divide integers.

Example Divide: **(a)** $15 \div (-3)$; **(b)** $-72 \div (-9)$.

a) The signs are different, so the answer is negative.

$15 \div (-3) = -5$

b) The signs are the same, so the answer is positive.

$-72 \div (-9) = 8$

Practice Exercise

7. Divide: $-48 \div 6$.

Objective 1.6c Divide real numbers.

Example Divide: **(a)** $-\frac{1}{4} \div \frac{3}{5}$; **(b)** $-22.4 \div (-4)$.

a) We multiply by the reciprocal of the divisor:

$$-\frac{1}{4} \div \frac{3}{5} = -\frac{1}{4} \cdot \frac{5}{3} = -\frac{5}{12}.$$

b) We carry out the long division:

$$-22.4 \div (-4) = 5.6.$$

Practice Exercise

8. Divide: $-\frac{3}{4} \div \left(-\frac{5}{3}\right)$.

Objective 1.7a Simplify fraction expressions.

Example Simplify: $-\frac{18x}{15x}$.

$$-\frac{18x}{15x} = -\frac{6 \cdot 3x}{5 \cdot 3x}$$ Factoring the numerator and the denominator

$$= -\frac{6}{5} \cdot \frac{3x}{3x}$$ Factoring the fraction expression

$$= -\frac{6}{5} \cdot 1$$ $\frac{3x}{3x} = 1$

$$= -\frac{6}{5}$$ Removing a factor of 1

Practice Exercise

9. Simplify: $\frac{45y}{27y}$.

Objective 1.7c Use the distributive laws to multiply expressions like 8 and $x - y$.

Example Multiply: $3(4x - y + 2z)$.

$$3(4x - y + 2z)$$
$$= 3 \cdot 4x - 3 \cdot y + 3 \cdot 2z$$
$$= 12x - 3y + 6z$$

Practice Exercise

10. Multiply: $5(x + 3y - 4z)$.

Objective 1.7d Use the distributive laws to factor expressions like $4x - 12 + 24y$.

Example Factor: $12a - 8b + 4c$.

$$12a - 8b + 4c$$
$$= 4 \cdot 3a - 4 \cdot 2b + 4 \cdot c$$
$$= 4(3a - 2b + c)$$

Practice Exercise

11. Factor: $27x + 9y - 36z$.

Objective 1.7e Collect like terms.

Example Collect like terms: $3x - 5y + 8x + y$.

$$3x - 5y + 8x + y$$
$$= 3x + 8x - 5y + y$$
$$= 3x + 8x - 5y + 1 \cdot y$$
$$= (3 + 8)x + (-5 + 1)y$$
$$= 11x - 4y$$

Practice Exercise

12. Collect like terms: $6a - 4b - a + 2b$.

Objective 1.8b Simplify expressions by removing parentheses and collecting like terms.

Example Remove parentheses and simplify:

$5x - 2(3x - y)$.

$5x - 2(3x - y) = 5x - 6x + 2y = -x + 2y$

Practice Exercise

13. Remove parentheses and simplify:

$8a - b - (4a + 3b)$.

Objective 1.8d Simplify expressions using the rules for order of operations.

Example Simplify: $12 - (7 - 3 \cdot 6)$.

$$\begin{aligned} 12 - (7 - 3 \cdot 6) &= 12 - (7 - 18) \\ &= 12 - (-11) \\ &= 12 + 11 \\ &= 23 \end{aligned}$$

Practice Exercise

14. Simplify: $75 \div (-15) + 24 \div 8$.

Review Exercises

The review exercises that follow are for practice. Answers are at the back of the book. If you miss an exercise, restudy the objective indicated in red after the exercise or the direction line that precedes it.

1. Evaluate $\dfrac{x - y}{3}$ when $x = 17$ and $y = 5$. [1.1a]

2. Translate to an algebraic expression: [1.1b]
Nineteen percent of some number.

3. Tell which integers correspond to this situation: [1.2a]
David has a debt of $45 and Joe has $72 in his savings account.

Find the absolute value. [1.2e]

4. $|-38|$

5. $|126|$

Graph the number on the number line. [1.2b]

6. -2.5

7. $\dfrac{8}{9}$

Use either < or > for □ to write a true sentence. [1.2d]

8. -3 □ 10

9. -1 □ -6

10. 0.126 □ -12.6

11. $-\dfrac{2}{3}$ □ $-\dfrac{1}{10}$

12. Write another inequality with the same meaning as $-3 < x$. [1.2d]

Write true or false. [1.2d]

13. $-9 \le 11$

14. $-11 \ge -3$

Find the opposite. [1.3b]

15. 3.8

16. $-\dfrac{3}{4}$

Find the reciprocal. [1.6b]

17. $\dfrac{3}{8}$

18. -7

19. Evaluate $-x$ when $x = -34$. [1.3b]

20. Evaluate $-(-x)$ when $x = 5$. [1.3b]

Compute and simplify.

21. $4 + (-7)$ [1.3a]

22. $6 + (-9) + (-8) + 7$ [1.3a]

23. $-3.8 + 5.1 + (-12) + (-4.3) + 10$ [1.3a]

24. $-3 - (-7) + 7 - 10$ [1.4a]

25. $-\frac{9}{10} - \frac{1}{2}$ [1.4a]

26. $-3.8 - 4.1$ [1.4a]

27. $-9 \cdot (-6)$ [1.5a]

28. $-2.7(3.4)$ [1.5a]

29. $\frac{2}{3} \cdot \left(-\frac{3}{7}\right)$ [1.5a]

30. $3 \cdot (-7) \cdot (-2) \cdot (-5)$ [1.5a]

31. $35 \div (-5)$ [1.6a]

32. $-5.1 \div 1.7$ [1.6c]

33. $-\frac{3}{11} \div \left(-\frac{4}{11}\right)$ [1.6c]

Simplify. [1.8d]

34. $(-3.4 - 12.2) - 8(-7)$

35. $\dfrac{-12(-3) - 2^3 - (-9)(-10)}{3 \cdot 10 + 1}$

36. $-16 \div 4 - 30 \div (-5)$

37. $\dfrac{-4[7 - (10 - 13)]}{|-2(8) - 4|}$

Solve.

38. On the first, second, and third downs, a football team had these gains and losses: 5-yd gain, 12-yd loss, and 15-yd gain, respectively. Find the total gain (or loss). [1.3c]

39. Kaleb's total assets are $170. He borrows $300. What are his total assets now? [1.4b]

40. *Stock Price.* The value of EFX Corp. stock began the day at $17.68 per share and dropped $1.63 per hour for 8 hr. What was the price of the stock after 8 hr? [1.5b]

41. *Checking Account Balance.* Yuri had $68 in his checking account. After writing a check to buy seven equally priced purchases of DVDs, the balance in his account was −$64.65. What was the price of each DVD? [1.6d]

Multiply. [1.7c]

42. $5(3x - 7)$

43. $-2(4x - 5)$

44. $10(0.4x + 1.5)$

45. $-8(3 - 6x)$

Factor. [1.7d]

46. $2x - 14$

47. $-6x + 6$

48. $5x + 10$

49. $-3x + 12y - 12$

Collect like terms. [1.7e]

50. $11a + 2b - 4a - 5b$

51. $7x - 3y - 9x + 8y$

52. $6x + 3y - x - 4y$

53. $-3a + 9b + 2a - b$

Remove parentheses and simplify.

54. $2a - (5a - 9)$ [1.8b]

55. $3(b + 7) - 5b$ [1.8b]

56. $3[11 - 3(4 - 1)]$ [1.8c]

57. $2[6(y - 4) + 7]$ [1.8c]

58. $[8(x + 4) - 10] - [3(x - 2) + 4]$ [1.8c]

59. $5\{[6(x - 1) + 7] - [3(3x - 4) + 8]\}$ [1.8c]

60. Factor out the greatest common factor: $18x - 6y + 30$. [1.7d]

A. $2(9x - 2y + 15)$ **B.** $3(6x - 2y + 10)$
C. $6(3x + 5)$ **D.** $6(3x - y + 5)$

61. Which expression is *not* equivalent to $mn + 5$? [1.7b]

A. $nm + 5$ **B.** $5n + m$
C. $5 + mn$ **D.** $5 + nm$

Synthesis

Simplify. [1.2e], [1.4a], [1.6a], [1.8d]

62. $-\left|\frac{7}{8} - \left(-\frac{1}{2}\right) - \frac{3}{4}\right|$

63. $(|2.7 - 3| + 3^2 - |-3|) \div (-3)$

64. $2000 - 1990 + 1980 - 1970 + \cdots + 20 - 10$

65. Find a formula for the perimeter of the figure below. [R.6a], [1.7e]

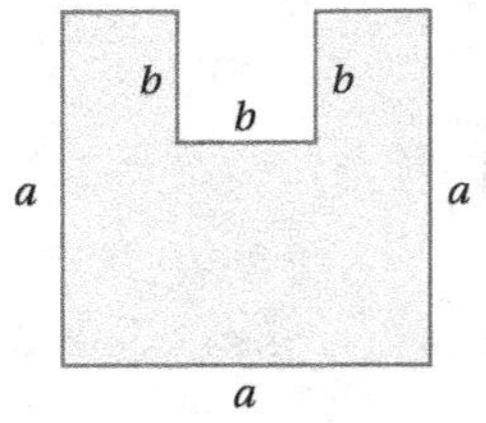

Understanding Through Discussion and Writing

1. Without actually performing the addition, explain why the sum of all integers from -50 to 50 is 0. [1.3b]
2. What rule have we developed that would tell you the sign of $(-7)^8$ and of $(-7)^{11}$ without doing the computations? Explain. [1.5a]
3. Explain how multiplication can be used to justify why a negative number divided by a negative number is positive. [1.6c]
4. Explain how multiplication can be used to justify why a negative number divided by a positive number is negative. [1.6c]
5. The distributive law was introduced before the discussion on collecting like terms. Why do you think this was done? [1.7c, e]
6. Jake keys in $18/2 \cdot 3$ on his calculator and expects the result to be 3. What mistake is he making? [1.8d]

CHAPTER 1 Test

For Extra Help

CHAPTER Test Prep VIDEOS

Step-by-step test solutions are found on the Chapter Test Prep Videos available via the Video Resources on DVD, in MyMathLab, and on YouTube (search "BittingerIntroAlg" and click on "Channels").

1. Evaluate $\frac{3x}{y}$ when $x = 10$ and $y = 5$.

2. Translate to an algebraic expression: Nine less than some number.

Use either $<$ or $>$ for $\square$ to write a true sentence.

3. $-3 \square -8$

4. $-\frac{1}{2} \square -\frac{1}{8}$

5. $-0.78 \square -0.87$

6. Write an inequality with the same meaning as $x < -2$.

7. Write true or false: $-13 \leq -3$.

Simplify.

8. $|-7|$

9. $\left|\frac{9}{4}\right|$

10. $|-2.7|$

Find the opposite.

11. $\frac{2}{3}$

12. -1.4

Find the reciprocal.

13. -2

14. $\frac{4}{7}$

15. Evaluate $-x$ when $x = -8$.

Compute and simplify.

16. $3.1 - (-4.7)$

17. $-8 + 4 + (-7) + 3$

18. $-\frac{1}{5} + \frac{3}{8}$

19. $2 - (-8)$

20. $3.2 - 5.7$

21. $\frac{1}{8} - \left(-\frac{3}{4}\right)$

22. $4 \cdot (-12)$

23. $-\frac{1}{2} \cdot \left(-\frac{3}{8}\right)$

24. $-45 \div 5$

25. $-\frac{3}{5} \div \left(-\frac{4}{5}\right)$

26. $4.864 \div (-0.5)$

27. $-2(16) - |2(-8) - 5^3|$

28. $-20 \div (-5) + 36 \div (-4)$

29. Maureen kept track of the changes in the stock market over a period of 5 weeks. By how many points had the market risen or fallen over this time?

WEEK 1	WEEK 2	WEEK 3	WEEK 4	WEEK 5
Down 13 pts	Down 16 pts	Up 36 pts	Down 11 pts	Up 19 pts

30. *Antarctica Highs and Lows.* The continent of Antarctica, which lies in the southern hemisphere, experiences winter in July. The average high temperature is $-67°F$ and the average low temperature is $-81°F$. How much higher is the average high than the average low?

Source: National Climatic Data Center

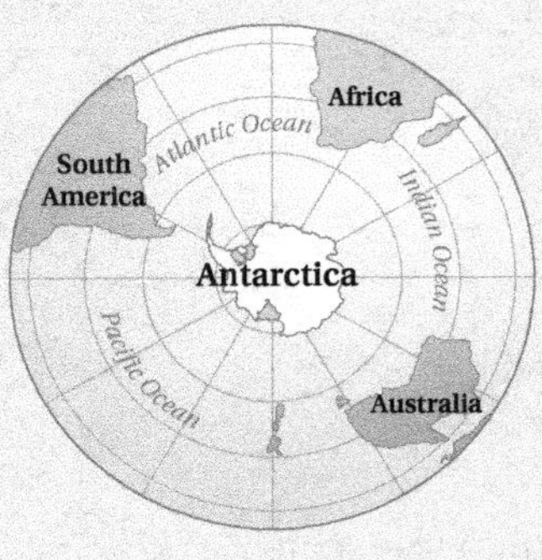

31. *Population Decrease.* The population of Mapleton was 18,600. It dropped 420 each year for 6 yr. What was the population of the city after 6 yr?

32. *Chemical Experiment.* During a chemical reaction, the temperature in a beaker decreased every minute by the same number of degrees. The temperature was 16°C at 11:08 A.M. By 11:52 A.M., the temperature had dropped to $-17°C$. By how many degrees did it change each minute?

Multiply.

33. $3(6 - x)$

34. $-5(y - 1)$

Factor.

35. $12 - 22x$

36. $7x + 21 + 14y$

Simplify.

37. $6 + 7 - 4 - (-3)$

38. $5x - (3x - 7)$

39. $4(2a - 3b) + a - 7$

40. $4\{3[5(y - 3) + 9] + 2(y + 8)\}$

41. $256 \div (-16) \div 4$

42. $2^3 - 10[4 - (-2 + 18)3]$

43. Which of the following is *not* a true statement?

A. $-5 \leq -5$ **B.** $-5 < -5$

C. $-5 \geq -5$ **D.** $-5 = -5$

Synthesis

Simplify.

44. $|-27 - 3(4)| - |-36| + |-12|$

45. $a - \{3a - [4a - (2a - 4a)]\}$

46. Find a formula for the perimeter of the figure shown here.

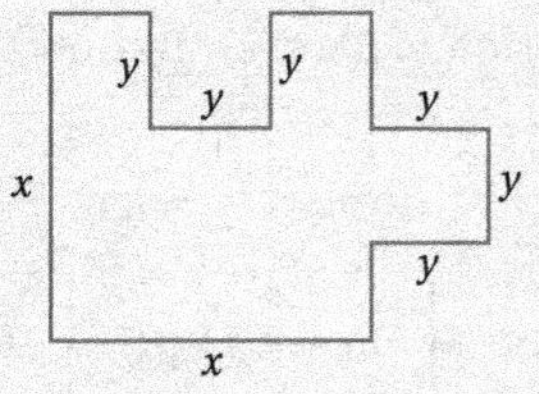

Solving Equations and Inequalities

CHAPTER

2

Real-World Application

The manatee, Florida's state marine mammal, is an endangered species. An aerial wintertime manatee census counted 2817 of these animals in 2007. This was 296 fewer than the number counted in 2006. What was Florida's manatee population in 2006?

Source: Florida Fish and Wildlife Conservation Commission

This problem appears as Exercise 1 in Exercise Set 2.6.

2.1 Solving Equations: The Addition Principle

OBJECTIVES

a Determine whether a given number is a solution of a given equation.

b Solve equations using the addition principle.

SKILL TO REVIEW

Objective 1.1a: Evaluate algebraic expressions by substitution.

1. Evaluate $x - 7$ when $x = 5$.

2. Evaluate $2x + 3$ when $x = -1$.

a Equations and Solutions

In order to solve problems, we must learn to solve equations.

EQUATION

An **equation** is a number sentence that says that the expressions on either side of the equals sign, =, represent the same number.

Here are some examples of equations:

$$3 + 2 = 5, \quad 14 - 10 = 1 + 3, \quad x + 6 = 13, \quad 3x - 2 = 7 - x.$$

Equations have expressions on each side of the equals sign. The sentence "$14 - 10 = 1 + 3$" asserts that the expressions $14 - 10$ and $1 + 3$ name the same number.

Some equations are true. Some are false. Some are neither true nor false.

EXAMPLES Determine whether each equation is true, false, or neither.

1. $3 + 2 = 5$ The equation is *true*.

2. $7 - 2 = 4$ The equation is *false*.

3. $x + 6 = 13$ The equation is *neither* true nor false, because we do not know what number x represents.

Do Margin Exercises 1–3.

Determine whether each equation is true, false, or neither.

1. $5 - 8 = -4$

2. $12 + 6 = 18$

3. $x + 6 = 7 - x$

SOLUTION OF AN EQUATION

Any replacement for the variable that makes an equation true is called a **solution** of the equation. To solve an equation means to find *all* of its solutions.

One way to determine whether a number is a solution of an equation is to evaluate the expression on each side of the equals sign by substitution. If the values are the same, then the number is a solution.

EXAMPLE 4 Determine whether 7 is a solution of $x + 6 = 13$.

We have

$x + 6 = 13$		Writing the equation
$7 + 6 \;?\; 13$		Substituting 7 for x
$13 \mid$		TRUE

Since the left-hand and the right-hand sides are the same, 7 is a solution. No other number makes the equation true, so the only solution is the number 7.

Answers

Skill to Review:
1. −2 **2.** 1

Margin Exercises:
1. False **2.** True **3.** Neither

EXAMPLE 5 Determine whether 19 is a solution of $7x = 141$.

$7x = 141$		Writing the equation
$7(19)$?	141	Substituting 19 for x
133		FALSE

Since the left-hand and the right-hand sides are not the same, 19 is not a solution of the equation.

Do Exercises 4–7.

Determine whether the given number is a solution of the given equation.

4. 8; $x + 4 = 12$

5. 0; $x + 4 = 12$

6. -3; $7 + x = -4$

7. $-\frac{3}{5}$; $-5x = 3$

b Using the Addition Principle

Consider the equation

$$x = 7.$$

We can easily see that the solution of this equation is 7. If we replace x with 7, we get

$$7 = 7, \quad \text{which is true.}$$

Now consider the equation of Example 4: $x + 6 = 13$. In Example 4, we discovered that the solution of this equation is also 7, but the fact that 7 is the solution is not as obvious. We now begin to consider principles that allow us to start with an equation like $x + 6 = 13$ and end up with an *equivalent equation*, like $x = 7$, in which the variable is alone on one side and for which the solution is easier to find.

EQUIVALENT EQUATIONS

Equations with the same solutions are called **equivalent equations.**

One of the principles that we use in solving equations involves addition. An equation $a = b$ says that a and b stand for the same number. Suppose this is true, and we add a number c to the number a. We get the same answer if we add c to b, because a and b are the same number.

THE ADDITION PRINCIPLE FOR EQUATIONS

For any real numbers a, b, and c,

$a = b$ is equivalent to $a + c = b + c$.

Let's solve the equation $x + 6 = 13$ using the addition principle. We want to get x alone on one side. To do so, we use the addition principle, choosing to add -6 because $6 + (-6) = 0$:

$x + 6 = 13$	
$x + 6 + (-6) = 13 + (-6)$	Using the addition principle: adding -6 on both sides
$x + 0 = 7$	Simplifying
$x = 7.$	Identity property of 0: $x + 0 = x$

The solution of $x + 6 = 13$ is 7.

Do Exercise 8.

8. Solve using the addition principle:

$$x + 2 = 11.$$

Answers

4. Yes **5.** No **6.** No **7.** Yes **8.** 9

When we use the addition principle, we sometimes say that we "add the same number on both sides of the equation." This is also true for subtraction, since we can express every subtraction as an addition. That is, since

$$a - c = b - c \quad \text{is equivalent to} \quad a + (-c) = b + (-c),$$

the addition principle tells us that we can "subtract the same number on both sides of the equation."

EXAMPLE 6 Solve: $x + 5 = -7$.

We have

$x + 5 = -7$	
$x + 5 - 5 = -7 - 5$	Using the addition principle: adding -5 on both sides or subtracting 5 on both sides
$x + 0 = -12$	Simplifying
$x = -12.$	Identity property of 0

To check the answer, we substitute -12 in the original equation.

Check: $x + 5 = -7$

$-12 + 5 \ ? \ -7$

-7 | TRUE

The solution of the original equation is -12.

In Example 6, to get x alone, we used the addition principle and subtracted 5 on both sides. This eliminated the 5 on the left. We started with $x + 5 = -7$, and, using the addition principle, we found a simpler equation $x = -12$ for which it was easy to *"see"* the solution. The equations $x + 5 = -7$ and $x = -12$ are *equivalent*.

9. Solve using the addition principle, subtracting 5 on both sides:

$x + 5 = -8.$

Do Exercise 9.

Now we use the addition principle to solve an equation that involves a subtraction.

EXAMPLE 7 Solve: $a - 4 = 10$.

We have

$a - 4 = 10$	
$a - 4 + 4 = 10 + 4$	Using the addition principle: adding 4 on both sides
$a + 0 = 14$	Simplifying
$a = 14.$	Identity property of 0

Check: $a - 4 = 10$

$14 - 4 \ ? \ 10$

10 | TRUE

The solution is 14.

10. Solve: $t - 3 = 19$.

Do Exercise 10.

Answers

9. -13 **10.** 22

EXAMPLE 8 Solve: $-6.5 = y - 8.4$.

We have

$$-6.5 = y - 8.4$$

$$-6.5 + 8.4 = y - 8.4 + 8.4$$ Using the addition principle: adding 8.4 on both sides to eliminate -8.4 on the right

$$1.9 = y.$$

Check:

$$\begin{array}{c|l} -6.5 = y - 8.4 & \\ \hline -6.5 \ ? \ 1.9 - 8.4 & \\ & -6.5 \quad \text{TRUE} \end{array}$$

The solution is 1.9.

Note that equations are reversible. That is, if $a = b$ is true, then $b = a$ is true. Thus when we solve $-6.5 = y - 8.4$, we can reverse it and solve $y - 8.4 = -6.5$ if we wish.

Do Exercises 11 and 12.

Solve.

11. $8.7 = n - 4.5$

12. $y + 17.4 = 10.9$

EXAMPLE 9 Solve: $-\frac{2}{3} + x = \frac{5}{2}$.

We have

$$-\frac{2}{3} + x = \frac{5}{2}$$

$$\frac{2}{3} - \frac{2}{3} + x = \frac{2}{3} + \frac{5}{2}$$ Adding $\frac{2}{3}$ on both sides

$$x = \frac{2}{3} + \frac{5}{2}$$

$$x = \frac{2}{3} \cdot \frac{2}{2} + \frac{5}{2} \cdot \frac{3}{3}$$ Multiplying by 1 to obtain equivalent fraction expressions with the least common denominator 6

$$x = \frac{4}{6} + \frac{15}{6}$$

$$x = \frac{19}{6}.$$

Check:

$$\begin{array}{l|l} -\frac{2}{3} + x = \frac{5}{2} & \\ \hline -\frac{2}{3} + \frac{19}{6} \ ? & \frac{5}{2} \\ -\frac{4}{6} + \frac{19}{6} & \\ \frac{15}{6} & \\ \frac{5}{2} & \quad \text{TRUE} \end{array}$$

The solution is $\frac{19}{6}$.

Do Exercises 13 and 14.

Solve.

13. $x + \frac{1}{2} = -\frac{3}{2}$

14. $t - \frac{13}{4} = \frac{5}{8}$

Answers

11. 13.2 **12.** -6.5 **13.** -2 **14.** $\frac{31}{8}$

2.1 Exercise Set

For Extra Help

MyMathLab | MathXL PRACTICE | WATCH | DOWNLOAD | READ | REVIEW

a Determine whether the given number is a solution of the given equation.

1. 15; $x + 17 = 32$

2. 35; $t + 17 = 53$

3. 21; $x - 7 = 12$

4. 36; $a - 19 = 17$

5. -7; $6x = 54$

6. -9; $8y = -72$

7. 30; $\frac{x}{6} = 5$

8. 49; $\frac{y}{8} = 6$

9. 20; $5x + 7 = 107$

10. 9; $9x + 5 = 86$

11. -10; $7(y - 1) = 63$

12. -5; $6(y - 2) = 18$

b Solve using the addition principle. Don't forget to check!

13. $x + 2 = 6$

Check: $x + 2 = 6$?

14. $y + 4 = 11$

Check: $y + 4 = 11$?

15. $x + 15 = -5$

Check: $x + 15 = -5$?

16. $t + 10 = 44$

Check: $t + 10 = 44$?

17. $x + 6 = -8$

Check: $x + 6 = -8$?

18. $z + 9 = -14$

19. $x + 16 = -2$

20. $m + 18 = -13$

21. $x - 9 = 6$

22. $x - 11 = 12$

23. $x - 7 = -21$

24. $x - 3 = -14$

25. $5 + t = 7$

26. $8 + y = 12$

27. $-7 + y = 13$

28. $-8 + y = 17$

29. $-3 + t = -9$

30. $-8 + t = -24$

31. $x + \frac{1}{2} = 7$

32. $24 = -\frac{7}{10} + r$

33. $12 = a - 7.9$

34. $2.8 + y = 11$

35. $r + \frac{1}{3} = \frac{8}{3}$

36. $t + \frac{3}{8} = \frac{5}{8}$

37. $m + \frac{5}{6} = -\frac{11}{12}$

38. $x + \frac{2}{3} = -\frac{5}{6}$

39. $x - \frac{5}{6} = \frac{7}{8}$

40. $y - \frac{3}{4} = \frac{5}{6}$

41. $-\frac{1}{5} + z = -\frac{1}{4}$

42. $-\frac{1}{8} + y = -\frac{3}{4}$

43. $7.4 = x + 2.3$

44. $8.4 = 5.7 + y$

45. $7.6 = x - 4.8$

46. $8.6 = x - 7.4$

47. $-9.7 = -4.7 + y$

48. $-7.8 = 2.8 + x$

49. $5\frac{1}{6} + x = 7$

50. $5\frac{1}{4} = 4\frac{2}{3} + x$

51. $q + \frac{1}{3} = -\frac{1}{7}$

52. $52\frac{3}{8} = -84 + x$

Skill Maintenance

53. Add: $-3 + (-8)$. [1.3a]

54. Subtract: $-3 - (-8)$. [1.4a]

55. Multiply: $-\frac{2}{3} \cdot \frac{5}{8}$. [1.5a]

56. Divide: $-\frac{3}{7} \div \left(-\frac{9}{7}\right)$. [1.6c]

57. Divide: $\frac{2}{3} \div \left(-\frac{4}{9}\right)$. [1.6c]

58. Add: $-8.6 + 3.4$. [1.3a]

59. Subtract: $-\frac{2}{3} - \left(-\frac{5}{8}\right)$. [1.4a]

60. Multiply: $(-25.4)(-6.8)$. [1.5a]

Translate to an algebraic expression. [1.1b]

61. Jane had $83 before paying x dollars for a pair of tennis shoes. How much does she have left?

62. Justin drove his S-10 pickup truck 65 mph for t hours. How far did he drive?

Synthesis

Solve.

63. $-356.788 = -699.034 + t$

64. $-\frac{4}{5} + \frac{7}{10} = x - \frac{3}{4}$

65. $x + \frac{4}{5} = -\frac{2}{3} - \frac{4}{15}$

66. $8 - 25 = 8 + x - 21$

67. $16 + x - 22 = -16$

68. $x + x = x$

69. $x + 3 = 3 + x$

70. $x + 4 = 5 + x$

71. $-\frac{3}{2} + x = -\frac{5}{17} - \frac{3}{2}$

72. $|x| = 5$

73. $|x| + 6 = 19$

2.2 Solving Equations: The Multiplication Principle

OBJECTIVE

a Solve equations using the multiplication principle.

SKILL TO REVIEW
Objective 1.6b: Find the reciprocal of a real number.

Find the reciprocal.

1. 5 **2.** $-\frac{5}{4}$

a Using the Multiplication Principle

Suppose that $a = b$ is true, and we multiply a by some number c. We get the same number if we multiply b by c, because a and b are the same number.

THE MULTIPLICATION PRINCIPLE FOR EQUATIONS

For any real numbers a, b, and c, $c \neq 0$,

$$a = b \quad \text{is equivalent to} \quad a \cdot c = b \cdot c.$$

When using the multiplication principle, we sometimes say that we "multiply on both sides of the equation by the same number."

EXAMPLE 1 Solve: $5x = 70$.

To get x alone, we multiply by the *multiplicative inverse*, or *reciprocal*, of 5. Then we get the *multiplicative identity* 1 times x, or $1 \cdot x$, which simplifies to x. This allows us to eliminate 5 on the left.

$5x = 70$ The reciprocal of 5 is $\frac{1}{5}$.

$\frac{1}{5} \cdot 5x = \frac{1}{5} \cdot 70$ Multiplying by $\frac{1}{5}$ to get $1 \cdot x$ and eliminate 5 on the left

$1 \cdot x = 14$ Simplifying

$x = 14$ Identity property of 1: $1 \cdot x = x$

Check:

$5x = 70$	
$5 \cdot 14 \; ? \; 70$	
$70 \mid$	TRUE

The solution is 14.

The multiplication principle also tells us that we can "divide on both sides of the equation by the same nonzero number." This is because dividing is the same as multiplying by a reciprocal. That is,

$$\frac{a}{c} = \frac{b}{c} \quad \text{is equivalent to} \quad a \cdot \frac{1}{c} = b \cdot \frac{1}{c}, \quad \text{when } c \neq 0.$$

In an expression like $5x$ in Example 1, the number 5 is called the **coefficient**. Example 1 could be done as follows, dividing on both sides by 5, the coefficient of x.

EXAMPLE 2 Solve: $5x = 70$.

$5x = 70$

$\frac{5x}{5} = \frac{70}{5}$ Dividing by 5 on both sides

$1 \cdot x = 14$ Simplifying

$x = 14$ Identity property of 1. The solution is 14.

Answers
Skill to Review:
1. $\frac{1}{5}$ 2. $-\frac{4}{5}$

Do Exercises 1 and 2.

EXAMPLE 3 Solve: $-4x = 92$.

We have

$$-4x = 92$$

$$\frac{-4x}{-4} = \frac{92}{-4}$$ Using the multiplication principle. Dividing by -4 on both sides is the same as multiplying by $-\frac{1}{4}$.

$$1 \cdot x = -23$$ Simplifying

$$x = -23.$$ Identity property of 1

Check:

$$\begin{array}{c|c} -4x & 92 \\ \hline -4(-23) \; ? & 92 \\ 92 & \end{array} \quad \text{TRUE}$$

The solution is -23.

Do Exercise 3.

EXAMPLE 4 Solve: $-x = 9$.

We have

$$-x = 9$$

$$-1 \cdot x = 9$$ Using the property of -1: $-x = -1 \cdot x$

$$\frac{-1 \cdot x}{-1} = \frac{9}{-1}$$ Dividing by -1 on both sides: $-1/(-1) = 1$

$$1 \cdot x = -9$$

$$x = -9.$$

Check:

$$\begin{array}{c|c} -x & 9 \\ \hline -(-9) \; ? & 9 \\ 9 & \end{array} \quad \text{TRUE}$$

The solution is -9.

Do Exercise 4.

We can also solve the equation $-x = 9$ by multiplying as follows.

EXAMPLE 5 Solve: $-x = 9$.

We have

$$-x = 9$$

$$-1 \cdot (-x) = -1 \cdot 9$$ Multiplying by -1 on both sides

$$-1 \cdot (-1) \cdot x = -9$$ $-x = (-1) \cdot x$

$$1 \cdot x = -9$$ $-1 \cdot (-1) = 1$

$$x = -9.$$

The solution is -9.

Do Exercise 5.

1. Solve. Multiply on both sides.
$6x = 90$

2. Solve. Divide on both sides.
$4x = -7$

3. Solve: $-6x = 108$.

4. Solve. Divide on both sides.
$-x = -10$

5. Solve. Multiply on both sides.
$-x = -10$

Answers

1. 15 **2.** $-\frac{7}{4}$ **3.** -18 **4.** 10 **5.** 10

In practice, it is generally more convenient to divide on both sides of the equation if the coefficient of the variable is in decimal notation or is an integer. If the coefficient is in fraction notation, it is usually more convenient to multiply by a reciprocal.

EXAMPLE 6 Solve: $\frac{3}{8} = -\frac{5}{4}x$.

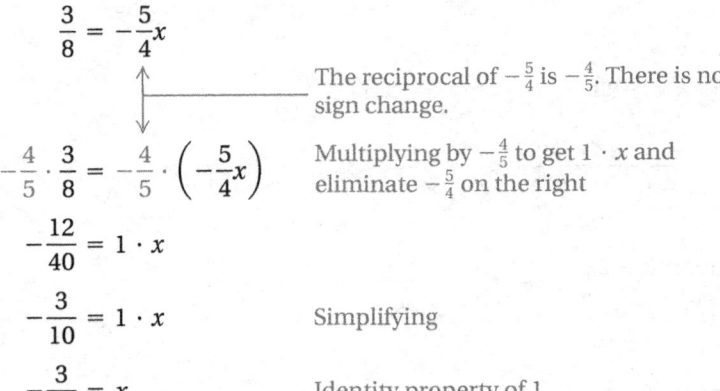

$$\frac{3}{8} = -\frac{5}{4}x$$

The reciprocal of $-\frac{5}{4}$ is $-\frac{4}{5}$. There is no sign change.

$$-\frac{4}{5} \cdot \frac{3}{8} = -\frac{4}{5} \cdot \left(-\frac{5}{4}x\right) \qquad \text{Multiplying by } -\tfrac{4}{5} \text{ to get } 1 \cdot x \text{ and eliminate } -\tfrac{5}{4} \text{ on the right}$$

$$-\frac{12}{40} = 1 \cdot x$$

$$-\frac{3}{10} = 1 \cdot x \qquad \text{Simplifying}$$

$$-\frac{3}{10} = x \qquad \text{Identity property of 1}$$

Check:

$$\frac{3}{8} = -\frac{5}{4}x$$

$$\frac{3}{8} \;?\; -\frac{5}{4}\left(-\frac{3}{10}\right)$$

$$\frac{3}{8} \qquad \text{TRUE}$$

The solution is $-\frac{3}{10}$.

As noted in Section 2.1, if $a = b$ is true, then $b = a$ is true. Thus we can reverse the equation $\frac{3}{8} = -\frac{5}{4}x$ and solve $-\frac{5}{4}x = \frac{3}{8}$ if we wish.

Do Exercise 6.

6. Solve: $\frac{2}{3} = -\frac{5}{6}y$.

EXAMPLE 7 Solve: $1.16y = 9744$.

$$1.16y = 9744$$

$$\frac{1.16y}{1.16} = \frac{9744}{1.16} \qquad \text{Dividing by 1.16 on both sides}$$

$$y = \frac{9744}{1.16}$$

$$y = 8400 \qquad \text{Simplifying}$$

Check:

$$1.16y = 9744$$

$$1.16(8400) \;?\; 9744$$

$$9744 \qquad \text{TRUE}$$

The solution is 8400.

Do Exercises 7 and 8.

Solve.

7. $1.12x = 8736$

8. $6.3 = -2.1y$

Answers

6. $-\frac{4}{5}$ **7.** 7800 **8.** -3

Now we use the multiplication principle to solve an equation that involves division.

EXAMPLE 8 Solve: $\frac{-y}{9} = 14$.

$$\frac{-y}{9} = 14$$

$$9 \cdot \frac{-y}{9} = 9 \cdot 14 \qquad \text{Multiplying by 9 on both sides}$$

$$-y = 126$$

$$-1 \cdot (-y) = -1 \cdot 126 \qquad \text{Multiplying by } -1 \text{ on both sides}$$

$$y = -126$$

Check:

$\frac{-y}{9} = 14$	
$\frac{-(-126)}{9}$	? 14
$\frac{126}{9}$	
14	TRUE

The solution is -126.

There are other ways to solve the equation in Example 8. One is by multiplying by -9 on both sides as follows:

$$-9 \cdot \frac{-y}{9} = -9 \cdot 14$$

$$\frac{(-9)(-y)}{9} = -126$$

$$\frac{9y}{9} = -126$$

$$y = -126.$$

Do Exercise 9.

9. Solve: $-14 = \frac{-y}{2}$.

STUDY TIPS

TIME MANAGEMENT

Having enough time to study is a critical factor in any course. Have realistic expectations about the amount of time you need to study for this course.

- **A rule of thumb for study time.** Budget two to three hours for homework and study per week for each hour of class time.
- **Balancing work and study.** Working 40 hours per week and taking 12 credit hours is equivalent to having two full-time jobs. It is challenging to handle such a load. If you work 40 hours per week, you will probably have more success in school if you take 3 to 6 credit hours. If you are carrying a full class-load, you can probably work 5 to 10 hours per week. Be honest with yourself about how much time you have available to work, attend class, and study.

Answer

9. 28

2.2 Exercise Set

For Extra Help
MyMathLab | MathXL PRACTICE | WATCH | DOWNLOAD | READ | REVIEW

a Solve using the multiplication principle. Don't forget to check!

1. $6x = 36$

Check: $6x = 36$?

2. $3x = 51$

Check: $3x = 51$?

3. $5y = 45$

Check: $5y = 45$?

4. $8y = 72$

Check: $8y = 72$?

5. $84 = 7x$

6. $63 = 9x$

7. $-x = 40$

8. $-x = 53$

9. $-1 = -z$

10. $-47 = -t$

11. $7x = -49$

12. $8x = -56$

13. $-12x = 72$

14. $-15x = 105$

15. $-21w = -126$

16. $-13w = -104$

17. $\frac{t}{7} = -9$

18. $\frac{y}{5} = -6$

19. $\frac{n}{-6} = 8$

20. $\frac{y}{-8} = 11$

21. $\frac{3}{4}x = 27$

22. $\frac{4}{5}x = 16$

23. $-\frac{2}{3}x = 6$

24. $-\frac{3}{8}x = 12$

25. $\frac{-t}{3} = 7$

26. $\frac{-x}{6} = 9$

27. $-\frac{m}{3} = \frac{1}{5}$

28. $\frac{1}{8} = -\frac{y}{5}$

29. $-\frac{3}{5}r = \frac{9}{10}$

30. $-\frac{2}{5}y = \frac{4}{15}$

31. $-\frac{3}{2}r = -\frac{27}{4}$

32. $-\frac{3}{8}x = -\frac{15}{16}$

33. $6.3x = 44.1$

34. $2.7y = 54$

35. $-3.1y = 21.7$

36. $-3.3y = 6.6$

37. $38.7m = 309.6$

38. $29.4m = 235.2$

39. $-\frac{2}{3}y = -10.6$

40. $-\frac{9}{7}y = 12.06$

41. $\frac{-x}{5} = 10$

42. $\frac{-x}{8} = -16$

43. $-\frac{t}{2} = 7$

44. $\frac{m}{-3} = 10$

Skill Maintenance

Collect like terms. [1.7e]

45. $3x + 4x$

46. $6x + 5 - 7x$

47. $-4x + 11 - 6x + 18x$

48. $8y - 16y - 24y$

Remove parentheses and simplify. [1.8b]

49. $3x - (4 + 2x)$

50. $2 - 5(x + 5)$

51. $8y - 6(3y + 7)$

52. $-2a - 4(5a - 1)$

Translate to an algebraic expression. [1.1b]

53. Patty drives her van for 8 hr at a speed of r miles per hour. How far does she drive?

54. A triangle has a height of 10 meters and a base of b meters. What is the area of the triangle?

Synthesis

Solve.

55. $-0.2344m = 2028.732$

56. $0 \cdot x = 0$

57. $0 \cdot x = 9$

58. $4|x| = 48$

59. $2|x| = -12$

Solve for x.

60. $ax = 5a$

61. $3x = \frac{b}{a}$

62. $cx = a^2 + 1$

63. $\frac{a}{b}x = 4$

64. A student makes a calculation and gets an answer of 22.5. On the last step, she multiplies by 0.3 when she should have divided by 0.3. What is the correct answer?

2.3 Using the Principles Together

OBJECTIVES

a Solve equations using both the addition principle and the multiplication principle.

b Solve equations in which like terms may need to be collected.

c Solve equations by first removing parentheses and collecting like terms; solve equations with an infinite number of solutions and equations with no solutions.

a Applying Both Principles

Consider the equation $3x + 4 = 13$. It is more complicated than those we discussed in the preceding two sections. In order to solve such an equation, we first isolate the x-term, $3x$, using the addition principle. Then we apply the multiplication principle to get x by itself.

EXAMPLE 1 Solve: $3x + 4 = 13$.

$$3x + 4 = 13$$

$$3x + 4 - 4 = 13 - 4 \quad \text{Using the addition principle: subtracting 4 on both sides}$$

First isolate the x-term. → $3x = 9$ Simplifying

$$\frac{3x}{3} = \frac{9}{3} \quad \text{Using the multiplication principle: dividing by 3 on both sides}$$

Then isolate x. → $x = 3$ Simplifying

Check:

$3x + 4$	$=$	13
$3 \cdot 3 + 4$	?	13
$9 + 4$		
13		TRUE

We use the rules for order of operations to carry out the check. We find the product $3 \cdot 3$. Then we add 4.

The solution is 3.

Do Exercise 1.

1. Solve: $9x + 6 = 51$.

EXAMPLE 2 Solve: $-5x - 6 = 16$.

$$-5x - 6 = 16$$

$$-5x - 6 + 6 = 16 + 6 \quad \text{Adding 6 on both sides}$$

$$-5x = 22$$

$$\frac{-5x}{-5} = \frac{22}{-5} \quad \text{Dividing by } -5 \text{ on both sides}$$

$$x = -\frac{22}{5}, \text{ or } -4\frac{2}{5} \quad \text{Simplifying}$$

Check:

$-5x - 6$	$=$	16
$-5\left(-\frac{22}{5}\right) - 6$	?	16
$22 - 6$		
16		TRUE

The solution is $-\frac{22}{5}$.

Do Exercises 2 and 3.

Solve.

2. $8x - 4 = 28$

3. $-\frac{1}{2}x + 3 = 1$

Answers

1. 5 2. 4 3. 4

EXAMPLE 3 Solve: $45 - t = 13$.

$$45 - t = 13$$
$$-45 + 45 - t = -45 + 13 \quad \text{Adding } -45 \text{ on both sides}$$
$$-t = -32$$
$$-1(-t) = -1(-32) \quad \text{Multiplying by } -1 \text{ on both sides}$$
$$t = 32$$

The number 32 checks and is the solution.

Do Exercise 4.

4. Solve: $-18 - m = -57$.

EXAMPLE 4 Solve: $16.3 - 7.2y = -8.18$.

$$16.3 - 7.2y = -8.18$$
$$-16.3 + 16.3 - 7.2y = -16.3 + (-8.18) \quad \text{Adding } -16.3 \text{ on both sides}$$
$$-7.2y = -24.48$$
$$\frac{-7.2y}{-7.2} = \frac{-24.48}{-7.2} \quad \text{Dividing by } -7.2 \text{ on both sides}$$
$$y = 3.4$$

Check:

$16.3 - 7.2y$	$=$	-8.18	
$16.3 - 7.2(3.4)$	?	-8.18	
$16.3 - 24.48$			
-8.18			TRUE

The solution is 3.4.

Do Exercises 5 and 6.

Solve.

5. $-4 - 8x = 8$

6. $41.68 = 4.7 - 8.6y$

b Collecting Like Terms

If there are like terms on one side of the equation, we collect them before using the addition principle or the multiplication principle.

EXAMPLE 5 Solve: $3x + 4x = -14$.

$$3x + 4x = -14$$
$$7x = -14 \quad \text{Collecting like terms}$$
$$\frac{7x}{7} = \frac{-14}{7} \quad \text{Dividing by 7 on both sides}$$
$$x = -2$$

The number -2 checks, so the solution is -2.

Do Exercises 7 and 8.

Solve.

7. $4x + 3x = -21$

8. $x - 0.09x = 728$

If there are like terms on opposite sides of the equation, we get them on the same side by using the addition principle. Then we collect them. In other words, we get all the terms with a variable on one side of the equation and all the terms without a variable on the other side.

Answers

4. 39 5. $-\frac{3}{2}$ 6. -4.3
7. -3 8. 800

EXAMPLE 6 Solve: $2x - 2 = -3x + 3$.

$$
\begin{aligned}
2x - 2 &= -3x + 3 \\
2x - 2 + 2 &= -3x + 3 + 2 && \text{Adding 2} \\
2x &= -3x + 5 && \text{Collecting like terms} \\
2x + 3x &= -3x + 3x + 5 && \text{Adding } 3x \\
5x &= 5 && \text{Simplifying} \\
\frac{5x}{5} &= \frac{5}{5} && \text{Dividing by 5} \\
x &= 1 && \text{Simplifying}
\end{aligned}
$$

Check:

$2x - 2$	$=$	$-3x + 3$	
$2 \cdot 1 - 2$	?	$-3 \cdot 1 + 3$	Substituting in the original equation
$2 - 2$		$-3 + 3$	
0		0	TRUE

The solution is 1.

Solve.

9. $7y + 5 = 2y + 10$

10. $5 - 2y = 3y - 5$

Do Exercises 9 and 10.

In Example 6, we used the addition principle to get all the terms with an x on one side of the equation and all the terms without an x on the other side. Then we collected like terms and proceeded as before. If there are like terms on one side at the outset, they should be collected first.

EXAMPLE 7 Solve: $6x + 5 - 7x = 10 - 4x + 3$.

$$
\begin{aligned}
6x + 5 - 7x &= 10 - 4x + 3 \\
-x + 5 &= 13 - 4x && \text{Collecting like terms} \\
4x - x + 5 &= 13 - 4x + 4x && \text{Adding } 4x \text{ to get all terms with a variable on one side} \\
3x + 5 &= 13 && \text{Simplifying; that is, collecting like terms} \\
3x + 5 - 5 &= 13 - 5 && \text{Subtracting 5} \\
3x &= 8 && \text{Simplifying} \\
\frac{3x}{3} &= \frac{8}{3} && \text{Dividing by 3} \\
x &= \frac{8}{3} && \text{Simplifying}
\end{aligned}
$$

The number $\frac{8}{3}$ checks, so it is the solution.

Solve.

11. $7x - 17 + 2x = 2 - 8x + 15$

12. $3x - 15 = 5x + 2 - 4x$

Do Exercises 11 and 12.

Clearing Fractions and Decimals

In general, equations are easier to solve if they do not contain fractions or decimals. Consider, for example, the equations

$$\frac{1}{2}x + 5 = \frac{3}{4} \quad \text{and} \quad 2.3x + 7 = 5.4.$$

Answers

9. 1 **10.** 2 **11.** 2 **12.** $\frac{17}{2}$

If we multiply by 4 on both sides of the first equation and by 10 on both sides of the second equation, we have

$$4\left(\frac{1}{2}x + 5\right) = 4 \cdot \frac{3}{4} \quad \text{and} \quad 10(2.3x + 7) = 10 \cdot 5.4$$

$$4 \cdot \frac{1}{2}x + 4 \cdot 5 = 4 \cdot \frac{3}{4} \quad \text{and} \quad 10 \cdot 2.3x + 10 \cdot 7 = 10 \cdot 5.4$$

$$2x + 20 = 3 \quad \text{and} \quad 23x + 70 = 54.$$

The first equation has been "cleared of fractions" and the second equation has been "cleared of decimals." Both resulting equations are equivalent to the original equations and are easier to solve. *It is your choice* whether to clear fractions or decimals, but doing so often eases computations.

The easiest way to clear an equation of fractions is to multiply *every term on both sides* by the **least common multiple of all the denominators.**

EXAMPLE 8 Solve: $\frac{2}{3}x - \frac{1}{6} + \frac{1}{2}x = \frac{7}{6} + 2x$.

The denominators are 3, 6, and 2. The number 6 is the least common multiple of all the denominators. We multiply by 6 on both sides of the equation.

$$6\left(\frac{2}{3}x - \frac{1}{6} + \frac{1}{2}x\right) = 6\left(\frac{7}{6} + 2x\right)$$ Multiplying by 6 on both sides

$$6 \cdot \frac{2}{3}x - 6 \cdot \frac{1}{6} + 6 \cdot \frac{1}{2}x = 6 \cdot \frac{7}{6} + 6 \cdot 2x$$ Using the distributive law (*Caution*! Be sure to multiply *all* the terms by 6.)

$$4x - 1 + 3x = 7 + 12x$$ Simplifying. Note that the fractions are cleared.

$$7x - 1 = 7 + 12x$$ Collecting like terms

$$7x - 1 - 12x = 7 + 12x - 12x$$ Subtracting $12x$

$$-5x - 1 = 7$$ Collecting like terms

$$-5x - 1 + 1 = 7 + 1$$ Adding 1

$$-5x = 8$$ Collecting like terms

$$\frac{-5x}{-5} = \frac{8}{-5}$$ Dividing by -5

$$x = -\frac{8}{5}$$

Check:

$$\begin{array}{c|c}
\multicolumn{2}{c}{\frac{2}{3}x - \frac{1}{6} + \frac{1}{2}x = \frac{7}{6} + 2x} \\
\hline
\frac{2}{3}\left(-\frac{8}{5}\right) - \frac{1}{6} + \frac{1}{2}\left(-\frac{8}{5}\right) \;?\; & \frac{7}{6} + 2\left(-\frac{8}{5}\right) \\
-\frac{16}{15} - \frac{1}{6} - \frac{8}{10} & \frac{7}{6} - \frac{16}{5} \\
-\frac{32}{30} - \frac{5}{30} - \frac{24}{30} & \frac{35}{30} - \frac{96}{30} \\
\frac{-32 - 5 - 24}{30} & \frac{35 - 96}{30} \\
-\frac{61}{30} & -\frac{61}{30}
\end{array}$$

TRUE

Caution!

Check the possible solution in the *original* equation rather than in the equation that has been cleared of fractions.

Calculator Corner

Checking Possible Solutions There are several ways to check the possible solutions of an equation on a calculator. One of the most straightforward methods is to substitute and carry out the calculations on each side of the equation just as we do when we check by hand. To check the possible solution, 1, in Example 6, for instance, we first substitute 1 for x in the expression on the left side of the equation. We press 2 × 1 − 2 ENTER. We get 0. Next, we substitute 1 for x in the expression on the right side of the equation. We then press (−) 3 × 1 + 3 ENTER. Again we get 0. Since the two sides of the equation have the same value when x is 1, we know that 1 is the solution of the equation.

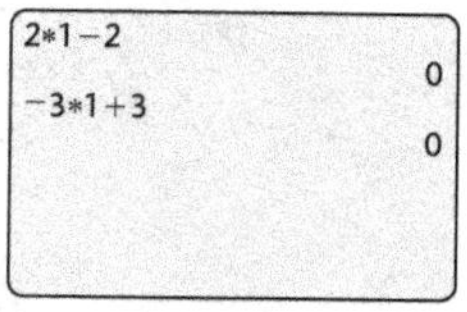

Exercise:

1. Use substitution to check the solutions found in Examples 1–5.

The solution is $-\frac{8}{5}$.

Do Exercise 13.

13. Solve: $\frac{7}{8}x - \frac{1}{4} + \frac{1}{2}x = \frac{3}{4} + x$.

To illustrate clearing decimals, we repeat Example 4, but this time we clear the equation of decimals first. Compare both methods.

To clear an equation of decimals, we count the greatest number of decimal places in any one number. If the greatest number of decimal places is 1, we multiply every term on both sides by 10; if it is 2, we multiply by 100; and so on.

EXAMPLE 9 Solve: $16.3 - 7.2y = -8.18$.

The greatest number of decimal places in any one number is *two*. Multiplying by 100, which has *two* 0's, will clear all decimals.

$$100(16.3 - 7.2y) = 100(-8.18) \quad \text{Multiplying by 100 on both sides}$$
$$100(16.3) - 100(7.2y) = 100(-8.18) \quad \text{Using the distributive law}$$
$$1630 - 720y = -818 \quad \text{Simplifying}$$
$$1630 - 720y - 1630 = -818 - 1630 \quad \text{Subtracting 1630}$$
$$-720y = -2448 \quad \text{Collecting like terms}$$
$$\frac{-720y}{-720} = \frac{-2448}{-720} \quad \text{Dividing by } -720$$
$$y = \frac{17}{5}, \text{ or } 3.4$$

The number $\frac{17}{5}$, or 3.4, checks, as shown in Example 4, so it is the solution.

Do Exercise 14.

14. Solve: $41.68 = 4.7 - 8.6y$.

C Equations Containing Parentheses

To solve certain kinds of equations that contain parentheses, we first use the distributive laws to remove the parentheses. Then we proceed as before.

EXAMPLE 10 Solve: $8x = 2(12 - 2x)$.

$$8x = 2(12 - 2x)$$
$$8x = 24 - 4x \quad \text{Using the distributive laws to multiply and remove parentheses}$$
$$8x + 4x = 24 - 4x + 4x \quad \text{Adding } 4x \text{ to get all the } x\text{-terms on one side}$$
$$12x = 24 \quad \text{Collecting like terms}$$
$$\frac{12x}{12} = \frac{24}{12} \quad \text{Dividing by 12}$$
$$x = 2$$

The number 2 checks, so the solution is 2.

Do Exercises 15 and 16.

Solve.

15. $2(2y + 3) = 14$

16. $5(3x - 2) = 35$

Answers

13. $\frac{8}{3}$ 14. $-\frac{43}{10}$, or -4.3
15. 2 16. 3

Here is a procedure for solving the types of equation discussed in this section.

AN EQUATION-SOLVING PROCEDURE

1. Multiply on both sides to clear the equation of fractions or decimals. (This is optional, but it can ease computations.)
2. If parentheses occur, multiply to remove them using the *distributive laws.*
3. Collect like terms on each side, if necessary.
4. Get all terms with variables on one side and all numbers (constant terms) on the other side, using the *addition principle.*
5. Collect like terms again, if necessary.
6. Multiply or divide to solve for the variable, using the *multiplication principle.*
7. Check all possible solutions in the original equation.

EXAMPLE 11 Solve: $2 - 5(x + 5) = 3(x - 2) - 1$.

$$2 - 5(x + 5) = 3(x - 2) - 1$$

$$2 - 5x - 25 = 3x - 6 - 1$$ Using the distributive laws to multiply and remove parentheses

$$-5x - 23 = 3x - 7$$ Collecting like terms

$$-5x - 23 + 5x = 3x - 7 + 5x$$ Adding $5x$

$$-23 = 8x - 7$$ Collecting like terms

$$-23 + 7 = 8x - 7 + 7$$ Adding 7

$$-16 = 8x$$ Collecting like terms

$$\frac{-16}{8} = \frac{8x}{8}$$ Dividing by 8

$$-2 = x$$

Check:

$2 - 5(x + 5)$	$= 3(x - 2) - 1$
$2 - 5(-2 + 5)$?	$3(-2 - 2) - 1$
$2 - 5(3)$	$3(-4) - 1$
$2 - 15$	$-12 - 1$
-13	-13 TRUE

The solution is -2.

Do Exercises 17 and 18.

Equations with Infinitely Many Solutions

The types of equations we have considered thus far in Sections 2.1–2.3 have all had exactly one solution. We now look at two other possibilities.

Consider

$$3 + x = x + 3.$$

Let's explore the equation and possible solutions in Margin Exercises 19–22.

Do Exercises 19–22.

Solve.

17. $3(7 + 2x) = 30 + 7(x - 1)$

18. $4(3 + 5x) - 4 = 3 + 2(x - 2)$

Determine whether the given number is a solution of the given equation.

19. 10; $3 + x = x + 3$

20. -7; $3 + x = x + 3$

21. $\frac{1}{2}$; $3 + x = x + 3$

22. 0; $3 + x = x + 3$

Answers

17. -2 **18.** $-\frac{1}{2}$ **19.** Yes **20.** Yes **21.** Yes **22.** Yes

We know by the commutative law of addition that the equation $3 + x = x + 3$ holds for any replacement of x with a real number. (See Section 1.7.) We have confirmed some of these solutions in Margin Exercises 19–22. Suppose we try to solve this equation using the addition principle:

$$\begin{aligned} 3 + x &= x + 3 \\ -x + 3 + x &= -x + x + 3 && \text{Adding } -x \\ 3 &= 3. && \text{True} \end{aligned}$$

We end with a true equation. The original equation holds for all real-number replacements. Every real number is a solution. Thus the number of solutions is **infinite**.

EXAMPLE 12 Solve: $7x - 17 = 4 + 7(x - 3)$.

$$\begin{aligned} 7x - 17 &= 4 + 7(x - 3) \\ 7x - 17 &= 4 + 7x - 21 && \text{Using the distributive law to multiply and remove parentheses} \\ 7x - 17 &= 7x - 17 && \text{Collecting like terms} \\ -7x + 7x - 17 &= -7x + 7x - 17 && \text{Adding } -7x \\ -17 &= -17 && \text{True for all real numbers} \end{aligned}$$

Every real number is a solution. There are infinitely many solutions.

Determine whether the given number is a solution of the given equation.

23. 10; $3 + x = x + 8$

24. -7; $3 + x = x + 8$

25. $\frac{1}{2}$; $3 + x = x + 8$

26. 0; $3 + x = x + 8$

Equations with No Solution

Now consider

$$3 + x = x + 8.$$

Let's explore the equation and possible solutions in Margin Exercises 23–26.

Do Exercises 23–26.

None of the replacements in Margin Exercises 23–26 is a solution of the given equation. In fact, there are no solutions. Let's try to solve this equation using the addition principle:

$$\begin{aligned} 3 + x &= x + 8 \\ -x + 3 + x &= -x + x + 8 && \text{Adding } -x \\ 3 &= 8. && \text{False} \end{aligned}$$

We end with a false equation. The original equation is false for all real-number replacements. Thus it has **no** solution.

Solve.

27. $30 + 5(x + 3) = -3 + 5x + 48$

28. $2x + 7(x - 4) = 13 + 9x$

EXAMPLE 13 Solve: $3x + 4(x + 2) = 11 + 7x$.

$$\begin{aligned} 3x + 4(x + 2) &= 11 + 7x \\ 3x + 4x + 8 &= 11 + 7x && \text{Using the distributive law to multiply and remove parentheses} \\ 7x + 8 &= 11 + 7x && \text{Collecting like terms} \\ 7x + 8 - 7x &= 11 + 7x - 7x && \text{Subtracting } 7x \\ 8 &= 11 && \text{False} \end{aligned}$$

There are no solutions.

Do Exercises 27 and 28.

When solving an equation, if the result is:

- an equation of the form $x = a$, where a is a real number, then there is one solution, the number a;
- a true equation like $3 = 3$ or $-1 = -1$, then every real number is a solution;
- a false equation like $3 = 8$ or $-4 = 5$, then there is no solution.

Answers

23. No **24.** No **25.** No **26.** No
27. All real numbers **28.** No solution

a Solve. Don't forget to check!

1. $5x + 6 = 31$

Check: $5x + 6 = 31$?

2. $7x + 6 = 13$

Check: $7x + 6 = 13$?

3. $8x + 4 = 68$

Check: $8x + 4 = 68$?

4. $4y + 10 = 46$

Check: $4y + 10 = 46$?

5. $4x - 6 = 34$

6. $5y - 2 = 53$

7. $3x - 9 = 33$

8. $4x - 19 = 5$

9. $7x + 2 = -54$

10. $5x + 4 = -41$

11. $-45 = 3 + 6y$

12. $-91 = 9t + 8$

13. $-4x + 7 = 35$

14. $-5x - 7 = 108$

15. $\frac{5}{4}x - 18 = -3$

16. $\frac{3}{2}x - 24 = -36$

b Solve.

17. $5x + 7x = 72$

Check: $5x + 7x = 72$?

18. $8x + 3x = 55$

Check: $8x + 3x = 55$?

19. $8x + 7x = 60$

Check: $8x + 7x = 60$?

20. $8x + 5x = 104$

Check: $8x + 5x = 104$?

21. $4x + 3x = 42$

22. $7x + 18x = 125$

23. $-6y - 3y = 27$

24. $-5y - 7y = 144$

25. $-7y - 8y = -15$

26. $-10y - 3y = -39$

27. $x + \frac{1}{3}x = 8$

28. $x + \frac{1}{4}x = 10$

29. $10.2y - 7.3y = -58$

30. $6.8y - 2.4y = -88$

31. $8y - 35 = 3y$

32. $4x - 6 = 6x$

33. $8x - 1 = 23 - 4x$

34. $5y - 2 = 28 - y$

35. $2x - 1 = 4 + x$

36. $4 - 3x = 6 - 7x$

37. $6x + 3 = 2x + 11$

38. $14 - 6a = -2a + 3$

39. $5 - 2x = 3x - 7x + 25$

40. $-7z + 2z - 3z - 7 = 17$

41. $4 + 3x - 6 = 3x + 2 - x$

42. $5 + 4x - 7 = 4x - 2 - x$

43. $4y - 4 + y + 24 = 6y + 20 - 4y$

44. $5y - 7 + y = 7y + 21 - 5y$

Solve. Clear fractions or decimals first.

45. $\frac{7}{2}x + \frac{1}{2}x = 3x + \frac{3}{2} + \frac{5}{2}x$

46. $\frac{7}{8}x - \frac{1}{4} + \frac{3}{4}x = \frac{1}{16} + x$

47. $\frac{2}{3} + \frac{1}{4}t = \frac{1}{3}$

48. $-\frac{3}{2} + x = -\frac{5}{6} - \frac{4}{3}$

49. $\frac{2}{3} + 3y = 5y - \frac{2}{15}$

50. $\frac{1}{2} + 4m = 3m - \frac{5}{2}$

51. $\frac{5}{3} + \frac{2}{3}x = \frac{25}{12} + \frac{5}{4}x + \frac{3}{4}$

52. $1 - \frac{2}{3}y = \frac{9}{5} - \frac{y}{5} + \frac{3}{5}$

53. $2.1x + 45.2 = 3.2 - 8.4x$

54. $0.96y - 0.79 = 0.21y + 0.46$

55. $1.03 - 0.62x = 0.71 - 0.22x$

56. $1.7t + 8 - 1.62t = 0.4t - 0.32 + 8$

57. $\frac{2}{7}x - \frac{1}{2}x = \frac{3}{4}x + 1$

58. $\frac{5}{16}y + \frac{3}{8}y = 2 + \frac{1}{4}y$

C Solve.

59. $3(2y - 3) = 27$

60. $8(3x + 2) = 30$

61. $40 = 5(3x + 2)$

62. $9 = 3(5x - 2)$

63. $-23 + y = y + 25$

64. $17 - t = -t + 68$

65. $-23 + x = x - 23$

66. $y - \frac{2}{3} = -\frac{2}{3} + y$

67. $2(3 + 4m) - 9 = 45$

68. $5x + 5(4x - 1) = 20$

69. $5r - (2r + 8) = 16$

70. $6b - (3b + 8) = 16$

71. $6 - 2(3x - 1) = 2$

72. $10 - 3(2x - 1) = 1$

73. $5x + 5 - 7x = 15 - 12x + 10x - 10$

74. $3 - 7x + 10x - 14 = 9 - 6x + 9x - 20$

75. $22x - 5 - 15x + 3 = 10x - 4 - 3x + 11$

76. $11x - 6 - 4x + 1 = 9x - 8 - 2x + 12$

77. $5(d + 4) = 7(d - 2)$

78. $3(t - 2) = 9(t + 2)$

79. $8(2t + 1) = 4(7t + 7)$

80. $7(5x - 2) = 6(6x - 1)$

81. $3(r - 6) + 2 = 4(r + 2) - 21$

82. $5(t + 3) + 9 = 3(t - 2) + 6$

83. $19 - (2x + 3) = 2(x + 3) + x$

84. $13 - (2c + 2) = 2(c + 2) + 3c$

85. $2[4 - 2(3 - x)] - 1 = 4[2(4x - 3) + 7] - 25$

86. $5[3(7 - t) - 4(8 + 2t)] - 20 = -6[2(6 + 3t) - 4]$

87. $11 - 4(x + 1) - 3 = 11 + 2(4 - 2x) - 16$

88. $6(2x - 1) - 12 = 7 + 12(x - 1)$

89. $22x - 1 - 12x = 5(2x - 1) + 4$

90. $2 + 14x - 9 = 7(2x + 1) - 14$

91. $0.7(3x + 6) = 1.1 - (x + 2)$

92. $0.9(2x + 8) = 20 - (x + 5)$

Skill Maintenance

93. Divide: $-22.1 \div 3.4$. [1.6c]

94. Multiply: $-22.1(3.4)$. [1.5a]

95. Factor: $7x - 21 - 14y$. [1.7d]

96. Factor: $8y - 88x + 8$. [1.7d]

Simplify.

97. $-3 + 2(-5)^2(-3) - 7$ [1.8d]

98. $3x + 2[4 - 5(2x - 1)]$ [1.8c]

99. $23(2x - 4) - 15(10 - 3x)$ [1.8b]

100. $256 \div 64 \div 4^2$ [1.8d]

Synthesis

Solve.

101. $\frac{2}{3}\left(\frac{7}{8} - 4x\right) - \frac{5}{8} = \frac{3}{8}$

102. $\frac{1}{4}(8y + 4) - 17 = -\frac{1}{2}(4y - 8)$

103. $\frac{4 - 3x}{7} = \frac{2 + 5x}{49} - \frac{x}{14}$

104. The width of a rectangle is 5 ft, its length is $(3x + 2)$ ft, and its area is 75 ft^2. Find x.

2.4 Formulas

(a) Evaluating Formulas

A **formula** is a "recipe" for doing a certain type of calculation. Formulas are often given as equations. When we replace the variables in an equation with numbers and calculate the result, we are **evaluating** the formula. Evaluating was introduced in Section 1.1.

Let's consider a formula that has to do with weather. Suppose you see a flash of lightning during a storm. Then a few seconds later, you hear the thunder that accompanies that lightning.

Your distance from the place where the lightning struck is given by the formula $M = \frac{1}{5}t$, where t is the number of seconds from the lightning flash to the sound of the thunder and M is in miles.

EXAMPLE 1 *Distance from Lightning.* Consider the formula $M = \frac{1}{5}t$. Suppose it takes 10 sec for the sound of thunder to reach you after you have seen a flash of lightning. How far away did the lightning strike?

We substitute 10 for t and calculate M:

$$M = \tfrac{1}{5}t = \tfrac{1}{5}(10) = 2.$$

The lightning struck 2 mi away.

EXAMPLE 2 *Socks from Cotton.* Consider the formula $S = 4321x$, where S is the number of socks of average size that can be produced from x bales of cotton. You see a shipment of 300 bales of cotton taken off a ship. How many socks can be made from the cotton?

Source: *Country Woman Magazine*

We substitute 300 for x and calculate S:

$$S = 4321x = 4321(300) = 1{,}296{,}300.$$

Thus, 1,296,300 socks can be made from 300 bales of cotton.

Do Exercises 1 and 2.

OBJECTIVES

(a) Evaluate a formula.

(b) Solve a formula for a specified letter.

1. **Storm Distance.** Refer to Example 1. Suppose that it takes the sound of thunder 14 sec to reach you. How far away is the storm?

2. **Socks from Cotton.** Refer to Example 2. Determine the number of socks that can be made from 65 bales of cotton.

Answers

1. 2.8 mi 2. 280,865 socks

EXAMPLE 3 *Distance, Rate, and Time.* The distance d that a car will travel at a rate, or speed, r in time t is given by

$$d = rt.$$

A car travels at 75 miles per hour (mph) for 4.5 hr. How far will it travel?

We substitute 75 for r and 4.5 for t and calculate d:

$$d = rt = (75)(4.5) = 337.5 \text{ mi.}$$

The car will travel 337.5 mi.

Do Exercise 3.

3. Distance, Rate, and Time. A car travels at 55 mph for 6.2 hr. How far will it travel?

b Solving Formulas

Refer to Example 2. Suppose a clothing company wants to produce S socks and needs to know how many bales of cotton to order. If this calculation is to be repeated many times, it might be helpful to first solve the formula for x:

$$S = 4321x$$

$$\frac{S}{4321} = x. \quad \text{Dividing by 4321}$$

Then we can substitute a number for S and calculate x. For example, if the number of socks S to be produced is 432,100, then

$$x = \frac{S}{4321} = \frac{432{,}100}{4321} = 100.$$

The company would need to order 100 bales of cotton.

EXAMPLE 4 Solve for z: $H = \frac{1}{4}z$.

$$H = \tfrac{1}{4}z \quad \text{We want this letter alone.}$$

$$4 \cdot H = 4 \cdot \tfrac{1}{4}z \quad \text{Multiplying by 4 on both sides}$$

$$4H = z$$

For $H = 2$ in Example 4, $z = 4H = 4(2)$, or 8.

EXAMPLE 5 *Distance, Rate, and Time.* Solve for t: $d = rt$.

$$d = rt \quad \text{We want this letter alone.}$$

$$\frac{d}{r} = \frac{rt}{r} \quad \text{Dividing by } r$$

$$\frac{d}{r} = \frac{r}{r} \cdot t$$

$$\frac{d}{r} = t \quad \text{Simplifying}$$

Do Exercises 4–6.

4. Solve for q: $B = \frac{1}{3}q$.

5. Solve for m: $n = mz$.

6. Electricity. Solve for I: $E = IR$. (This formula relates voltage E, current I, and resistance R.)

Answers

3. 341 mi **4.** $q = 3B$
5. $m = \frac{n}{z}$ **6.** $I = \frac{E}{R}$

EXAMPLE 6 Solve for x: $y = x + 3$.

$y = x + 3$	We want this letter alone.
$y - 3 = x + 3 - 3$	Subtracting 3
$y - 3 = x$	Simplifying

EXAMPLE 7 Solve for x: $y = x - a$.

$y = x - a$	We want this letter alone.
$y + a = x - a + a$	Adding a
$y + a = x$	Simplifying

Do Exercises 7–9.

Solve for x.

7. $y = x + 5$

8. $y = x - 7$

9. $y = x - b$

EXAMPLE 8 Solve for y: $6y = 3x$.

$6y = 3x$	We want this letter alone.
$\frac{6y}{6} = \frac{3x}{6}$	Dividing by 6
$y = \frac{x}{2}$, or $\frac{1}{2}x$	Simplifying

EXAMPLE 9 Solve for y: $by = ax$.

$by = ax$	We want this letter alone.
$\frac{by}{b} = \frac{ax}{b}$	Dividing by b
$y = \frac{ax}{b}$	Simplifying

Do Exercises 10 and 11.

10. Solve for y: $9y = 5x$.

11. Solve for p: $ap = bt$.

EXAMPLE 10 Solve for x: $ax + b = c$.

$ax + b = c$	We want this letter alone.
$ax + b - b = c - b$	Subtracting b
$ax = c - b$	Simplifying
$\frac{ax}{a} = \frac{c - b}{a}$	Dividing by a
$x = \frac{c - b}{a}$	Simplifying

Do Exercises 12 and 13.

12. Solve for x: $y = mx + b$.

13. Solve for Q: $tQ - p = a$.

Answers

7. $x = y - 5$ 8. $x = y + 7$
9. $x = y + b$ 10. $y = \frac{5x}{9}$, or $\frac{5}{9}x$
11. $p = \frac{bt}{a}$ 12. $x = \frac{y - b}{m}$
13. $Q = \frac{a + p}{t}$

To solve a formula for a given letter, identify the letter and:

1. Multiply on both sides to clear fractions or decimals, if that is needed.
2. Collect like terms on each side, if necessary.
3. Get all terms with the letter to be solved for on one side of the equation and all other terms on the other side.
4. Collect like terms again, if necessary.
5. Solve for the letter in question.

EXAMPLE 11 *Circumference.* Solve for r: $C = 2\pi r$. This is a formula for the circumference C of a circle of radius r.

$C = 2\pi r$ We want this letter alone.

$\frac{C}{2\pi} = \frac{2\pi r}{2\pi}$ Dividing by 2π

$\frac{C}{2\pi} = r$

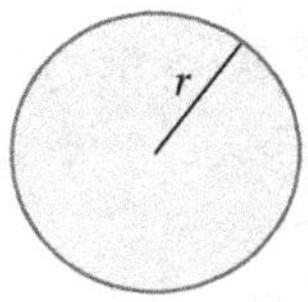

EXAMPLE 12 *Averages.* Solve for a: $A = \frac{a + b + c}{3}$. This is a formula for the average A of three numbers a, b, and c.

$A = \frac{a + b + c}{3}$ We want the letter a alone.

$3 \cdot A = 3 \cdot \frac{a + b + c}{3}$ Multiplying by 3 on both sides

$3A = a + b + c$ Simplifying

$3A - b - c = a$ Subtracting b and c

Do Exercises 14 and 15.

14. Circumference. Solve for D:

$C = \pi D$.

This is a formula for the circumference C of a circle of diameter D.

15. Averages. Solve for c:

$A = \frac{a + b + c + d}{4}$.

STUDY TIPS

HIGHLIGHTING

- **Try to keep one section ahead of your syllabus.** Reading and highlighting a section before your instructor lectures on it allows you to listen carefully and concentrate on what is being said in class. Then you can take notes only on special points and on questions related to the lecture.
- **Highlight important points.** You are probably used to highlighting key points as you study. If that works for you, continue to do so. But you will notice many design features throughout this book that already highlight important points. Thus you may not need to highlight as much as you generally do.
- **Highlight points that you do not understand.** Use a special marker to indicate trouble spots that can lead to questions to be asked during class or in a tutoring session.

Answers

14. $D = \frac{C}{\pi}$ 15. $c = 4A - a - b - d$

For Extra Help
MyMathLab | Math XL PRACTICE | WATCH | DOWNLOAD | READ | REVIEW

a, b Solve.

1. *Furnace Output.* The formula

$$B = 30a$$

is used in New England to estimate the minimum furnace output B, in Btu's, for a modern house with a square feet of flooring.

Source: U.S. Department of Energy

a) Determine the minimum furnace output for a 1900-ft^2 modern house.
b) Solve for a. That is, solve $B = 30a$ for a.

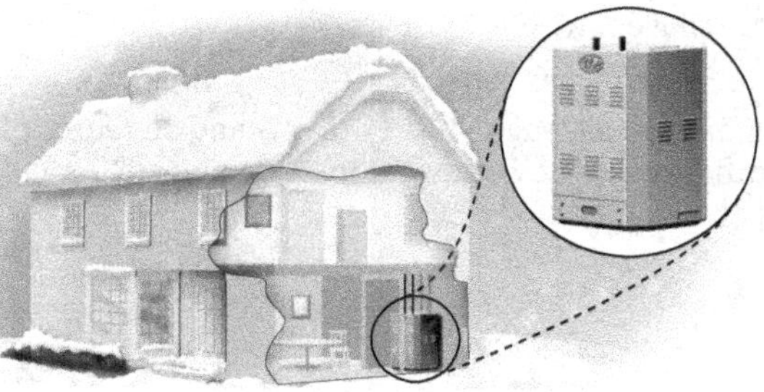

2. *Furnace Output.* The formula

$$B = 50a$$

is used in New England to estimate the minimum furnace output B, in Btu's, for an old, poorly insulated house with a square feet of flooring.

Source: U.S. Department of Energy

a) Determine the minimum furnace output for a 3200-ft^2 old, poorly insulated house.
b) Solve for a. That is, solve $B = 50a$ for a.

3. *Distance from Lightning.* The formula

$$M = \tfrac{1}{5}t$$

can be used to determine how far M, in miles, you are from lightning when its thunder takes t seconds to reach your ears.

a) It takes 8 sec for the sound of thunder to reach you after you have seen the lightning. How far away did the lightning strike?
b) Solve for t.

4. *Electrical Power.* The power rating P, in watts, of an electrical appliance is determined by

$$P = I \cdot V,$$

where I is the current, in amperes, and V is measured in volts.

a) A microwave oven requires 12 amps of current and the voltage in the house is 115 volts. What is the wattage of the microwave?
b) Solve for I; for V.

5. *College Enrollment.* At many colleges, the number of "full-time-equivalent" students f is given by

$$f = \frac{n}{15},$$

where n is the total number of credits for which students have enrolled in a given semester.

a) Determine the number of full-time-equivalent students on a campus in which students registered for a total of 21,345 credits.
b) Solve for n.

6. *Surface Area of a Cube.* The surface area A of a cube with side s is given by

$$A = 6s^2.$$

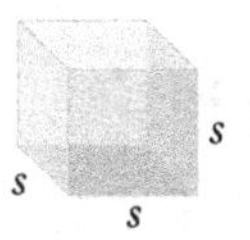

a) Find the surface area of a cube with sides of 3 in.
b) Solve for s^2.

7. *Calorie Density.* The calorie density D, in calories per ounce, of a food that contains c calories and weighs w ounces is given by

$$D = \frac{c}{w}.$$

Eight ounces of fat-free milk contains 84 calories. Find the calorie density of fat-free milk.

Source: *Nutrition Action Healthletter*, March 2000, p. 9. Center for Science in the Public Interest, Suite 300; 1875 Connecticut Ave NW, Washington, D.C. 20008.

8. *Wavelength of a Musical Note.* The wavelength w, in meters per cycle, of a musical note is given by

$$w = \frac{r}{f},$$

where r is the speed of the sound, in meters per second, and f is the frequency, in cycles per second. The speed of sound in air is 344 m/sec. What is the wavelength of a note whose frequency in air is 24 cycles per second?

9. *Size of a League Schedule.* When all n teams in a league play every other team twice, a total of N games are played, where

$$N = n^2 - n.$$

A soccer league has 7 teams and all teams play each other twice. How many games are played?

10. *Size of a League Schedule.* When all n teams in a league play every other team twice, a total of N games are played, where

$$N = n^2 - n.$$

A basketball league has 11 teams and all teams play each other twice. How many games are played?

b Solve for the indicated letter.

11. $y = 5x$, for x

12. $d = 55t$, for t

13. $a = bc$, for c

14. $y = mx$, for x

15. $n = m + 11$, for m

16. $z = t + 21$, for t

17. $y = x - \frac{3}{5}$, for x

18. $y = x - \frac{2}{3}$, for x

19. $y = 13 + x$, for x

20. $t = 6 + s$, for s

21. $y = x + b$, for x

22. $y = x + A$, for x

23. $y = 5 - x$, for x

24. $y = 10 - x$, for x

25. $y = a - x$, for x

26. $y = q - x$, for x

27. $8y = 5x$, for y

28. $10y = -5x$, for y

29. $By = Ax$, for x

30. $By = Ax$, for y

31. $W = mt + b$, for t

32. $W = mt - b$, for t

33. $y = bx + c$, for x

34. $y = bx - c$, for x

35. *Area of a Parallelogram:*

$A = bh$, for h

(Area A, base b, height h)

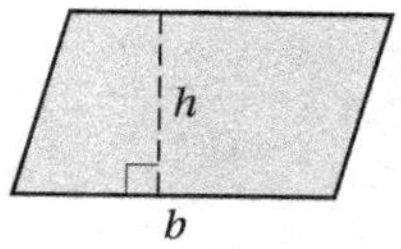

36. *Distance, Rate, Time:*

$d = rt$, for r

(Distance d, speed r, time t)

37. *Perimeter of a Rectangle:*

$P = 2l + 2w$, for w

(Perimeter P, length l, width w)

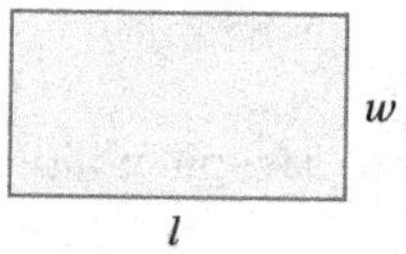

38. *Area of a Circle:*

$A = \pi r^2$, for r^2

(Area A, radius r)

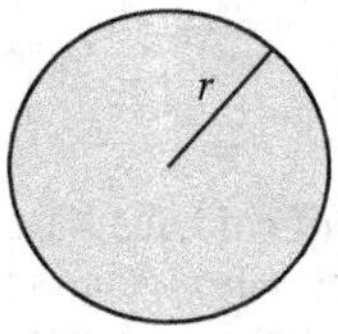

39. *Average of Two Numbers:*

$A = \dfrac{a + b}{2}$, for a

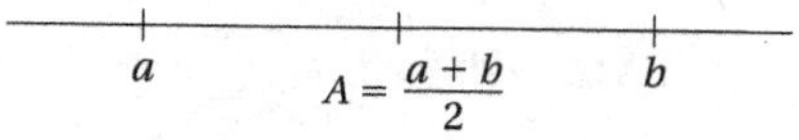

40. *Area of a Triangle:*

$A = \dfrac{1}{2}bh$, for b

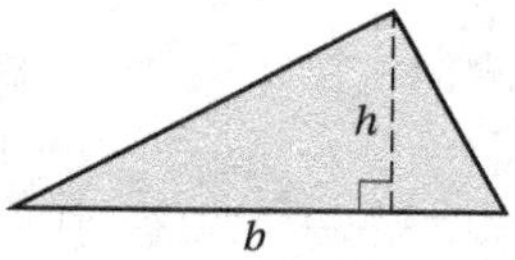

41. $A = \dfrac{a + b + c}{3}$, for b

42. $A = \dfrac{a + b + c}{3}$, for c

43. $A = at + b$, for t

44. $S = rx + s$, for x

45. $Ax + By = c$, for x

46. $Q = \dfrac{p - q}{2}$, for p

47. *Force:*

$F = ma$, for a

(Force F, mass m, acceleration a)

48. *Simple Interest:*

$I = Prt$, for P

(Interest I, principal P, interest rate r, time t)

49. *Relativity:*

$E = mc^2$, for c^2

(Energy E, mass m, speed of light c)

50. $Ax + By = c$, for y

51. $v = \frac{3k}{t}$, for t

52. $P = \frac{ab}{c}$, for c

Skill Maintenance

53. Convert to decimal notation: $\frac{23}{25}$. [R.3b]

54. Add: $-23 + (-67)$. [1.3a]

55. Add: $0.082 + (-9.407)$. [1.3a]

56. Subtract: $-23 - (-67)$. [1.4a]

57. Subtract: $-45.8 - (-32.6)$. [1.4a]

58. Remove parentheses and simplify: [1.8b]

$4a - 8b - 5(5a - 4b)$.

Convert to decimal notation. [R.4a]

59. 3.1%

60. 67.1%

61. Add: $-\frac{2}{3} + \frac{5}{6}$. [1.3a]

62. Subtract: $-\frac{2}{3} - \frac{5}{6}$. [1.4a]

Synthesis

63. *Female Caloric Needs.* The number of calories K needed each day by a moderately active woman who weighs w pounds, is h inches tall, and is a years old can be estimated by the formula

$$K = 917 + 6(w + h - a).$$

Source: Parker, M., *She Does Math.* Mathematical Association of America, p. 96

a) Elaine is moderately active, weighs 120 lb, is 67 in. tall, and is 23 yr old. What are her caloric needs?

b) Solve the formula for a; for h; for w.

64. *Male Caloric Needs.* The number of calories K needed each day by a moderately active man who weighs w kilograms, is h centimeters tall, and is a years old can be estimated by the formula

$$K = 19.18w + 7h - 9.52a + 92.4.$$

Source: Parker, M., *She Does Math.* Mathematical Association of America, p. 96

a) Marv is moderately active, weighs 97 kg, is 185 cm tall, and is 55 yr old. What are his caloric needs?

b) Solve the formula for a; for h; for w.

Solve.

65. $H = \frac{2}{a - b}$, for b; for a

66. $P = 4m + 7mn$, for m

67. In $A = lw$, if l and w both double, what is the effect on A?

68. In $P = 2a + 2b$, if P doubles, do a and b necessarily both double?

69. In $A = \frac{1}{2}bh$, if b increases by 4 units and h does not change, what happens to A?

70. Solve for F: $D = \frac{1}{E + F}$.

Mid-Chapter Review

Concept Reinforcement

Determine whether each statement is true or false.

__________ **1.** $3 - x = 4x$ and $5x = -3$ are equivalent equations. [2.1b]

__________ **2.** For any real numbers a, b, and c, $a = b$ is equivalent to $a + c = b + c$. [2.1b]

__________ **3.** We can use the multiplication principle to divide on both sides of an equation by the same nonzero number. [2.2a]

__________ **4.** Every equation has at least one solution. [2.3c]

Guided Solutions

Fill in each blank with the number, variable, or expression that creates a correct statement or solution.

Solve. [2.1b], [2.2a]

5.
$$\begin{aligned} x + 5 &= -3 \\ x + 5 - 5 &= -3 - \square \\ x + \square &= -8 \\ x &= \square \end{aligned}$$

6.
$$\begin{aligned} -6x &= 42 \\ \frac{-6x}{-6} &= \frac{42}{\square} \\ \square \cdot x &= -7 \\ x &= \square \end{aligned}$$

7. Solve for y: $5y + z = t$. [2.4b]
$$\begin{aligned} 5y + z &= t \\ 5y + z - z &= t - \square \\ 5y &= \square \\ \frac{5y}{5} &= \frac{t - z}{\square} \\ y &= \frac{\square}{5} \end{aligned}$$

Mixed Review

Solve. [2.1b], [2.2a], [2.3a, b, c]

8. $x + 5 = 11$

9. $x + 9 = -3$

10. $8 = t + 1$

11. $-7 = y + 3$

12. $x - 6 = 14$

13. $y - 7 = -2$

14. $-\frac{3}{2} + z = -\frac{3}{4}$

15. $-3.3 = -1.9 + t$

16. $7x = 42$

17. $17 = -t$

18. $6x = -54$

19. $-5y = -85$

20. $\frac{x}{7} = 3$

21. $\frac{2}{3}x = 12$

22. $-\frac{t}{5} = 3$

23. $\frac{3}{4}x = -\frac{9}{8}$

24. $3x + 2 = 5$

25. $5x + 4 = -11$

26. $6x - 7 = 2$

27. $-4x - 9 = -5$

28. $6x + 5x = 33$

29. $-3y - 4y = 49$

30. $3x - 4 = 12 - x$

31. $5 - 6x = 9 - 8x$

32. $4y - \frac{3}{2} = \frac{3}{4} + 2y$

33. $\frac{4}{5} + \frac{1}{6}t = \frac{1}{10}$

34. $0.21n - 1.05 = 2.1 - 0.14n$

35. $5(3y - 1) = -35$

36. $7 - 2(5x + 3) = 1$

37. $-8 + t = t - 8$

38. $z + 12 = -12 + z$

39. $4(3x + 2) = 5(2x - 1)$

40. $8x - 6 - 2x = 3(2x - 4) + 6$

Solve for the indicated letter. [2.4b]

41. $A = 4b$, for b

42. $y = x - 1.5$, for x

43. $n = s - m$, for m

44. $4t = 9w$, for t

45. $B = at - c$, for t

46. $M = \frac{x + y + z}{2}$, for y

Understanding Through Discussion and Writing

47. Explain the difference between equivalent expressions and equivalent equations. [1.7a], [2.1b]

48. Are the equations $x = 5$ and $x^2 = 25$ equivalent? Why or why not? [2.1b]

49. When solving an equation using the addition principle, how do you determine which number to add or subtract on both sides of the equation? [2.1b]

50. Explain the following mistake made by a fellow student. [2.1b]

$$x + \frac{1}{3} = -\frac{5}{3}$$
$$x = -\frac{4}{3}$$

51. When solving an equation using the multiplication principle, how do you determine by what number to multiply or divide on both sides of the equation? [2.2a]

52. Devise an application in which it would be useful to solve the equation $d = rt$ for r. [2.4b]

2.5 Applications of Percent

(a) Translating and Solving

OBJECTIVE

(a) Solve applied problems involving percent.

Many applied problems involve percent. Here we begin to see how equation solving can enhance our problem-solving skills. For background on the manipulative skills of percent notation, see Section R.4.

In solving percent problems, we first *translate* the problem to an equation. Then we *solve* the equation using the techniques discussed in Sections 2.1–2.3. The key words in the translation are as follows.

KEY WORDS IN PERCENT TRANSLATIONS

"**Of**" translates to "$\cdot$" or "$\times$".

"**Is**" translates to "$=$".

"**What number**" or "**what percent**" translates to any letter.

"**%**" translates to "$\times \frac{1}{100}$" or "$\times 0.01$".

EXAMPLE 1 Translate:

28% of 5 is what number?

$$28\% \cdot 5 = a$$

This is a percent equation.

EXAMPLE 2 Translate:

45% of what number is 28?

$$45\% \times b = 28$$

EXAMPLE 3 Translate:

What percent of 90 is 7?

$$n \cdot 90 = 7$$

Do Exercises 1–6.

Translate to an equation. Do not solve.

1. 13% of 80 is what number?
2. What number is 60% of 70?
3. 43 is 20% of what number?
4. 110% of what number is 30?
5. 16 is what percent of 80?
6. What percent of 94 is 10.5?

Percent problems are actually of three different types. Although the method we present does *not* require that you be able to identify which type we are studying, it is helpful to know them. Let's begin by using a specific example to find a standard form for a percent problem.

We know that

15 is 25% of 60, or $15 = 25\% \times 60$.

We can think of this as:

Amount = Percent number × Base.

Answers

1. $13\% \cdot 80 = a$ 2. $a = 60\% \cdot 70$ 3. $43 = 20\% \cdot b$ 4. $110\% \cdot b = 30$ 5. $16 = n \cdot 80$ 6. $n \cdot 94 = 10.5$

STUDY TIPS

SOLVING APPLIED PROBLEMS

Don't be discouraged if, at first, you find the exercises in this section to be more challenging than those in earlier sections or if you have had difficulty doing applied problems in the past. Your skill will improve with each problem you solve. After you have done your homework for this section, you might want to do extra problems from the text or from the online tutorial that accompanies the text. As you gain experience solving applied problems, you will find yourself becoming comfortable with them.

Each of the three types of percent problem depends on which of the three pieces of information is missing in the statement

Amount = Percent number × Base.

1. Finding the ***amount*** (the result of taking the percent)

   Example: What number is 25% of 60?

   Translation: $y = 25\% \cdot 60$

2. Finding the ***base*** (the number you are taking the percent of)

   Example: 15 is 25% of what number?

   Translation: $15 = 25\% \cdot y$

3. Finding the ***percent number*** (the percent itself)

   Example: 15 is what percent of 60?

   Translation: $15 = y \cdot 60$

Finding the Amount

EXAMPLE 4 What number is 11% of 49?

What number is 11% of 49?

Translate: $a = 11\% \times 49$

Solve: The letter is by itself. To solve the equation, we need only convert 11% to decimal notation and multiply:

$$a = 11\% \times 49 = 0.11 \times 49 = 5.39.$$

Thus, 5.39 is 11% of 49. The answer is 5.39.

7. What number is 2.4% of 80?

Do Exercise 7.

Finding the Base

EXAMPLE 5 3 is 16% of what number?

3 is 16% of what number?

Translate: $3 = 16\% \times b$

$3 = 0.16 \times b$ Converting 16% to decimal notation

Solve: In this case, the letter is not by itself. To solve the equation, we divide by 0.16 on both sides:

$$3 = 0.16 \times b$$

$$\frac{3}{0.16} = \frac{0.16 \times b}{0.16} \quad \text{Dividing by 0.16}$$

$$18.75 = b. \quad \text{Simplifying}$$

The answer is 18.75.

8. 25.3 is 22% of what number?

Do Exercise 8.

Answers

7. 1.92 **8.** 115

Finding the Percent Number

In solving these problems, you *must* remember to convert to percent notation after you have solved the equation.

EXAMPLE 6 $32 is what percent of $50?

	$32	is	what percent	of	$50?
	↓	↓	↓	↓	↓
Translate:	32	=	p	×	50

Solve: To solve the equation, we divide by 50 on both sides and convert the answer to percent notation:

$$32 = p \times 50$$

$$\frac{32}{50} = \frac{p \times 50}{50} \quad \text{Dividing by 50}$$

$$0.64 = p$$

$$64\% = p. \quad \text{Converting to percent notation}$$

Thus, $32 is 64% of $50. The answer is 64%.

Do Exercise 9.

9. What percent of $50 is $18?

EXAMPLE 7 *Foreign Visitors to China.* About 22 million foreign travelers visited China in 2006. Of this number, 9% were from the United States. How many Americans visited China in 2006?

Source: *TIME Magazine*, March 8, 2007

To solve this problem, we first reword and then translate. We let a = the number of Americans, in millions, who visited China in 2006.

	What number	is	9%	of	22?
Rewording:	↓	↓	↓	↓	↓
Translating:	a	=	9%	×	22

Solve: The letter is by itself. To solve the equation, we need only convert 9% to decimal notation and multiply:

$$a = 9\% \times 22 = 0.09 \times 22 = 1.98.$$

Thus, 1.98 million is 9% of 22 million, so 1.98 million Americans visited China in 2006.

Do Exercise 10.

10. Chinese Visitors to the United States. About 51 million foreign travelers visited the United States in 2006. Of this number, 1% were from China. How many Chinese travelers visited the United States in 2006?

Source: *TIME Magazine*, March 8, 2007

EXAMPLE 8 *Public School Enrollment.* In the fall of 2008, 14.9 million students enrolled in grades 9–12 in U.S. public schools. This was 30% of the total enrollment in public schools. What was the total enrollment?

Source: National Center for Educational Statistics

To solve this problem, we first reword and then translate. We let T = the total enrollment, in millions, in U.S. public schools in 2008.

	14.9	is	30%	of	what number?
Rewording:	↓	↓	↓	↓	↓
Translating:	14.9	=	30%	×	T

Answers

9. 36% **10.** 0.51 million travelers

11. Areas of Texas and Alaska. The area of the second largest state, Texas, is 268,581 mi^2. This is about 40.5% of the area of the largest state, Alaska. What is the area of Alaska?

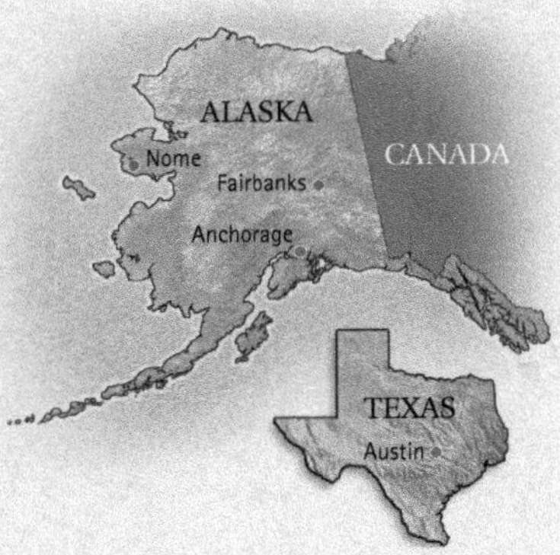

Solve: To solve the equation, we convert 30% to decimal notation and divide by 0.3 on both sides:

$$14.9 = 30\% \times T$$
$$14.9 = 0.3 \times T \quad \text{Converting to decimal notation}$$
$$\frac{14.9}{0.3} = \frac{0.3 \times T}{0.3} \quad \text{Dividing by 0.3}$$
$$49.7 \approx T. \quad \text{Simplifying and rounding to the nearest tenth}$$

About 49.7 million students enrolled in U.S. public schools in 2008.

Do Exercise 11.

EXAMPLE 9 *Employment Outlook.* There were 280 thousand dental assistants in 2006. This number is expected to grow to 362 thousand in 2016. What is the percent of increase?

Source: *Occupational Outlook Handbook*

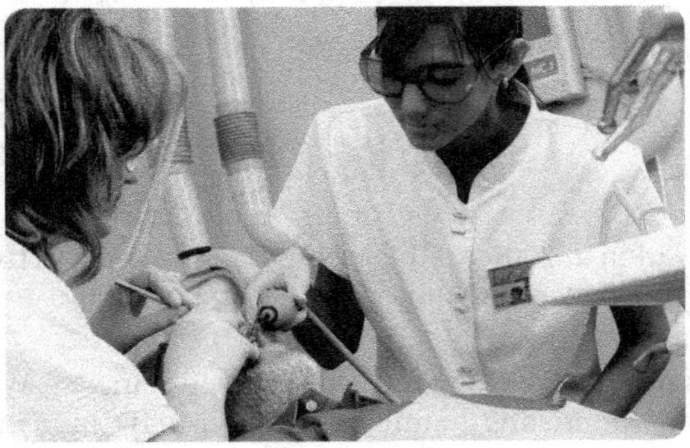

To solve the problem, we must first determine the amount of the increase, in thousands:

Jobs in 2016	minus	Jobs in 2006	=	Increase
↓	↓	↓	↓	↓
362	−	280	=	82.

Using the job increase of 82 thousand, we reword and then translate. We let p = the percent of increase. We want to know, "what percent of the number of jobs in 2006 is 82 thousand?"

Rewording:	82	is	what percent	of	280?
	↓	↓	↓	↓	↓
Translating:	82	=	p	×	280

12. Employment Outlook. There were 234 thousand file clerks in 2006. This number is expected to decrease to 137 thousand in 2016. What is the percent of decrease?

Source: *Occupational Outlook Handbook*

Solve: To solve the equation, we divide by 280 on both sides and convert the answer to percent notation:

$$82 = p \times 280$$
$$\frac{82}{280} = \frac{p \times 280}{280} \quad \text{Dividing by 280}$$
$$0.293 \approx p \quad \text{Simplifying}$$
$$29.3\% \approx p. \quad \text{Converting to percent notation}$$

The percent of increase is about 29.3%.

Do Exercise 12.

Answers

11. About 663,163 mi^2
12. About 41.5%

2.5 Exercise Set

For Extra Help
MyMathLab
Math XL PRACTICE | WATCH | DOWNLOAD | READ | REVIEW

a Solve.

1. What percent of 180 is 36?

2. What percent of 76 is 19?

3. 45 is 30% of what number?

4. 20.4 is 24% of what number?

5. What number is 65% of 840?

6. What number is 50% of 50?

7. 30 is what percent of 125?

8. 57 is what percent of 300?

9. 12% of what number is 0.3?

10. 7 is 175% of what number?

11. 2 is what percent of 40?

12. 16 is what percent of 40?

13. What percent of 68 is 17?

14. What percent of 150 is 39?

15. What number is 35% of 240?

16. What number is 1% of one million?

17. What percent of 125 is 30?

18. What percent of 60 is 75?

19. What percent of 300 is 48?

20. What percent of 70 is 70?

21. 14 is 30% of what number?

22. 54 is 24% of what number?

23. What number is 2% of 40?

24. What number is 40% of 2?

25. 0.8 is 16% of what number?

26. 40 is 2% of what number?

27. 54 is 135% of what number?

28. 8 is 2% of what number?

Amount Spent on Pets. In 2007, \$41.2 billion was spent on pets in the United States. The circle graph below shows the breakdown of this spending.

Amount Spent on Pets

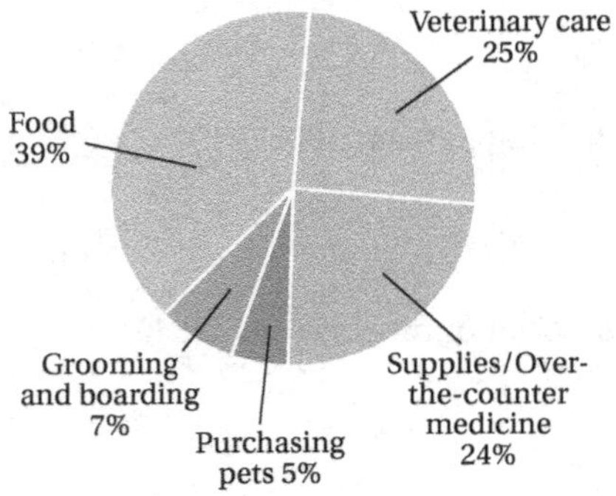

SOURCE: American Pet Products Association

Complete the following table of amounts spent on pets. Round to the nearest tenth.

	CATEGORY	AMOUNT (in billions)		CATEGORY	AMOUNT (in billions)
29.	Food		**30.**	Veterinary care	
31.	Purchasing pets		**32.**	Grooming and boarding	

33. *Smart TV Market.* Smart TVs, which are designed to be easily connected to the Internet or to a home computer network, are a small but growing part of the TV market. Total TV sales in 2010 are projected to be 209 million units, with smart TVs comprising 25.1 million units. What percent of total sales are projected to be smart TV sales?
Source: IDC

34. *Automobile Sales.* Sales of cars averaged \$26 million per dealership in 2007. Of this amount, new car sales accounted for receipts of \$24 million. What percent of total sales are new cars?
Source: U.S. Census Bureau

35. *Graduation Gifts.* American consumers spent \$4.5 billion on graduation gifts in 2008. Cash accounted for 58.8% of this amount. How much cash was given as graduation gifts?
Source: National Retail Federation

36. *Graduation Gifts.* Refer to Exercise 35. Gift cards accounted for 35.7% of the amount spent on graduation gifts in 2008. What is the total value of these gift cards?
Source: National Retail Federation

37. *Student Loans.* To finance her community college education, Sarah takes out a Stafford loan for \$6500. After a year, Sarah decides to pay off the interest, which is 6% of \$6500. How much will she pay?

38. *Student Loans.* Paul takes out a PLUS loan for \$5400. After a year, Paul decides to pay off the interest, which is 8.5% of \$5400. How much will he pay?

39. *Tipping.* Leon left a \$4 tip for a meal that cost \$25.

a) What percent of the cost of the meal was the tip?
b) What was the total cost of the meal including the tip?

40. *Tipping.* Selena left a \$12.76 tip for a meal that cost \$58.

a) What percent of the cost of the meal was the tip?
b) What was the total cost of the meal including the tip?

41. *Tipping.* Leon left a 15% tip for a meal that cost \$25.

a) How much was the tip?
b) What was the total cost of the meal including the tip?

42. *Tipping.* Sam, Selena, Rachel, and Clement left a 15% tip for a meal that cost \$58.

a) How much was the tip?
b) What was the total cost of the meal including the tip?

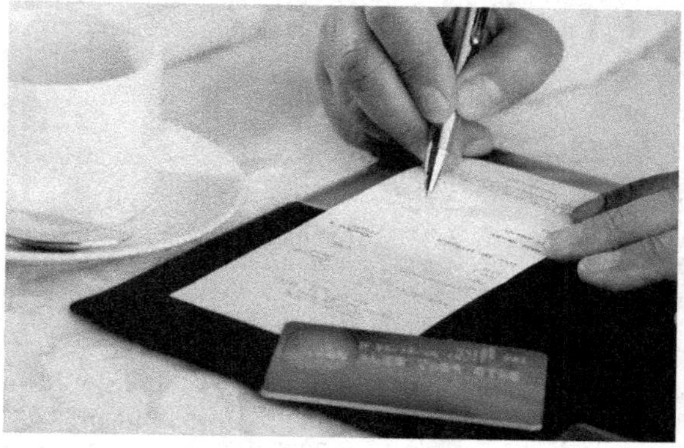

43. *Tipping.* Leon left a 15% tip of \$4.50 for a meal.

a) What was the cost of the meal before the tip?
b) What was the total cost of the meal including the tip?

44. *Tipping.* Selena left a 15% tip of \$8.40 for a meal.

a) What was the cost of the meal before the tip?
b) What was the total cost of the meal including the tip?

45. *City Park Space.* Portland, Oregon, has 12,959 acres of park space. This is 15.1% of the acreage of the entire city. What is the total acreage of Portland?

Source: Indy Parks and Recreation master plan

46. *Junk Mail.* About 46.2 billion pieces of unopened junk mail ends up in landfills each year. This is about 44% of all the junk mail that is sent annually. How many pieces of junk mail are sent annually?

Source: Globaljunkmailcrisis.org

47. *Size of New Homes.* The median size of a new single-family home grew from 1879 ft^2 in 1997 to 2304 ft^2 in 2008. What is the percent of increase?

Source: U.S. Census Bureau

48. *Health Technology Spending.* With growth in traditional technology markets slowing, many companies are developing products for the health-care market. Worldwide, \$68.4 billion was spent on health-care technology in 2005. This amount was expected to increase to \$83.6 billion in 2009. What is the percent of increase?

Source: Gartner

49. *Renewable Fuel.* In 2006, about 4 billion gal of renewable fuels, such as ethanol and other biofuels, were used in the United States. The energy law passed in 2007 requires that 36 billion gal of such fuels be used by 2022. What is the percent of increase?
Source: U.S. Senate Committee on Energy and Natural Resources

50. *Accidents at Railroad Crossings.* In 1997, 3865 accidents occurred at railroad crossings in the United States. This number dropped to 2918 in 2006. What is the percent of decrease?
Source: Federal Railroad Administration

51. *Employment Outlook.* In 2006, there were 50 thousand pharmacy aides in the United States. This number is expected to drop to 45 thousand by 2016. What is the percent of decrease?
Source: Occupational Outlook Handbook

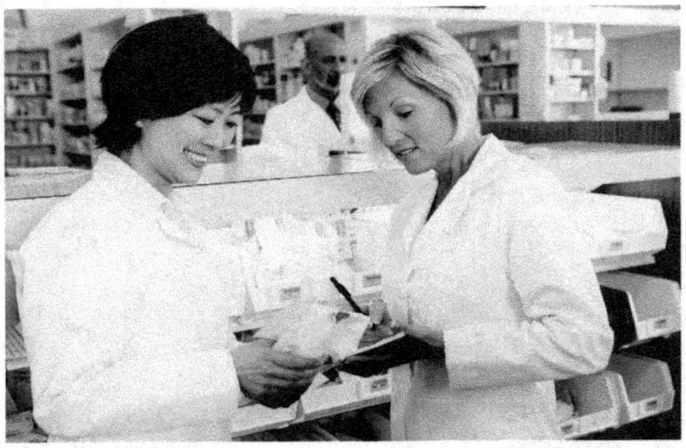

52. *Employment Outlook.* In 2006, there were 767,000 personal and home-care aides in the United States. This number is expected to grow to 1,156,000 by 2016. What is the percent of increase?
Source: Occupational Outlook Handbook

53. *Debit IDs.* A growing number of colleges are teaming up with banks to issue student ID cards that double as debit cards. There were 52 such partnerships in 2002. This number grew to 127 in 2007. What is the percent of increase?
Source: CR80News

54. *Decline in Tuberculosis Cases.* The number of cases of tuberculosis in the United States has plunged from 69,895 in 1956 to 13,299 in 2007. What is the percent of decrease?
Source: U.S. Centers for Disease Control and Prevention

Skill Maintenance

Compute. [R.3b]

55. $9.076 \div 0.05$

56. 9.076×0.05

57. $1.089 + 10.89 + 0.1089$

58. $1000.23 - 156.0893$

Remove parentheses and simplify. [1.8b]

59. $-5a + 3c - 2(c - 3a)$

60. $4(x - 2y) - (y - 3x)$

Add. [1.3a]

61. $-6.5 + 2.6$

62. $-\frac{3}{8} + (-5) + \frac{1}{4} + (-1)$

Fill in each blank with a word that makes the statement true. [1.8d]

63. To simplify the calculation $18 - 24 \div 3 - 48 \div (-4)$, do all the ______ calculations first, and then the ______ calculations.

64. To simplify the calculation $18 - 24^3 \div 48 \div (-4)^2$, do all the ______ calculations first, and then the ______ calculations, and finally the ______ calculation.

Synthesis

65. It has been determined that at the age of 15, a boy has reached 96.1% of his final adult height. Jaraan is 6 ft 4 in. at the age of 15. What will his final adult height be?

66. It has been determined that at the age of 10, a girl has reached 84.4% of her final adult height. Dana is 4 ft 8 in. at the age of 10. What will her final adult height be?

2.6 Applications and Problem Solving

a Five Steps for Solving Problems

We have discussed many new equation-solving tools in this chapter and used them for applications and problem solving. Here we consider a five-step strategy that can be very helpful in solving problems.

FIVE STEPS FOR PROBLEM SOLVING IN ALGEBRA

1. *Familiarize* yourself with the problem situation.
2. *Translate* the problem to an equation.
3. *Solve* the equation.
4. *Check* the answer in the original problem.
5. *State* the answer to the problem clearly.

Of the five steps, the most important is probably the first one: becoming familiar with the problem situation. The box below lists some hints for familiarization.

TO FAMILIARIZE YOURSELF WITH A PROBLEM

- If a problem is given in words, read it carefully. Reread the problem, perhaps aloud. Try to verbalize the problem as if you were explaining it to someone else.
- Choose a variable (or variables) to represent the unknown and clearly state what the variable represents. Be descriptive! For example, let $L =$ the length, $d =$ the distance, and so on.
- Make a drawing and label it with known information, using specific units if given. Also, indicate unknown information.
- Find further information. Look up formulas or definitions with which you are not familiar. (Geometric formulas appear on the inside back cover of this text.) Consult a reference librarian or the Internet.
- Create a table that lists all the information you have available. Look for patterns that may help in the translation to an equation.
- Think of a possible answer and check the guess. Note the manner in which the guess is checked.

EXAMPLE 1 *Knitted Scarf.* Lily knitted a scarf in three shades of blue, starting with a light-blue section, then a medium-blue section, and finally a dark-blue section. The medium-blue section is one-half the length of the light-blue section. The dark-blue section is one-fourth the length of the light-blue section. The scarf is 7 ft long. Find the length of each section of the scarf.

OBJECTIVE

a Solve applied problems by translating to equations.

SKILL TO REVIEW
Objective 1.1b: Translate phrases to algebraic expressions.

Translate each phrase to an algebraic expression.

1. One-third of a number
2. Two more than a number

Answers

Skill to Review:

1. $\frac{1}{3}n$, or $\frac{n}{3}$ 2. $x + 2$, or $2 + x$

1. **Familiarize.** Because the lengths of the medium-blue section and the dark-blue section are expressed in terms of the length of the light-blue section, we let

$$x = \text{the length of the light-blue section.}$$

Then $\frac{1}{2}x =$ the length of the medium-blue section

and $\frac{1}{4}x =$ the length of the dark-blue section.

We make a drawing and label it.

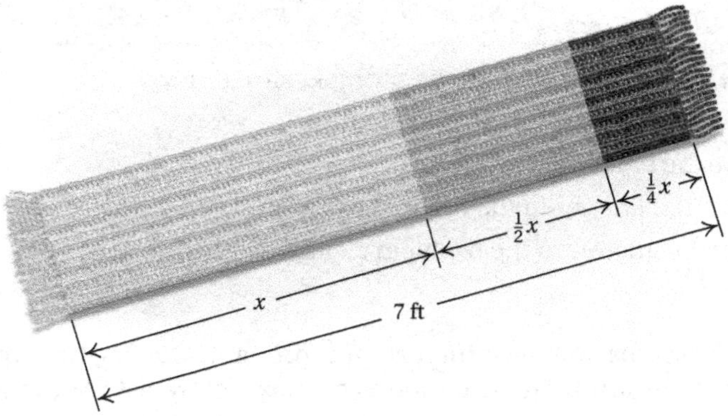

2. **Translate.** From the statement of the problem and the drawing, we know that the lengths add up to 7 ft. This gives us our translation:

Length of light-blue section	plus	Length of medium-blue section	plus	Length of dark-blue section	is	Total length
↓	↓	↓	↓	↓	↓	↓
x	$+$	$\frac{1}{2}x$	$+$	$\frac{1}{4}x$	$=$	$7.$

3. **Solve.** First, we clear fractions and then carry out the solution as follows:

$$x + \frac{1}{2}x + \frac{1}{4}x = 7 \qquad \text{The LCM of the denominators is 4.}$$

$$4\left(x + \frac{1}{2}x + \frac{1}{4}x\right) = 4 \cdot 7 \qquad \text{Multiplying by the LCM, 4}$$

$$4 \cdot x + 4 \cdot \frac{1}{2}x + 4 \cdot \frac{1}{4}x = 4 \cdot 7 \qquad \text{Using the distributive law}$$

$$4x + 2x + x = 28 \qquad \text{Simplifying}$$

$$7x = 28 \qquad \text{Collecting like terms}$$

$$\frac{7x}{7} = \frac{28}{7} \qquad \text{Dividing by 7}$$

$$x = 4.$$

4. **Check.** Do we have an answer to the *original problem*? If the length of the light-blue section is 4 ft, then the length of the medium-blue section is $\frac{1}{2} \cdot 4$ ft, or 2 ft, and the length of the dark-blue section is $\frac{1}{4} \cdot 4$ ft, or 1 ft. The sum of these lengths is 7 ft, so the answer checks.

5. **State.** The length of the light-blue section is 4 ft, the length of the medium-blue section is 2 ft, and the length of the dark-blue section is 1 ft. (Note that we must include the unit, feet, in the answer.)

Do Exercise 1.

EXAMPLE 2 *Hiking.* At age 79, Earl Shaffer became the oldest person to through-hike all 2100 miles of the Appalachian Trail—from Springer Mountain, Georgia, to Mount Katahdin, Maine. Shaffer through-hiked the trail three times, in 1948 (Georgia to Maine), in 1965 (Maine to Georgia), and in 1998 (Georgia to Maine) near the 50th anniversary of his first hike. At one point in 1998, Shaffer stood atop Big Walker Mountain, Virginia, which is three times as far from the northern end as from the southern end. How far was Shaffer from each end of the trail?

Source: Appalachian Trail Conference; Earl Shaffer Foundation

1. **Familiarize.** Let's consider a drawing.

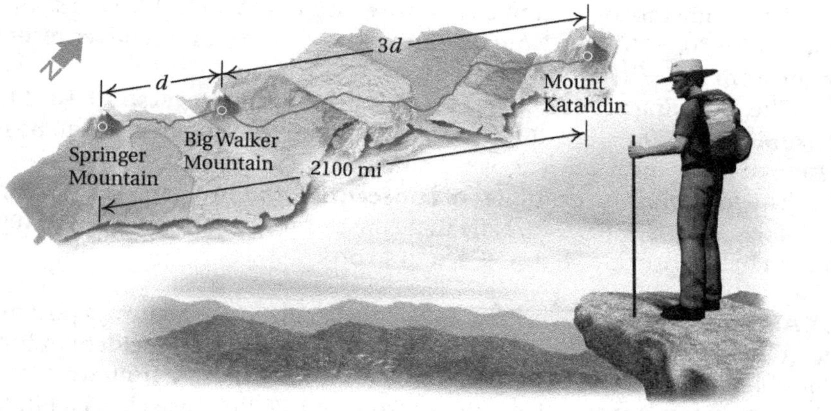

To become familiar with the problem, let's guess a possible distance that Shaffer stood from Springer Mountain—say, 600 mi. Three times 600 mi is 1800 mi. Since 600 mi + 1800 mi = 2400 mi and 2400 mi is greater than 2100 mi, we see that our guess is too large. Rather than guess again, let's use the equation-solving skills that we have learned in this chapter. We let

d = the distance, in miles, to the southern end, and

$3d$ = the distance, in miles, to the northern end.

(We could also let x = the distance to the northern end and $\frac{1}{3}x$ = the distance to the southern end.)

2. **Translate.** From the drawing, we see that the lengths of the two parts of the trail must add up to 2100 mi. This leads to our translation:

Distance to southern end	plus	Distance to northern end	is	2100 mi
↓	↓	↓	↓	↓
d	$+$	$3d$	$=$	$2100.$

1. **Gourmet Sandwiches.** A sandwich shop specializes in sandwiches prepared in buns of length 18 in. Jenny, Emma, and Sarah buy one of these sandwiches and take it back to their apartment. Since they have different appetites, Jenny cuts the sandwich in such a way that Emma gets one-half of what Jenny gets and Sarah gets three-fourths of what Jenny gets. Find the length of each person's sandwich.

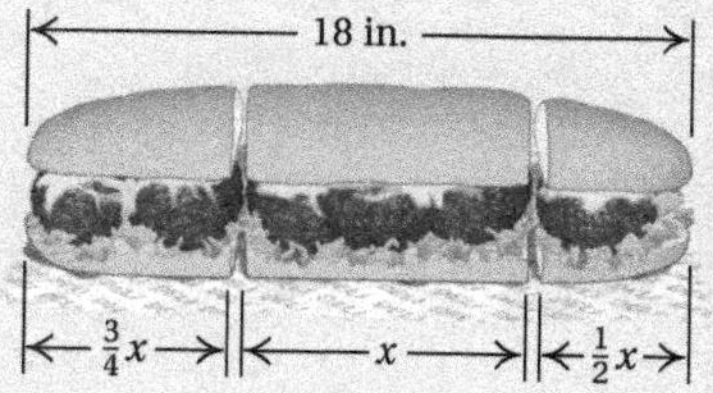

Answer

1. Jenny: 8 in.; Emma: 4 in.; Sarah: 6 in.

3. **Solve.** We solve the equation:

$$
\begin{aligned}
d + 3d &= 2100 \\
4d &= 2100 && \text{Collecting like terms} \\
\frac{4d}{4} &= \frac{2100}{4} && \text{Dividing by 4} \\
d &= 525.
\end{aligned}
$$

4. **Check.** As expected, d is less than 600 mi. If $d = 525$ mi, then $3d = 1575$ mi. Since 525 mi + 1575 mi = 2100 mi, we have a check.
5. **State.** Atop Big Walker Mountain, Shaffer stood 525 mi from Springer Mountain and 1575 mi from Mount Katahdin.

Do Exercise 2.

2. **Running.** Yiannis Kouros of Australia holds the record for the greatest distance run in 24 hr by running 188 mi. After 8 hr, he was approximately twice as far from the finish line as he was from the start. How far had he run?
Source: Australian Ultra Runners Association

Recall that the set of integers = $\{\ldots, -5, -4, -3, -2, -1, 0, 1, 2, 3, 4, 5, \ldots\}$. Before we solve the next problem, we need to learn some additional terminology regarding integers.

The following are examples of **consecutive integers:** 16, 17, 18, 19, 20; and −31, −30, −29, −28. Note that consecutive integers can be represented in the form $x, x + 1, x + 2$, and so on.

The following are examples of **consecutive even integers:** 16, 18, 20, 22, 24; and −52, −50, −48, −46. Note that consecutive even integers can be represented in the form $x, x + 2, x + 4$, and so on.

The following are examples of **consecutive odd integers:** 21, 23, 25, 27, 29; and −71, −69, −67, −65. Note that consecutive odd integers can be represented in the form $x, x + 2, x + 4$, and so on.

EXAMPLE 3 *Interstate Mile Markers.* U.S. interstate highways post numbered markers every mile to indicate location in case of an accident or breakdown. In many states, the numbers on the markers increase from west to east. The sum of two consecutive mile markers on I-70 in Kansas is 559. Find the numbers on the markers.

Source: Federal Highway Administration, Ed Rotalewski

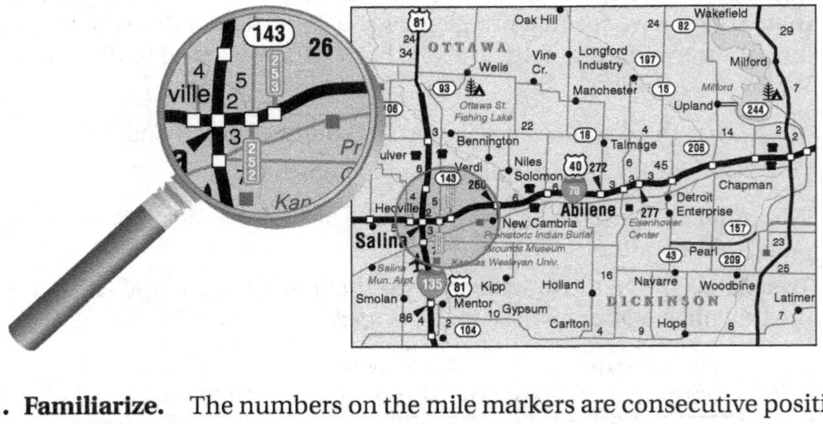

1. **Familiarize.** The numbers on the mile markers are consecutive positive integers. Thus if we let x = the smaller number, then $x + 1$ = the larger number.

To become familiar with the problem, we can make a table, as shown at left. First, we guess a value for x; then we find $x + 1$. Finally, we add the two numbers and check the sum.

x	$x + 1$	Sum of x and $x + 1$
114	115	229
252	253	505
302	303	605

Answer

2. $62\frac{2}{3}$ mi

From the table, we see that the first marker will be between 252 and 302. We could continue guessing and solve the problem this way, but let's work on developing our algebra skills.

2. **Translate.** We reword the problem and translate as follows.

Rewording:	First integer	plus	Second integer	is	559
	↓	↓	↓	↓	↓
Translating:	x	$+$	$(x + 1)$	$=$	559

3. **Solve.** We solve the equation:

$$
\begin{aligned}
x + (x + 1) &= 559 \\
2x + 1 &= 559 && \text{Collecting like terms} \\
2x + 1 - 1 &= 559 - 1 && \text{Subtracting 1} \\
2x &= 558 \\
\frac{2x}{2} &= \frac{558}{2} && \text{Dividing by 2} \\
x &= 279.
\end{aligned}
$$

If x is 279, then $x + 1$ is 280.

4. **Check.** Our possible answers are 279 and 280. These are consecutive positive integers and $279 + 280 = 559$, so the answers check.

5. **State.** The mile markers are 279 and 280.

Do Exercise 3.

3. Interstate Mile Markers. The sum of two consecutive mile markers on I-90 in upstate New York is 627. (On I-90 in New York, the marker numbers increase from east to west.) Find the numbers on the markers.

Source: New York State Department of Transportation

EXAMPLE 4 *Copy Machine Rental.* It costs the Drake law firm \$225 per month plus 1.2¢ per copy to rent a copy machine. The firm needs to lease a machine for use during a special case that they anticipate will take 3 months. If they allot a budget of \$1100, how many copies can they make?

1. **Familiarize.** Suppose that the law firm makes 20,000 copies. Then the cost is given by monthly charges plus copy charges, or

3(\$225)	plus	Cost per copy	times	Number of copies
↓	↓	↓	↓	↓
\$675	$+$	\$0.012	$\cdot$	20,000,

Answer

3. 313 and 314

which is \$915. We see that the firm can make more than 20,000 copies. This process familiarizes us with the way in which a calculation is made. Note that we convert 1.2¢ to \$0.012 so that all information is in the same unit, dollars. Otherwise, we will not get the correct answer.

We let $c =$ the number of copies that can be made for the budget of \$1100.

2. **Translate.** We reword the problem and translate as follows:

Monthly cost	plus	Cost per copy	times	Number of copies	is	Budget
↓	↓	↓	↓	↓	↓	↓
3(\$225)	$+$	\$0.012	$\cdot$	c	$=$	\$1100.

3. **Solve.** We solve the equation:

$$3(225) + 0.012c = 1100$$
$$675 + 0.012c = 1100$$
$$0.012c = 425 \qquad \text{Subtracting 675}$$
$$\frac{0.012c}{0.012} = \frac{425}{0.012} \qquad \text{Dividing by 0.012}$$
$$c \approx 35{,}417. \qquad \text{Rounding to the nearest one}$$

4. **Check.** We check in the original problem. The cost for 35,417 pages is 35,417(\$0.012) = \$425.004. The rental for 3 months is 3(\$225) = \$675. The total cost is then \$425.004 + \$675 ≈ \$1100, which is the \$1100 that was allotted.

5. **State.** The law firm can make 35,417 copies on the copy rental allotment of \$1100.

4. Copy Machine Rental. The Drake law firm in Example 4 decides to increase its budget to \$1400 for the 3-month period. How many copies can they make for \$1400?

Do Exercise 4.

EXAMPLE 5 *Perimeter of NBA Court.* The perimeter of an NBA basketball court is 288 ft. The length is 44 ft longer than the width. Find the dimensions of the court.

Source: National Basketball Association

1. **Familiarize.** We first make a drawing.

We let $w =$ the width of the rectangle. Then $w + 44 =$ the length. The perimeter P of a rectangle is the distance around the rectangle and is given by the formula $2l + 2w = P$, where

$l =$ the length and $w =$ the width.

Answer

4. 60,417 copies

2. Translate. To translate the problem, we substitute $w + 44$ for l and 288 for P:

$$2l + 2w = P$$
$$2(w + 44) + 2w = 288.$$

Caution!

Parentheses are necessary here.

3. Solve. We solve the equation:

$$2(w + 44) + 2w = 288$$
$$2 \cdot w + 2 \cdot 44 + 2w = 288 \quad \text{Using the distributive law}$$
$$4w + 88 = 288 \quad \text{Collecting like terms}$$
$$4w + 88 - 88 = 288 - 88 \quad \text{Subtracting 88}$$
$$4w = 200$$
$$\frac{4w}{4} = \frac{200}{4} \quad \text{Dividing by 4}$$
$$w = 50.$$

Thus possible dimensions are

$w = 50$ ft and $l = w + 44 = 50 + 44$, or 94 ft.

4. Check. If the width is 50 ft and the length is 94 ft, then the perimeter is $2(50 \text{ ft}) + 2(94 \text{ ft})$, or 288 ft. This checks.

5. State. The width is 50 ft and the length is 94 ft.

Do Exercise 5.

5. Perimeter of High School Basketball Court. The perimeter of a standard high school basketball court is 268 ft. The length is 34 ft longer than the width. Find the dimensions of the court.

Source: Indiana High School Athletic Association

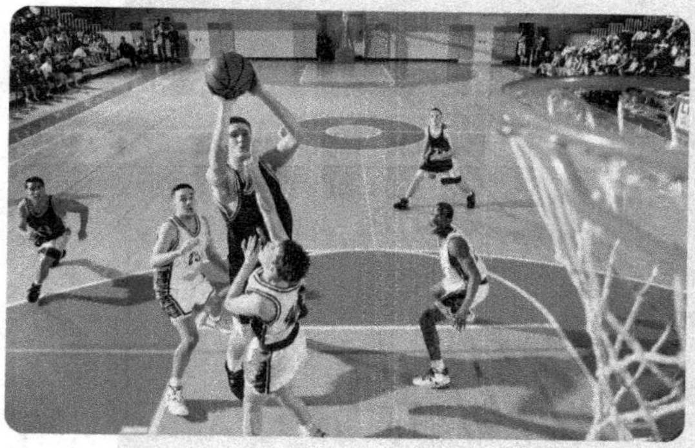

Caution!

Always be sure to answer the original problem completely. For instance, in Example 2, we need to find *two* numbers: the distances from *each* end of the trail to the hiker. Similarly, in Example 3, we need to find two mile markers, and in Example 5, we need to find two dimensions, not just the width.

EXAMPLE 6 *Roof Gable.* In a triangular gable end of a roof, the angle of the peak is twice as large as the angle of the back side of the house. The measure of the angle on the front side is 20° greater than the angle on the back side. How large are the angles?

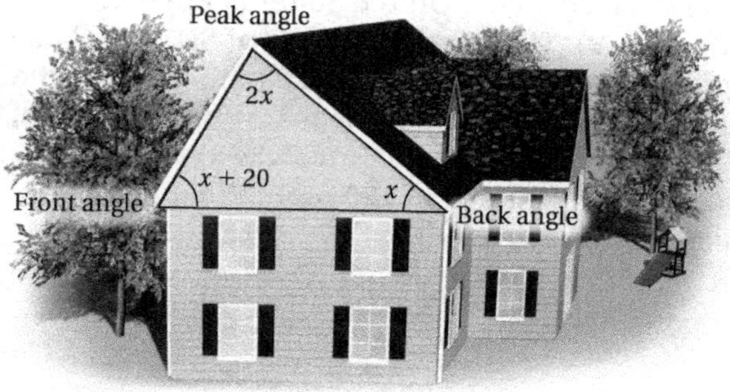

1. Familiarize. We first make a drawing as shown above. We let

measure of back angle $= x$.

Then measure of peak angle $= 2x$

and measure of front angle $= x + 20$.

Answer

5. Length: 84 ft; width: 50 ft

2. **Translate.** To translate, we need to know that the sum of the measures of the angles of a triangle is 180°. You might recall this fact from geometry or you can look it up in a geometry book or in the list of formulas inside the back cover of this book. We translate as follows:

$$\underbrace{\text{Measure of back angle}}_{x} \;\; \underset{+}{\text{plus}} \;\; \underbrace{\text{Measure of peak angle}}_{2x} \;\; \underset{+}{\text{plus}} \;\; \underbrace{\text{Measure of front angle}}_{(x + 20)} \;\; \underset{=}{\text{is}} \;\; \underset{180°.}{180°}$$

3. **Solve.** We solve the equation:

$$\begin{aligned} x + 2x + (x + 20) &= 180 \\ 4x + 20 &= 180 \\ 4x + 20 - 20 &= 180 - 20 \\ 4x &= 160 \\ \frac{4x}{4} &= \frac{160}{4} \\ x &= 40. \end{aligned}$$

Possible measures for the angles are as follows:

Back angle: $x = 40°$;
Peak angle: $2x = 2(40) = 80°$;
Front angle: $x + 20 = 40 + 20 = 60°$.

4. **Check.** Consider our answers: 40°, 80°, and 60°. The peak is twice the back and the front is 20° greater than the back. The sum is 180°. The angles check.

5. **State.** The measures of the angles are 40°, 80°, and 60°.

Caution!

Units are important in answers. Remember to include them, where appropriate.

Do Exercise 6.

6. The second angle of a triangle is three times as large as the first. The third angle measures 30° more than the first angle. Find the measures of the angles.

EXAMPLE 7 *Fastest Roller Coasters.* The average top speed of the three fastest steel roller coasters in the United States is 116 mph. The third-fastest roller coaster, Superman: The Escape (located at Six Flags Magic Mountain, Valencia, California), reaches a top speed of 28 mph less than the fastest roller coaster, Kingda Ka (located at Six Flags Great Adventure, Jackson, New Jersey). The second-fastest roller coaster, Top Thrill Dragster (located at Cedar Point, Sandusky, Ohio), has a top speed of 120 mph. What is the top speed of the fastest steel roller coaster?

Source: Coaster Grotto

Answer

6. First: 30°; second: 90°; third: 60°

1. **Familiarize.** The **average** of a set of numbers is the sum of the numbers divided by the number of addends.

We are given that the second-fastest speed is 120 mph. Suppose the three top speeds are 131, 120, and 103. The average is then

$$\frac{131 + 120 + 103}{3} = \frac{354}{3} = 118,$$

which is too high. Instead of continuing to guess, let's use the equation-solving skills we have learned in this chapter. We let x represent the top speed of the fastest roller coaster. Then $x - 28$ is the top speed of the third-fastest roller coaster.

2. **Translate.** We reword the problem and translate as follows:

$$\frac{\text{Speed of fastest coaster} + \text{Speed of second-fastest coaster} + \text{Speed of third-fastest coaster}}{\text{Number of roller coasters}} = \text{Average speed of three fastest roller coasters}$$

$$\frac{x + 120 + (x - 28)}{3} = 116.$$

3. **Solve.** We solve as follows:

$$\frac{x + 120 + (x - 28)}{3} = 116$$

$$3 \cdot \frac{x + 120 + (x - 28)}{3} = 3 \cdot 116 \qquad \text{Multiplying by 3 on both sides to clear the fraction}$$

$$x + 120 + (x - 28) = 348$$

$$2x + 92 = 348 \qquad \text{Collecting like terms}$$

$$2x = 256 \qquad \text{Subtracting 92}$$

$$x = 128. \qquad \text{Dividing by 2}$$

4. **Check.** If the top speed of the fastest roller coaster is 128 mph, then the top speed of the third-fastest is $128 - 28$, or 100 mph. The average of the top speeds of the three fastest is

$$\frac{128 + 120 + 100}{3} = \frac{348}{3} = 116 \text{ mph.}$$

The answer checks.

5. **State.** The top speed of the fastest steel roller coaster in the United States is 128 mph.

Do Exercise 7.

7. **Average Test Score.** Sam's average score on his first three math tests is 77. He scored 62 on the first test. On the third test, he scored 9 more than he scored on his second test. What did he score on the second and third tests?

Answer

7. Second: 80; third: 89

EXAMPLE 8 *Simple Interest.* An investment is made at 3% simple inter-est for 1 year. It grows to \$746.75. How much was originally invested (the principal)?

1. **Familiarize.** Suppose that \$100 was invested. Recalling the formula for simple interest, $I = Prt$, we know that the interest for 1 year on \$100 at 3% simple interest is given by $I = \$100 \cdot 0.03 \cdot 1 = \$3$. Then, at the end of the year, the amount in the account is found by adding the principal and the interest:

$$\begin{array}{ccccc} \text{Principal} & + & \text{Interest} & = & \text{Amount} \\ \downarrow & & \downarrow & & \downarrow \\ \$100 & + & \$3 & = & \$103. \end{array}$$

In this problem, we are working backward. We are trying to find the prin-cipal, which is the original investment. We let $x =$ the principal. Then the interest earned is $3\%x$.

2. **Translate.** We reword the problem and then translate:

$$\begin{array}{ccccc} \text{Principal} & + & \text{Interest} & = & \text{Amount} \\ \downarrow & & \downarrow & & \downarrow \\ x & + & 3\%x & = & 746.75. \end{array}$$

Interest is 3% of the principal.

3. **Solve.** We solve the equation:

$$x + 3\%x = 746.75$$

$$x + 0.03x = 746.75 \quad \text{Converting to decimal notation}$$

$$1x + 0.03x = 746.75 \quad \text{Identity property of 1}$$

$$(1 + 0.03)x = 746.75$$

$$1.03x = 746.75 \quad \text{Collecting like terms}$$

$$\frac{1.03x}{1.03} = \frac{746.75}{1.03} \quad \text{Dividing by 1.03}$$

$$x = 725.$$

4. **Check.** We check by taking 3% of \$725 and adding it to \$725:

$$3\% \times \$725 = 0.03 \times 725 = \$21.75.$$

Then $\$725 + \$21.75 = \$746.75$, so \$725 checks.

5. **State.** The original investment was \$725.

Do Exercise 8.

8. Simple Interest. An investment is made at 7% simple interest for 1 year. It grows to \$8988. How much was originally invested (the principal)?

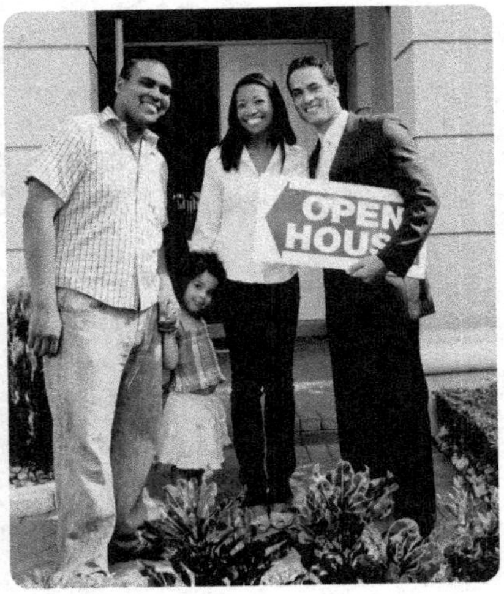

EXAMPLE 9 *Selling a Home.* The Landers are planning to sell their home. If they want to be left with \$117,500 after paying 6% of the selling price to a realtor as a commission, for how much must they sell the house?

1. **Familiarize.** Suppose the Landers sell the house for \$120,000. A 6% commission can be determined by finding 6% of \$120,000:

$$6\% \text{ of } \$120{,}000 = 0.06(\$120{,}000) = \$7200.$$

Subtracting this commission from \$120,000 would leave the Landers with

$$\$120{,}000 - \$7200 = \$112{,}800.$$

This shows that in order for the Landers to clear \$117,500, the house must sell for more than \$120,000. Our guess shows us how to translate to an equation. We let $x =$ the selling price, in dollars. With a 6% commis-sion, the realtor would receive $0.06x$.

Answer

8. \$8400

2. **Translate.** We reword the problem and translate as follows:

Selling price	less	Commission	is	Amount remaining.
↓	↓	↓	↓	↓
x	$-$	$0.06x$	$=$	$117{,}500.$

3. **Solve.** We solve the equation:

$$x - 0.06x = 117{,}500$$
$$1x - 0.06x = 117{,}500$$
$$(1 - 0.06)x = 117{,}500$$
$$0.94x = 117{,}500$$

Collecting like terms. Had we noted that after the commission has been paid, 94% remains, we could have begun with this equation.

$$\frac{0.94x}{0.94} = \frac{117{,}500}{0.94}$$

Dividing by 0.94

$$x = 125{,}000.$$

4. **Check.** To check, we first find 6% of \$125,000:

$$6\% \text{ of } \$125{,}000 = 0.06(\$125{,}000) = \$7500.$$ This is the commission.

Next, we subtract the commission to find the remaining amount:

$$\$125{,}000 - \$7500 = \$117{,}500.$$

Since, after the commission, the Landers are left with \$117,500, our answer checks. Note that the \$125,000 selling price is greater than \$120,000, as predicted in the *Familiarize* step.

5. **State.** To be left with \$117,500, the Landers must sell the house for \$125,000.

Do Exercise 9.

9. Price Before Sale. The price of a suit was decreased to a sale price of \$526.40. This was a 20% reduction. What was the former price?

Caution!

The problem in Example 9 is easy to solve with algebra. Without algebra, it is not. A common error in such a problem is to take 6% of the price after commission and then subtract or add. Note that 6% of the selling price ($6\% \cdot \$125{,}000 = \$7500$) is not equal to 6% of the amount that the Landers want to be left with ($6\% \cdot \$117{,}500 = \$7050$).

STUDY TIPS

PROBLEM-SOLVING TIPS

The more problems you solve, the more your skills will improve.

1. Look for patterns when solving problems. Each time you study an example in a text, you may observe a pattern for problems that you will encounter later in the exercise sets or in other practical situations.
2. When translating in mathematics, consider the dimensions of the variables and the constants in the equation. The variables that represent length should all be in the same unit, those that represent money should all be in dollars or all in cents, and so on.
3. Make sure that units appear in the answer whenever appropriate and that you have completely answered the original problem.

Answer

9. \$658

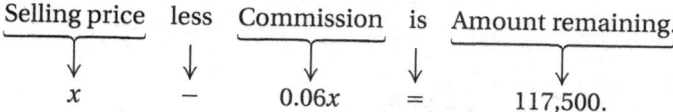

Translating for Success

The goal of these matching questions is to practice step (2), *Translate,* of the five-step problem-solving process. Translate each word problem to an equation and select a correct translation from equations A–O.

1. *Angle Measures.* The measure of the second angle of a triangle is 51° more than that of the first angle. The measure of the third angle is 3° less than twice the first angle. Find the measures of the angles.

2. *Sales Tax.* Tina paid $3976 for a used car. This amount included 5% for sales tax. How much did the car cost before tax?

3. *Perimeter.* The perimeter of a rectangle is 2347 ft. The length is 28 ft greater than the width. Find the length and the width.

4. *Fraternity or Sorority Membership.* At Arches Tech University, 3976 students belong to a fraternity or a sorority. This is 35% of the total enrollment. What is the total enrollment at Arches Tech?

5. *Fraternity or Sorority Membership.* At Moab Tech University, thirty-five percent of the students belong to a fraternity or a sorority. The total enrollment of the university is 11,360 students. How many students belong to either a fraternity or a sorority?

A. $x + (x - 3) + \frac{4}{5}x = 384$

B. $x + (x + 51) + (2x - 3) = 180$

C. $x + (x + 96) = 180$

D. $2 \cdot 96 + 2x = 3976$

E. $x + (x + 1) + (x + 2) = 384$

F. $3976 = x \cdot 11{,}360$

G. $2x + 2(x + 28) = 2347$

H. $3976 = x + 5\%x$

I. $x + (x + 28) = 2347$

J. $x = 35\% \cdot 11{,}360$

K. $x + 96 = 3976$

L. $x + (x + 3) + \frac{4}{5}x = 384$

M. $x + (x + 2) + (x + 4) = 384$

N. $35\% \cdot x = 3976$

O. $2x + (x + 28) = 2347$

Answers on page A-5

6. *Island Population.* There are 180 thousand people living on a small Caribbean island. The women outnumber the men by 96 thousand. How many men live on the island?

7. *Wire Cutting.* A 384-m wire is cut into three pieces. The second piece is 3 m longer than the first. The third is four-fifths as long as the first. How long is each piece?

8. *Locker Numbers.* The numbers on three adjoining lockers are consecutive integers whose sum is 384. Find the integers.

9. *Fraternity or Sorority Membership.* The total enrollment at Canyonlands Tech University is 11,360 students. Of these, 3976 students belong to a fraternity or a sorority. What percent of the students belong to a fraternity or a sorority?

10. *Width of a Rectangle.* The length of a rectangle is 96 ft. The perimeter of the rectangle is 3976 ft. Find the width.

For Extra Help MyMathLab Math XL PRACTICE WATCH DOWNLOAD READ REVIEW

a Solve. *Although you might find the answer quickly in some other way, practice using the five-step problem-solving strategy.*

1. *Manatee Population.* The manatee, Florida's state marine mammal, is an endangered species. An aerial wintertime manatee census counted 2817 of these animals in 2007. This was 296 fewer than the number counted in 2006. What was Florida's manatee population in 2006?

Source: Florida Fish and Wildlife Conservation Commission

2. *Mass Transit Boom.* Americans took 2.8 billion rides on public transit from April through June in 2008. This was the highest ridership for that period in 50 yr and represented an increase of 0.7 billion rides over the same period in 1998. How many rides were taken from April through June in 1998?

Source: American Public Transportation Association

3. *Pipe Cutting.* A 240-in. pipe is cut into two pieces. One piece is three times the length of the other. Find the lengths of the pieces.

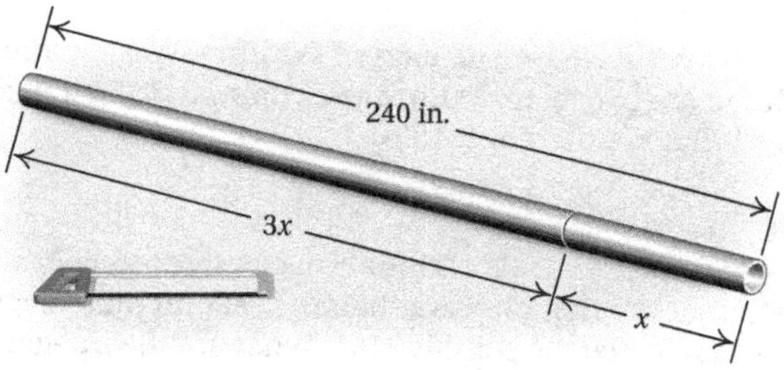

4. *Board Cutting.* A 72-in. board is cut into two pieces. One piece is 2 in. longer than the other. Find the lengths of the pieces.

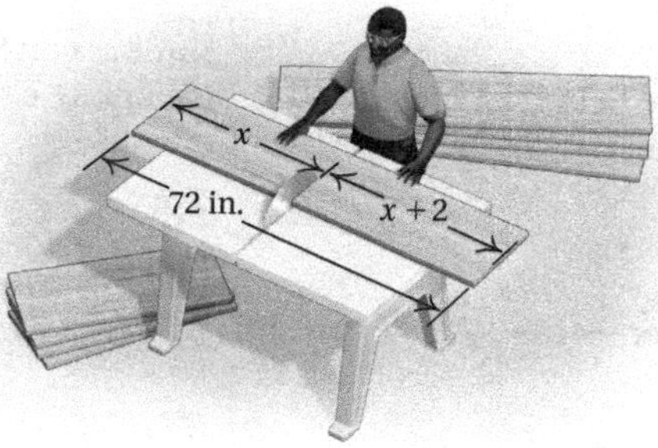

5. *Cost of Movie Tickets.* The average cost of movie tickets for a family of four was $28.32 in 2008. This was $11.76 more than the cost in 1993. What was the average cost of movie tickets for a family of four in 1993? (These prices include senior discounts and children's prices.)

Source: Motion Picture Association of America

6. *Area of Lake Ontario.* The area of Lake Superior is about four times the area of Lake Ontario. The area of Lake Superior is 30,172 mi^2. What is the area of Lake Ontario?

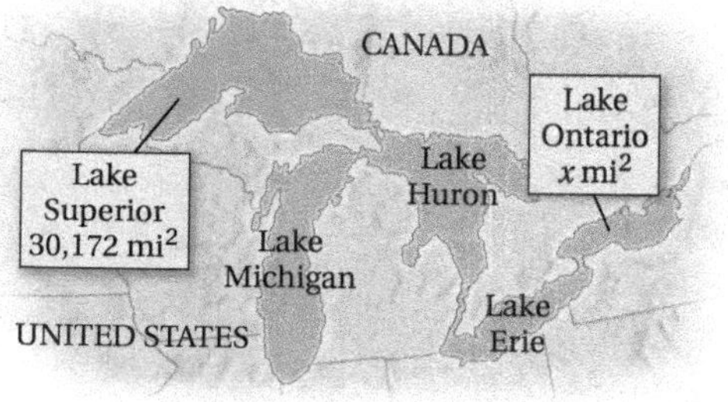

7. *Iditarod Race.* The Iditarod sled dog race in Alaska extends for 1049 mi from Anchorage to Nome. If a musher is twice as far from Anchorage as from Nome, how many miles of the race has the musher completed?

Source: Iditarod Trail Commission

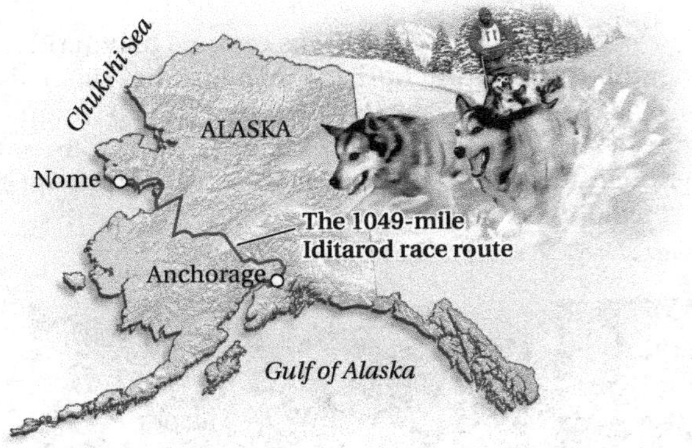

8. *Statue of Liberty.* The height of the Eiffel Tower is 974 ft, which is about 669 ft higher than the Statue of Liberty. What is the height of the Statue of Liberty?

9. *Consecutive Apartment Numbers.* The apartments in Vincent's apartment house are numbered consecutively on each floor. The sum of his number and his next-door neighbor's number is 2409. What are the two numbers?

10. *Consecutive Post Office Box Numbers.* The sum of the numbers on two consecutive post office boxes is 547. What are the numbers?

11. *Consecutive Ticket Numbers.* The numbers on Sam's three raffle tickets are consecutive integers. The sum of the numbers is 126. What are the numbers?

12. *Consecutive Ages.* The ages of Whitney, Wesley, and Wanda are consecutive integers. The sum of their ages is 108. What are their ages?

13. *Consecutive Odd Integers.* The sum of three consecutive odd integers is 189. What are the integers?

14. *Consecutive Integers.* Three consecutive integers are such that the first plus one-half the second plus seven less than twice the third is 2101. What are the integers?

15. *Standard Billboard Sign.* A standard rectangular highway billboard sign has a perimeter of 124 ft. The length is 6 ft more than three times the width. Find the dimensions of the sign.

16. *Two-by-Four.* The perimeter of a cross section or end of a "two-by-four" piece of lumber is 10 in. The length is 2 in. more than the width. Find the actual dimensions of the cross section of a two-by-four.

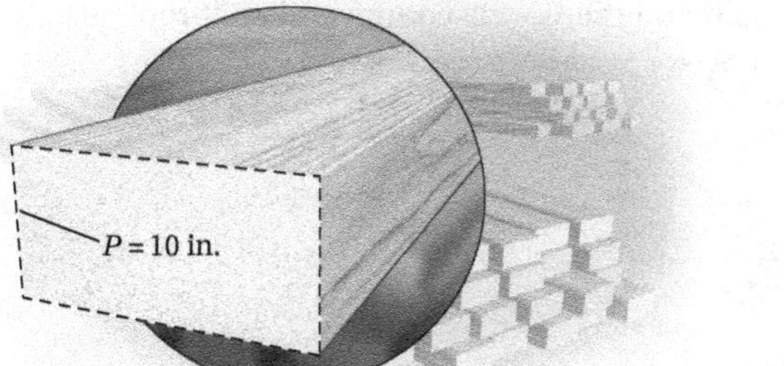

17. *Price of Walking Shoes.* Amy paid $63.75 for a pair of walking shoes during a 15%-off sale. What was the regular price?

18. *Price of a CD Player.* Doug paid $72 for a shockproof portable CD player during a 20%-off sale. What was the regular price?

19. *Price of a Jacket.* Evelyn paid $89.25, including 5% tax, for a jacket. How much did the jacket itself cost?

20. *Price of a Printer.* Jake paid $100.70, including 6% tax, for a color printer. How much did the printer itself cost?

21. *Parking Costs.* A hospital parking lot charges $1.50 for the first hour or part thereof, and $1.00 for each additional hour or part thereof. A weekly pass costs $27.00 and allows unlimited parking for 7 days. Suppose that each visit Ed makes to the hospital lasts $1\frac{1}{2}$ hr. What is the minimum number of times that Ed would have to visit per week to make it worthwhile for him to buy the pass?

22. *Van Rental.* Value Rent-A-Car rents vans at a daily rate of $84.45 plus 55¢ per mile. Molly rents a van to deliver electrical parts to her customers. She is allotted a daily budget of $250. How many miles can she drive for $250? (*Hint*: 60¢ = $0.60.)

23. *Triangular Field.* The second angle of a triangular field is three times as large as the first angle. The third angle is 40° greater than the first angle. How large are the angles?

24. *Triangular Parking Lot.* The second angle of a triangular parking lot is four times as large as the first angle. The third angle is 45° less than the sum of the other two angles. How large are the angles?

25. *Triangular Backyard.* A home has a triangular backyard. The second angle of the triangle is 5° more than the first angle. The third angle is 10° more than three times the first angle. Find the angles of the triangular yard.

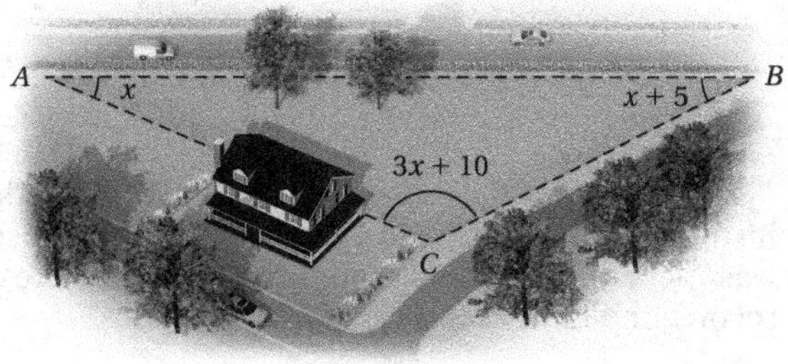

26. *Boarding Stable.* A rancher needs to form a triangular horse pen using ropes next to a stable. The second angle is three times the first angle. The third angle is 15° less than the first angle. Find the angles of the triangular pen.

27. *Stock Prices.* Sarah's investment in a technology stock grew 28% to $448. How much did she invest?

28. *Savings Interest.* Sharon invested money in a savings account at a rate of 6% simple interest. After 1 year, she has $6996 in the account. How much did Sharon originally invest?

29. *Credit Cards.* The balance on Will's credit card grew 2%, to $870, in one month. What was his balance at the beginning of the month?

30. *Loan Interest.* Alvin borrowed money from a cousin at a rate of 10% simple interest. After 1 year, $7194 paid off the loan. How much did Alvin borrow?

31. *Taxi Fares.* In Beniford, taxis charge $3 plus 75¢ per mile for an airport pickup. How far from the airport can Courtney travel for $12?

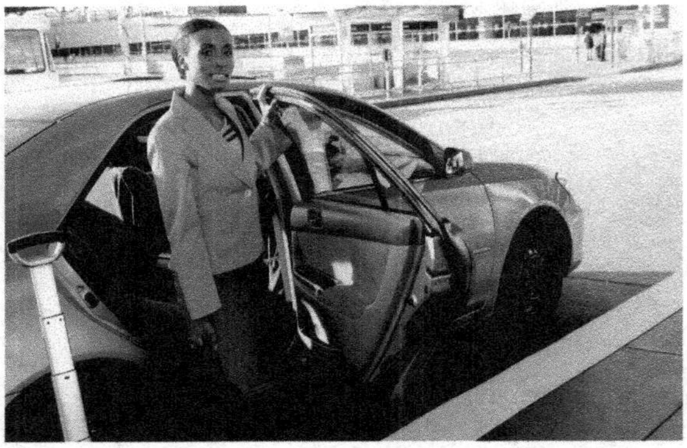

32. *Taxi Fares.* In Cranston, taxis charge $4 plus 90¢ per mile for an airport pickup. How far from the airport can Ralph travel for $17.50?

33. *Tipping.* Leon left a 15% tip for a meal. The total cost of the meal, including the tip, was $41.40. What was the cost of the meal before the tip was added?

34. *Tipping.* Selena left an 18% tip for a meal. The total cost of the meal, including the tip, was $40.71. What was the cost of the meal before the tip was added?

35. *Average Price.* Tom paid an average of $34 per tie for a recent purchase of three ties. The price of one tie was twice as much as another, and the remaining tie cost $27. What were the prices of the other two ties?

36. *Average Test Score.* Jaci averaged 84 on her first three history exams. The first score was 67. The second score was 7 less than the third score. What did she score on the second and third exams?

37. If you double a number and then add 16, you get $\frac{2}{3}$ of the original number. What is the original number?

38. If you double a number and then add 85, you get $\frac{3}{4}$ of the original number. What is the original number?

Skill Maintenance

Calculate.

39. $-\frac{4}{5} - \frac{3}{8}$ [1.4a]

40. $-\frac{4}{5} + \frac{3}{8}$ [1.3a]

41. $-\frac{4}{5} \cdot \frac{3}{8}$ [1.5a]

42. $-\frac{4}{5} \div \frac{3}{8}$ [1.6c]

43. $\frac{1}{10} \div \left(-\frac{1}{100}\right)$ [1.6c]

44. $-25.6 \div (-16)$ [1.6c]

45. $-25.6(-16)$ [1.5a]

46. $-25.6 - (-16)$ [1.4a]

47. $-25.6 + (-16)$ [1.3a]

48. $(-0.02) \div (-0.2)$ [1.6c]

Synthesis

49. Apples are collected in a basket for six people. One-third, one-fourth, one-eighth, and one-fifth are given to four people, respectively. The fifth person gets ten apples, leaving one apple for the sixth person. Find the original number of apples in the basket.

50. *Test Questions.* A student scored 78 on a test that had 4 seven-point fill-ins and 24 three-point multiple-choice questions. The student answered one fill-in incorrectly. How many multiple-choice questions did the student answer correctly?

51. The area of this triangle is 2.9047 in^2. Find x.

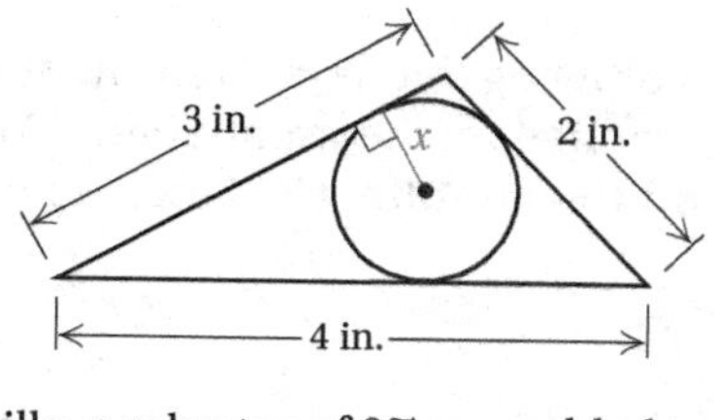

52. Susanne goes to the bank to get $20 in quarters, dimes, and nickels to use to make change at her yard sale. She gets twice as many quarters as dimes and 10 more nickels than dimes. How many of each type of coin does she get?

53. In Connerville, a sales tax of 9% was added to the price of gasoline as registered on the pump. Suppose a driver asked for $10 worth of gas. The attendant filled the tank until the pump read $9.10 and charged the driver $10. Something was wrong. Use algebra to correct the error.

2.7 Solving Inequalities

OBJECTIVES

a) Determine whether a given number is a solution of an inequality.

b) Graph an inequality on the number line.

c) Solve inequalities using the addition principle.

d) Solve inequalities using the multiplication principle.

e) Solve inequalities using the addition principle and the multiplication principle together.

SKILL TO REVIEW

Objective 1.2d: Determine whether an inequality like $-3 \leq 5$ is true or false.

Write true or false.

1. $-6 \leq -8$ **2.** $1 \geq 1$

Determine whether each number is a solution of the inequality.

1. $x > 3$

a) 2 b) 0

c) -5 d) 15.4

e) 3 f) $-\frac{2}{5}$

2. $x \leq 6$

a) 6 b) 0

c) -4.3 d) 25

e) -6 f) $\frac{5}{8}$

Answers

Skill to Review:

1. False **2.** True

Margin Exercises:

1. (a) No; (b) no; (c) no; (d) yes; (e) no; (f) no

2. (a) Yes; (b) yes; (c) yes; (d) no; (e) yes; (f) yes

We now extend our equation-solving principles to the solving of inequalities.

a Solutions of Inequalities

In Section 1.2, we defined the symbols $>$ (is greater than), $<$ (is less than), $\geq$ (is greater than or equal to), and $\leq$ (is less than or equal to).

An **inequality** is a number sentence with $>, <, \geq$, or $\leq$ as its verb—for example,

$$-4 > t, \quad x < 3, \quad 2x + 5 \geq 0, \quad \text{and} \quad -3y + 7 \leq -8.$$

Some replacements for a variable in an inequality make it true and some make it false. (There are some exceptions to this statement, but we will not consider them here.)

SOLUTION

A replacement that makes an inequality true is called a **solution**. The set of all solutions is called the **solution set**. When we have found the set of all solutions of an inequality, we say that we have **solved** the inequality.

EXAMPLES Determine whether each number is a solution of $x < 2$.

1. -2.7 Since $-2.7 < 2$ is true, -2.7 is a solution.

2. 2 Since $2 < 2$ is false, 2 is not a solution.

EXAMPLES Determine whether each number is a solution of $y \geq 6$.

3. 6 Since $6 \geq 6$ is true, 6 is a solution.

4. $-\frac{4}{3}$ Since $-\frac{4}{3} \geq 6$ is false, $-\frac{4}{3}$ is not a solution.

Do Margin Exercises 1 and 2.

b Graphs of Inequalities

Some solutions of $x < 2$ are $-3, 0, 1, 0.45, -8.9, -\pi, \frac{5}{8}$, and so on. In fact, there are infinitely many real numbers that are solutions. Because we cannot list them all individually, it is helpful to make a drawing that represents all the solutions.

A **graph** of an inequality is a drawing that represents its solutions. An inequality in one variable can be graphed on the number line. An inequality in two variables can be graphed on the coordinate plane. We will study such graphs in Chapter 3.

EXAMPLE 5 Graph: $x < 2$.

The solutions of $x < 2$ are all those numbers less than 2. They are shown on the number line by shading all points to the left of 2. The open circle at 2 indicates that 2 is *not* part of the graph.

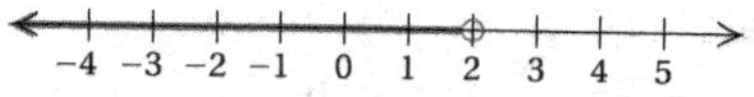

EXAMPLE 6 Graph: $x \geq -3$.

The solutions of $x \geq -3$ are shown on the number line by shading the point for -3 and all points to the right of -3. The closed circle at -3 indicates that -3 *is* part of the graph.

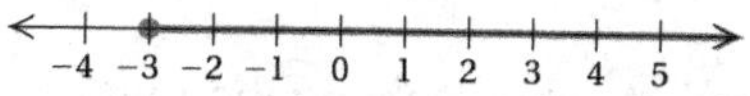

EXAMPLE 7 Graph: $-3 \leq x < 2$.

The inequality $-3 \leq x < 2$ is read "-3 is less than or equal to x *and* x is less than 2," or "x is greater than or equal to -3 *and* x is less than 2." In order to be a solution of this inequality, a number must be a solution of both $-3 \leq x$ and $x < 2$. The number 1 is a solution, as are -1.7, 0, 1.5, and $\frac{3}{8}$. We can see from the graphs below that the solution set consists of the numbers that overlap in the two solution sets in Examples 5 and 6.

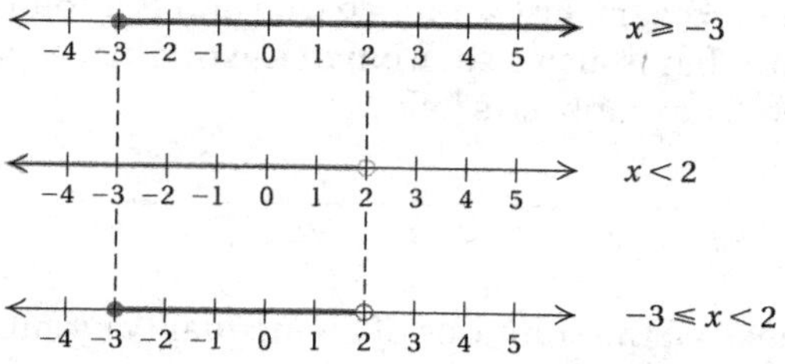

The open circle at 2 means that 2 is *not* part of the graph. The closed circle at -3 means that -3 *is* part of the graph. The other solutions are shaded.

Do Exercises 3–5.

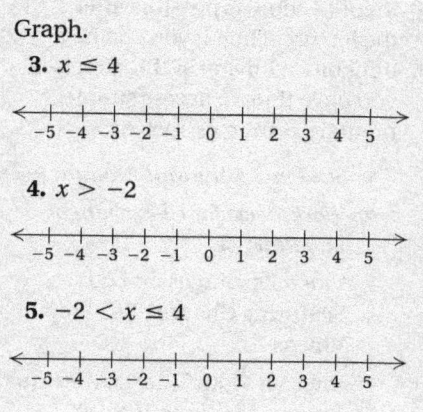

C Solving Inequalities Using the Addition Principle

Consider the true inequality $3 < 7$. If we add 2 on both sides, we get another true inequality:

$$3 + 2 < 7 + 2, \quad \text{or} \quad 5 < 9.$$

Similarly, if we add -4 on both sides of $x + 4 < 10$, we get an *equivalent* inequality:

$$x + 4 + (-4) < 10 + (-4),$$

or

$$x < 6.$$

To say that $x + 4 < 10$ and $x < 6$ are **equivalent** is to say that they have the same solution set. For example, the number 3 is a solution of $x + 4 < 10$. It is also a solution of $x < 6$. The number -2 is a solution of $x < 6$. It is also a solution of $x + 4 < 10$. Any solution of one inequality is a solution of the other—they are equivalent.

Graph.

3. $x \leq 4$

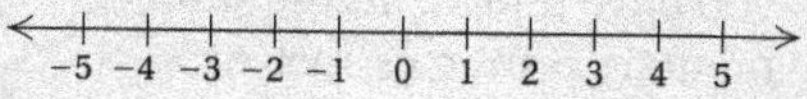

4. $x > -2$

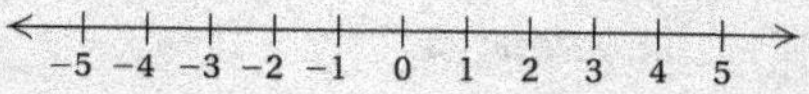

5. $-2 < x \leq 4$

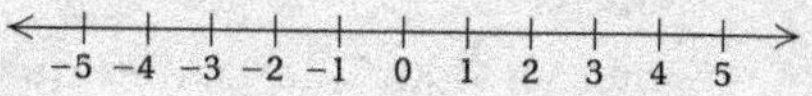

Answers

3.

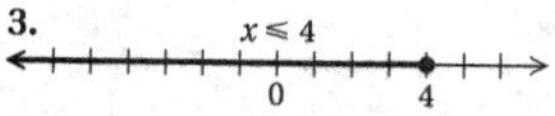

4.

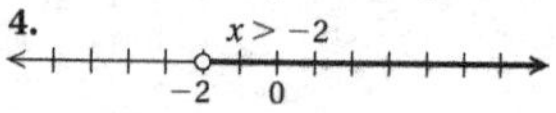

5.

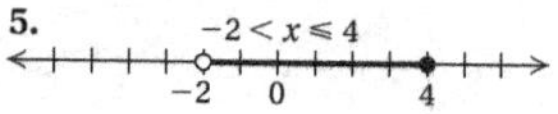

THE ADDITION PRINCIPLE FOR INEQUALITIES

For any real numbers a, b, and c:

$a < b$ is equivalent to $a + c < b + c$;

$a > b$ is equivalent to $a + c > b + c$;

$a \leq b$ is equivalent to $a + c \leq b + c$;

$a \geq b$ is equivalent to $a + c \geq b + c$.

In other words, when we add or subtract the same number on both sides of an inequality, the direction of the inequality symbol is not changed.

As with equation solving, when solving inequalities, our goal is to isolate the variable on one side. Then it is easier to determine the solution set.

STUDY TIPS

USING THE SUPPLEMENTS

The new mathematical skills and concepts presented in lectures will be of increased value to you if you begin the homework assignment as soon as possible after the lecture. Then if you still have difficulty with any of the exercises, you have time to access supplementary resources such as:

- *Student's Solutions Manual*
- *Worksheets for Classroom or Lab Practice*
- Video Resources on DVD Featuring Chapter Test Prep Videos
- InterAct Math Tutorial Website (www.interactmath.com)
- MathXL® Tutorials on CD

Please see the Preface for more information on these and other supplements.

EXAMPLE 8 Solve: $x + 2 > 8$. Then graph.

We use the addition principle, subtracting 2 on both sides:

$$x + 2 - 2 > 8 - 2$$
$$x > 6.$$

From the inequality $x > 6$, we can determine the solutions directly. Any number greater than 6 makes the last sentence true and is a solution of that sentence. Any such number is also a solution of the original sentence. Thus the inequality is solved. The graph is as follows:

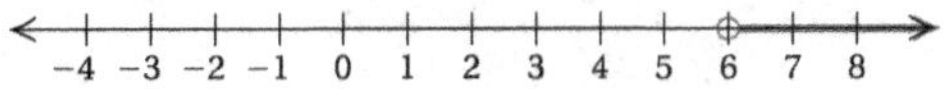

We cannot check all the solutions of an inequality by substitution, as we usually can for an equation, because there are too many of them. A partial check can be done by substituting a number greater than 6—say, 7—into the original inequality:

$x + 2 > 8$	
$7 + 2 \ ? \ 8$	
9	TRUE

Since $9 > 8$ is true, 7 is a solution. This is a partial check that any number greater than 6 is a solution.

EXAMPLE 9 Solve: $3x + 1 \leq 2x - 3$. Then graph.

We have

$3x + 1 \leq 2x - 3$	
$3x + 1 - 1 \leq 2x - 3 - 1$	Subtracting 1
$3x \leq 2x - 4$	Simplifying
$3x - 2x \leq 2x - 4 - 2x$	Subtracting $2x$
$x \leq -4.$	Simplifying

Any number less than or equal to -4 is a solution. The graph is as follows:

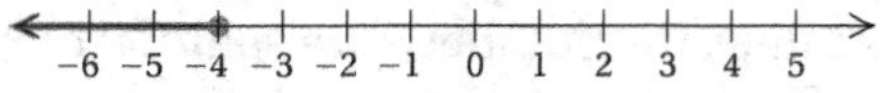

In Example 9, any number less than or equal to -4 is a solution. The following are some solutions:

$$-4, \quad -5, \quad -6, \quad -\frac{13}{3}, \quad -204.5, \quad \text{and} \quad -18\pi.$$

Besides drawing a graph, we can also describe all the solutions of an inequality using **set notation**. We could just begin to list them in a set using roster notation (see p. 63), as follows:

$$\left\{-4, -5, -6, -\frac{13}{3}, -204.5, -18\pi, \ldots\right\}.$$

We can never list them all this way, however. Seeing this set without knowing the inequality makes it difficult for us to know what real numbers we are considering. There is, however, another kind of notation that we can use. It is

$$\{x \mid x \leq -4\},$$

which is read

"The set of all x such that x is less than or equal to -4."

This shorter notation for sets is called **set-builder notation**.

From now on, we will use this notation when solving inequalities.

Do Exercises 6–8.

Solve. Then graph.

6. $x + 3 > 5$

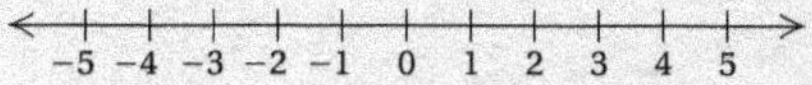

7. $x - 1 \leq 2$

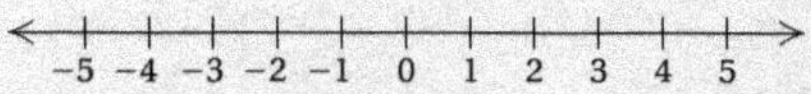

8. $5x + 1 < 4x - 2$

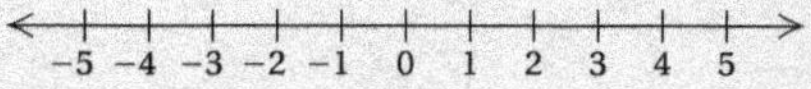

EXAMPLE 10 Solve: $x + \frac{1}{3} > \frac{5}{4}$.

We have

$$\begin{aligned} x + \tfrac{1}{3} &> \tfrac{5}{4} \\ x + \tfrac{1}{3} - \tfrac{1}{3} &> \tfrac{5}{4} - \tfrac{1}{3} && \text{Subtracting } \tfrac{1}{3} \\ x &> \tfrac{5}{4} \cdot \tfrac{3}{3} - \tfrac{1}{3} \cdot \tfrac{4}{4} && \text{Multiplying by 1 to obtain a common denominator} \\ x &> \tfrac{15}{12} - \tfrac{4}{12} \\ x &> \tfrac{11}{12}. \end{aligned}$$

Any number greater than $\frac{11}{12}$ is a solution. The solution set is

$$\left\{x \mid x > \tfrac{11}{12}\right\},$$

which is read

"The set of all x such that x is greater than $\frac{11}{12}$."

When solving inequalities, you may obtain an answer like $\frac{11}{12} < x$. Recall from Chapter 1 that this has the same meaning as $x > \frac{11}{12}$. Thus the solution set in Example 10 can be described as $\left\{x \mid \frac{11}{12} < x\right\}$ or as $\left\{x \mid x > \frac{11}{12}\right\}$. The latter is used most often.

Do Exercises 9 and 10.

Solve.

9. $x + \dfrac{2}{3} \geq \dfrac{4}{5}$

10. $5y + 2 \leq -1 + 4y$

d Solving Inequalities Using the Multiplication Principle

There is a multiplication principle for inequalities that is similar to that for equations, but it must be modified. When we are multiplying on both sides by a negative number, the direction of the inequality symbol must be changed.

Answers

6. $\{x \mid x > 2\}$;

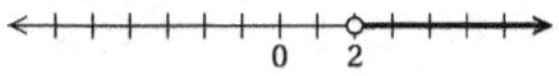

7. $\{x \mid x \leq 3\}$;

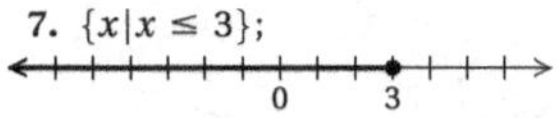

8. $\{x \mid x < -3\}$;

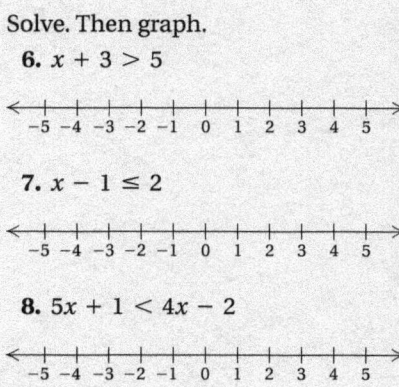

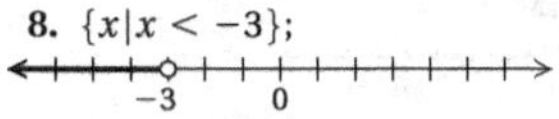

9. $\left\{x \mid x \geq \dfrac{2}{15}\right\}$

10. $\{y \mid y \leq -3\}$

Consider the true inequality $3 < 7$. If we multiply on both sides by a *positive* number, like 2, we get another true inequality:

$$3 \cdot 2 < 7 \cdot 2, \quad \text{or} \quad 6 < 14. \qquad \text{True}$$

If we multiply on both sides by a *negative* number, like -2, and we do not change the direction of the inequality symbol, we get a *false* inequality:

$$3 \cdot (-2) < 7 \cdot (-2), \quad \text{or} \quad -6 < -14. \qquad \text{False}$$

The fact that $6 < 14$ is true but $-6 < -14$ is false stems from the fact that the negative numbers, in a sense, mirror the positive numbers. That is, whereas 14 is to the *right* of 6 on the number line, the number -14 is to the *left* of -6. Thus, if we reverse (change the direction of) the inequality symbol, we get a *true* inequality: $-6 > -14$.

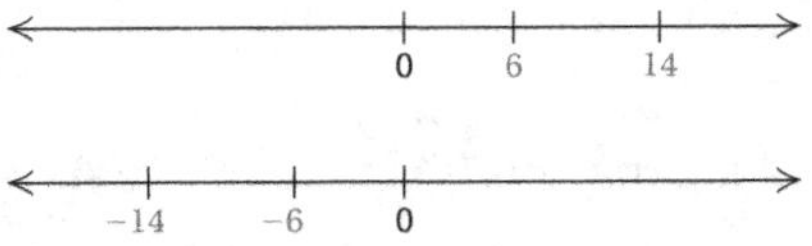

THE MULTIPLICATION PRINCIPLE FOR INEQUALITIES

For any real numbers a and b, and any *positive* number c:

$a < b$ is equivalent to $ac < bc$;

$a > b$ is equivalent to $ac > bc$.

For any real numbers a and b, and any *negative* number c:

$a < b$ is equivalent to $ac > bc$;

$a > b$ is equivalent to $ac < bc$.

Similar statements hold for $\leq$ and $\geq$.

In other words, when we multiply or divide by a positive number on both sides of an inequality, the direction of the inequality symbol stays the same. When we multiply or divide by a negative number on both sides of an inequality, the direction of the inequality symbol is reversed.

EXAMPLE 11 Solve: $4x < 28$. Then graph.

We have

$$4x < 28$$

$$\frac{4x}{4} < \frac{28}{4} \qquad \text{Dividing by 4}$$

The symbol stays the same.

$$x < 7. \qquad \text{Simplifying}$$

The solution set is $\{x | x < 7\}$. The graph is as follows:

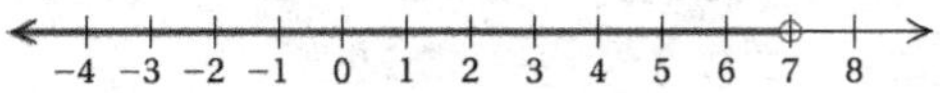

Do Exercises 11 and 12.

Solve. Then graph.

11. $8x < 64$

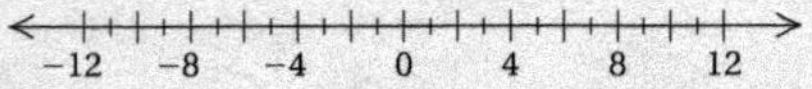

12. $5y \geq 160$

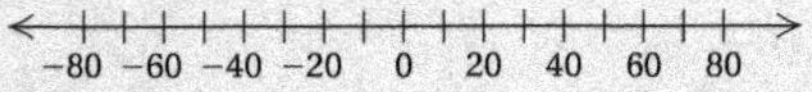

Answers

11. $\{x | x < 8\}$;

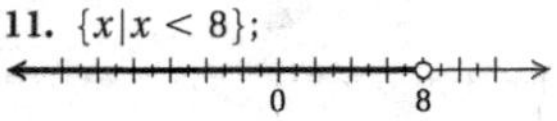

12. $\{y | y \geq 32\}$;

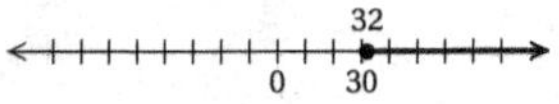

EXAMPLE 12 Solve: $-2y < 18$. Then graph.

$$-2y < 18$$
$$\frac{-2y}{-2} > \frac{18}{-2}$$ Dividing by -2

The symbol must be reversed!

$$y > -9.$$ Simplifying

The solution set is $\{y|y > -9\}$. The graph is as follows:

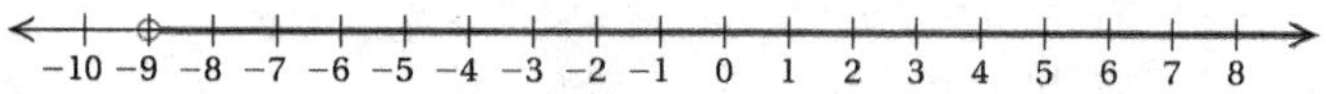

Do Exercises 13 and 14.

Solve.

13. $-4x \leq 24$

14. $-5y > 13$

e Using the Principles Together

All of the equation-solving techniques used in Sections 2.1–2.3 can be used with inequalities, provided we remember to reverse the inequality symbol when multiplying or dividing on both sides by a negative number.

EXAMPLE 13 Solve: $6 - 5x > 7$.

$$6 - 5x > 7$$
$$-6 + 6 - 5x > -6 + 7$$ Adding -6. The symbol stays the same.
$$-5x > 1$$ Simplifying
$$\frac{-5x}{-5} < \frac{1}{-5}$$ Dividing by -5

The symbol must be reversed because we are dividing by a *negative* number, -5.

$$x < -\frac{1}{5}.$$ Simplifying

The solution set is $\left\{x|x < -\frac{1}{5}\right\}$.

Do Exercise 15.

15. Solve: $7 - 4x < 8$.

EXAMPLE 14 Solve: $17 - 5y > 8y - 9$.

$$-17 + 17 - 5y > -17 + 8y - 9$$ Adding -17. The symbol stays the same.
$$-5y > 8y - 26$$ Simplifying
$$-8y - 5y > -8y + 8y - 26$$ Adding $-8y$
$$-13y > -26$$ Simplifying
$$\frac{-13y}{-13} < \frac{-26}{-13}$$ Dividing by -13

The symbol must be reversed because we are dividing by a *negative* number, -13.

$$y < 2$$

The solution set is $\{y|y < 2\}$.

Do Exercise 16.

16. Solve. Begin by subtracting 24 on both sides.

$$24 - 7y \leq 11y - 14$$

Answers

13. $\{x|x \geq -6\}$ **14.** $\left\{y|y < -\frac{13}{5}\right\}$
15. $\left\{x|x > -\frac{1}{4}\right\}$ **16.** $\left\{y|y \geq \frac{19}{9}\right\}$

Typically, we solve an equation or an inequality by isolating the variable on the left side. When we are solving an inequality, however, there are situations in which isolating the variable on the right side will eliminate the need to reverse the inequality symbol. Let's solve the inequality in Example 14 again, but this time we will isolate the variable on the right side.

EXAMPLE 15 Solve: $17 - 5y > 8y - 9$.

Note that if we add $5y$ on both sides, the coefficient of the y-term will be positive after like terms have been collected.

$17 - 5y + 5y > 8y - 9 + 5y$	Adding $5y$
$17 > 13y - 9$	Simplifying
$17 + 9 > 13y - 9 + 9$	Adding 9
$26 > 13y$	Simplifying
$\frac{26}{13} > \frac{13y}{13}$	Dividing by 13. We leave the inequality symbol the same because we are dividing by a positive number.
$2 > y$	

The solution set is $\{y \mid 2 > y\}$, or $\{y \mid y < 2\}$.

Do Exercise 17.

17. Solve. Begin by adding $7y$ on both sides.

$24 - 7y \le 11y - 14$

EXAMPLE 16 Solve: $3(x - 2) - 1 < 2 - 5(x + 6)$.

First, we use the distributive law to remove parentheses. Next, we collect like terms and then use the addition and multiplication principles for inequalities to get an equivalent inequality with x alone on one side.

$3(x - 2) - 1 < 2 - 5(x + 6)$	
$3x - 6 - 1 < 2 - 5x - 30$	Using the distributive law to multiply and remove parentheses
$3x - 7 < -5x - 28$	Collecting like terms
$3x + 5x < -28 + 7$	Adding $5x$ and 7 to get all x-terms on one side and all other terms on the other side
$8x < -21$	Simplifying
$x < \frac{-21}{8}$, or $-\frac{21}{8}$.	Dividing by 8

The solution set is $\left\{x \mid x < -\frac{21}{8}\right\}$.

Do Exercise 18.

18. Solve:

$3(7 + 2x) \le 30 + 7(x - 1)$.

Answers

17. $\left\{y \mid y \ge \frac{19}{9}\right\}$ **18.** $\{x \mid x \ge -2\}$

EXAMPLE 17 Solve: $16.3 - 7.2p \leq -8.18$.

The greatest number of decimal places in any one number is *two.* Multiplying by 100, which has two 0's, will clear decimals. Then we proceed as before.

$$16.3 - 7.2p \leq -8.18$$
$$100(16.3 - 7.2p) \leq 100(-8.18) \quad \text{Multiplying by 100}$$
$$100(16.3) - 100(7.2p) \leq 100(-8.18) \quad \text{Using the distributive law}$$
$$1630 - 720p \leq -818 \quad \text{Simplifying}$$
$$1630 - 720p - 1630 \leq -818 - 1630 \quad \text{Subtracting 1630}$$
$$-720p \leq -2448 \quad \text{Simplifying}$$
$$\frac{-720p}{-720} \geq \frac{-2448}{-720} \quad \text{Dividing by } -720$$

The symbol must be reversed.

$$p \geq 3.4$$

The solution set is $\{p \mid p \geq 3.4\}$.

Do Exercise 19.

19. Solve:
$2.1x + 43.2 \geq 1.2 - 8.4x.$

EXAMPLE 18 Solve: $\frac{2}{3}x - \frac{1}{6} + \frac{1}{2}x > \frac{7}{6} + 2x.$

The number 6 is the least common multiple of all the denominators. Thus we first multiply by 6 on both sides to clear the fractions.

$$\frac{2}{3}x - \frac{1}{6} + \frac{1}{2}x > \frac{7}{6} + 2x$$
$$6\left(\frac{2}{3}x - \frac{1}{6} + \frac{1}{2}x\right) > 6\left(\frac{7}{6} + 2x\right) \quad \text{Multiplying by 6 on both sides}$$
$$6 \cdot \frac{2}{3}x - 6 \cdot \frac{1}{6} + 6 \cdot \frac{1}{2}x > 6 \cdot \frac{7}{6} + 6 \cdot 2x \quad \text{Using the distributive law}$$
$$4x - 1 + 3x > 7 + 12x \quad \text{Simplifying}$$
$$7x - 1 > 7 + 12x \quad \text{Collecting like terms}$$
$$7x - 1 - 7x > 7 + 12x - 7x \quad \text{Subtracting } 7x\text{. The coefficient of the } x\text{-term will be positive.}$$
$$-1 > 7 + 5x \quad \text{Simplifying}$$
$$-1 - 7 > 7 + 5x - 7 \quad \text{Subtracting 7}$$
$$-8 > 5x \quad \text{Simplifying}$$
$$\frac{-8}{5} > \frac{5x}{5} \quad \text{Dividing by 5}$$
$$-\frac{8}{5} > x$$

The solution set is $\left\{x \mid -\frac{8}{5} > x\right\}$, or $\left\{x \mid x < -\frac{8}{5}\right\}$.

Do Exercise 20.

20. Solve:
$\frac{3}{4} + x < \frac{7}{8}x - \frac{1}{4} + \frac{1}{2}x.$

Answers

19. $\{x \mid x \geq -4\}$ **20.** $\left\{x \mid x > \frac{8}{3}\right\}$

For Extra Help
MyMathLab | MathXL PRACTICE | WATCH | DOWNLOAD | READ | REVIEW

a Determine whether each number is a solution of the given inequality.

1. $x > -4$
a) 4
b) 0
c) -4
d) 6
e) 5.6

2. $x \le 5$
a) 0
b) 5
c) -1
d) -5
e) $7\frac{1}{4}$

3. $x \ge 6.8$
a) -6
b) 0
c) 6
d) 8
e) $-3\frac{1}{2}$

4. $x < 8$
a) 8
b) -10
c) 0
d) 11
e) -4.7

b Graph on the number line.

5. $x > 4$

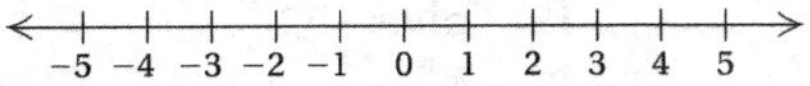

6. $x < 0$

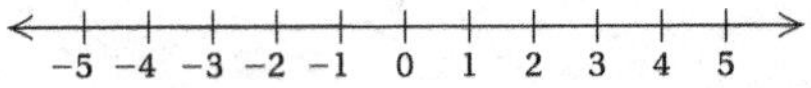

7. $t < -3$

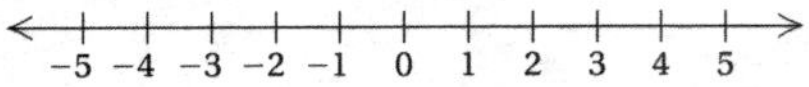

8. $y > 5$

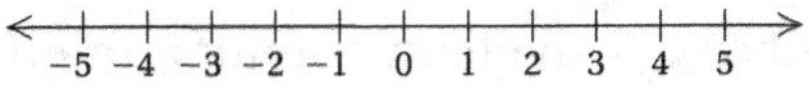

9. $m \ge -1$

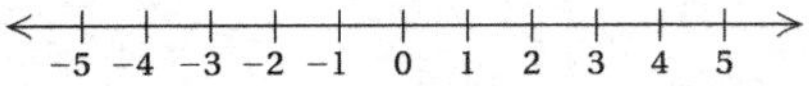

10. $x \le -2$

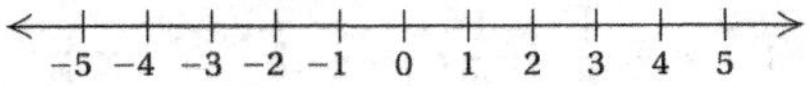

11. $-3 < x \le 4$

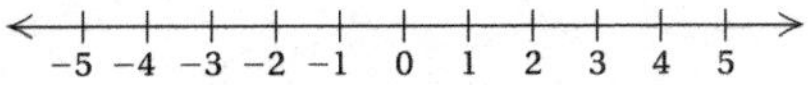

12. $-5 \le x < 2$

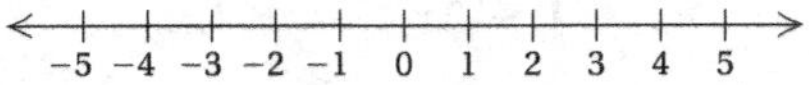

13. $0 < x < 3$

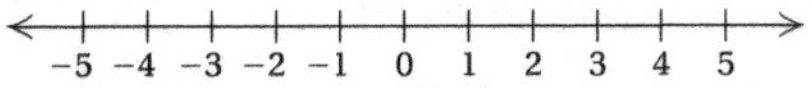

14. $-5 \le x \le 0$

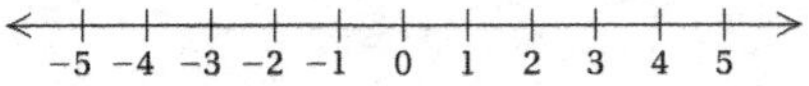

c Solve using the addition principle. Then graph.

15. $x + 7 > 2$

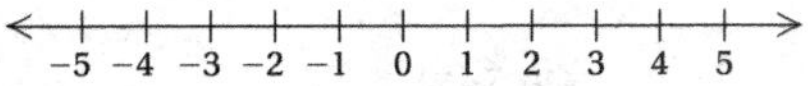

16. $x + 5 > 2$

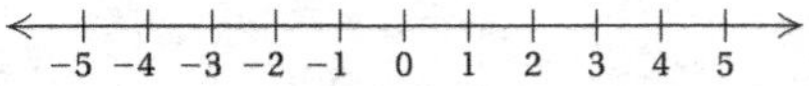

17. $x + 8 \le -10$

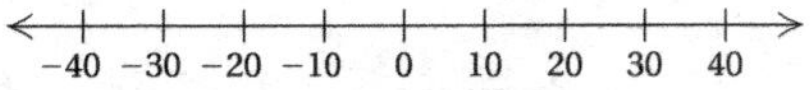

18. $x + 8 \le -11$

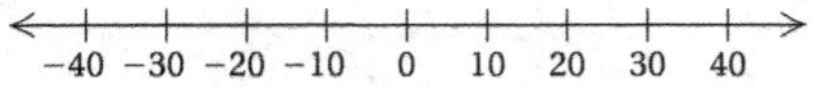

Solve using the addition principle.

19. $y - 7 > -12$

20. $y - 9 > -15$

21. $2x + 3 > x + 5$

22. $2x + 4 > x + 7$

23. $3x + 9 \leq 2x + 6$

24. $3x + 18 \leq 2x + 16$

25. $5x - 6 < 4x - 2$

26. $9x - 8 < 8x - 9$

27. $-9 + t > 5$

28. $-8 + p > 10$

29. $y + \frac{1}{4} \leq \frac{1}{2}$

30. $x - \frac{1}{3} \leq \frac{5}{6}$

31. $x - \frac{1}{3} > \frac{1}{4}$

32. $x + \frac{1}{8} > \frac{1}{2}$

d Solve using the multiplication principle. Then graph.

33. $5x < 35$

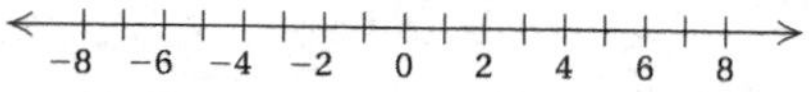

34. $8x \geq 32$

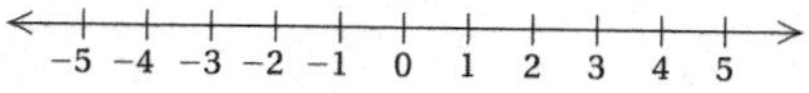

35. $-12x > -36$

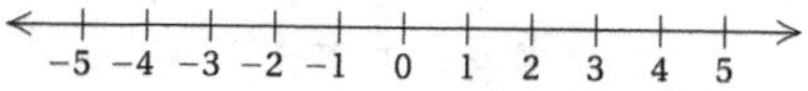

36. $-16x > -64$

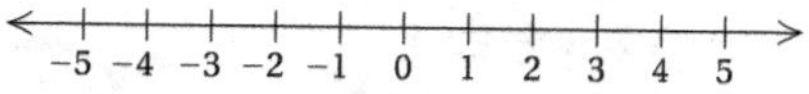

Solve using the multiplication principle.

37. $5y \geq -2$

38. $3x < -4$

39. $-2x \leq 12$

40. $-3x \leq 15$

41. $-4y \geq -16$

42. $-7x < -21$

43. $-3x < -17$

44. $-5y > -23$

45. $-2y > \frac{1}{7}$

46. $-4x \leq \frac{1}{9}$

47. $-\frac{6}{5} \leq -4x$

48. $-\frac{7}{9} > 63x$

e Solve using the addition principle and the multiplication principle.

49. $4 + 3x < 28$

50. $3 + 4y < 35$

51. $3x - 5 \leq 13$

52. $5y - 9 \leq 21$

53. $13x - 7 < -46$

54. $8y - 6 < -54$

55. $30 > 3 - 9x$

56. $48 > 13 - 7y$

57. $4x + 2 - 3x \leq 9$

58. $15x + 5 - 14x \leq 9$

59. $-3 < 8x + 7 - 7x$

60. $-8 < 9x + 8 - 8x - 3$

61. $6 - 4y > 4 - 3y$

62. $9 - 8y > 5 - 7y + 2$

63. $5 - 9y \leq 2 - 8y$

64. $6 - 18x \leq 4 - 12x - 5x$

65. $19 - 7y - 3y < 39$

66. $18 - 6y - 4y < 63 + 5y$

67. $0.9x + 19.3 > 5.3 - 2.6x$

68. $0.96y - 0.79 \leq 0.21y + 0.46$

69. $\frac{x}{3} - 2 \leq 1$

70. $\frac{2}{3} + \frac{x}{5} < \frac{4}{15}$

71. $\frac{y}{5} + 1 \leq \frac{2}{5}$

72. $\frac{3x}{4} - \frac{7}{8} \geq -15$

73. $3(2y - 3) < 27$

74. $4(2y - 3) > 28$

75. $2(3 + 4m) - 9 \geq 45$

76. $3(5 + 3m) - 8 \leq 88$

77. $8(2t + 1) > 4(7t + 7)$

78. $7(5y - 2) > 6(6y - 1)$

79. $3(r - 6) + 2 < 4(r + 2) - 21$

80. $5(x + 3) + 9 \le 3(x - 2) + 6$

81. $0.8(3x + 6) \ge 1.1 - (x + 2)$

82. $0.4(2x + 8) \ge 20 - (x + 5)$

83. $\frac{5}{3} + \frac{2}{3}x < \frac{25}{12} + \frac{5}{4}x + \frac{3}{4}$

84. $1 - \frac{2}{3}y \ge \frac{9}{5} - \frac{y}{5} + \frac{3}{5}$

Skill Maintenance

Add or subtract. [1.3a], [1.4a]

85. $-56 + (-18)$

86. $-2.3 + 7.1$

87. $-\frac{3}{4} + \frac{1}{8}$

88. $8.12 - 9.23$

89. $-56 - (-18)$

90. $-\frac{3}{4} - \frac{1}{8}$

91. $-2.3 - 7.1$

92. $-8.12 + 9.23$

Simplify.

93. $5 - 3^2 + (8 - 2)^2 \cdot 4$ [1.8d]

94. $10 \div 2 \cdot 5 - 3^2 + (-5)^2$ [1.8d]

95. $5(2x - 4) - 3(4x + 1)$ [1.8b]

96. $9(3 + 5x) - 4(7 + 2x)$ [1.8b]

Synthesis

97. Determine whether each number is a solution of the inequality $|x| < 3$.

a) 0
b) -2
c) -3
d) 4
e) 3
f) 1.7
g) -2.8

98. Graph $|x| < 3$ on the number line.

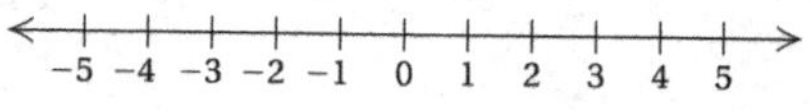

Solve.

99. $x + 3 < 3 + x$

100. $x + 4 > 3 + x$

2.8 Applications and Problem Solving with Inequalities

OBJECTIVES

a Translate number sentences to inequalities.

b Solve applied problems using inequalities.

The five steps for problem solving can be used for problems involving inequalities.

a Translating to Inequalities

Before solving problems that involve inequalities, we list some important phrases to look for. Sample translations are listed as well.

IMPORTANT WORDS	SAMPLE SENTENCE	TRANSLATION
is at least	Bill is at least 21 years old.	$b \geq 21$
is at most	At most 5 students dropped the course.	$n \leq 5$
cannot exceed	To qualify, earnings cannot exceed \$12,000.	$r \leq 12{,}000$
must exceed	The speed must exceed 15 mph.	$s > 15$
is less than	Tucker's weight is less than 50 lb.	$w < 50$
is more than	Boston is more than 200 mi away.	$d > 200$
is between	The film was between 90 and 100 min long.	$90 < t < 100$
no more than	Bing weighs no more than 90 lb.	$w \leq 90$
no less than	Valerie scored no less than 8.3.	$s \geq 8.3$

The following phrases deserve special attention.

TRANSLATING "AT LEAST" AND "AT MOST"

A quantity x is at least some amount q: $x \geq q$.
(If x is at least q, it cannot be less than q.)

A quantity x is at most some amount q: $x \leq q$.
(If x is at most q, it cannot be more than q.)

Do Exercises 1–8.

Translate.

1. Maggie worked no fewer than 15 hr last week.
2. The price of that PT Cruiser is at most \$21,900.
3. The time of the test was between 45 and 55 min.
4. Tania's weight is less than 110 lb.
5. That number is more than -2.
6. The costs of production of that CD-ROM cannot exceed \$12,500.
7. At most 1250 people attended the concert.
8. Yesterday, at least 23 people got tickets for speeding.

b Solving Problems

EXAMPLE 1 *Catering Costs.* To cater a party, Curtis' Barbeque charges a \$150 setup fee plus \$15.50 per person. The cost of Berry Manufacturing's annual picnic cannot exceed \$2100. How many people can attend the picnic?

Source: Curtis' All American Barbeque, Putney, Vermont

1. **Familiarize.** Suppose that 110 people were to attend the picnic. The cost would then be $\$150 + \$15.50(110)$, or \$1855. This shows that more than 110 people could attend the picnic without exceeding \$2100. Instead of making another guess, we let $n =$ the number of people in attendance.

Answers

1. $h \geq 15$ 2. $p \leq 21{,}900$
3. $45 < t < 55$ 4. $w < 110$
5. $n > -2$ 6. $c \leq 12{,}500$
7. $p \leq 1250$ 8. $s \geq 23$

2. **Translate.** Our guess shows us how to translate. The cost of the picnic will be the \$150 setup fee plus \$15.50 times the number of people attending. We translate to an inequality:

Rewording:	The setup fee	plus	the cost of the meals	cannot exceed	\$2100.
	↓	↓	↓	↓	↓
Translating:	150	+	$15.50n$	$\leq$	2100.

3. **Solve.** We solve the inequality for n:

$$150 + 15.50n \leq 2100$$

$$150 + 15.50n - 150 \leq 2100 - 150 \quad \text{Subtracting 150}$$

$$15.50n \leq 1950 \quad \text{Simplifying}$$

$$\frac{15.50n}{15.50} \leq \frac{1950}{15.50} \quad \text{Dividing by 15.50}$$

$$n \leq 125.8. \quad \text{Rounding to the nearest tenth}$$

4. **Check.** Although the solution set of the inequality is all numbers less than or equal to about 125.8, since n = the number of people in attendance, we round *down* to 125 people. If 125 people attend, the cost will be \$150 + \$15.50(125), or \$2087.50. If 126 attend, the cost will exceed \$2100.

5. **State.** At most, 125 people can attend the picnic.

Do Exercise 9.

Translate to an inequality and solve.

9. **Butter Temperatures.** Butter stays solid at Fahrenheit temperatures below 88°. The formula

$$F = \tfrac{9}{5}C + 32$$

can be used to convert Celsius temperatures C to Fahrenheit temperatures F. Determine (in terms of an inequality) those Celsius temperatures for which butter stays solid.

Caution!

Solutions of problems should always be checked using the original wording of the problem. In some cases, answers might need to be whole numbers or integers or rounded off in a particular direction.

EXAMPLE 2 *Nutrition.* The U.S. Department of Agriculture recommends that for a typical 2000-calorie daily diet, no more than 20 g of saturated fat be consumed. In the first three days of a four-day vacation, Anthony consumed 26 g, 17 g, and 22 g of saturated fat. Determine (in terms of an inequality) how many grams of saturated fat Anthony can consume on the fourth day if he is to average no more than 20 g of saturated fat per day.

SOURCES: U.S. Department of Health and Human Services; U.S. Department of Agriculture

Answer

9. $\frac{9}{5}C + 32 < 88$; $\{C \mid C < 31\tfrac{1}{9}°\}$

1. **Familiarize.** Suppose Anthony consumed 19 g of saturated fat on the fourth day. His daily average for the vacation would then be

$$\frac{26\text{ g} + 17\text{ g} + 22\text{ g} + 19\text{ g}}{4} = \frac{84\text{ g}}{4} = 21\text{ g}.$$

This shows that Anthony cannot consume 19 g of saturated fat on the fourth day, if he is to average no more than 20 g of fat per day. We let $x =$ the number of grams of fat that Anthony consumes on the fourth day.

2. **Translate.** We reword the problem and translate to an inequality as follows:

Rewording:	The average consumption of saturated fat	should be no more than	20 g.
Translating:	$\frac{26 + 17 + 22 + x}{4}$	$\leq$	20.

3. **Solve.** Because of the fraction expression, it is convenient to use the multiplication principle first to solve the inequality:

$$\frac{26 + 17 + 22 + x}{4} \leq 20$$

$$4\left(\frac{26 + 17 + 22 + x}{4}\right) \leq 4 \cdot 20 \qquad \text{Multiplying by 4}$$

$$26 + 17 + 22 + x \leq 80$$

$$65 + x \leq 80 \qquad \text{Simplifying}$$

$$x \leq 15. \qquad \text{Subtracting 65}$$

4. **Check.** As a partial check, we show that Anthony can consume 15 g of saturated fat on the fourth day and not exceed a 20-g average for the four days:

$$\frac{26 + 17 + 22 + 15}{4} = \frac{80}{4} = 20.$$

5. **State.** Anthony's average intake of saturated fat for the vacation will not exceed 20 g per day if he consumes no more than 15 g of saturated fat on the fourth day.

Do Exercise 10.

Translate to an inequality and solve.

10. Test Scores. A pre-med student is taking a chemistry course in which four tests are given. To get an A, she must average at least 90 on the four tests. The student got scores of 91, 86, and 89 on the first three tests. Determine (in terms of an inequality) what scores on the last test will allow her to get an A.

STUDY TIPS

CHECKLIST

- Are you approaching your study of mathematics with a positive attitude?
- Are you making use of the textbook supplements, such as the *Student's Solutions Manual* and the videos?
- Have you determined the location of the learning resource centers on your campus, such as a math lab, a tutor center, and your instructor's office?
- Are you stopping to work the margin exercises when directed to do so?
- Are you keeping one section ahead in your syllabus?

Answer

10. $\frac{91 + 86 + 89 + s}{4} \geq 90$; $\{s | s \geq 94\}$

2.8 Exercise Set

For Extra Help
MyMathLab
Math XL PRACTICE | WATCH | DOWNLOAD | READ | REVIEW

a Translate to an inequality.

1. A number is at least 7.

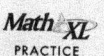

2. A number is greater than or equal to 5.

3. The baby weighs more than 2 kilograms (kg).

4. Between 75 and 100 people attended the concert.

5. The speed of the train was between 90 and 110 mph.

6. The attendance was no more than 180.

7. Leah works no more than 20 hr per week.

8. The amount of acid must exceed 40 liters (L).

9. The cost of gasoline is no less than $1.50 per gallon.

10. The temperature is at most $-2°$.

11. A number is greater than 8.

12. A number is less than 5.

13. A number is less than or equal to -4.

14. A number is greater than or equal to 18.

15. The number of people is at least 1300.

16. The cost is at most $4857.95.

17. The amount of water is not to exceed 500 liters.

18. The cost of lettuce is no less than 94 cents per pound.

19. Two more than three times a number is less than 13.

20. Five less than one-half a number is greater than 17.

b Solve.

21. *Test Scores.* James is taking a literature course in which four tests are given. To get a B, he must average at least 80 on the four tests. He got scores of 82, 76, and 78 on the first three tests. Determine (in terms of an inequality) what scores on the last test will allow him to get at least a B.

22. *Test Scores.* Rebecca's quiz grades are 73, 75, 89, and 91. Determine (in terms of an inequality) what scores on the last quiz will allow her to get an average quiz grade of at least 85.

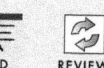

23. *Gold Temperatures.* Gold stays solid at Fahrenheit temperatures below 1945.4°. Determine (in terms of an inequality) those Celsius temperatures for which gold stays solid. Use the formula given in Margin Exercise 9.

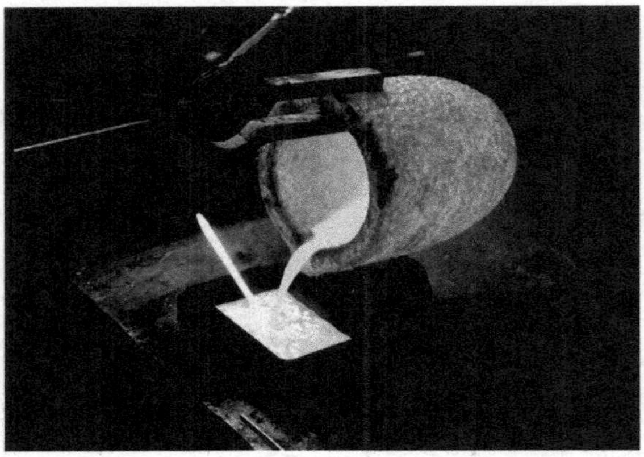

24. *Body Temperatures.* The human body is considered to be fevered when its temperature is higher than 98.6°F. Using the formula given in Margin Exercise 9, determine (in terms of an inequality) those Celsius temperatures for which the body is fevered.

25. *World Records in the 1500-m Run.* The formula

$$R = -0.075t + 3.85$$

can be used to predict the world record in the 1500-m run t years after 1930. Determine (in terms of an inequality) those years for which the world record will be less than 3.5 min.

26. *World Records in the 200-m Dash.* The formula

$$R = -0.028t + 20.8$$

can be used to predict the world record in the 200-m dash t years after 1920. Determine (in terms of an inequality) those years for which the world record will be less than 19.0 sec.

27. *Envelope Size.* For a direct-mail campaign, Laramore Advertising determines that any envelope with a fixed width of $3\frac{1}{2}$ in. and an area of at least $17\frac{1}{2}$ in^2 can be used. Determine (in terms of an inequality) those lengths that will satisfy the company constraints.

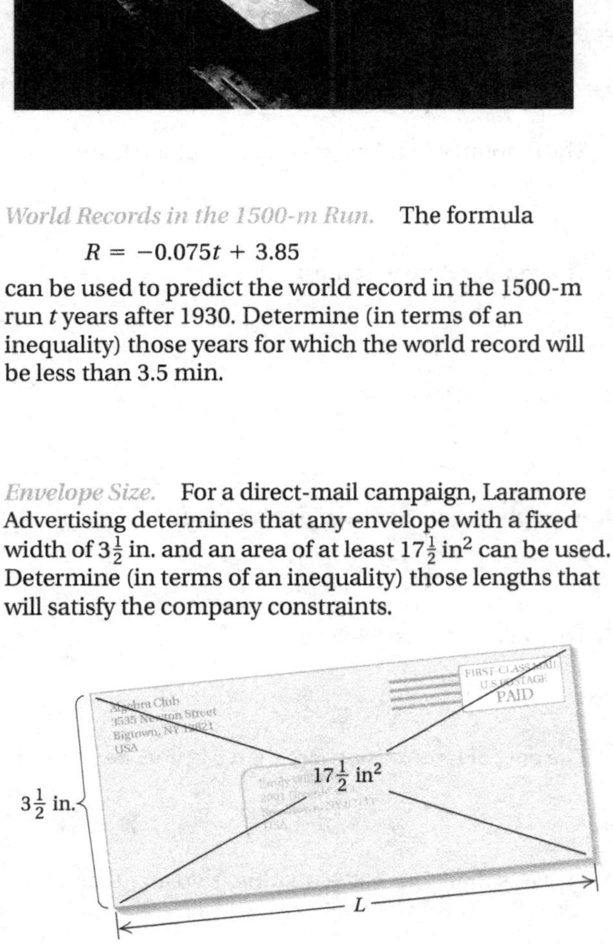

28. *Package Sizes.* Logan Delivery Service accepts packages of up to 165 in. in length and girth combined. (Girth is the distance around the package.) A package has a fixed girth of 53 in. Determine (in terms of an inequality) those lengths for which a package is acceptable.

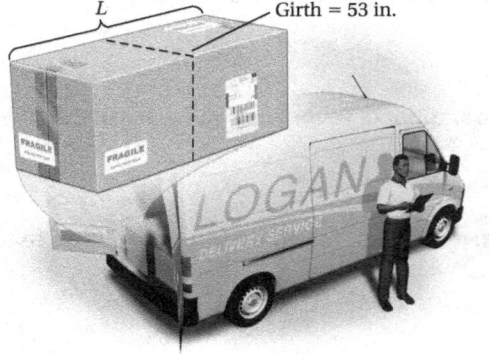

29. *Blueprints.* To make copies of blueprints, Vantage Reprographics charges a \$5 setup fee plus \$4 per copy. Myra can spend no more than \$65 for copying her blueprints. What numbers of copies will allow her to stay within budget?

30. *Banquet Costs.* The Shepard College women's volleyball team can spend at most \$450 for its awards banquet at a local restaurant. If the restaurant charges a \$40 setup fee plus \$16 per person, at most how many can attend?

31. *Phone Costs.* Simon claims that it costs him at least \$3.00 every time he calls an overseas customer. If his typical call costs 75¢ plus 45¢ for each minute, how long do his calls typically last? (*Hint*: 75¢ = \$0.75.)

32. *Parking Costs.* Laura is certain that every time she parks in the municipal garage it costs her at least \$6.75. If the garage charges \$1.50 plus 75¢ for each half hour, for how long is Laura's car generally parked?

33. *College Tuition.* Angelica's financial aid stipulates that her tuition cannot exceed \$1000. If her local community college charges a \$35 registration fee plus \$375 per course, what is the greatest number of courses for which Angelica can register?

34. *Furnace Repairs.* RJ's Plumbing and Heating charges \$45 plus \$30 per hour for emergency service. Gary remembers being billed over \$150 for an emergency call. How long was RJ's there?

35. *Nutrition.* Following the guidelines of the Food and Drug Administration, Dale tries to eat at least 5 servings of fruits or vegetables each day. For the first six days of one week, he had 4, 6, 7, 4, 6, and 4 servings. How many servings of fruits or vegetables should Dale eat on Saturday, in order to average at least 5 servings per day for the week?

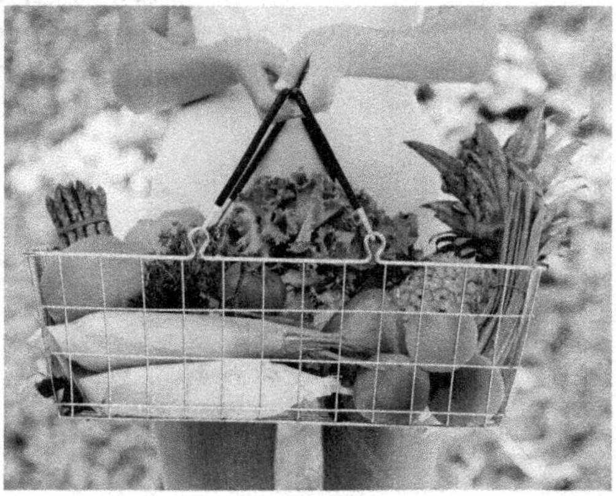

36. *College Course Load.* To remain on financial aid, Millie needs to complete an average of at least 7 credits per quarter each year. In the first three quarters of 2009, Millie completed 5, 7, and 8 credits. How many credits of course work must Millie complete in the fourth quarter if she is to remain on financial aid?

37. *Perimeter of a Rectangle.* The width of a rectangle is fixed at 8 ft. What lengths will make the perimeter at least 200 ft? at most 200 ft?

38. *Perimeter of a Triangle.* One side of a triangle is 2 cm shorter than the base. The other side is 3 cm longer than the base. What lengths of the base will allow the perimeter to be greater than 19 cm?

39. *Area of a Rectangle.* The width of a rectangle is fixed at 4 cm. For what lengths will the area be less than 86 cm^2?

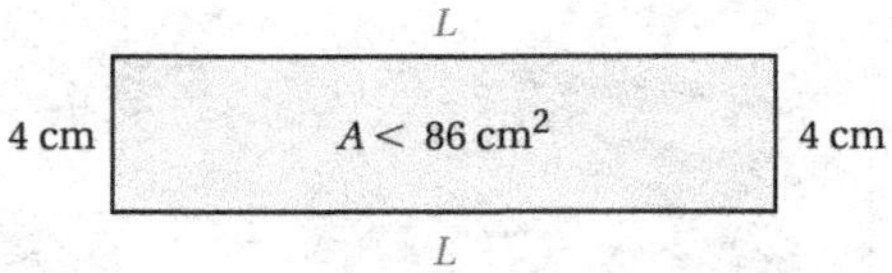

40. *Area of a Rectangle.* The width of a rectangle is fixed at 16 yd. For what lengths will the area be at least 264 yd^2?

41. *Insurance-Covered Repairs.* Most insurance companies will replace a vehicle if an estimated repair exceeds 80% of the "blue-book" value of the vehicle. Michelle's insurance company paid $8500 for repairs to her Subaru after an accident. What can be concluded about the blue-book value of the car?

42. *Insurance-Covered Repairs.* Following an accident, Jeff's Ford pickup was replaced by his insurance company because the damage was so extensive. Before the damage, the blue-book value of the truck was $21,000. How much would it have cost to repair the truck? (See Exercise 41.)

43. *Reduced-Fat Foods.* In order for a food to be labeled "reduced fat," it must have at least 25% less fat than the regular item. One brand of reduced-fat peanut butter contains 12 g of fat per serving. What can you conclude about the fat content in a serving of the brand's regular peanut butter?

44. *Reduced-Fat Foods.* One brand of reduced-fat chocolate chip cookies contains 5 g of fat per serving. What can you conclude about the fat content of the brand's regular chocolate chip cookies? (See Exercise 43.)

45. *Pond Depth.* On July 1, Garrett's Pond was 25 ft deep. Since that date, the water level has dropped $\frac{2}{3}$ ft per week. For what dates will the water level not exceed 21 ft?

46. *Weight Gain.* A 3-lb puppy is gaining weight at a rate of $\frac{3}{4}$ lb per week. When will the puppy's weight exceed $22\frac{1}{2}$ lb?

47. *Area of a Triangular Flag.* As part of an outdoor education course, Wendy needs to make a bright-colored triangular flag with an area of at least 3 ft^2. What heights can the triangle be if the base is $1\frac{1}{2}$ ft?

48. *Area of a Triangular Sign.* Zoning laws in Harrington prohibit displaying signs with areas exceeding 12 ft^2. If Flo's Marina is ordering a triangular sign with an 8-ft base, how tall can the sign be?

49. *Electrician Visits.* Dot's Electric made 17 customer calls last week and 22 calls this week. How many calls must be made next week in order to maintain a weekly average of at least 20 calls for the three-week period?

50. *Volunteer Work.* George and Joan do volunteer work at a hospital. Joan worked 3 more hr than George, and together they worked more than 27 hr. What possible numbers of hours did each work?

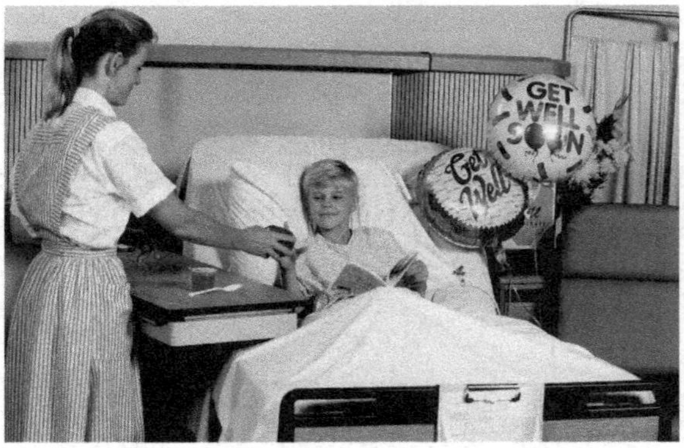

Skill Maintenance

In each of Exercises 51–58, fill in the blank with the correct term from the given list. Some of the choices may not be used.

51. The product of a(n) ______________ number of negative numbers is always positive. [1.5a]

52. The product of a(n) ______________ number of negative numbers is always negative. [1.5a]

53. The ______________ inverse of a negative number is always positive. [1.3b]

54. The ______________ inverse of a negative number is always negative. [1.6b]

55. Equations with the same solutions are called ______________ equations. [2.1b]

56. The ______________ for equations asserts that when we add the same number to the expressions on each side of the equation, we get equivalent equations. [2.1b]

57. The ______________ for inequalities asserts that when we multiply or divide by a negative number on both sides of an inequality, the direction of the inequality symbol ______________. [2.7d]

58. Any replacement for the variable that makes an equation true is called a(n) ______________ of the equation. [2.1a]

addition principle
multiplication principle
solution
value
is reversed
stays the same
even
odd
multiplicative
additive
equivalent

Synthesis

59. *Ski Wax.* Green ski wax works best between 5° and 15° Fahrenheit. Determine those Celsius temperatures for which green ski wax works best. Use the formula given in Margin Exercise 9.

60. *Parking Fees.* Mack's Parking Garage charges $4.00 for the first hour and $2.50 for each additional hour. For how long has a car been parked when the charge exceeds $16.50?

61. *Low-Fat Foods.* In order for a food to be labeled "low fat," it must have fewer than 3 g of fat per serving. One brand of reduced-fat tortilla chips contains 60% less fat than regular nacho cheese tortilla chips, but still cannot be labeled low fat. What can you conclude about the fat content of a serving of nacho cheese tortilla chips?

62. *Parking Fees.* When asked how much the parking charge is for a certain car, Mack replies "between 14 and 24 dollars." For how long has the car been parked? (See Exercise 60.)

CHAPTER 2

Summary and Review

Key Terms and Properties

equation, p. 126
solution of an equation, p. 126
equivalent equations, p. 127
clearing fractions, p. 141
clearing decimals, p. 141
formula, p. 149
evaluating a formula, p. 149
inequality, p. 184
solution set, p. 184
graph of an inequality, p. 184
equivalent inequalities, p. 185
set-builder notation, p.187

The Addition Principle for Equations: For any real numbers a, b, and c, $a = b$ is equivalent to $a + c = b + c$.

The Multiplication Principle for Equations: For any real numbers a, b, and c, $c \neq 0$: $a = b$ is equivalent to $a \cdot c = b \cdot c$.

The Addition Principle for Inequalities: For any real numbers a, b, and c:
$a < b$ is equivalent to $a + c < b + c$;
$a > b$ is equivalent to $a + c > b + c$.
Similar statements hold for $\leq$ and $\geq$.

The Multiplication Principle for Inequalities: For any real numbers a and b, and any *positive* number c:
$a < b$ is equivalent to $ac < bc$; $a > b$ is equivalent to $ac > bc$.
For any real numbers a and b, and any *negative* number c:
$a < b$ is equivalent to $ac > bc$; $a > b$ is equivalent to $ac < bc$.
Similar statements hold for $\leq$ and $\geq$.

Concept Reinforcement

Determine whether each statement is true or false.

_____ **1.** Some equations have no solution. [2.3c]

_____ **2.** For any number n, $n \geq n$. [2.7a]

_____ **3.** $2x - 7 < 11$ and $x < 2$ are equivalent inequalities. [2.7e]

_____ **4.** If $x > y$, then $-x < -y$. [2.7d]

Important Concepts

Objective 2.3a Solve equations using both the addition principle and the multiplication principle.
Objective 2.3b Solve equations in which like terms may need to be collected.
Objective 2.3c Solve equations by first removing parentheses and collecting like terms.

Example Solve: $6y - 2(2y - 3) = 12$.

$$6y - 2(2y - 3) = 12$$
$$6y - 4y + 6 = 12 \quad \text{Removing parentheses}$$
$$2y + 6 = 12 \quad \text{Collecting like terms}$$
$$2y + 6 - 6 = 12 - 6 \quad \text{Subtracting 6}$$
$$2y = 6$$
$$\frac{2y}{2} = \frac{6}{2} \quad \text{Dividing by 2}$$
$$y = 3$$

The solution is 3.

Practice Exercise

1. Solve: $4(x - 3) = 6(x + 2)$.

Objective 2.3c Solve equations with no solutions and equations with an infinite number of solutions.

Example Solve: $8 + 2x - 4 = 6 + 2(x - 1)$.

$$8 + 2x - 4 = 6 + 2(x - 1)$$
$$8 + 2x - 4 = 6 + 2x - 2$$
$$2x + 4 = 2x + 4$$
$$2x + 4 - 2x = 2x + 4 - 2x$$
$$4 = 4$$

Every real number is a solution of the equation $4 = 4$, so all real numbers are solutions of the original equation. The equation has infinitely many solutions.

Example Solve: $2 + 5(x - 1) = -6 + 5x + 7$.

$$2 + 5(x - 1) = -6 + 5x + 7$$
$$2 + 5x - 5 = -6 + 5x + 7$$
$$5x - 3 = 5x + 1$$
$$5x - 3 - 5x = 5x + 1 - 5x$$
$$-3 = 1$$

This is a false equation, so the original equation has no solution.

Practice Exercises

2. Solve: $4 + 3y - 7 = 3 + 3(y - 2)$.

3. Solve: $4(x - 3) + 7 = -5 + 4x + 10$.

Objective 2.4b Solve a formula for a specified letter.

Example Solve for n: $M = \dfrac{m + n}{5}$.

$$M = \frac{m + n}{5}$$
$$5 \cdot M = 5\left(\frac{m + n}{5}\right)$$
$$5M = m + n$$
$$5M - m = m + n - m$$
$$5M - m = n$$

Practice Exercise

4. Solve for b: $A = \frac{1}{2}bh$.

Objective 2.7b Graph an inequality on the number line.

Example Graph each inequality: **(a)** $x < 2$; **(b)** $x \geq -3$.

a) The solutions of $x < 2$ are all numbers less than 2. We shade all points to the left of 2, and we use an open circle at 2 to indicate that 2 *is not* part of the graph.

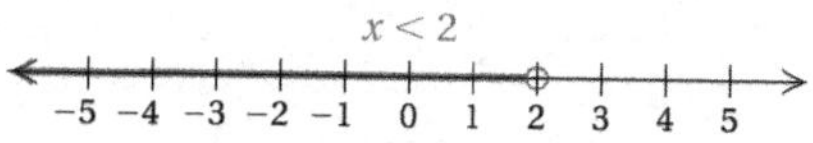

b) The solutions of $x \geq -3$ are all numbers greater than −3 and the number −3 as well. We shade all points to the right of −3, and we use a closed circle at −3 to indicate that −3 *is* part of the graph.

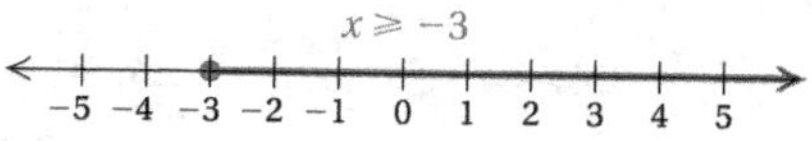

Practice Exercises

5. Graph: $x > 1$.

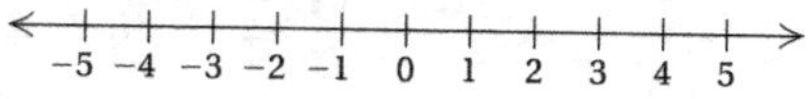

6. Graph: $x \leq -1$.

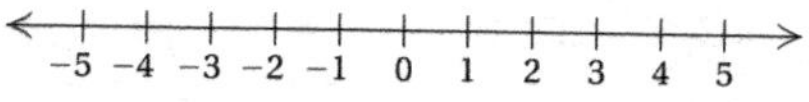

Objective 2.7e Solve inequalities using the addition principle and the multiplication principle together.

Example Solve: $8y - 7 \le 5y + 2$.

$$8y - 7 \le 5y + 2$$
$$8y - 7 - 8y \le 5y + 2 - 8y$$
$$-7 \le -3y + 2$$
$$-7 - 2 \le -3y + 2 - 2$$
$$-9 \le -3y$$
$$\frac{-9}{-3} \ge \frac{-3y}{-3} \quad \text{Reversing the symbol}$$
$$3 \ge y$$

The solution set is $\{y \mid 3 \ge y\}$, or $\{y \mid y \le 3\}$.

Practice Exercise

7. Solve: $6y + 5 > 3y - 7$.

Review Exercises

Solve. [2.1b]

1. $x + 5 = -17$

2. $n - 7 = -6$

3. $x - 11 = 14$

4. $y - 0.9 = 9.09$

Solve. [2.2a]

5. $-\frac{2}{3}x = -\frac{1}{6}$

6. $-8x = -56$

7. $-\frac{x}{4} = 48$

8. $15x = -35$

9. $\frac{4}{5}y = -\frac{3}{16}$

Solve. [2.3a]

10. $5 - x = 13$

11. $\frac{1}{4}x - \frac{5}{8} = \frac{3}{8}$

Solve. [2.3b, c]

12. $5t + 9 = 3t - 1$

13. $7x - 6 = 25x$

14. $14y = 23y - 17 - 10$

15. $0.22y - 0.6 = 0.12y + 3 - 0.8y$

16. $\frac{1}{4}x - \frac{1}{8}x = 3 - \frac{1}{16}x$

17. $14y + 17 + 7y = 9 + 21y + 8$

18. $4(x + 3) = 36$

19. $3(5x - 7) = -66$

20. $8(x - 2) - 5(x + 4) = 20 + x$

21. $-5x + 3(x + 8) = 16$

22. $6(x - 2) - 16 = 3(2x - 5) + 11$

Determine whether the given number is a solution of the inequality $x \le 4$. [2.7a]

23. -3

24. 7

25. 4

Solve. Write set notation for the answers. [2.7c, d, e]

26. $y + \frac{2}{3} \geq \frac{1}{6}$

27. $9x \geq 63$

28. $2 + 6y > 14$

29. $7 - 3y \geq 27 + 2y$

30. $3x + 5 < 2x - 6$

31. $-4y < 28$

32. $4 - 8x < 13 + 3x$

33. $-4x \leq \frac{1}{3}$

Graph on the number line. [2.7b, e]

34. $4x - 6 < x + 3$

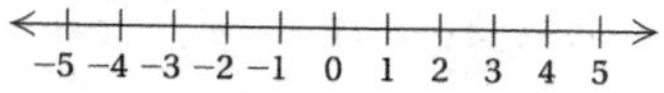

35. $-2 < x \leq 5$

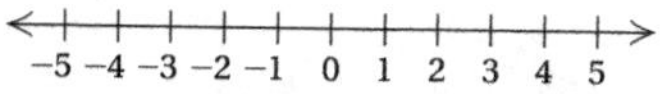

36. $y > 0$

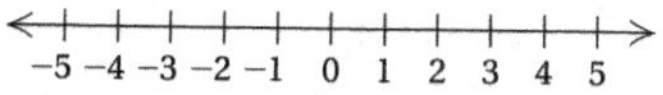

Solve. [2.4b]

37. $C = \pi d$, for d

38. $V = \frac{1}{3}Bh$, for B

39. $A = \frac{a + b}{2}$, for a

40. $y = mx + b$, for x

Solve. [2.6a]

41. *Dimensions of Wyoming.* The state of Wyoming is roughly in the shape of a rectangle whose perimeter is 1280 mi. The length is 90 mi more than the width. Find the dimensions.

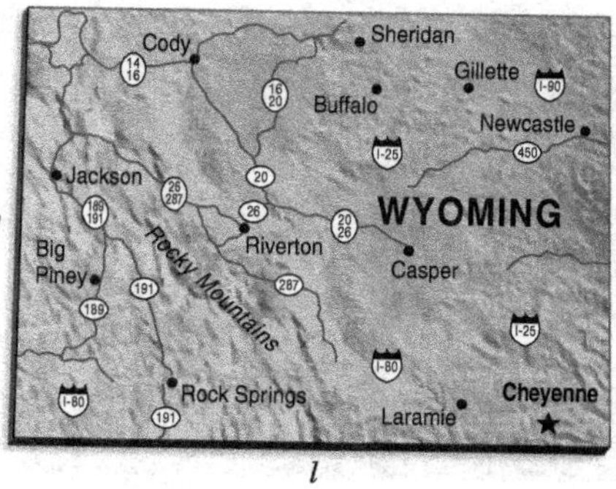

w

l

42. *Interstate Mile Markers.* The sum of two consecutive mile markers on I-5 in California is 691. Find the numbers on the markers.

43. An entertainment center sold for $2449 in June. This was $332 more than the cost in February. What was the cost in February?

44. Ty is paid a commission of $4 for each magazine subscription he sells. One week, he received $108 in commissions. How many subscriptions did he sell?

45. The measure of the second angle of a triangle is 50° more than that of the first angle. The measure of the third angle is 10° less than twice the first angle. Find the measures of the angles.

Solve. [2.5a]

46. What number is 20% of 75?

47. Fifteen is what percent of 80?

48. 18 is 3% of what number?

49. *Job Opportunities.* There were 1.388 million child-care workers in 2006. The number of job opportunities in that field is expected to grow to 1.636 million by 2016. What is the percent of increase?

Source: *Occupational Outlook Handbook*

Solve. [2.6a]

50. After a 30% reduction, a bread maker is on sale for \$154. What was the marked price (the price before the reduction)?

51. A hotel manager's salary is \$61,410, which is a 15% increase over the previous year's salary. What was the previous salary?

52. A tax-exempt organization received a bill of \$145.90 for janitorial supplies. The bill incorrectly included sales tax of 5%. How much does the organization actually owe?

Solve. [2.8b]

53. *Test Scores.* Jacinda's test grades are 71, 75, 82, and 86. What is the lowest grade that she can get on the next test and still have an average test score of at least 80?

54. The length of a rectangle is 43 cm. What widths will make the perimeter greater than 120 cm?

55. The solution of the equation $4(3x - 5) + 6 = 8 + x$ is which of the following? [2.3c]

A. Less than -1
B. Between -1 and 1
C. Between 1 and 5
D. Greater than 5

56. Solve for y: $3x + 4y = P$. [2.4b]

A. $y = \dfrac{P - 3x}{4}$
B. $y = \dfrac{P + 3x}{4}$
C. $y = P - \dfrac{3x}{4}$
D. $y = \dfrac{P}{4} - 3x$

Synthesis

Solve.

57. $2|x| + 4 = 50$ [1.2e], [2.3a]

58. $|3x| = 60$ [1.2e], [2.2a]

59. $y = 2a - ab + 3$, for a [2.4b]

Understanding Through Discussion and Writing

1. Would it be better to receive a 5% raise and then an 8% raise or the other way around? Why? [2.5a]

2. Erin returns a tent that she bought during a storewide 25%-off sale that has ended. She is offered store credit for 125% of what she paid (not to be used on sale items). Is this fair to Erin? Why or why not? [2.5a]

3. Are the inequalities $x > -5$ and $-x < 5$ equivalent? Why or why not? [2.7d]

4. Explain in your own words why it is necessary to reverse the inequality symbol when multiplying on both sides of an inequality by a negative number. [2.7d]

5. If f represents Fran's age and t represents Todd's age, write a sentence that would translate to $t + 3 < f$. [2.8a]

6. Explain how the meanings of "Five more than a number" and "Five is more than a number" differ. [2.8a]

CHAPTER 2

Test

For Extra Help

CHAPTER Test Prep VIDEOS

Step-by-step test solutions are found on the Chapter Test Prep Videos available via the Video Resources on DVD, in MyMathLab, and on YouTube (search "BittingerIntroAlg" and click on "Channels").

Solve.

1. $x + 7 = 15$

2. $t - 9 = 17$

3. $3x = -18$

4. $-\frac{4}{7}x = -28$

5. $3t + 7 = 2t - 5$

6. $\frac{1}{2}x - \frac{3}{5} = \frac{2}{5}$

7. $8 - y = 16$

8. $-\frac{2}{5} + x = -\frac{3}{4}$

9. $3(x + 2) = 27$

10. $-3x - 6(x - 4) = 9$

11. $0.4p + 0.2 = 4.2p - 7.8 - 0.6p$

12. $4(3x - 1) + 11 = 2(6x + 5) - 8$

13. $-2 + 7x + 6 = 5x + 4 + 2x$

Solve. Write set notation for the answers.

14. $x + 6 \le 2$

15. $14x + 9 > 13x - 4$

16. $12x \le 60$

17. $-2y \ge 26$

18. $-4y \le -32$

19. $-5x \ge \frac{1}{4}$

20. $4 - 6x > 40$

21. $5 - 9x \ge 19 + 5x$

Graph on the number line.

22. $y \le 9$

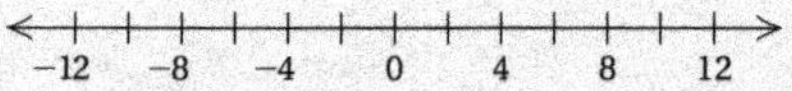

23. $6x - 3 < x + 2$

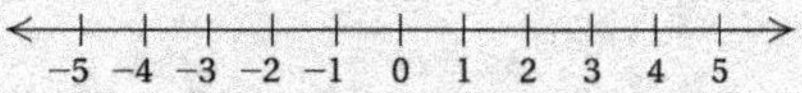

24. $-2 \le x \le 2$

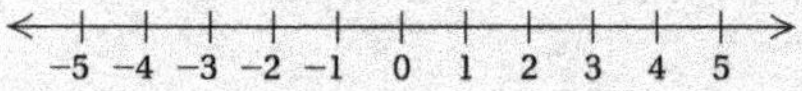

Solve.

25. What number is 24% of 75?

26. 15.84 is what percent of 96?

27. 800 is 2% of what number?

28. *Job Opportunities.* The number of job opportunities for physician's assistants is expected to increase from 66,000 in 2006 to 83,000 in 2016. What is the percent of increase?

Source: *Occupational Outlook Handbook*

29. *Perimeter of a Photograph.* The perimeter of a rectangular photograph is 36 cm. The length is 4 cm greater than the width. Find the width and the length.

30. *Charitable Contributions.* About $102.3 billion was given to religious organizations in 2007. This represents 33% of all charitable donations that year. How much was donated to all charities?

Sources: Giving USA Foundation; Center on Philanthropy at Indiana University

31. *Raffle Tickets.* The numbers on three raffle tickets are consecutive integers whose sum is 7530. Find the integers.

32. *Savings Account.* Money is invested in a savings account at 5% simple interest. After 1 year, there is $924 in the account. How much was originally invested?

33. *Board Cutting.* An 8-m board is cut into two pieces. One piece is 2 m longer than the other. How long are the pieces?

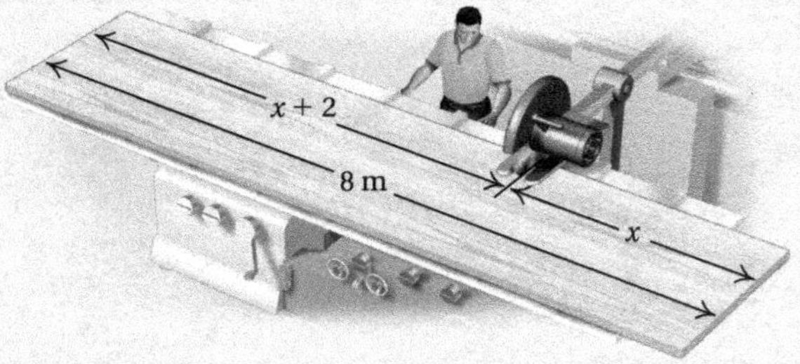

34. *Lengths of a Rectangle.* The width of a rectangle is 96 yd. Find all possible lengths such that the perimeter of the rectangle will be at least 540 yd.

35. *Budgeting.* Jason has budgeted an average of $95 per month for entertainment. For the first five months of the year, he has spent $98, $89, $110, $85, and $83. How much can Jason spend in the sixth month without exceeding his average budget?

36. *Copy Machine Rental.* A catalog publisher needs to lease a copy machine for use during a special project that they anticipate will take 3 months. It costs $225 per month plus 1.2¢ per copy to rent the machine. The company must stay within a budget of $2400 for copies. Determine (in terms of an inequality) the number of copies they can make and still remain within budget.

37. Solve $A = 2\pi rh$ for r.

38. Solve $y = 8x + b$ for x.

39. *Senior Population.* The number of Americans age 65 and older is projected to grow from 40.4 million to 70.3 million between 2011 and 2030. Find the percent of increase.

Source: U.S. Census Bureau

A. 42.5% **B.** 47%
C. 57.5% **D.** 74%

Synthesis

40. Solve $c = \dfrac{1}{a - d}$ for d.

41. Solve: $3|w| - 8 = 37$.

42. A movie theater had a certain number of tickets to give away. Five people got the tickets. The first got one-third of the tickets, the second got one-fourth of the tickets, and the third got one-fifth of the tickets. The fourth person got eight tickets, and there were five tickets left for the fifth person. Find the total number of tickets given away.

CHAPTERS 1-2

Cumulative Review

Evaluate.

1. $\frac{y - x}{4}$, when $y = 12$ and $x = 6$

2. $\frac{3x}{y}$, when $x = 5$ and $y = 4$

3. $x - 3$, when $x = 3$

4. Translate to an algebraic expression: Four less than twice w.

Use $<$ or $>$ for □ to write a true sentence.

5. -4 □ -6

6. 0 □ -5

7. -8 □ 7

8. Find the opposite and the reciprocal of $\frac{2}{5}$.

Find the absolute value.

9. $|3|$

10. $\left|-\frac{3}{4}\right|$

11. $|0|$

Compute and simplify.

12. $-6.7 + 2.3$

13. $-\frac{1}{6} - \frac{7}{3}$

14. $-\frac{5}{8}\left(-\frac{4}{3}\right)$

15. $(-7)(5)(-6)(-0.5)$

16. $81 \div (-9)$

17. $-10.8 \div 3.6$

18. $-\frac{4}{5} \div -\frac{25}{8}$

Multiply.

19. $5(3x + 5y + 2z)$

20. $4(-3x - 2)$

21. $-6(2y - 4x)$

Factor.

22. $64 + 18x + 24y$

23. $16y - 56$

24. $5a - 15b + 25$

Collect like terms.

25. $9b + 18y + 6b + 4y$

26. $3y + 4 + 6z + 6y$

27. $-4d - 6a + 3a - 5d + 1$

28. $3.2x + 2.9y - 5.8x - 8.1y$

Simplify.

29. $7 - 2x - (-5x) - 8$

30. $-3x - (-x + y)$

31. $-3(x - 2) - 4x$

32. $10 - 2(5 - 4x)$

33. $[3(x + 6) - 10] - [5 - 2(x - 8)]$

Solve.

34. $x + 1.75 = 6.25$

35. $\frac{5}{2}y = \frac{2}{5}$

36. $-2.6 + x = 8.3$

37. $4\frac{1}{2} + y = 8\frac{1}{3}$

38. $-\frac{3}{4}x = 36$

39. $\frac{2}{5}x = -\frac{3}{20}$

40. $5.8x = -35.96$

41. $-4x + 3 = 15$

42. $-3x + 5 = -8x - 7$

43. $4y - 4 + y = 6y + 20 - 4y$

44. $-3(x - 2) = -15$

45. $\frac{1}{3}x - \frac{5}{6} = \frac{1}{2} + 2x$

46. $-3.7x + 6.2 = -7.3x - 5.8$

47. $4(x + 2) = 4(x - 2) + 16$

48. $0(x + 3) + 4 = 0$

49. $3x - 1 < 2x + 1$

50. $3y + 7 > 5y + 13$

51. $5 - y \leq 2y - 7$

52. $H = 65 - m$, for m
(To determine the number of heating degree days H for a day with m degrees Fahrenheit as the average temperature)

53. $I = Prt$, for t
(Simple-interest formula, where I is interest, P is principal, r is interest rate, and t is time)

54. What number is 24% of 105?

55. 39.6 is what percent of 88?

56. $163.35 is 45% of what?

57. *Price Reduction.* After a 25% reduction, a tie is on sale for $18.45. What was the price before reduction?

58. *Rollerblade Costs.* Susan and Melinda purchased rollerblades for a total of $107. Susan paid $17 more for her rollerblades than Melinda did. What did Melinda pay?

59. *Savings Investment.* Money is invested in a savings account at 8% simple interest. After 1 year, there is $1134 in the account. How much was originally invested?

60. *Wire Cutting.* A 143-m wire is cut into three pieces. The second piece is 3 m longer than the first. The third is four-fifths as long as the first. How long is each piece?

61. *Grade Average.* Nadia is taking a literature course in which four tests are given. To get a B, a student must average at least 80 on the four tests. Nadia scored 82, 76, and 78 on the first three tests. What scores on the last test will earn her at least a B?

62. Simplify: $-125 \div 25 \cdot 625 \div 5$.

A. $-390{,}625$ **B.** -125
C. -625 **D.** 25

Synthesis

63. An engineer's salary at the end of a year is $48,418.24. This reflects a 4% salary increase and a later 3% cost-of-living adjustment during the year. What was the salary at the beginning of the year?

64. Grace needs to use a copier to reduce a drawing to fit on a page. The original drawing is 9 in. long and it must fit into a space that is 6.3 in. long. By what percent should she reduce the drawing on the copier?

Solve.

65. $4|x| - 13 = 3$

66. $\frac{2 + 5x}{4} = \frac{11}{28} + \frac{8x + 3}{7}$

67. $p = \frac{2}{m + Q}$, for Q

Polynomials: Operations

CHAPTER

3

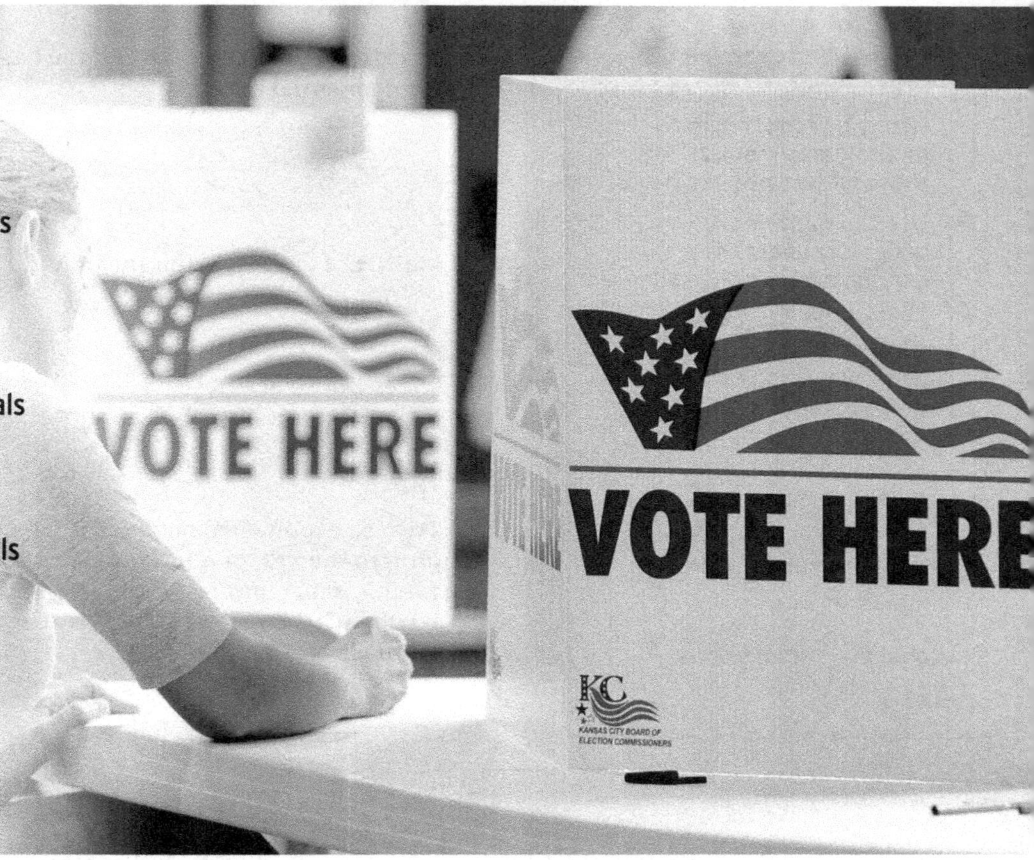

Real-World Application

About 22,750,000 young people, ages 18–29, voted in the 2008 presidential election. Convert the number 22,750,000 to scientific notation.

Source: Center for Information & Research on Civic Learning and Engagement, Tufts University

This problem appears as Exercise 64 in Section 3.2.

3.1 Integers as Exponents

OBJECTIVES

- **a** Tell the meaning of exponential notation.
- **b** Evaluate exponential expressions with exponents of 0 and 1.
- **c** Evaluate algebraic expressions containing exponents.
- **d** Use the product rule to multiply exponential expressions with like bases.
- **e** Use the quotient rule to divide exponential expressions with like bases.
- **f** Express an exponential expression involving negative exponents with positive exponents.

SKILL TO REVIEW
Objective 1.1a: Evaluate algebraic expressions by substitution.

1. Evaluate $6y$ when $y = 4$.
2. Evaluate $\frac{m}{n}$ when $m = 48$ and $n = 8$.

We introduced integer exponents of 2 or higher in Section R.5. Here we consider 0, 1, and negative integers as exponents.

a Exponential Notation

An exponent of 2 or greater tells how many times the base is used as a factor. For example,

$$a \cdot a \cdot a \cdot a = a^4.$$

In this case, the **exponent** is 4 and the **base** is a. An expression for a power is called **exponential notation**.

a^n ← This is the exponent.
↑
This is the base.

EXAMPLE 1 What is the meaning of 3^5? of n^4? of $(2n)^3$? of $50x^2$? of $(-n)^3$? of $-n^3$?

3^5 means $3 \cdot 3 \cdot 3 \cdot 3 \cdot 3$; n^4 means $n \cdot n \cdot n \cdot n$;
$(2n)^3$ means $2n \cdot 2n \cdot 2n$; $50x^2$ means $50 \cdot x \cdot x$;
$(-n)^3$ means $(-n) \cdot (-n) \cdot (-n)$; $-n^3$ means $-1 \cdot n \cdot n \cdot n$

Do Margin Exercises 1–6.

What is the meaning of each of the following?

1. 5^4
2. x^5
3. $(3t)^2$
4. $3t^2$
5. $(-x)^4$
6. $-y^3$

We read exponential notation as follows: a^n is read the ***n*th power of *a***, or simply ***a* to the *n*th**, or ***a* to the *n***. We often read x^2 as "***x*-squared**." The reason for this is that the area of a square of side x is $x \cdot x$, or x^2. We often read x^3 as "***x*-cubed**." The reason for this is that the volume of a cube with length, width, and height x is $x \cdot x \cdot x$, or x^3.

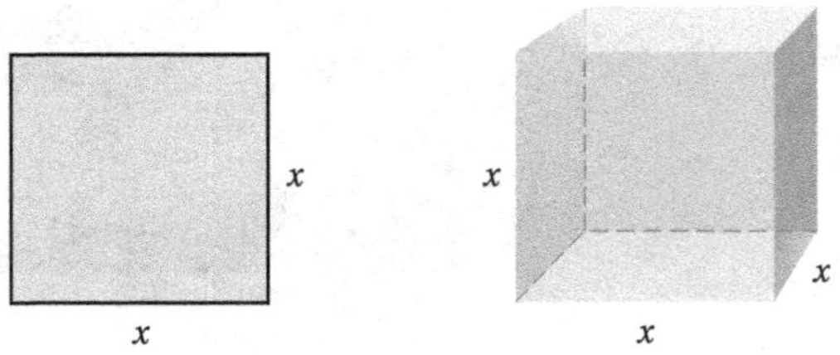

b One and Zero as Exponents

Look for a pattern in the following:

On each side, we **divide** by 8 at each step.		On this side, the exponents **decrease** by 1 at each step.
	$8 \cdot 8 \cdot 8 \cdot 8 = 8^4$	
	$8 \cdot 8 \cdot 8 = 8^3$	
	$8 \cdot 8 = 8^2$	
	$8 = 8^?$	
	$1 = 8^?$.	

To continue the pattern, we would say that

$$8 = 8^1 \quad \text{and} \quad 1 = 8^0.$$

Answers

Skill to Review:
1. 24 2. 6

Margin Exercises:
1. $5 \cdot 5 \cdot 5 \cdot 5$ 2. $x \cdot x \cdot x \cdot x \cdot x$
3. $3t \cdot 3t$ 4. $3 \cdot t \cdot t$
5. $(-x) \cdot (-x) \cdot (-x) \cdot (-x)$
6. $-1 \cdot y \cdot y \cdot y$

We make the following definition.

EXPONENTS OF 0 AND 1

$a^1 = a$, for any number a;
$a^0 = 1$, for any nonzero number a

We consider 0^0 to be not defined. We will explain why later in this section.

EXAMPLE 2 Evaluate 5^1, $(-8)^1$, 3^0, $(-7.3)^0$, and $(186{,}892{,}046)^0$.

$5^1 = 5$; $(-8)^1 = -8$; $3^0 = 1$;
$(-7.3)^0 = 1$; $(186{,}892{,}046)^0 = 1$

Do Exercises 7-12.

Evaluate.

7. 6^1
8. 7^0
9. $(8.4)^1$
10. 8654^0
11. $(-1.4)^1$
12. 0^1

c Evaluating Algebraic Expressions

Algebraic expressions can involve exponential notation. For example, the following are algebraic expressions:

$$x^4, \quad (3x)^3 - 2, \quad a^2 + 2ab + b^2.$$

We evaluate algebraic expressions by replacing variables with numbers and following the rules for order of operations.

EXAMPLE 3 Evaluate $1000 - x^4$ when $x = 5$.

$$\begin{aligned} 1000 - x^4 &= 1000 - 5^4 \quad \text{Substituting} \\ &= 1000 - 5 \cdot 5 \cdot 5 \cdot 5 \\ &= 1000 - 625 \\ &= 375 \end{aligned}$$

EXAMPLE 4 *Area of a Compact Disc.* The standard compact disc used for software and music has a radius of 6 cm. Find the area of such a CD (ignoring the hole in the middle).

$$\begin{aligned} A &= \pi r^2 \\ &= \pi \cdot (6\text{ cm})^2 \\ &= \pi \cdot 6\text{ cm} \cdot 6\text{ cm} \\ &\approx 3.14 \times 36\text{ cm}^2 \\ &= 113.04\text{ cm}^2 \end{aligned}$$

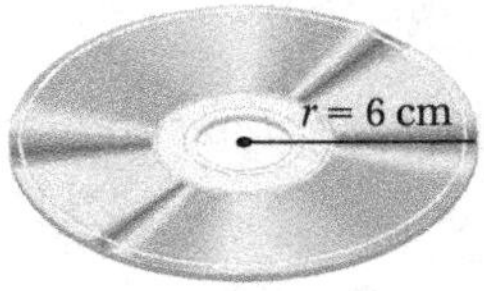

In Example 4, "cm^2" means "square centimeters" and "$\approx$" means "is approximately equal to."

EXAMPLE 5 Evaluate $(5x)^3$ when $x = -2$.

When we evaluate with a negative number, we often use extra parentheses to show the substitution.

$$\begin{aligned} (5x)^3 &= [5 \cdot (-2)]^3 \quad \text{Substituting} \\ &= [-10]^3 \quad \text{Multiplying within brackets first} \\ &= [-10] \cdot [-10] \cdot [-10] \\ &= -1000 \quad \text{Evaluating the power} \end{aligned}$$

STUDY TIPS

HELPING OTHERS HELPS YOU

When you are confident in your command of a topic, don't hesitate to help classmates who are having trouble understanding it. You will find that your understanding and retention of a concept will deepen when you explain it to someone else.

Answers

7. 6 8. 1 9. 8.4 10. 1
11. −1.4 12. 0

13. Evaluate t^3 when $t = 5$.

14. Evaluate $-5x^5$ when $x = -2$.

15. Find the area of a circle when $r = 32$ cm. Use 3.14 for π.

16. Evaluate $200 - a^4$ when $a = 3$.

17. Evaluate $t^1 - 4$ and $t^0 - 4$ when $t = 7$.

18. a) Evaluate $(4t)^2$ when $t = -3$.
    b) Evaluate $4t^2$ when $t = -3$.
    c) Determine whether $(4t)^2$ and $4t^2$ are equivalent.

EXAMPLE 6 Evaluate $5x^3$ when $x = -2$.

$$\begin{aligned} 5x^3 &= 5 \cdot (-2)^3 && \text{Substituting} \\ &= 5 \cdot (-2) \cdot (-2) \cdot (-2) && \text{Evaluating the power first} \\ &= 5(-8) && (-2)(-2)(-2) = -8 \\ &= -40 \end{aligned}$$

Recall that two expressions are equivalent if they have the same value for all meaningful replacements. Note that Examples 5 and 6 show that $(5x)^3$ and $5x^3$ are *not* equivalent—that is, $(5x)^3 \neq 5x^3$.

Do Exercises 13–18.

d Multiplying Powers with Like Bases

There are several rules for manipulating exponential notation to obtain equivalent expressions. We first consider multiplying powers with like bases:

$$a^3 \cdot a^2 = \underbrace{(a \cdot a \cdot a)}_{\text{3 factors}}\underbrace{(a \cdot a)}_{\text{2 factors}} = \underbrace{a \cdot a \cdot a \cdot a \cdot a}_{\text{5 factors}} = a^5.$$

Since an integer exponent greater than 1 tells how many times we use a base as a factor, then $(a \cdot a \cdot a)(a \cdot a) = a \cdot a \cdot a \cdot a \cdot a = a^5$ by the associative law. Note that the exponent in a^5 is the sum of those in $a^3 \cdot a^2$. That is, $3 + 2 = 5$. Likewise,

$$b^4 \cdot b^3 = (b \cdot b \cdot b \cdot b)(b \cdot b \cdot b) = b^7, \quad \text{where} \quad 4 + 3 = 7.$$

Adding the exponents gives the correct result.

THE PRODUCT RULE

For any number a and any positive integers m and n,

$$a^m \cdot a^n = a^{m+n}.$$

(When multiplying with exponential notation, if the bases are the same, keep the base and add the exponents.)

EXAMPLES Multiply and simplify.

7. $5^6 \cdot 5^2 = 5^{6+2}$ Adding exponents: $a^m \cdot a^n = a^{m+n}$
   $= 5^8$

8. $m^5 m^{10} m^3 = m^{5+10+3} = m^{18}$

9. $x \cdot x^8 = x^1 \cdot x^8$ Writing x as x^1
   $= x^{1+8}$
   $= x^9$

10. $(a^3b^2)(a^3b^5) = (a^3a^3)(b^2b^5)$
    $= a^6b^7$

11. $(4y)^6(4y)^3 = (4y)^{6+3} = (4y)^9$

Do Exercises 19–23.

Multiply and simplify.

19. $3^5 \cdot 3^5$

20. $x^4 \cdot x^6$

21. $p^4p^{12}p^8$

22. $x \cdot x^4$

23. $(a^2b^3)(a^7b^5)$

Answers

13. 125 14. 160 15. 3215.36 cm^2 16. 119 17. 3; −3 18. (a) 144; (b) 36; (c) no 19. 3^{10} 20. x^{10} 21. p^{24} 22. x^5 23. a^9b^8

e Dividing Powers with Like Bases

The following suggests a rule for dividing powers with like bases, such as a^5/a^2:

$$\frac{a^5}{a^2} = \frac{a \cdot a \cdot a \cdot a \cdot a}{a \cdot a} = \frac{a \cdot a \cdot a \cdot a \cdot a}{1 \cdot a \cdot a} = \frac{a \cdot a \cdot a}{1} \cdot \frac{a \cdot a}{a \cdot a}$$

$$= \frac{a \cdot a \cdot a}{1} \cdot 1 = a \cdot a \cdot a = a^3.$$

Note that the exponent in a^3 is the difference of those in $a^5 \div a^2$. That is, $5 - 2 = 3$. In a similar way, we have

$$\frac{t^9}{t^4} = \frac{t \cdot t \cdot t \cdot t \cdot t \cdot t \cdot t \cdot t \cdot t}{t \cdot t \cdot t \cdot t} = t^5, \text{ where } 9 - 4 = 5.$$

Subtracting exponents gives the correct answer.

THE QUOTIENT RULE

For any nonzero number a and any positive integers m and n,

$$\frac{a^m}{a^n} = a^{m-n}.$$

(When dividing with exponential notation, if the bases are the same, keep the base and subtract the exponent of the denominator from the exponent of the numerator.)

EXAMPLES Divide and simplify.

12. $\dfrac{6^5}{6^3} = 6^{5-3}$ Subtracting exponents

$= 6^2$

13. $\dfrac{x^8}{x^1} = x^{8-1}$

$= x^7$

14. $\dfrac{(3t)^{12}}{(3t)^2} = (3t)^{12-2}$

$= (3t)^{10}$

15. $\dfrac{p^5q^7}{p^2q^5} = \dfrac{p^5}{p^2} \cdot \dfrac{q^7}{q^5} = p^{5-2}q^{7-5}$

$= p^3q^2$

The quotient rule can also be used to explain the definition of 0 as an exponent. Consider the expression a^4/a^4, where a is nonzero:

$$\frac{a^4}{a^4} = \frac{a \cdot a \cdot a \cdot a}{a \cdot a \cdot a \cdot a} = 1.$$

This is true because the numerator and the denominator are the same. Now suppose we apply the rule for dividing powers with the same base:

$$\frac{a^4}{a^4} = a^{4-4} = a^0.$$

Since $a^4/a^4 = 1$ and $a^4/a^4 = a^0$, it follows that $a^0 = 1$, when $a \neq 0$.

We can explain why we do not define 0^0 using the quotient rule. We know that 0^0 is 0^{1-1}. But 0^{1-1} is also equal to $0^1/0^1$, or $0/0$. We have already seen that division by 0 is not defined, so 0^0 is also not defined.

Do Exercises 24–27.

Divide and simplify.

24. $\dfrac{4^5}{4^2}$

25. $\dfrac{y^6}{y^2}$

26. $\dfrac{p^{10}}{p}$

27. $\dfrac{a^7b^6}{a^3b^4}$

Answers

24. 4^3 25. y^4 26. p^9 27. a^4b^2

f Negative Integers as Exponents

We can use the rule for dividing powers with like bases to lead us to a definition of exponential notation when the exponent is a negative integer. Consider $5^3/5^7$ and first simplify it using procedures we have learned for working with fractions:

$$\frac{5^3}{5^7} = \frac{5 \cdot 5 \cdot 5}{5 \cdot 5 \cdot 5 \cdot 5 \cdot 5 \cdot 5 \cdot 5} = \frac{5 \cdot 5 \cdot 5 \cdot 1}{5 \cdot 5 \cdot 5 \cdot 5 \cdot 5 \cdot 5 \cdot 5}$$

$$= \frac{5 \cdot 5 \cdot 5}{5 \cdot 5 \cdot 5} \cdot \frac{1}{5 \cdot 5 \cdot 5 \cdot 5} = \frac{1}{5^4}.$$

Now we apply the rule for dividing exponential expressions with the same bases. Then

$$\frac{5^3}{5^7} = 5^{3-7} = 5^{-4}.$$

From these two expressions for $5^3/5^7$, it follows that

$$5^{-4} = \frac{1}{5^4}.$$

This leads to our definition of negative exponents.

NEGATIVE EXPONENT

For any real number a that is nonzero and any integer n,

$$a^{-n} = \frac{1}{a^n}.$$

In fact, the numbers a^n and a^{-n} are reciprocals because

$$a^n \cdot a^{-n} = a^n \cdot \frac{1}{a^n} = \frac{a^n}{a^n} = 1.$$

The following is another way to arrive at the definition of negative exponents.

On each side, we **divide** by 5 at each step.

$$5 \cdot 5 \cdot 5 \cdot 5 = 5^4$$
$$5 \cdot 5 \cdot 5 = 5^3$$
$$5 \cdot 5 = 5^2$$
$$5 = 5^1$$
$$1 = 5^0$$
$$\frac{1}{5} = 5^?$$
$$\frac{1}{25} = 5^?$$

On this side, the exponents **decrease** by 1 at each step.

To continue the pattern, it should follow that

$$\frac{1}{5} = \frac{1}{5^1} = 5^{-1} \quad \text{and} \quad \frac{1}{25} = \frac{1}{5^2} = 5^{-2}.$$

EXAMPLES Express using positive exponents. Then simplify.

16. $4^{-2} = \frac{1}{4^2} = \frac{1}{16}$

17. $(-3)^{-2} = \frac{1}{(-3)^2} = \frac{1}{(-3)(-3)} = \frac{1}{9}$

18. $m^{-3} = \frac{1}{m^3}$

19. $ab^{-1} = a\left(\frac{1}{b^1}\right) = a\left(\frac{1}{b}\right) = \frac{a}{b}$

20. $\frac{1}{x^{-3}} = x^{-(-3)} = x^3$

21. $3c^{-5} = 3\left(\frac{1}{c^5}\right) = \frac{3}{c^5}$

Example 20 might also be done as follows:

$$\frac{1}{x^{-3}} = \frac{1}{\frac{1}{x^3}} = 1 \cdot \frac{x^3}{1} = x^3.$$

Caution!

As shown in Examples 16 and 17, a negative exponent does not necessarily mean that an expression is negative.

Do Exercises 28–33.

Express with positive exponents. Then simplify.

28. 4^{-3}

29. 5^{-2}

30. 2^{-4}

31. $(-2)^{-3}$

32. $4p^{-3}$

33. $\frac{1}{x^{-2}}$

The rules for multiplying and dividing powers with like bases hold when exponents are 0 or negative.

EXAMPLES Simplify. Write the result using positive exponents.

22. $7^{-3} \cdot 7^6 = 7^{-3+6}$ Adding exponents

$= 7^3$

23. $x^4 \cdot x^{-3} = x^{4+(-3)} = x^1 = x$

24. $\frac{5^4}{5^{-2}} = 5^{4-(-2)}$ Subtracting exponents

$= 5^{4+2} = 5^6$

25. $\frac{x}{x^7} = x^{1-7} = x^{-6} = \frac{1}{x^6}$

26. $\frac{b^{-4}}{b^{-5}} = b^{-4-(-5)}$

$= b^{-4+5} = b^1 = b$

27. $y^{-4} \cdot y^{-8} = y^{-4+(-8)}$

$= y^{-12} = \frac{1}{y^{12}}$

Do Exercises 34–38.

Simplify.

34. $5^{-2} \cdot 5^4$

35. $x^{-3} \cdot x^{-4}$

36. $\frac{7^{-2}}{7^3}$

37. $\frac{b^{-2}}{b^{-3}}$

38. $\frac{t}{t^{-5}}$

The following is a summary of the definitions and rules for exponents that we have considered in this section.

DEFINITIONS AND RULES FOR EXPONENTS

1 as an exponent:	$a^1 = a$
0 as an exponent:	$a^0 = 1, a \neq 0$
Negative integers as exponents:	$a^{-n} = \frac{1}{a^n}, \frac{1}{a^{-n}} = a^n; a \neq 0$
Product Rule:	$a^m \cdot a^n = a^{m+n}$
Quotient Rule:	$\frac{a^m}{a^n} = a^{m-n}, a \neq 0$

Answers

28. $\frac{1}{4^3} = \frac{1}{64}$ 29. $\frac{1}{5^2} = \frac{1}{25}$ 30. $\frac{1}{2^4} = \frac{1}{16}$
31. $\frac{1}{(-2)^3} = -\frac{1}{8}$ 32. $\frac{4}{p^3}$ 33. x^2
34. 5^2 35. $\frac{1}{x^7}$ 36. $\frac{1}{7^5}$ 37. b 38. t^6

3.1 Exercise Set

For Extra Help
MyMathLab Math XL PRACTICE WATCH DOWNLOAD READ REVIEW

a What is the meaning of each of the following?

1. 3^4

2. 4^3

3. $(-1.1)^5$

4. $(87.2)^6$

5. $\left(\frac{2}{3}\right)^4$

6. $\left(-\frac{5}{8}\right)^3$

7. $(7p)^2$

8. $(11c)^3$

9. $8k^3$

10. $17x^2$

11. $-6y^4$

12. $-q^5$

b Evaluate.

13. $a^0, a \neq 0$

14. $t^0, t \neq 0$

15. b^1

16. c^1

17. $\left(\frac{2}{3}\right)^0$

18. $\left(-\frac{5}{8}\right)^0$

19. $(-7.03)^1$

20. $\left(\frac{4}{5}\right)^1$

21. 8.38^0

22. 8.38^1

23. $(ab)^1$

24. $(ab)^0, a, b \neq 0$

25. ab^0

26. ab^1

c Evaluate.

27. m^3, when $m = 3$

28. x^6, when $x = 2$

29. p^1, when $p = 19$

30. x^{19}, when $x = 0$

31. $-x^4$, when $x = -3$

32. $-2y^7$, when $x = 2$

33. x^4, when $x = 4$

34. y^{15}, when $y = 1$

35. $y^2 - 7$, when $y = -10$

36. $z^5 + 5$, when $z = -2$

37. $161 - b^2$, when $b = 5$

38. $325 - v^3$, when $v = -3$

39. $x^1 + 3$ and $x^0 + 3$, when $x = 7$

40. $y^0 - 8$ and $y^1 - 8$, when $y = -3$

41. Find the area of a circle when $r = 34$ ft. Use 3.14 for π.

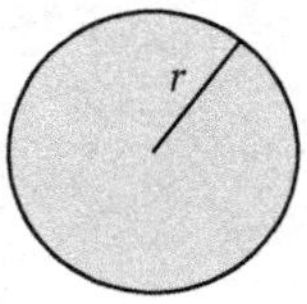

42. The area A of a square with sides of length s is given by $A = s^2$. Find the area of a square with sides of length 24 m.

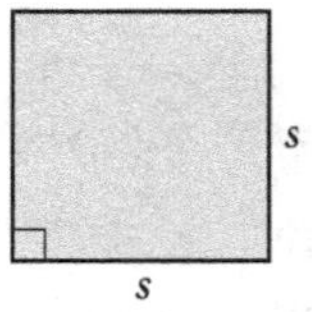

f Express using positive exponents. Then simplify.

43. 3^{-2}

44. 2^{-3}

45. 10^{-3}

46. 5^{-4}

47. a^{-3}

48. x^{-2}

49. $\frac{1}{8^{-2}}$

50. $\frac{1}{2^{-5}}$

51. $\frac{1}{y^{-4}}$

52. $\frac{1}{t^{-7}}$

53. $5z^{-4}$

54. $6n^{-5}$

55. xy^{-2}

56. ab^{-3}

Express using negative exponents.

57. $\frac{1}{4^3}$

58. $\frac{1}{5^2}$

59. $\frac{1}{x^3}$

60. $\frac{1}{y^2}$

61. $\frac{1}{a^5}$

62. $\frac{1}{b^7}$

d, **f** Multiply and simplify.

63. $2^4 \cdot 2^3$

64. $3^5 \cdot 3^2$

65. $8^5 \cdot 8^9$

66. $n^3 \cdot n^{20}$

67. $x^4 \cdot x$

68. $y \cdot y^9$

69. $9^{17} \cdot 9^{21}$

70. $t^0 \cdot t^{16}$

71. $(3y)^4(3y)^8$

72. $(2t)^8(2t)^{17}$

73. $(7y)^1(7y)^{16}$

74. $(8x)^0(8x)^1$

75. $3^{-5} \cdot 3^8$

76. $5^{-8} \cdot 5^9$

77. $x^{-2} \cdot x^2$

78. $x \cdot x^{-1}$

79. $x^{14} \cdot x^3$

80. $x^9 \cdot x^4$

81. $x^{-7} \cdot x^{-6}$

82. $y^{-5} \cdot y^{-8}$

83. $a^{11} \cdot a^{-3} \cdot a^{-18}$

84. $a^{-11} \cdot a^{-3} \cdot a^{-7}$

85. $(s^2t^3)(st^4)$

86. $(m^4n)(m^2n^7)$

e, **f** Divide and simplify.

87. $\frac{7^5}{7^2}$

88. $\frac{5^8}{5^6}$

89. $\frac{y^9}{y}$

90. $\frac{x^{11}}{x}$

91. $\frac{16^2}{16^8}$

92. $\frac{7^2}{7^9}$

93. $\frac{m^6}{m^{12}}$

94. $\frac{a^3}{a^4}$

95. $\frac{(8x)^6}{(8x)^{10}}$

96. $\frac{(8t)^4}{(8t)^{11}}$

97. $\frac{(2y)^9}{(2y)^9}$

98. $\frac{(6y)^7}{(6y)^7}$

99. $\frac{x}{x^{-1}}$

100. $\frac{y^8}{y}$

101. $\frac{x^7}{x^{-2}}$

102. $\frac{t^8}{t^{-3}}$

103. $\frac{z^{-6}}{z^{-2}}$

104. $\frac{x^{-9}}{x^{-3}}$

105. $\frac{x^{-5}}{x^{-8}}$

106. $\frac{y^{-2}}{y^{-9}}$

107. $\frac{m^{-9}}{m^{-9}}$

108. $\frac{x^{-7}}{x^{-7}}$

109. $\frac{a^5b^3}{a^2b}$

110. $\frac{s^8t^4}{st^3}$

Matching. In Exercises 111 and 112, match each item in the first column with the appropriate item in the second column by drawing connecting lines. Items in the second column may be used more than once.

111.

5^2	$-\frac{1}{10}$
5^{-2}	$\frac{1}{10}$
$\left(\frac{1}{5}\right)^2$	$-\frac{1}{25}$
$\left(\frac{1}{5}\right)^{-2}$	10
-5^2	25
$(-5)^2$	-25
$-\left(-\frac{1}{5}\right)^2$	$\frac{1}{25}$
$\left(-\frac{1}{5}\right)^{-2}$	-10

112.

$-\left(\frac{1}{8}\right)^2$	16
$\left(\frac{1}{8}\right)^{-2}$	-16
8^{-2}	64
8^2	-64
-8^2	$\frac{1}{64}$
$(-8)^2$	$-\frac{1}{64}$
$\left(-\frac{1}{8}\right)^{-2}$	$-\frac{1}{16}$
$\left(-\frac{1}{8}\right)^2$	$\frac{1}{16}$

Skill Maintenance

Solve. [2.6a]

113. *Cutting a Submarine Sandwich.* A 12-in. submarine sandwich is cut into two pieces. One piece is twice as long as the other. How long are the pieces?

114. *Book Pages.* The sum of the page numbers on the facing pages of a book is 457. Find the page numbers.

115. The perimeter of a rectangle is 640 ft. The length is 15 ft more than the width. Find the area of the rectangle.

116. The first angle of a triangle is 24° more than the second. The third angle is twice the first. Find the measures of the angles of the triangle.

Solve. [2.3c]

117. $-6(2 - x) + 10(5x - 7) = 10$

118. $-10(x - 4) = 5(2x + 5) - 7$

Factor. [1.7d]

119. $4x - 12 + 24y$

120. $256 - 2a - 4b$

Synthesis

Determine whether each of the following is correct.

121. $(x + 1)^2 = x^2 + 1$

122. $(x - 1)^2 = x^2 - 2x + 1$

123. $(5x)^0 = 5x^0$

124. $\dfrac{x^3}{x^5} = x^2$

Simplify.

125. $(y^{2x})(y^{3x})$

126. $a^{5k} \div a^{3k}$

127. $\dfrac{a^{6t}(a^{7t})}{a^{9t}}$

128. $\dfrac{\left(\frac{1}{2}\right)^4}{\left(\frac{1}{2}\right)^5}$

129. $\dfrac{(0.8)^5}{(0.8)^3(0.8)^2}$

130. $\dfrac{(x - 3)^5}{x - 3}$

Use $>$, $<$, or $=$ for $\square$ to write a true sentence.

131. $3^5 \square 3^4$

132. $4^2 \square 4^3$

133. $4^3 \square 5^3$

134. $4^3 \square 3^4$

Evaluate.

135. $\dfrac{1}{-z^4}$, when $z = -10$

136. $\dfrac{1}{-z^5}$, when $z = -0.1$

137. Determine whether $(a + b)^2$ and $a^2 + b^2$ are equivalent. (*Hint*: Choose values for a and b and evaluate.)

3.2 Exponents and Scientific Notation

OBJECTIVES

- **a** Use the power rule to raise powers to powers.
- **b** Raise a product to a power and a quotient to a power.
- **c** Convert between scientific notation and decimal notation.
- **d** Multiply and divide using scientific notation.
- **e** Solve applied problems using scientific notation.

We now add to our ability to work with exponential expressions by considering three more rules. The rules are also applied to a new way to name numbers called *scientific notation.*

a Raising Powers to Powers

Consider an expression like $(3^2)^4$. We are raising 3^2 to the fourth power:

$$\begin{aligned}(3^2)^4 &= (3^2)(3^2)(3^2)(3^2)\\ &= (3\cdot 3)(3\cdot 3)(3\cdot 3)(3\cdot 3)\\ &= 3\cdot 3\cdot 3\cdot 3\cdot 3\cdot 3\cdot 3\cdot 3\\ &= 3^8.\end{aligned}$$

Note that in this case we could have multiplied the exponents:

$$(3^2)^4 = 3^{2\cdot 4} = 3^8.$$

Likewise, $(y^8)^3 = (y^8)(y^8)(y^8) = y^{24}$. Once again, we get the same result if we multiply the exponents:

$$(y^8)^3 = y^{8\cdot 3} = y^{24}.$$

THE POWER RULE

For any real number a and any integers m and n,

$$(a^m)^n = a^{mn}.$$

(To raise a power to a power, multiply the exponents.)

EXAMPLES Simplify. Express the answers using positive exponents.

1. $(3^5)^4 = 3^{5\cdot 4}$ Multiplying exponents
   $= 3^{20}$

2. $(2^2)^5 = 2^{2\cdot 5} = 2^{10}$

3. $(y^{-5})^7 = y^{-5\cdot 7} = y^{-35} = \dfrac{1}{y^{35}}$

4. $(x^4)^{-2} = x^{4(-2)} = x^{-8} = \dfrac{1}{x^8}$

5. $(a^{-4})^{-6} = a^{(-4)(-6)} = a^{24}$

Do Exercises 1–4.

Simplify. Express the answers using positive exponents.

1. $(3^4)^5$
2. $(x^{-3})^4$
3. $(y^{-5})^{-3}$
4. $(x^4)^{-8}$

b Raising a Product or a Quotient to a Power

When an expression inside parentheses is raised to a power, the inside expression is the base. Let's compare $2a^3$ and $(2a)^3$:

$2a^3 = 2\cdot a\cdot a\cdot a;$ The base is a.

$(2a)^3 = (2a)(2a)(2a)$ The base is $2a$.

$= (2\cdot 2\cdot 2)(a\cdot a\cdot a)$ Using the associative and commutative laws of multiplication to regroup the factors

$= 2^3a^3$

$= 8a^3.$

Answers

1. 3^{20} 2. $\dfrac{1}{x^{12}}$ 3. y^{15} 4. $\dfrac{1}{x^{32}}$

We see that $2a^3$ and $(2a)^3$ are *not* equivalent. We also see that we can evaluate the power $(2a)^3$ by raising each factor to the power 3. This leads us to the following rule for raising a product to a power.

RAISING A PRODUCT TO A POWER

For any real numbers a and b and any integer n,

$$(ab)^n = a^n b^n.$$

(To raise a product to the nth power, raise each factor to the nth power.)

EXAMPLES Simplify.

6. $(4x^2)^3 = (4^1x^2)^3$ — Since $4 = 4^1$
$= (4^1)^3 \cdot (x^2)^3$ — Raising *each* factor to the third power
$= 4^3 \cdot x^6 = 64x^6$

7. $(5x^3y^5z^2)^4 = 5^4(x^3)^4(y^5)^4(z^2)^4$ — Raising *each* factor to the fourth power
$= 625x^{12}y^{20}z^8$

8. $(-5x^4y^3)^3 = (-5)^3(x^4)^3(y^3)^3$
$= -125x^{12}y^9$

9. $[(-x)^{25}]^2 = (-x)^{50}$ — Using the power rule
$= (-1 \cdot x)^{50}$ — Using the property of -1 (Section 1.8)
$= (-1)^{50}x^{50}$
$= 1 \cdot x^{50}$ — The product of an even number of negative factors is positive.
$= x^{50}$

10. $(5x^2y^{-2})^3 = 5^3(x^2)^3(y^{-2})^3 = 125x^6y^{-6}$ — Be sure to raise *each* factor to the third power.
$= \dfrac{125x^6}{y^6}$

11. $(3x^3y^{-5}z^2)^4 = 3^4(x^3)^4(y^{-5})^4(z^2)^4 = 81x^{12}y^{-20}z^8 = \dfrac{81x^{12}z^8}{y^{20}}$

12. $(-x^4)^{-3} = (-1 \cdot x^4)^{-3} = (-1)^{-3} \cdot x^{4(-3)} = (-1)^{-3} \cdot x^{-12}$
$= \dfrac{1}{(-1)^3} \cdot \dfrac{1}{x^{12}} = \dfrac{1}{-1} \cdot \dfrac{1}{x^{12}} = -\dfrac{1}{x^{12}}$

13. $(-2x^{-5}y^4)^{-4} = (-2)^{-4}(x^{-5})^{-4}(y^4)^{-4} = \dfrac{1}{(-2)^4} \cdot x^{20} \cdot y^{-16}$
$= \dfrac{1}{16} \cdot x^{20} \cdot \dfrac{1}{y^{16}} = \dfrac{x^{20}}{16y^{16}}$

Do Exercises 5–11.

Simplify.

5. $(2x^5y^{-3})^4$

6. $(5x^5y^{-6}z^{-3})^2$

7. $[(-x)^{37}]^2$

8. $(3y^{-2}x^{-5}z^8)^3$

9. $(-y^8)^{-3}$

10. $(-2x^4)^{-2}$

11. $(-3x^2y^{-5})^{-3}$

Answers

5. $\dfrac{16x^{20}}{y^{12}}$ 6. $\dfrac{25x^{10}}{y^{12}z^6}$ 7. x^{74} 8. $\dfrac{27z^{24}}{y^6x^{15}}$
9. $-\dfrac{1}{y^{24}}$ 10. $\dfrac{1}{4x^8}$ 11. $-\dfrac{y^{15}}{27x^6}$

There is a similar rule for raising a quotient to a power.

RAISING A QUOTIENT TO A POWER

For any real numbers a and b, $b \neq 0$, and any integer n,

$$\left(\frac{a}{b}\right)^n = \frac{a^n}{b^n}.$$

(To raise a quotient to the nth power, raise both the numerator and the denominator to the nth power.) Also,

$$\left(\frac{a}{b}\right)^{-n} = \left(\frac{b}{a}\right)^n = \frac{b^n}{a^n}, \quad a \neq 0.$$

EXAMPLES Simplify.

14. $\left(\frac{x^2}{4}\right)^3 = \frac{(x^2)^3}{4^3} = \frac{x^6}{64}$

15. $\left(\frac{3a^4}{b^3}\right)^2 = \frac{(3a^4)^2}{(b^3)^2} = \frac{3^2(a^4)^2}{b^{3\cdot 2}} = \frac{9a^8}{b^6}$

16. $\left(\frac{y^2}{2z^{-5}}\right)^4 = \frac{(y^2)^4}{(2z^{-5})^4} = \frac{(y^2)^4}{2^4(z^{-5})^4} = \frac{y^8}{16z^{-20}} = \frac{y^8z^{20}}{16}$

17. $\left(\frac{y^3}{5}\right)^{-2} = \frac{(y^3)^{-2}}{5^{-2}} = \frac{y^{-6}}{5^{-2}} = \frac{\frac{1}{y^6}}{\frac{1}{5^2}} = \frac{1}{y^6} \div \frac{1}{5^2} = \frac{1}{y^6} \cdot \frac{5^2}{1} = \frac{25}{y^6}$

Example 17 might also be done as follows:

$$\left(\frac{y^3}{5}\right)^{-2} = \left(\frac{5}{y^3}\right)^2 \qquad \left(\frac{a}{b}\right)^{-n} = \left(\frac{b}{a}\right)^n$$

$$= \frac{5^2}{(y^3)^2} = \frac{25}{y^6}.$$

Do Exercises 12–15.

Simplify.

12. $\left(\frac{x^6}{5}\right)^2$

13. $\left(\frac{2t^5}{w^4}\right)^3$

14. $\left(\frac{a^4}{3b^{-2}}\right)^3$

15. $\left(\frac{x^4}{3}\right)^{-2}$

Do this two ways.

C Scientific Notation

There are many kinds of symbols, or notation, for numbers. You are already familiar with fraction notation, decimal notation, and percent notation. Now we study another, **scientific notation**, which makes use of exponential notation. Scientific notation is especially useful when calculations involve very large or very small numbers. The following are examples of scientific notation.

①

① *Niagara Falls*: On the Canadian side, the amount of water that spills over the falls in 1 day during the summer is about

$$4.9793 \times 10^{10} \text{ gal} = 49{,}793{,}000{,}000 \text{ gal}.$$

Answers

12. $\frac{x^{12}}{25}$ 13. $\frac{8t^{15}}{w^{12}}$ 14. $\frac{a^{12}b^6}{27}$ 15. $\frac{9}{x^8}$

② *The mass of the earth*:

6.615×10^{21} tons = 6,615,000,000,000,000,000,000 tons.

③ *The mass of a hydrogen atom*:

1.7×10^{-24} g = 0.0000000000000000000000017 g.

②

③

SCIENTIFIC NOTATION

Scientific notation for a number is an expression of the type

$M \times 10^n$,

where n is an integer, M is greater than or equal to 1 and less than 10 ($1 \leq M < 10$), and M is expressed in decimal notation. 10^n is also considered to be scientific notation when $M = 1$.

You should try to make conversions to scientific notation mentally as much as possible. Here is a handy mental device.

A positive exponent in scientific notation indicates a large number (greater than or equal to 10) and a negative exponent indicates a small number (between 0 and 1).

EXAMPLES Convert to scientific notation.

18. $78{,}000 = 7.8 \times 10^4$

7.8,000.
4 places

Large number, so the exponent is positive.

19. $0.0000057 = 5.7 \times 10^{-6}$

0.000005.7
6 places

Small number, so the exponent is negative.

Convert to scientific notation.

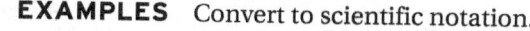

16. 0.000517

17. 523,000,000

Do Exercises 16 and 17.

EXAMPLES Convert mentally to decimal notation.

20. $7.893 \times 10^5 = 789{,}300$

7.89300.
5 places

Positive exponent, so the answer is a large number.

21. $4.7 \times 10^{-8} = 0.000000047$

.00000004.7
8 places

Negative exponent, so the answer is a small number.

Caution!

Each of the following is *not* scientific notation.

12.46×10^7

This number is greater than 10.

0.347×10^{-5}

This number is less than 1.

Answers

16. 5.17×10^{-4} **17.** 5.23×10^8

Do Exercises 18 and 19.

d Multiplying and Dividing Using Scientific Notation

Multiplying

Consider the product

$$400 \cdot 2000 = 800{,}000.$$

In scientific notation, this is

$$(4 \times 10^2) \cdot (2 \times 10^3) = (4 \cdot 2)(10^2 \cdot 10^3) = 8 \times 10^5.$$

By applying the commutative and associative laws, we can find this product by multiplying $4 \cdot 2$, to get 8, and $10^2 \cdot 10^3$, to get 10^5.

EXAMPLE 22 Multiply: $(1.8 \times 10^6) \cdot (2.3 \times 10^{-4})$.

We apply the commutative and associative laws to get

$$(1.8 \times 10^6) \cdot (2.3 \times 10^{-4}) = (1.8 \cdot 2.3) \times (10^6 \cdot 10^{-4})$$
$$= 4.14 \times 10^{6+(-4)}$$
$$= 4.14 \times 10^2.$$

We get 4.14 by multiplying 1.8 and 2.3. We get 10^2 by adding the exponents 6 and -4.

EXAMPLE 23 Multiply: $(3.1 \times 10^5) \cdot (4.5 \times 10^{-3})$.

$$(3.1 \times 10^5) \cdot (4.5 \times 10^{-3}) = (3.1 \times 4.5)(10^5 \cdot 10^{-3})$$
$$= 13.95 \times 10^2$$ Not scientific notation; 13.95 is greater than 10.
$$= (1.395 \times 10^1) \times 10^2$$ Substituting 1.395×10^1 for 13.95
$$= 1.395 \times (10^1 \times 10^2)$$ Associative law
$$= 1.395 \times 10^3$$ Adding exponents. The answer is now in scientific notation.

Do Exercises 20 and 21.

Dividing

Consider the quotient $800{,}000 \div 400 = 2000$. In scientific notation, this is

$$(8 \times 10^5) \div (4 \times 10^2) = \frac{8 \times 10^5}{4 \times 10^2} = \frac{8}{4} \times \frac{10^5}{10^2} = 2 \times 10^3.$$

We found this product by dividing 8 by 4, to get 2, and 10^5 by 10^2, to get 10^3.

EXAMPLE 24 Divide: $(3.41 \times 10^5) \div (1.1 \times 10^{-3})$.

$$(3.41 \times 10^5) \div (1.1 \times 10^{-3}) = \frac{3.41 \times 10^5}{1.1 \times 10^{-3}} = \frac{3.41}{1.1} \times \frac{10^5}{10^{-3}}$$
$$= 3.1 \times 10^{5-(-3)}$$
$$= 3.1 \times 10^8$$

Convert to decimal notation.

18. 6.893×10^{11}

19. 5.67×10^{-5}

Multiply and write scientific notation for the result.

20. $(1.12 \times 10^{-8})(5 \times 10^{-7})$

21. $(9.1 \times 10^{-17})(8.2 \times 10^3)$

Calculator Corner

To find the product in Example 22 and express the result in scientific notation on a graphing calculator, we first set the calculator in Scientific mode by pressing MODE, positioning the cursor over Sci on the first line, and pressing ENTER. Then we go to the home screen and enter the computation by pressing 1 . 8 2ND EE 6 × 2 . 3 2ND EE (−) 4 ENTER. (EE is the second operation associated with the , key.) The decimal portion of a number written in scientific notation appears before a small E and the exponent follows the E.

```
1.8E6*2.3E-4
          4.14E2
```

Exercises: Multiply or divide and express the answer in scientific notation.

1. $(3.15 \times 10^7)(4.3 \times 10^{-12})$
2. $(8 \times 10^9)(4 \times 10^{-5})$
3. $\dfrac{4.5 \times 10^6}{1.5 \times 10^{12}}$
4. $\dfrac{4 \times 10^{-9}}{5 \times 10^{16}}$

Answers

18. 689,300,000,000 **19.** 0.0000567
20. 5.6×10^{-15} **21.** 7.462×10^{-13}

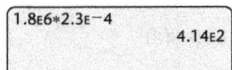

EXAMPLE 25 Divide: $(6.4 \times 10^{-7}) \div (8.0 \times 10^{6})$.

$$(6.4 \times 10^{-7}) \div (8.0 \times 10^{6}) = \frac{6.4 \times 10^{-7}}{8.0 \times 10^{6}}$$
$$= \frac{6.4}{8.0} \times \frac{10^{-7}}{10^{6}}$$
$$= 0.8 \times 10^{-7-6}$$
$$= 0.8 \times 10^{-13}$$ Not scientific notation; 0.8 is less than 1.
$$= (8.0 \times 10^{-1}) \times 10^{-13}$$ Substituting 8.0×10^{-1} for 0.8
$$= 8.0 \times (10^{-1} \times 10^{-13})$$ Associative law
$$= 8.0 \times 10^{-14}$$ Adding exponents

Do Exercises 22 and 23.

Divide and write scientific notation for the result.

22. $\dfrac{4.2 \times 10^{5}}{2.1 \times 10^{2}}$

23. $\dfrac{1.1 \times 10^{-4}}{2.0 \times 10^{-7}}$

e Applications with Scientific Notation

EXAMPLE 26 *Distance from the Sun to Earth.* Light from the sun traveling at a rate of 300,000 kilometers per second (km/s) reaches Earth in 499 sec. Find the distance, expressed in scientific notation, from the sun to Earth.

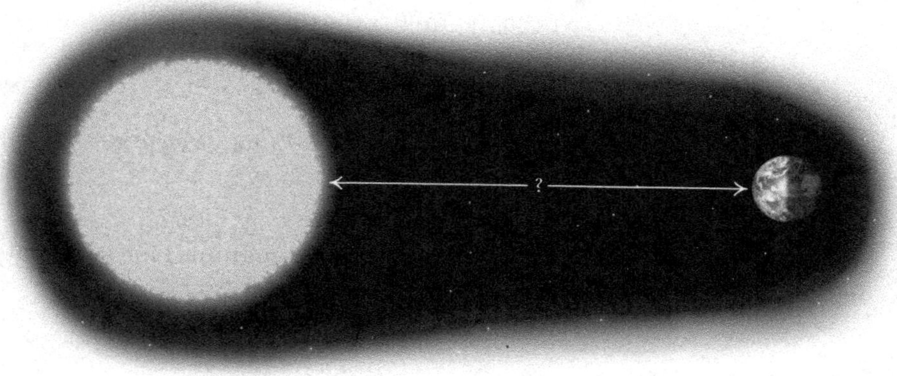

The time t that it takes for light to reach Earth from the sun is 4.99×10^{2} sec (s). The speed is 3.0×10^{5} km/s. Recall that distance can be expressed in terms of speed and time as

Distance = Speed · Time

$$d = rt.$$

We substitute 3.0×10^{5} for r and 4.99×10^{2} for t:

$$d = rt$$
$$= (3.0 \times 10^{5})(4.99 \times 10^{2})$$ Substituting
$$= 14.97 \times 10^{7}$$
$$= (1.497 \times 10^{1}) \times 10^{7}$$
$$= 1.497 \times (10^{1} \times 10^{7})$$
$$= 1.497 \times 10^{8}\text{ km.}$$ Converting to scientific notation

Thus the distance from the sun to Earth is 1.497×10^{8} km.

Do Exercise 24.

STUDY TIPS

WRITING ALL THE STEPS

Take the time to write all the steps when doing your homework. Doing so will help you organize your thinking and avoid computational errors. If you get a wrong answer, having all the steps allows easier checking of your work. It will also give you complete, step-by-step solutions of the exercises that can be used to study for an exam.

24. **Niagara Falls Water Flow.** On the Canadian side, the amount of water that spills over Niagara Falls in 1 min during the summer is about

$$1.3088 \times 10^{8}\text{ L.}$$

How much water spills over the falls in one day? Express the answer in scientific notation.

Answers

22. 2.0×10^{3} 23. 5.5×10^{2}
24. 1.884672×10^{11} L

EXAMPLE 27 *DNA.* A strand of DNA (deoxyribonucleic acid) is about 150 cm long and 1.3×10^{-10} cm wide. The length of a strand of DNA is how many times the width?

Source: Human Genome Project Information

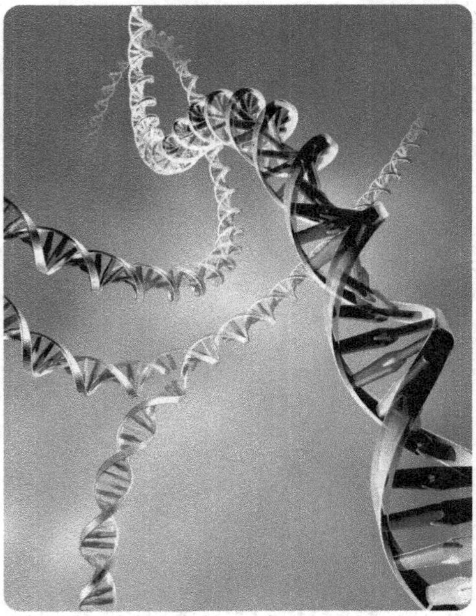

To determine how many times longer DNA is than it is wide, we divide the length by the width:

$$\frac{150}{1.3 \times 10^{-10}} = \frac{150}{1.3} \times \frac{1}{10^{-10}}$$
$$\approx 115.385 \times 10^{10}$$
$$= (1.15385 \times 10^{2}) \times 10^{10}$$
$$= 1.15385 \times 10^{12}.$$

Thus the length of DNA is about 1.15385×10^{12} times its width.

Do Exercise 25.

25. Earth vs. Saturn. The mass of Earth is about 6×10^{21} metric tons. The mass of Saturn is about 5.7×10^{23} metric tons. About how many times the mass of Earth is the mass of Saturn? Express the answer in scientific notation.

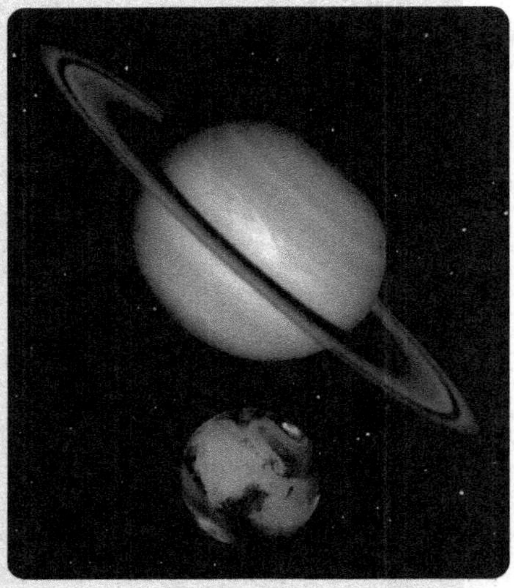

The following is a summary of the definitions and rules for exponents that we have considered in this section and the preceding one.

DEFINITIONS AND RULES FOR EXPONENTS

Exponent of 1:	$a^1 = a$
Exponent of 0:	$a^0 = 1, a \neq 0$
Negative exponents:	$a^{-n} = \frac{1}{a^n}, \frac{1}{a^{-n}} = a^n, a \neq 0$
Product Rule:	$a^m \cdot a^n = a^{m+n}$
Quotient Rule:	$\frac{a^m}{a^n} = a^{m-n}, a \neq 0$
Power Rule:	$(a^m)^n = a^{mn}$
Raising a product to a power:	$(ab)^n = a^n b^n$
Raising a quotient to a power:	$\left(\frac{a}{b}\right)^n = \frac{a^n}{b^n}, b \neq 0;$
	$\left(\frac{a}{b}\right)^{-n} = \frac{b^n}{a^n}, b \neq 0, a \neq 0$
Scientific notation:	$M \times 10^n$, or 10^n, where $1 \leq M < 10$

Answer

25. The mass of Saturn is 9.5×10 times the mass of Earth.

For Extra Help
MyMathLab
MathXL PRACTICE | WATCH | DOWNLOAD | READ | REVIEW

a, **b** Simplify.

1. $(2^3)^2$

2. $(5^2)^4$

3. $(5^2)^{-3}$

4. $(7^{-3})^5$

5. $(x^{-3})^{-4}$

6. $(a^{-5})^{-6}$

7. $(a^{-2})^9$

8. $(x^{-5})^6$

9. $(t^{-3})^{-6}$

10. $(a^{-4})^{-7}$

11. $(t^4)^{-3}$

12. $(t^5)^{-2}$

13. $(x^{-2})^{-4}$

14. $(t^{-6})^{-5}$

15. $(ab)^3$

16. $(xy)^2$

17. $(ab)^{-3}$

18. $(xy)^{-6}$

19. $(mn^2)^{-3}$

20. $(x^3y)^{-2}$

21. $(4x^3)^2$

22. $4(x^3)^2$

23. $(3x^{-4})^2$

24. $(2a^{-5})^3$

25. $(x^4y^5)^{-3}$

26. $(t^5x^3)^{-4}$

27. $(x^{-6}y^{-2})^{-4}$

28. $(x^{-2}y^{-7})^{-5}$

29. $(a^{-2}b^7)^{-5}$

30. $(q^5r^{-1})^{-3}$

31. $(5r^{-4}t^3)^2$

32. $(4x^5y^{-6})^3$

33. $(a^{-5}b^7c^{-2})^3$

34. $(x^{-4}y^{-2}z^9)^2$

35. $(3x^3y^{-8}z^{-3})^2$

36. $(2a^2y^{-4}z^{-5})^3$

37. $(-4x^3y^{-2})^2$

38. $(-8x^3y^{-2})^3$

39. $(-a^{-3}b^{-2})^{-4}$

40. $(-p^{-4}q^{-3})^{-2}$

41. $\left(\frac{y^3}{2}\right)^2$

42. $\left(\frac{a^5}{3}\right)^3$

43. $\left(\frac{a^2}{b^3}\right)^4$

44. $\left(\frac{x^3}{y^4}\right)^5$

45. $\left(\frac{y^2}{2}\right)^{-3}$

46. $\left(\frac{a^4}{3}\right)^{-2}$

47. $\left(\frac{7}{x^{-3}}\right)^2$

48. $\left(\frac{3}{a^{-2}}\right)^3$

49. $\left(\frac{x^2y}{z}\right)^3$

50. $\left(\frac{m}{n^4p}\right)^3$

51. $\left(\frac{a^2b}{cd^3}\right)^{-2}$

52. $\left(\frac{2a^2}{3b^4}\right)^{-3}$

c Convert to scientific notation.

53. 28,000,000,000

54. 4,900,000,000,000

55. 907,000,000,000,000,000

56. 168,000,000,000,000

57. 0.00000304

58. 0.000000000865

59. 0.000000018

60. 0.00000000002

61. 100,000,000,000

62. 0.0000001

63. *Population of the United States.* It is estimated that the population of the United States will be 419,854,000 in 2050. Convert 419,854,000 to scientific notation.
Source: U.S. Census Bureau

64. *Young Voters.* About 22,750,000 young people, ages 18–29, voted in the 2008 presidential election. Convert 22,750,000 to scientific notation.
Source: Center for Information & Research on Civic Learning and Engagement, Tufts University

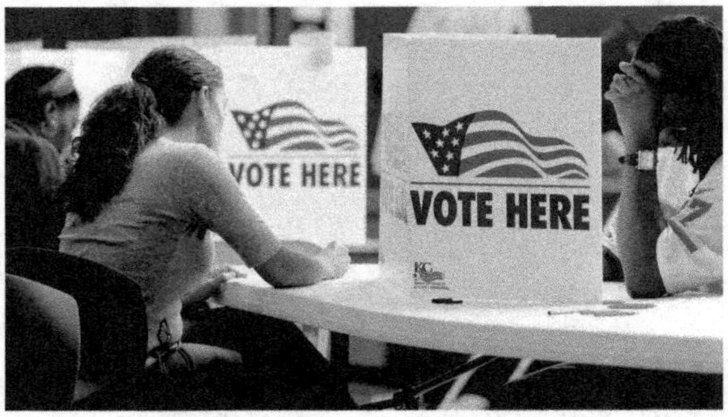

65. *Political Spending.* A record \$2,400,000,000 was spent on campaigning, advertising, conventions, and other political activities in the 2008 presidential election. Convert \$2,400,000,000 to scientific notation.
Source: Center for Responsive Politics

66. *Advertising Spending.* Coca-Cola spent \$2,600,000,000 on advertising in a recent year. Convert \$2,600,000,000 to scientific notation.
Source: Nielsen Media Research

Convert to decimal notation.

67. 8.74×10^7

68. 1.85×10^8

69. 5.704×10^{-8}

70. 8.043×10^{-4}

71. 10^7

72. 10^6

73. 10^{-5}

74. 10^{-8}

d Multiply or divide and write scientific notation for the result.

75. $(3 \times 10^4)(2 \times 10^5)$

76. $(3.9 \times 10^8)(8.4 \times 10^{-3})$

77. $(5.2 \times 10^5)(6.5 \times 10^{-2})$

78. $(7.1 \times 10^{-7})(8.6 \times 10^{-5})$

79. $(9.9 \times 10^{-6})(8.23 \times 10^{-8})$

80. $(1.123 \times 10^4) \times 10^{-9}$

81. $\dfrac{8.5 \times 10^{8}}{3.4 \times 10^{-5}}$

82. $\dfrac{5.6 \times 10^{-2}}{2.5 \times 10^{5}}$

83. $(3.0 \times 10^{6}) \div (6.0 \times 10^{9})$

84. $(1.5 \times 10^{-3}) \div (1.6 \times 10^{-6})$

85. $\dfrac{7.5 \times 10^{-9}}{2.5 \times 10^{12}}$

86. $\dfrac{4.0 \times 10^{-3}}{8.0 \times 10^{20}}$

e Solve.

87. *River Discharge.* The average discharge at the mouths of the Amazon River is 4,200,000 cubic feet per second. How much water is discharged from the Amazon River in 1 yr? Express the answer in scientific notation.

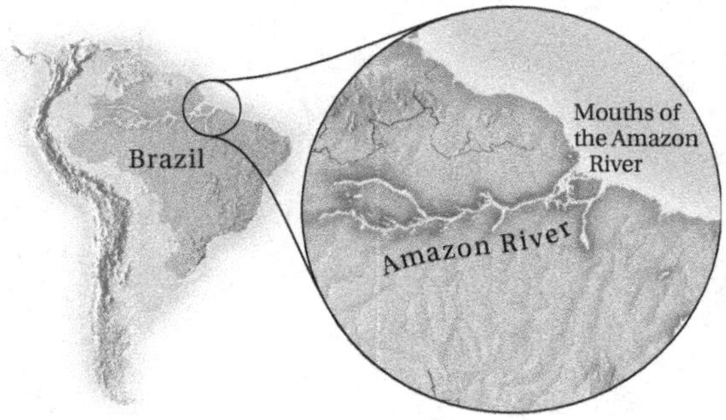

88. *Water Contamination.* Americans who change their own motor oil generate about 150 million gallons of used oil annually. If this oil is not disposed of properly, it can contaminate drinking water and soil. One gallon of used oil can contaminate one million gallons of drinking water. How many gallons of drinking water can 150 million gallons of oil contaminate? Express the answer in scientific notation. (1 million = 10^{6}).

Source: *New Car Buying Guide*

89. *Earth vs. Jupiter.* The mass of Earth is about 6×10^{21} metric tons. The mass of Jupiter is about 1.908×10^{24} metric tons. About how many times the mass of Earth is the mass of Jupiter? Express the answer in scientific notation.

90. *Computers.* A gigabyte is a measure of a computer's storage capacity. One gigabyte holds about one billion bytes of information. If a firm's computer network contains 2500 gigabytes of memory, how many bytes are in the network? Express the answer in scientific notation. (1 billion = 10^{9})

91. *Stars.* It is estimated that there are 10 billion trillion stars in the known universe. Express the number of stars in scientific notation. (1 billion $= 10^9$; 1 trillion $= 10^{12}$)

92. *Closest Star.* Excluding the sun, the closest star to Earth is Proxima Centauri, which is 4.3 light-years away. (One light-year $= 5.88 \times 10^{12}$ mi.) How far, in miles, is Proxima Centauri from Earth? Express the answer in scientific notation.

93. *Red Light.* The wavelength of light is given by the velocity divided by the frequency. The velocity of red light is 300,000,000 m/sec, and its frequency is 400,000,000,000,000 cycles per second. What is the wavelength of red light? Express the answer in scientific notation.

94. *Earth vs. Sun.* The mass of Earth is about 6×10^{21} metric tons. The mass of the sun is about 1.998×10^{27} metric tons. About how many times the mass of Earth is the mass of the sun? Express the answer in scientific notation.

Space Travel. Use the following information for Exercises 95 and 96.

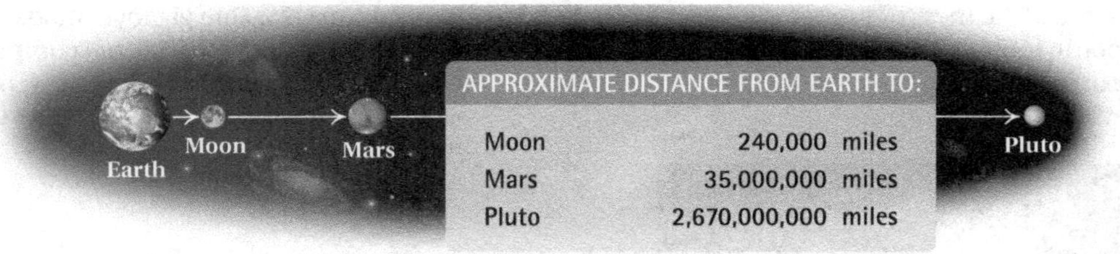

Earth
Moon
Mars
Pluto
APPROXIMATE DISTANCE FROM EARTH TO:
Moon 240,000 miles
Mars 35,000,000 miles
Pluto 2,670,000,000 miles

95. *Time to Reach Mars.* Suppose that it takes about 3 days for a space vehicle to travel from Earth to the moon. About how long would it take the same space vehicle traveling at the same speed to reach Mars? Express the answer in scientific notation.

96. *Time to Reach Pluto.* Suppose that it takes about 3 days for a space vehicle to travel from Earth to the moon. About how long would it take the same space vehicle traveling at the same speed to reach the dwarf planet Pluto? Express the answer in scientific notation.

Skill Maintenance

Factor. [1.7d]

97. $9x - 36$

98. $4x - 2y + 16$

99. $3s + 3t + 24$

100. $-7x - 14$

Solve. [2.3b]

101. $2x - 4 - 5x + 8 = x - 3$

102. $8x + 7 - 9x = 12 - 6x + 5$

Solve. [2.3c]

103. $8(2x + 3) - 2(x - 5) = 10$

104. $4(x - 3) + 5 = 6(x + 2) - 8$

Graph.

105. $y = x - 5$

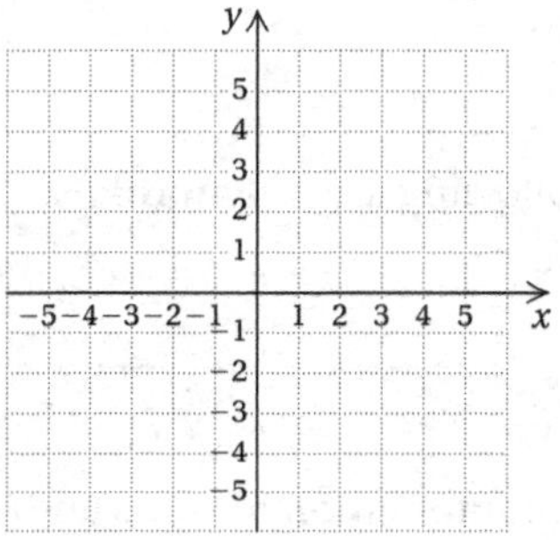

106. $2x + y = 4$

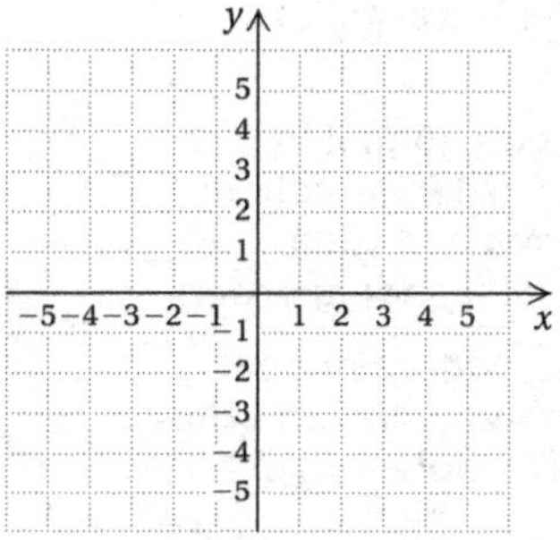

Synthesis

107. Carry out the indicated operations. Express the result in scientific notation.

$$\frac{(5.2 \times 10^{6})(6.1 \times 10^{-11})}{1.28 \times 10^{-3}}$$

108. Find the reciprocal and express it in scientific notation.

$$6.25 \times 10^{-3}$$

Simplify.

109. $\dfrac{(5^{12})^2}{5^{25}}$

110. $\dfrac{a^{22}}{(a^2)^{11}}$

111. $\dfrac{(3^5)^4}{3^5 \cdot 3^4}$

112. $\left(\dfrac{5x^{-2}}{3y^{-2}z}\right)^0$

113. $\dfrac{49^{18}}{7^{35}}$

114. $\left(\dfrac{1}{a}\right)^{-n}$

115. $\dfrac{(0.4)^5}{[(0.4)^3]^2}$

116. $\left(\dfrac{4a^3b^{-2}}{5c^{-3}}\right)^1$

Determine whether each of the following is true for all pairs of integers m and n and all positive numbers x and y.

117. $x^m \cdot y^n = (xy)^{mn}$

118. $x^m \cdot y^m = (xy)^{2m}$

119. $(x - y)^m = x^m - y^m$

120. $-x^m = (-x)^m$

121. $(-x)^{2m} = x^{2m}$

122. $x^{-m} = \dfrac{-1}{x^m}$

3.3 Introduction to Polynomials

OBJECTIVES

a Evaluate a polynomial for a given value of the variable.

b Identify the terms of a polynomial.

c Identify the like terms of a polynomial.

d Identify the coefficients of a polynomial.

e Collect the like terms of a polynomial.

f Arrange a polynomial in descending order, or collect the like terms and then arrange in descending order.

g Identify the degree of each term of a polynomial and the degree of the polynomial.

h Identify the missing terms of a polynomial.

i Classify a polynomial as a monomial, a binomial, a trinomial, or none of these.

SKILL TO REVIEW
Objective 1.7e: Collect like terms.

Collect like terms.

1. $3x - 4y + 5x + y$
2. $2a - 7b + 6 - 3a + 4b - 1$

We have already learned to evaluate and to manipulate certain kinds of algebraic expressions. We will now consider algebraic expressions called *polynomials*.

The following are examples of *monomials in one variable*:

$$3x^2, \quad 2x, \quad -5, \quad 37p^4, \quad 0.$$

Each expression is a constant or a constant times some variable to a nonnegative integer power.

MONOMIAL

A **monomial** is an expression of the type ax^n, where a is a real-number constant and n is a nonnegative integer.

Algebraic expressions like the following are **polynomials**:

$$\tfrac{3}{4}y^5, \quad -2, \quad 5y + 3, \quad 3x^2 + 2x - 5, \quad -7a^3 + \tfrac{1}{2}a, \quad 6x, \quad 37p^4, \quad x, \quad 0.$$

POLYNOMIAL

A **polynomial** is a monomial or a combination of sums and/or differences of monomials.

The following algebraic expressions are *not* polynomials:

$$\textbf{(1)}\ \frac{x+3}{x-4}, \qquad \textbf{(2)}\ 5x^3 - 2x^2 + \frac{1}{x}, \qquad \textbf{(3)}\ \frac{1}{x^3 - 2}.$$

Expressions (1) and (3) are not polynomials because they represent quotients, not sums or differences. Expression (2) is not a polynomial because

$$\frac{1}{x} = x^{-1},$$

and this is not a monomial because the exponent is negative.

Do Margin Exercise 1.

1. Write three polynomials.

a Evaluating Polynomials and Applications

When we replace the variable in a polynomial with a number, the polynomial then represents a number called a **value** of the polynomial. Finding that number, or value, is called **evaluating the polynomial**. We evaluate a polynomial using the rules for order of operations (Section 1.8).

EXAMPLE 1 Evaluate the polynomial when $x = 2$.

a) $3x + 5 = 3 \cdot 2 + 5$
$= 6 + 5$
$= 11$

b) $2x^2 - 7x + 3 = 2 \cdot 2^2 - 7 \cdot 2 + 3$
$= 2 \cdot 4 - 7 \cdot 2 + 3$
$= 8 - 14 + 3$
$= -3$

Answers

Skill to Review:
1. $8x - 3y$ 2. $-a - 3b + 5$

Margin Exercise:
1. $4x^2 - 3x + \frac{5}{4}$; $15y^3$; $-7x^3 + 1.1$; answers may vary

EXAMPLE 2 Evaluate the polynomial when $x = -4$.

a) $2 - x^3 = 2 - (-4)^3 = 2 - (-64)$
$= 2 + 64 = 66$

b) $-x^2 - 3x + 1 = -(-4)^2 - 3(-4) + 1$
$= -16 + 12 + 1 = -3$

Do Exercises 2–5.

Evaluate each polynomial when $x = 3$.

2. $-4x - 7$

3. $-5x^3 + 7x + 10$

Evaluate each polynomial when $x = -5$.

4. $5x + 7$

5. $2x^2 + 5x - 4$

Algebraic–Graphical Connection

Recall from Chapter 3 that in order to plot points before graphing an equation, we choose values for x and compute the corresponding y-values. An equation like $y = 2x - 2$, which has a polynomial on one side and only y on the other, is called a **polynomial equation**. For such an equation, determining y is the same as evaluating the polynomial. Once the graph of such an equation has been drawn, we can evaluate the polynomial for a given x-value by finding the y-value that is paired with it on the graph.

EXAMPLE 3 Use *only* the given graph of $y = 2x - 2$ to evaluate the polynomial $2x - 2$ when $x = 3$.

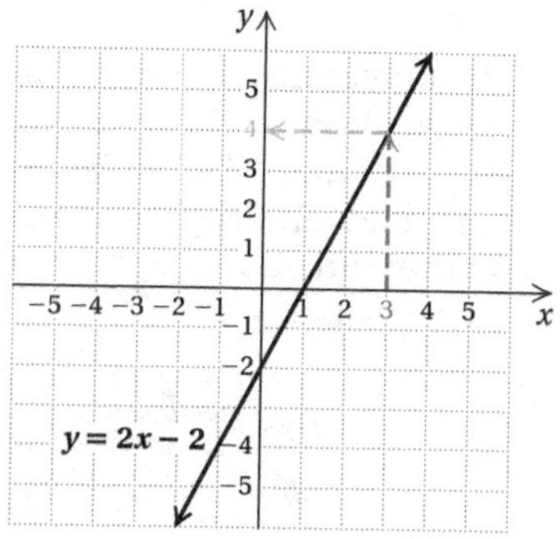

First, we locate 3 on the x-axis. From there we move vertically to the graph of the equation and then horizontally to the y-axis. There we locate the y-value that is paired with 3. Although our drawing may not be precise, it appears that the y-value 4 is paired with 3. Thus the value of $2x - 2$ is 4 when $x = 3$.

Do Exercise 6.

6. Use *only* the graph shown in Example 3 to evaluate the polynomial $2x - 2$ when $x = 4$ and when $x = -1$.

Polynomial equations can be used to model many real-world situations.

EXAMPLE 4 *Games in a Sports League.* In a sports league of x teams in which each team plays every other team twice, the total number of games N to be played is given by the polynomial equation

$$N = x^2 - x.$$

A women's slow-pitch softball league has 10 teams. What is the total number of games to be played?

We evaluate the polynomial when $x = 10$:

$$N = x^2 - x = 10^2 - 10 = 100 - 10 = 90.$$

The league plays 90 games.

Do Exercises 7 and 8.

7. Referring to Example 4, determine the total number of games to be played in a league of 12 teams.

8. Perimeter of a Baseball Diamond. The perimeter P of a square of side x is given by the polynomial equation $P = 4x$.

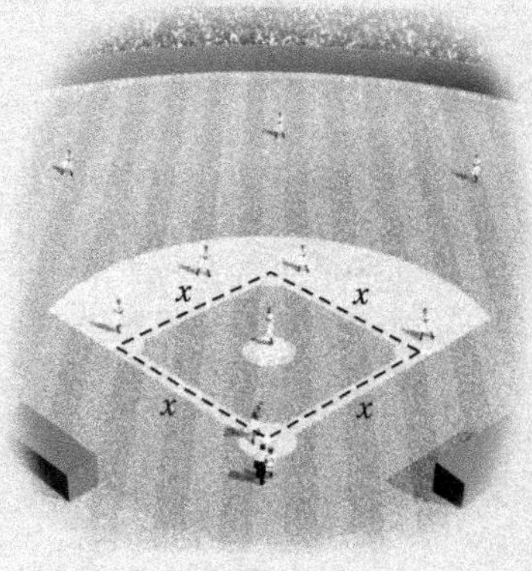

A baseball diamond is a square 90 ft on a side. Find the perimeter of a baseball diamond.

Answers

2. −19 **3.** −104 **4.** −18 **5.** 21
6. 6; −4 **7.** 132 games **8.** 360 ft

Calculator Corner

We can use the Value feature from the CALC menu to evaluate a polynomial on a graphing calculator. To evaluate the polynomial in Example 2(b), $-x^2 - 3x + 1$, when $x = -4$, we first graph $y_1 = -x^2 - 3x + 1$ in a window that includes the x-value -4. We will use the standard window. Then we press 2ND CALC 1 or 2ND CALC ENTER to access the CALC menu and select item 1, Value. Now we supply the desired x-value by pressing (−) 4. We then press ENTER to see X = −4, Y = −3 at the bottom of the screen. Thus, when $x = -4$, the value of $-x^2 - 3x + 1$ is -3.

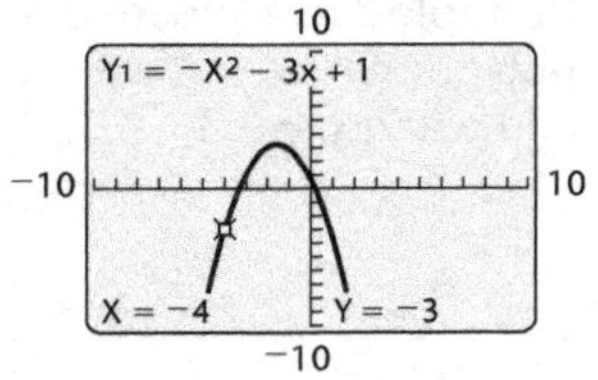

Exercises: Use the Value feature to evaluate each polynomial for the given values of x.

1. $-x^2 - 3x + 1$, when $x = -2$, $x = -0.5$, and $x = 4$
2. $3x^2 - 5x + 2$, when $x = -3$, $x = 1$, and $x = 2.6$

EXAMPLE 5 *Medical Dosage.* The concentration C, in parts per million, of a certain antibiotic in the bloodstream after t hours is given by the polynomial equation

$$C = -0.05t^2 + 2t + 2.$$

Find the concentration after 2 hr.

To find the concentration after 2 hr, we evaluate the polynomial when $t = 2$:

$$\begin{aligned} C &= -0.05t^2 + 2t + 2 \\ &= -0.05(2)^2 + 2(2) + 2 && \text{Substituting 2 for } t \\ &= -0.05(4) + 2(2) + 2 && \text{Carrying out the calculation using the rules for order of operations} \\ &= -0.2 + 4 + 2 \\ &= 3.8 + 2 \\ &= 5.8. \end{aligned}$$

The concentration after 2 hr is 5.8 parts per million.

Algebraic–Graphical Connection

The polynomial equation in Example 5 can be graphed if we evaluate the polynomial for several values of t. We list the values in a table and show the graph below. Note that the concentration peaks at the 20-hr mark and after slightly more than 40 hr, the concentration is 0. Since neither time nor concentration can be negative, our graph uses only the first quadrant.

	C	
t	$C = -0.05t^2 + 2t + 2$	
0	2	
2	5.8	← Example 5
10	17	
20	22	
30	17	

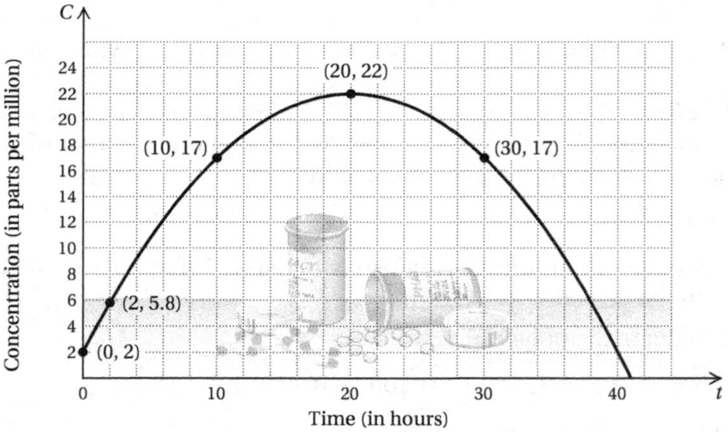

Do Exercises 9 and 10.

9. Medical Dosage.

a) Referring to Example 5, determine the concentration after 3 hr by evaluating the polynomial when $t = 3$.

b) Use *only* the graph showing medical dosage to check the value found in part (a).

10. Medical Dosage. Referring to Example 5, use *only* the graph showing medical dosage to estimate the value of the polynomial when $t = 26$.

Answers

9. (a) 7.55 parts per million; (b) When $t = 3$, $C \approx 7.5$ so the value found in part (a) appears to be correct. **10.** 20 parts per million

b Identifying Terms

As we saw in Section 1.4, subtractions can be rewritten as additions. For any polynomial that has some subtractions, we can find an equivalent polynomial using only additions.

EXAMPLES Find an equivalent polynomial using only additions.

6. $-5x^2 - x = -5x^2 + (-x)$

7. $4x^5 - 2x^6 + 4x - 7 = 4x^5 + (-2x^6) + 4x + (-7)$

Do Exercises 11 and 12.

Find an equivalent polynomial using only additions.

11. $-9x^3 - 4x^5$

12. $-2y^3 + 3y^7 - 7y - 9$

When a polynomial is written using only additions, the monomials being added are called **terms.** In Example 6, the terms are $-5x^2$ and $-x$. In Example 7, the terms are $4x^5$, $-2x^6$, $4x$, and -7.

EXAMPLE 8 Identify the terms of the polynomial

$$4x^7 + 3x + 12 + 8x^3 + 5x.$$

Terms: $4x^7$, $3x$, 12, $8x^3$, and $5x$.

If there are subtractions, you can *think* of them as additions without rewriting.

EXAMPLE 9 Identify the terms of the polynomial

$$3t^4 - 5t^6 - 4t + 2.$$

Terms: $3t^4$, $-5t^6$, $-4t$, and 2.

Do Exercises 13 and 14.

Identify the terms of each polynomial.

13. $3x^2 + 6x + \frac{1}{2}$

14. $-4y^5 + 7y^2 - 3y - 2$

c Like Terms

When terms have the same variable and the same exponent power, we say that they are **like terms.**

EXAMPLES Identify the like terms in the polynomials.

10. $4x^3 + 5x - 4x^2 + 2x^3 + x^2$

Like terms: $4x^3$ and $2x^3$ — Same variable and exponent

Like terms: $-4x^2$ and x^2 — Same variable and exponent

11. $6 - 3a^2 - 8 - a - 5a$

Like terms: 6 and -8 — Constant terms are like terms because $6 = 6x^0$ and $-8 = -8x^0$.

Like terms: $-a$ and $-5a$

Do Exercises 15–17.

Identify the like terms in each polynomial.

15. $4x^3 - x^3 + 2$

16. $4t^4 - 9t^3 - 7t^4 + 10t^3$

17. $5x^2 + 3x - 10 + 7x^2 - 8x + 11$

d Coefficients

The coefficient of the term $5x^3$ is 5. In the following polynomial, the red numbers are the **coefficients**, 3, -2, 5, and 4:

$$3x^5 - 2x^3 + 5x + 4.$$

Answers

11. $-9x^3 + (-4x^5)$
12. $-2y^3 + 3y^7 + (-7y) + (-9)$
13. $3x^2, 6x, \frac{1}{2}$ **14.** $-4y^5, 7y^2, -3y, -2$
15. $4x^3$ and $-x^3$ **16.** $4t^4$ and $-7t^4$; $-9t^3$ and $10t^3$ **17.** $5x^2$ and $7x^2$; $3x$ and $-8x$; -10 and 11

EXAMPLE 12 Identify the coefficient of each term in the polynomial

$$3x^4 - 4x^3 + \frac{1}{2}x^2 + x - 8.$$

The coefficient of the first term is 3.

The coefficient of the second term is -4.

The coefficient of the third term is $\frac{1}{2}$.

The coefficient of the fourth term is 1. $x = 1x$

The coefficient of the fifth term is -8.

18. Identify the coefficient of each term in the polynomial $2x^4 - 7x^3 - 8.5x^2 - x - 4$.

Do Exercise 18.

e Collecting Like Terms

We can often simplify polynomials by **collecting like terms**, or **combining like terms**. To do this, we use the distributive laws. We factor out the variable expression and add or subtract the coefficients. We try to do this mentally as much as possible.

EXAMPLES Collect like terms.

13. $2x^3 - 6x^3 = (2 - 6)x^3$ Using a distributive law

$= -4x^3$

14. $5x^2 + 7 + 4x^4 + 2x^2 - 11 - 2x^4 = (5 + 2)x^2 + (4 - 2)x^4 + (7 - 11)$

$= 7x^2 + 2x^4 - 4$

Collect like terms.

19. $3x^2 + 5x^2$

20. $4x^3 - 2x^3 + 2 + 5$

21. $\frac{1}{2}x^5 - \frac{3}{4}x^5 + 4x^2 - 2x^2$

22. $24 - 4x^3 - 24$

23. $5x^3 - 8x^5 + 8x^5$

24. $-2x^4 + 16 + 2x^4 + 9 - 3x^5$

Note that using the distributive laws in this manner allows us to collect like terms by adding or subtracting the coefficients. Often the middle step is omitted and we add or subtract mentally, writing just the answer. In collecting like terms, we may get 0.

EXAMPLE 15 Collect like terms: $3x^5 + 2x^2 - 3x^5 + 8$.

$3x^5 + 2x^2 - 3x^5 + 8 = (3 - 3)x^5 + 2x^2 + 8$

$= 0x^5 + 2x^2 + 8$

$= 2x^2 + 8$

Do Exercises 19–24.

Expressing a term like x^2 by showing 1 as a factor, $1 \cdot x^2$, may make it easier to understand how to factor or collect like terms.

EXAMPLES Collect like terms.

16. $5x^2 + x^2 = 5x^2 + 1x^2$ Replacing x^2 with $1x^2$

$= (5 + 1)x^2$ Using a distributive law

$= 6x^2$

Answers

18. 2, −7, −8.5, −1, −4 **19.** $8x^2$

20. $2x^3 + 7$ **21.** $-\frac{1}{4}x^5 + 2x^2$ **22.** $-4x^3$

23. $5x^3$ **24.** $25 - 3x^5$

17. $5x^8 - 6x^5 - x^8 = 5x^8 - 6x^5 - 1x^8$ $x^8 = 1x^8$
$= (5 - 1)x^8 - 6x^5$
$= 4x^8 - 6x^5$

18. $\frac{2}{3}x^4 - x^3 - \frac{1}{6}x^4 + \frac{2}{5}x^3 - \frac{3}{10}x^3$
$= \left(\frac{2}{3} - \frac{1}{6}\right)x^4 + \left(-1 + \frac{2}{5} - \frac{3}{10}\right)x^3$ $-x^3 = -1 \cdot x^3$
$= \left(\frac{4}{6} - \frac{1}{6}\right)x^4 + \left(-\frac{10}{10} + \frac{4}{10} - \frac{3}{10}\right)x^3$
$= \frac{3}{6}x^4 - \frac{9}{10}x^3$
$= \frac{1}{2}x^4 - \frac{9}{10}x^3$

Do Exercises 25–28.

Collect like terms.

25. $7x - x$

26. $5x^3 - x^3 + 4$

27. $\frac{3}{4}x^3 + 4x^2 - x^3 + 7$

28. $\frac{4}{5}x^4 - x^4 + x^5 - \frac{1}{5} - \frac{1}{4}x^4 + 10$

f Descending and Ascending Order

Note in the following polynomial that the exponents decrease from left to right. We say that the polynomial is arranged in **descending order**:

$$2x^4 - 8x^3 + 5x^2 - x + 3.$$

The term with the largest exponent is first. The term with the next largest exponent is second, and so on. The associative and commutative laws allow us to arrange the terms of a polynomial in descending order.

EXAMPLES Arrange the polynomial in descending order.

19. $6x^5 + 4x^7 + x^2 + 2x^3 = 4x^7 + 6x^5 + 2x^3 + x^2$

20. $\frac{2}{3} + 4x^5 - 8x^2 + 5x - 3x^3 = 4x^5 - 3x^3 - 8x^2 + 5x + \frac{2}{3}$

Do Exercises 29–31.

Arrange each polynomial in descending order.

29. $x + 3x^5 + 4x^3 + 5x^2 + 6x^7 - 2x^4$

30. $4x^2 - 3 + 7x^5 + 2x^3 - 5x^4$

31. $-14 + 7t^2 - 10t^5 + 14t^7$

EXAMPLE 21 Collect like terms and then arrange in descending order:

$$2x^2 - 4x^3 + 3 - x^2 - 2x^3.$$

$2x^2 - 4x^3 + 3 - x^2 - 2x^3 = x^2 - 6x^3 + 3$ Collecting like terms
$= -6x^3 + x^2 + 3$ Arranging in descending order

Do Exercises 32 and 33.

Collect like terms and then arrange in descending order.

32. $3x^2 - 2x + 3 - 5x^2 - 1 - x$

33. $-x + \frac{1}{2} + 14x^4 - 7x - 1 - 4x^4$

We usually arrange polynomials in descending order, but not always. The opposite order is called **ascending order**. Generally, if an exercise is written in a certain order, we give the answer in that same order.

g Degrees

The **degree** of a term is the exponent of the variable. The degree of the term $-5x^3$ is 3.

EXAMPLE 22 Identify the degree of each term of $8x^4 - 3x + 7$.

The degree of $8x^4$ is 4.
The degree of $-3x$ is 1.   Recall that $x = x^1$.
The degree of 7 is 0.   Think of 7 as $7x^0$. Recall that $x^0 = 1$.

Answers

25. $6x$ 26. $4x^3 + 4$ 27. $-\frac{1}{4}x^3 + 4x^2 + 7$
28. $x^5 - \frac{9}{20}x^4 + \frac{49}{5}$
29. $6x^7 + 3x^5 - 2x^4 + 4x^3 + 5x^2 + x$
30. $7x^5 - 5x^4 + 2x^3 + 4x^2 - 3$
31. $14t^7 - 10t^5 + 7t^2 - 14$
32. $-2x^2 - 3x + 2$ 33. $10x^4 - 8x - \frac{1}{2}$

The **degree of a polynomial** is the largest of the degrees of the terms, unless it is the polynomial 0. The polynomial 0 is a special case. We agree that it has *no* degree either as a term or as a polynomial. This is because we can express 0 as $0 = 0x^5 = 0x^7$, and so on, using any exponent we wish.

EXAMPLE 23 Identify the degree of the polynomial $5x^3 - 6x^4 + 7$.

$5x^3 - 6x^4 + 7.$ The largest exponent is 4.

The degree of the polynomial is 4.

Do Exercises 34 and 35.

Identify the degree of each term and the degree of the polynomial.

34. $-6x^4 + 8x^2 - 2x + 9$

35. $4 - x^3 + \frac{1}{2}x^6 - x^5$

Let's summarize the terminology that we have learned, using the polynomial $3x^4 - 8x^3 + x^2 + 7x - 6$.

TERM	COEFFICIENT	DEGREE OF THE TERM	DEGREE OF THE POLYNOMIAL
$3x^4$	3	4	
$-8x^3$	-8	3	
x^2	1	2	4
$7x$	7	1	
-6	-6	0	

h Missing Terms

If a coefficient is 0, we generally do not write the term. We say that we have a **missing term**.

EXAMPLE 24 Identify the missing terms in the polynomial

$$8x^5 - 2x^3 + 5x^2 + 7x + 8.$$

There is no term with x^4. We say that the x^4-term is missing.

Do Exercises 36–39.

Identify the missing terms in each polynomial.

36. $2x^3 + 4x^2 - 2$

37. $-3x^4$

38. $x^3 + 1$

39. $x^4 - x^2 + 3x + 0.25$

For certain skills or manipulations, we can write missing terms with zero coefficients or leave space.

EXAMPLE 25 Write the polynomial $x^4 - 6x^3 + 2x - 1$ in two ways: with its missing term and by leaving space for it.

a) $x^4 - 6x^3 + 2x - 1 = x^4 - 6x^3 + 0x^2 + 2x - 1$ Writing with the missing x^2-term

b) $x^4 - 6x^3 + 2x - 1 = x^4 - 6x^3 \qquad + 2x - 1$ Leaving space for the missing x^2-term

EXAMPLE 26 Write the polynomial $y^5 - 1$ in two ways: with its missing terms and by leaving space for them.

a) $y^5 - 1 = y^5 + 0y^4 + 0y^3 + 0y^2 + 0y - 1$

b) $y^5 - 1 = y^5 \qquad\qquad\qquad - 1$

Do Exercises 40 and 41.

Write each polynomial in two ways: with its missing terms and by leaving space for them.

40. $2x^3 + 4x^2 - 2$

41. $a^4 + 10$

Answers

34. 4, 2, 1, 0; 4 **35.** 0, 3, 6, 5; 6 **36.** x
37. x^3, x^2, x, x^0 **38.** x^2, x **39.** x^3
40. $2x^3 + 4x^2 + 0x - 2$; $2x^3 + 4x^2 \qquad - 2$
41. $a^4 + 0a^3 + 0a^2 + 0a + 10$; $a^4 \qquad\qquad + 10$

Classifying Polynomials

Polynomials with just one term are called **monomials**. Polynomials with just two terms are called **binomials**. Those with just three terms are called **trinomials**. Those with more than three terms are generally not specified with a name.

EXAMPLE 27

MONOMIALS	BINOMIALS	TRINOMIALS	NONE OF THESE
$4x^2$	$2x + 4$	$3x^3 + 4x + 7$	$4x^3 - 5x^2 + x - 8$
9	$3x^5 + 6x$	$6x^7 - 7x^2 + 4$	$z^5 + 2z^4 - z^3 + 7z + 3$
$-23x^{19}$	$-9x^7 - 6$	$4x^2 - 6x - \frac{1}{2}$	$4x^6 - 3x^5 + x^4 - x^3 + 2x - 1$

Do Exercises 42–45.

Classify each polynomial as a monomial, a binomial, a trinomial, or none of these.

42. $3x^2 + x$

43. $5x^4$

44. $4x^3 - 3x^2 + 4x + 2$

45. $3x^2 + 2x - 4$

Answers

42. Binomial **43.** Monomial **44.** None of these **45.** Trinomial

3.3 Exercise Set

For Extra Help
MyMathLab
MathXL PRACTICE WATCH DOWNLOAD READ REVIEW

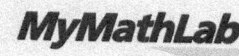

a Evaluate each polynomial when $x = 4$ and when $x = -1$.

1. $-5x + 2$

2. $-8x + 1$

3. $2x^2 - 5x + 7$

4. $3x^2 + x - 7$

5. $x^3 - 5x^2 + x$

6. $7 - x + 3x^2$

Evaluate each polynomial when $x = -2$ and when $x = 0$.

7. $\frac{1}{3}x + 5$

8. $8 - \frac{1}{4}x$

9. $x^2 - 2x + 1$

10. $5x + 6 - x^2$

11. $-3x^3 + 7x^2 - 3x - 2$

12. $-2x^3 + 5x^2 - 4x + 3$

13. *Skydiving.* During the first 13 sec of a jump, the distance S, in feet, that a skydiver falls in t seconds can be approximated by the polynomial equation

$$S = 11.12t^2.$$

Approximately how far has a skydiver fallen 10 sec after having jumped from a plane?

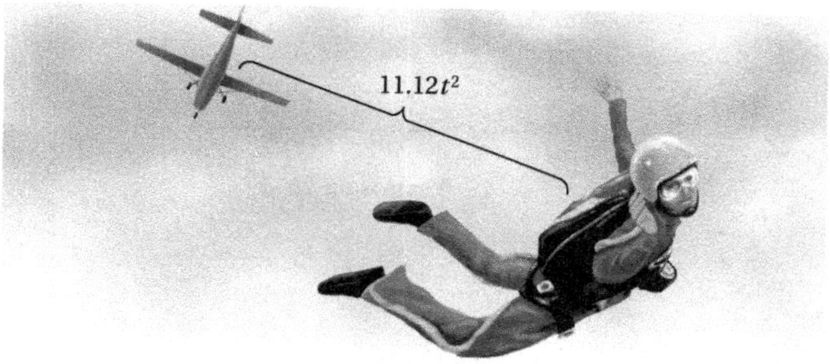

14. *Skydiving.* For jumps that exceed 13 sec, the polynomial equation

$$S = 173t - 369$$

can be used to approximate the distance S, in feet, that a skydiver has fallen in t seconds. Approximately how far has a skydiver fallen 20 sec after having jumped from a plane?

15. *Total Revenue.* Hadley Electronics is marketing a new type of plasma TV. The firm determines that when it sells x TVs, its total revenue R (the total amount of money taken in) will be

$$R = 280x - 0.4x^2 \text{ dollars.}$$

What is the total revenue from the sale of 75 TVs? 100 TVs?

16. *Total Cost.* Hadley Electronics determines that the total cost C of producing x plasma TVs is given by

$$C = 5000 + 0.6x^2 \text{ dollars.}$$

What is the total cost of producing 500 TVs? 650 TVs?

17. The graph of the polynomial equation $y = 5 - x^2$ is shown below. Use *only* the graph to estimate the value of the polynomial when $x = -3$, $x = -1$, $x = 0$, $x = 1.5$, and $x = 2$.

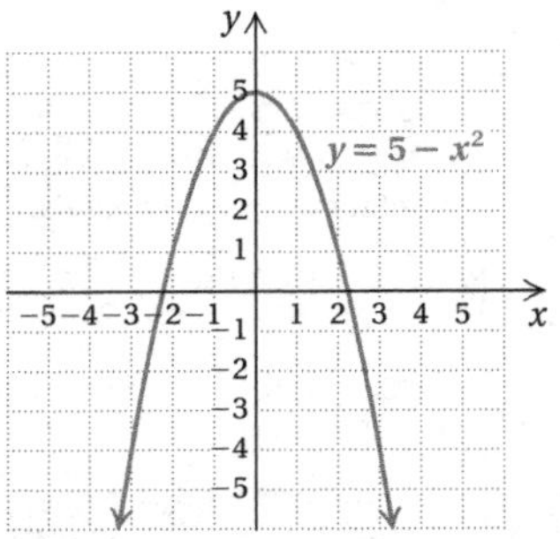

18. The graph of the polynomial equation $y = 6x^3 - 6x$ is shown below. Use *only* the graph to estimate the value of the polynomial when $x = -1$, $x = -0.5$, $x = 0.5$, $x = 1$, and $x = 1.1$.

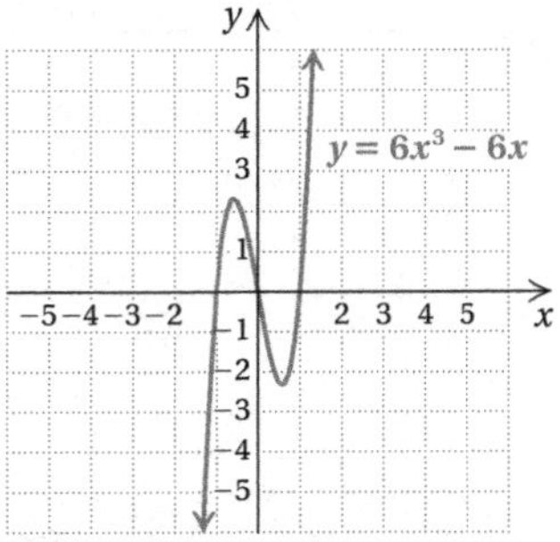

19. *Electricity Consumption.* The net consumption of electricity in China can be estimated by the polynomial equation

$$E = 158.68t + 2728.4,$$

where E is the consumption of electricity, in billions of kilowatt-hours, and t is the number of years after 2010. That is, $t = 0$ corresponds to 2010, $t = 5$ corresponds to 2015, and so on.

Source: Energy Information Administration

a) Use the equation to estimate the consumption of electricity, in billions of kilowatt-hours, in 2010, 2015, 2020, 2025, and 2030.

b) Check the results of part (a) using the graph below.

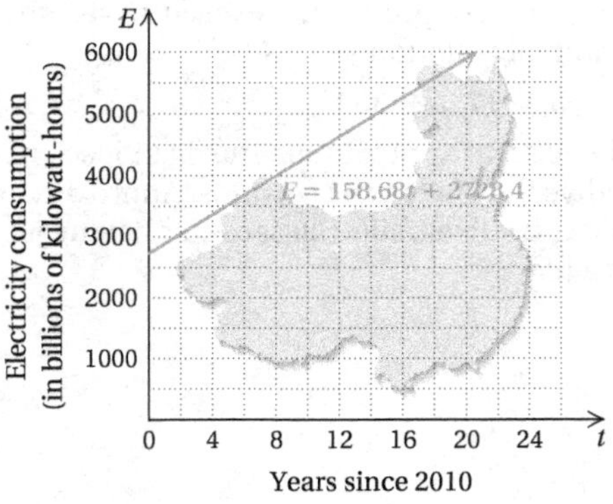

20. *Electricity Consumption.* The net consumption of electricity in the United States can be estimated by the polynomial equation

$$E = 72.9t + 4134.4,$$

where E is the consumption of electricity, in billions of kilowatt-hours, and t is the number of years after 2010. That is, $t = 0$ corresponds to 2010, $t = 5$ corresponds to 2015, and so on.

Source: Energy Information Administration

a) Use the equation to estimate the consumption of electricity, in billions of kilowatt-hours, in 2010, 2015, 2020, 2025, and 2030.

b) Check the results of part (a) using the graph below.

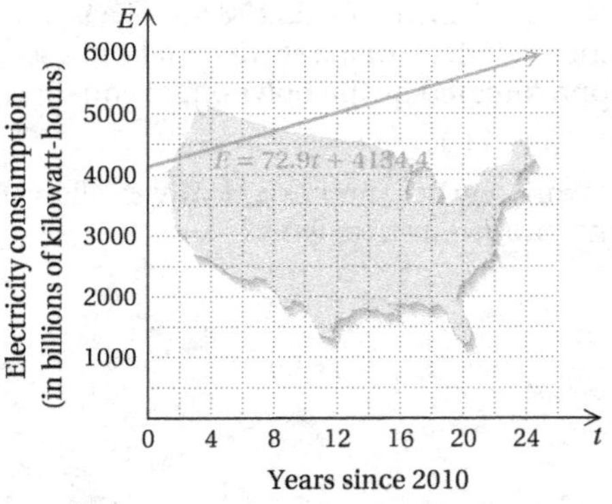

Memorizing Words. Participants in a psychology experiment were able to memorize an average of M words in t minutes, where $M = -0.001t^3 + 0.1t^2$. Use the graph below for Exercises 21–26.

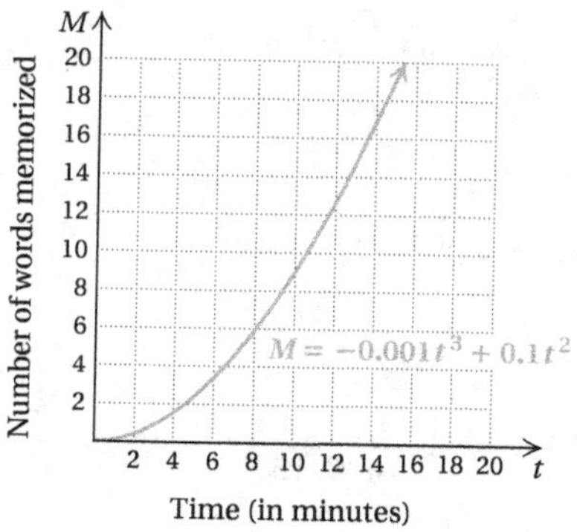

21. Estimate the number of words memorized after 10 min.

22. Estimate the number of words memorized after 14 min.

23. Find the approximate value of M for $t = 8$.

24. Find the approximate value of M for $t = 12$.

25. Estimate the value of M when t is 13.

26. Estimate the value of M when t is 7.

b Identify the terms of each polynomial.

27. $2 - 3x + x^2$

28. $2x^2 + 3x - 4$

29. $-2x^4 + \frac{1}{3}x^3 - x + 3$

30. $-\frac{2}{5}x^5 - x^3 + 6$

c Identify the like terms in each polynomial.

31. $5x^3 + 6x^2 - 3x^2$

32. $3x^2 + 4x^3 - 2x^2$

33. $2x^4 + 5x - 7x - 3x^4$

34. $-3t + t^3 - 2t - 5t^3$

35. $3x^5 - 7x + 8 + 14x^5 - 2x - 9$

36. $8x^3 + 7x^2 - 11 - 4x^3 - 8x^2 - 29$

d Identify the coefficient of each term of the polynomial.

37. $-3x + 6$

38. $2x - 4$

39. $5x^2 + \frac{3}{4}x + 3$

40. $\frac{2}{3}x^2 - 5x + 2$

41. $-5x^4 + 6x^3 - 2.7x^2 + x - 2$

42. $7x^3 - x^2 - 4.2x + 5$

e Collect like terms.

43. $2x - 5x$

44. $2x^2 + 8x^2$

45. $x - 9x$

46. $x - 5x$

47. $5x^3 + 6x^3 + 4$

48. $6x^4 - 2x^4 + 5$

49. $5x^3 + 6x - 4x^3 - 7x$

50. $3a^4 - 2a + 2a + a^4$

51. $6b^5 + 3b^2 - 2b^5 - 3b^2$

52. $2x^2 - 6x + 3x + 4x^2$

53. $\frac{1}{4}x^5 - 5 + \frac{1}{2}x^5 - 2x - 37$

54. $\frac{1}{3}x^3 + 2x - \frac{1}{6}x^3 + 4 - 16$

55. $6x^2 + 2x^4 - 2x^2 - x^4 - 4x^2$

56. $8x^2 + 2x^3 - 3x^3 - 4x^2 - 4x^2$

57. $\frac{1}{4}x^3 - x^2 - \frac{1}{6}x^2 + \frac{3}{8}x^3 + \frac{5}{16}x^3$

58. $\frac{1}{5}x^4 + \frac{1}{5} - 2x^2 + \frac{1}{10} - \frac{3}{15}x^4 + 2x^2 - \frac{3}{10}$

f Arrange each polynomial in descending order.

59. $x^5 + x + 6x^3 + 1 + 2x^2$

60. $3 + 2x^2 - 5x^6 - 2x^3 + 3x$

61. $5y^3 + 15y^9 + y - y^2 + 7y^8$

62. $9p - 5 + 6p^3 - 5p^4 + p^5$

Collect like terms and then arrange in descending order.

63. $3x^4 - 5x^6 - 2x^4 + 6x^6$

64. $-1 + 5x^3 - 3 - 7x^3 + x^4 + 5$

65. $-2x + 4x^3 - 7x + 9x^3 + 8$

66. $-6x^2 + x - 5x + 7x^2 + 1$

67. $3x + 3x + 3x - x^2 - 4x^2$

68. $-2x - 2x - 2x + x^3 - 5x^3$

69. $-x + \frac{3}{4} + 15x^4 - x - \frac{1}{2} - 3x^4$

70. $2x - \frac{5}{6} + 4x^3 + x + \frac{1}{3} - 2x$

g Identify the degree of each term of the polynomial and the degree of the polynomial.

71. $2x - 4$

72. $6 - 3x$

73. $3x^2 - 5x + 2$

74. $5x^3 - 2x^2 + 3$

75. $-7x^3 + 6x^2 + \frac{3}{5}x + 7$

76. $5x^4 + \frac{1}{4}x^2 - x + 2$

77. $x^2 - 3x + x^6 - 9x^4$

78. $8x - 3x^2 + 9 - 8x^3$

79. Complete the following table for the polynomial $-7x^4 + 6x^3 - x^2 + 8x - 2$.

TERM	COEFFICIENT	DEGREE OF THE TERM	DEGREE OF THE POLYNOMIAL
$-7x^4$			
$6x^3$	6		
		2	
$8x$		1	
	-2		

80. Complete the following table for the polynomial $3x^2 + x^5 - 46x^3 + 6x - 2.4 - \frac{1}{2}x^4$.

TERM	COEFFICIENT	DEGREE OF THE TERM	DEGREE OF THE POLYNOMIAL
		5	
$-\frac{1}{2}x^4$		4	
	-46		
$3x^2$		2	
	6		
-2.4			

h Identify the missing terms in each polynomial.

81. $x^3 - 27$

82. $x^5 + x$

83. $x^4 - x$

84. $5x^4 - 7x + 2$

85. $2x^3 - 5x^2 + x - 3$

86. $-6x^3$

Write each polynomial in two ways: with its missing terms and by leaving space for them.

87. $x^3 - 27$

88. $x^5 + x$

89. $x^4 - x$

90. $5x^4 - 7x + 2$

91. $2x^3 - 5x^2 + x - 3$

92. $-6x^3$

i Classify each polynomial as a monomial, a binomial, a trinomial, or none of these.

93. $x^2 - 10x + 25$

94. $-6x^4$

95. $x^3 - 7x^2 + 2x - 4$

96. $x^2 - 9$

97. $4x^2 - 25$

98. $2x^4 - 7x^3 + x^2 + x - 6$

99. $40x$

100. $4x^2 + 12x + 9$

Skill Maintenance

101. Three tired hikers camped overnight. All they had to eat was a bag of apples. During the night, one awoke and ate one-third of the apples. Later, a second camper awoke and ate one-third of the apples that remained. Much later, the third camper awoke and ate one-third of those apples yet remaining after the other two had eaten. When they got up the next morning, 8 apples were left. How many apples did they begin with? [2.6a]

Subtract. [1.4a]

102. $1 - 20$

103. $\frac{1}{8} - \frac{5}{6}$

104. $\frac{3}{8} - \left(-\frac{1}{4}\right)$

105. $5.6 - 8.2$

106. Solve: $3(x + 2) = 5x - 9$. [2.3c]

107. Solve $C = ab - r$ for b. [2.4b]

108. A warehouse stores 1800 lb of peanuts, 1500 lb of cashews, and 700 lb of almonds. What percent of the total is peanuts? cashews? almonds? [2.5a]

109. Factor: $3x - 15y + 63$. [1.7d]

Synthesis

Collect like terms.

110. $6x^3 \cdot 7x^2 - (4x^3)^2 + (-3x^3)^2 - (-4x^2)(5x^3) - 10x^5 + 17x^6$

111. $(3x^2)^3 + 4x^2 \cdot 4x^4 - x^4(2x)^2 + ((2x)^2)^3 - 100x^2(x^2)^2$

112. Construct a polynomial in x (meaning that x is the variable) of degree 5 with four terms and coefficients that are integers.

113. What is the degree of $(5m^5)^2$?

114. A polynomial in x has degree 3. The coefficient of x^2 is 3 less than the coefficient of x^3. The coefficient of x is three times the coefficient of x^2. The remaining coefficient is 2 more than the coefficient of x^3. The sum of the coefficients is -4. Find the polynomial.

Use the CALC feature and choose VALUE on your graphing calculator to find the values in each of the following. (Refer to the Calculator Corner on p. 238.)

115. Exercise 17

116. Exercise 18

117. Exercise 21

118. Exercise 22

3.4 Addition and Subtraction of Polynomials

OBJECTIVES

a Add polynomials.

b Simplify the opposite of a polynomial.

c Subtract polynomials.

d Use polynomials to represent perimeter and area.

SKILL TO REVIEW
Objective 1.4a: Subtract real numbers and simplify combinations of additions and subtractions.

Simplify.

1. $-4 - (-8)$
2. $-5 - 6 + 4$

a Addition of Polynomials

To add two polynomials, we can write a plus sign between them and then collect like terms. Depending on the situation, you may see polynomials written in descending order, ascending order, or neither. Generally, if an exercise is written in a particular order, we write the answer in that same order.

EXAMPLE 1 Add: $(-3x^3 + 2x - 4) + (4x^3 + 3x^2 + 2)$.

$$\begin{aligned}(-3x^3 + 2x - 4) &+ (4x^3 + 3x^2 + 2)\\ &= (-3 + 4)x^3 + 3x^2 + 2x + (-4 + 2) \quad \text{Collecting like terms}\\ &= x^3 + 3x^2 + 2x - 2\end{aligned}$$

EXAMPLE 2 Add:

$$\left(\tfrac{2}{3}x^4 + 3x^2 - 2x + \tfrac{1}{2}\right) + \left(-\tfrac{1}{3}x^4 + 5x^3 - 3x^2 + 3x - \tfrac{1}{2}\right).$$

We have

$$\begin{aligned}&\left(\tfrac{2}{3}x^4 + 3x^2 - 2x + \tfrac{1}{2}\right) + \left(-\tfrac{1}{3}x^4 + 5x^3 - 3x^2 + 3x - \tfrac{1}{2}\right)\\ &\quad = \left(\tfrac{2}{3} - \tfrac{1}{3}\right)x^4 + 5x^3 + (3 - 3)x^2 + (-2 + 3)x + \left(\tfrac{1}{2} - \tfrac{1}{2}\right) \quad \text{Collecting like terms}\\ &\quad = \tfrac{1}{3}x^4 + 5x^3 + x.\end{aligned}$$

We can add polynomials as we do because they represent numbers. After some practice, you will be able to add mentally.

Do Margin Exercises 1–4.

EXAMPLE 3 Add: $(3x^2 - 2x + 2) + (5x^3 - 2x^2 + 3x - 4)$.

$$\begin{aligned}(3x^2 - 2x + 2) &+ (5x^3 - 2x^2 + 3x - 4)\\ &= 5x^3 + (3 - 2)x^2 + (-2 + 3)x + (2 - 4) \quad \text{You might do this step mentally.}\\ &= 5x^3 + x^2 + x - 2 \quad \text{Then you would write only this.}\end{aligned}$$

Do Exercises 5 and 6 on the following page.

We can also add polynomials by writing like terms in columns.

EXAMPLE 4 Add: $9x^5 - 2x^3 + 6x^2 + 3$ and $5x^4 - 7x^2 + 6$ and $3x^6 - 5x^5 + x^2 + 5$.

We arrange the polynomials with the like terms in columns.

$$\begin{array}{rrrrrr} & 9x^5 & & -\,2x^3 & +\,6x^2 & +\ 3\\ & & 5x^4 & & -\,7x^2 & +\ 6\\ 3x^6 & -\,5x^5 & & & +\ x^2 & +\ 5\\ \hline 3x^6 & +\,4x^5 & +\,5x^4 & -\,2x^3 & & +\,14\end{array}$$

We leave spaces for missing terms. Adding

We write the answer as $3x^6 + 4x^5 + 5x^4 - 2x^3 + 14$ without the space.

Add.

1. $(3x^2 + 2x - 2) + (-2x^2 + 5x + 5)$
2. $(-4x^5 + x^3 + 4) + (7x^4 + 2x^2)$
3. $(31x^4 + x^2 + 2x - 1) + (-7x^4 + 5x^3 - 2x + 2)$
4. $(17x^3 - x^2 + 3x + 4) + \left(-15x^3 + x^2 - 3x - \dfrac{2}{3}\right)$

Answers

Skill to Review:
1. 4 2. −7

Margin Exercises:
1. $x^2 + 7x + 3$
2. $-4x^5 + 7x^4 + x^3 + 2x^2 + 4$
3. $24x^4 + 5x^3 + x^2 + 1$
4. $2x^3 + \dfrac{10}{3}$

Add mentally. Try to write just the answer.

5. $(4x^2 - 5x + 3) + (-2x^2 + 2x - 4)$

6. $(3x^3 - 4x^2 - 5x + 3) + \left(5x^3 + 2x^2 - 3x - \frac{1}{2}\right)$

Add.

7.
$$\begin{array}{r} -2x^3 + 5x^2 - 2x + 4 \\ x^4 \quad + 6x^2 + 7x - 10 \\ -9x^4 + 6x^3 + x^2 \quad - 2 \\ \hline \end{array}$$

8. $-3x^3 + 5x + 2$ and $x^3 + x^2 + 5$ and $x^3 - 2x - 4$

Simplify.

9. $-(4x^3 - 6x + 3)$

10. $-(5x^4 + 3x^2 + 7x - 5)$

11. $-\left(14x^{10} - \frac{1}{2}x^5 + 5x^3 - x^2 + 3x\right)$

Subtract.

12. $(7x^3 + 2x + 4) - (5x^3 - 4)$

13. $(-3x^2 + 5x - 4) - (-4x^2 + 11x - 2)$

Answers

5. $2x^2 - 3x - 1$ 6. $8x^3 - 2x^2 - 8x + \frac{5}{2}$
7. $-8x^4 + 4x^3 + 12x^2 + 5x - 8$
8. $-x^3 + x^2 + 3x + 3$ 9. $-4x^3 + 6x - 3$
10. $-5x^4 - 3x^2 - 7x + 5$
11. $-14x^{10} + \frac{1}{2}x^5 - 5x^3 + x^2 - 3x$
12. $2x^3 + 2x + 8$ 13. $x^2 - 6x - 2$

Do Exercises 7 and 8.

b Opposites of Polynomials

In Section 1.8, we used the property of -1 to show that we can find the opposite of an expression. For example, the opposite of $x - 2y + 5$ can be written as

$$-(x - 2y + 5).$$

We find an equivalent expression by changing the sign of every term:

$$-(x - 2y + 5) = -x + 2y - 5.$$

We use this concept when we subtract polynomials.

OPPOSITES OF POLYNOMIALS

To find an equivalent polynomial for the **opposite**, or **additive inverse**, of a polynomial, change the sign of every term. This is the same as multiplying by -1.

EXAMPLE 5 Simplify: $-(x^2 - 3x + 4)$.

$$-(x^2 - 3x + 4) = -x^2 + 3x - 4$$

EXAMPLE 6 Simplify: $-(-t^3 - 6t^2 - t + 4)$.

$$-(-t^3 - 6t^2 - t + 4) = t^3 + 6t^2 + t - 4$$

EXAMPLE 7 Simplify: $-\left(-7x^4 - \frac{5}{9}x^3 + 8x^2 - x + 67\right)$.

$$-\left(-7x^4 - \frac{5}{9}x^3 + 8x^2 - x + 67\right) = 7x^4 + \frac{5}{9}x^3 - 8x^2 + x - 67$$

Do Exercises 9–11.

c Subtraction of Polynomials

Recall that we can subtract a real number by adding its opposite, or additive inverse: $a - b = a + (-b)$. This allows us to subtract polynomials.

EXAMPLE 8 Subtract:

$$(9x^5 + x^3 - 2x^2 + 4) - (2x^5 + x^4 - 4x^3 - 3x^2).$$

We have

$(9x^5 + x^3 - 2x^2 + 4) - (2x^5 + x^4 - 4x^3 - 3x^2)$

$= 9x^5 + x^3 - 2x^2 + 4 + [-(2x^5 + x^4 - 4x^3 - 3x^2)]$ Adding the opposite

$= 9x^5 + x^3 - 2x^2 + 4 - 2x^5 - x^4 + 4x^3 + 3x^2$ Finding the opposite by changing the sign of *each* term

$= 7x^5 - x^4 + 5x^3 + x^2 + 4.$ Adding (collecting like terms)

Do Exercises 12 and 13.

As with similar work in Section 1.8, we combine steps by changing the sign of each term of the polynomial being subtracted and collecting like terms. Try to do this mentally as much as possible.

EXAMPLE 9 Subtract: $(9x^5 + x^3 - 2x) - (-2x^5 + 5x^3 + 6)$.

$(9x^5 + x^3 - 2x) - (-2x^5 + 5x^3 + 6)$

$= 9x^5 + x^3 - 2x + 2x^5 - 5x^3 - 6$ Finding the opposite by changing the sign of each term

$= 11x^5 - 4x^3 - 2x - 6$ Adding (collecting like terms)

Do Exercises 14 and 15.

Subtract.

14. $(-6x^4 + 3x^2 + 6) - (2x^4 + 5x^3 - 5x^2 + 7)$

15. $\left(\frac{3}{2}x^3 - \frac{1}{2}x^2 + 0.3\right) - \left(\frac{1}{2}x^3 + \frac{1}{2}x^2 + \frac{4}{3}x + 1.2\right)$

We can use columns to subtract. We replace coefficients with their opposites, as shown in Example 9.

EXAMPLE 10 Write in columns and subtract:

$(5x^2 - 3x + 6) - (9x^2 - 5x - 3)$.

a) $\begin{array}{r} 5x^2 - 3x + 6 \\ -(9x^2 - 5x - 3) \\ \hline \end{array}$ Writing like terms in columns

b) $\begin{array}{r} 5x^2 - 3x + 6 \\ -9x^2 + 5x + 3 \\ \hline \end{array}$ Changing signs

c) $\begin{array}{r} 5x^2 - 3x + 6 \\ -9x^2 + 5x + 3 \\ \hline -4x^2 + 2x + 9 \end{array}$ Adding

If you can do so without error, you can arrange the polynomials in columns and write just the answer, remembering to change the signs and add.

EXAMPLE 11 Write in columns and subtract:

$(x^3 + x^2 + 2x - 12) - (-2x^3 + x^2 - 3x)$.

$\begin{array}{rrrr} x^3 + x^2 + 2x - 12 \\ -(-2x^3 + x^2 - 3x \qquad) \\ \hline 3x^3 \qquad + 5x - 12 \end{array}$

Leaving space for the missing term

Changing the signs and adding

Do Exercises 16 and 17.

Write in columns and subtract.

16. $(4x^3 + 2x^2 - 2x - 3) - (2x^3 - 3x^2 + 2)$

17. $(2x^3 + x^2 - 6x + 2) - (x^5 + 4x^3 - 2x^2 - 4x)$

d Polynomials and Geometry

EXAMPLE 12 Find a polynomial for the sum of the areas of these rectangles.

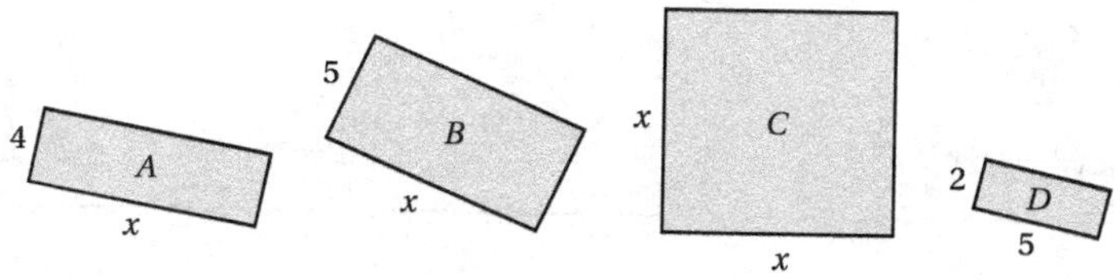

Recall that the area of a rectangle is the product of the length and the width. The sum of the areas is a sum of products. We find these products and then collect like terms.

Answers

14. $-8x^4 - 5x^3 + 8x^2 - 1$
15. $x^3 - x^2 - \frac{4}{3}x - 0.9$
16. $2x^3 + 5x^2 - 2x - 5$
17. $-x^5 - 2x^3 + 3x^2 - 2x + 2$

Area of A	plus	Area of B	plus	Area of C	plus	Area of D
$4 \cdot x$	$+$	$5 \cdot x$	$+$	$x \cdot x$	$+$	$2 \cdot 5$

We collect like terms:

$$4x + 5x + x^2 + 10 = x^2 + 9x + 10.$$

Do Exercise 18.

18. Find a polynomial for the sums of the perimeters and of the areas of the rectangles.

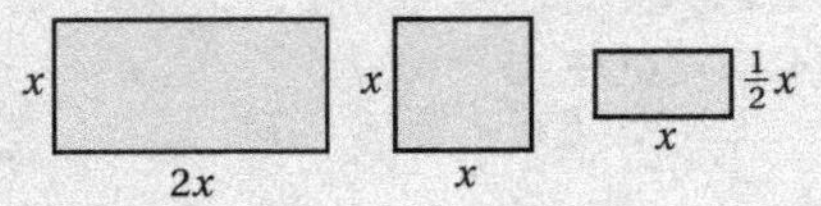

EXAMPLE 13 *Lawn Area.* A water fountain with a 4-ft by 4-ft square base is placed in a park in a square grassy area that is x ft on a side. To determine the amount of grass seed needed for the lawn, find a polynomial for the grassy area.

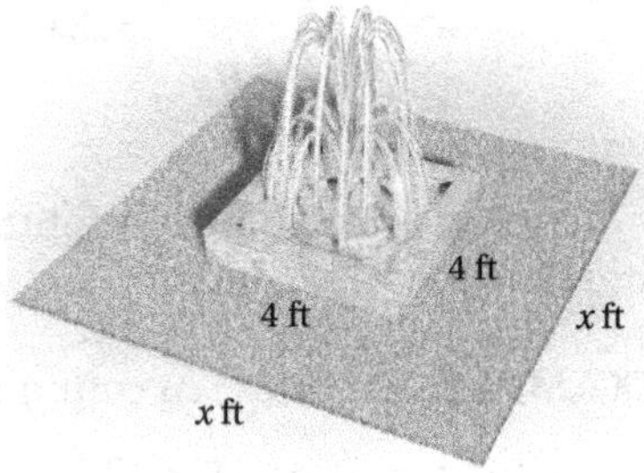

We make a drawing of the situation as shown here. We then reword the problem and write the polynomial as follows:

Area of grassy area	$-$	Area of base of fountain	$=$	Area left over
$x \cdot x$	$-$	$4 \cdot 4$	$=$	Area left over.

Then $(x^2 - 16)\ \text{ft}^2$ = Area left over.

Do Exercise 19.

19. Lawn Area. An 8-ft by 8-ft shed is placed on a lawn x ft on a side. Find a polynomial for the remaining area.

Calculator Corner

Checking Addition and Subtraction of Polynomials A table set in AUTO mode can be used to perform a partial check that polynomials have been added or subtracted correctly. To check Example 3, we enter $y_1 = (3x^2 - 2x + 2) + (5x^3 - 2x^2 + 3x - 4)$ and $y_2 = 5x^3 + x^2 + x - 2$. If the addition has been done correctly, the values of y_1 and y_2 will be the same regardless of the table settings used.

X	Y1	Y2
−2	−40	−40
−1	−7	−7
0	−2	−2
1	5	5
2	44	44
3	145	145
4	338	338

X = −2

A graph can also be used to check addition and subtraction. See the Calculator Corner on p. 262 for the procedure.

Exercises: Use a table to determine whether the sum or the difference is correct.

1. $(-3x^3 + 2x - 4) + (4x^3 + 3x^2 + 2) = x^3 + 3x^2 + 2x - 2$
2. $(x^3 - 2x^2 + 3x - 7) + (3x^2 - 4x + 5) = x^3 + x^2 - x - 2$
3. $(5x^2 - 7x + 4) + (2x^2 + 3x - 6) = 7x^2 + 4x - 2$
4. $(9x^5 + x^3 - 2x) - (-2x^5 + 5x^3 + 6) = 11x^5 - 4x^3 - 2x - 6$
5. $(3x^4 - 2x^2 - 1) - (2x^4 - 3x^2 - 4) = x^4 + x^2 - 5$
6. $(-2x^3 + 3x^2 - 4x + 5) - (3x^2 + 2x + 8) = -2x^3 - 6x - 3$

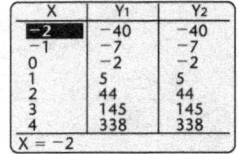

Answers

18. Sum of perimeters: $13x$; sum of areas: $\frac{7}{2}x^2$

19. $(x^2 - 64)\ \text{ft}^2$

3.4 Exercise Set

For Extra Help

MyMathLab | Math XL PRACTICE | WATCH | DOWNLOAD | READ | REVIEW

a Add.

1. $(3x + 2) + (-4x + 3)$

2. $(6x + 1) + (-7x + 2)$

3. $(-6x + 2) + \left(x^2 + \frac{1}{2}x - 3\right)$

4. $\left(x^2 - \frac{5}{3}x + 4\right) + (8x - 9)$

5. $(x^2 - 9) + (x^2 + 9)$

6. $(x^3 + x^2) + (2x^3 - 5x^2)$

7. $(3x^2 - 5x + 10) + (2x^2 + 8x - 40)$

8. $(6x^4 + 3x^3 - 1) + (4x^2 - 3x + 3)$

9. $(1.2x^3 + 4.5x^2 - 3.8x) + (-3.4x^3 - 4.7x^2 + 23)$

10. $(0.5x^4 - 0.6x^2 + 0.7) + (2.3x^4 + 1.8x - 3.9)$

11. $(1 + 4x + 6x^2 + 7x^3) + (5 - 4x + 6x^2 - 7x^3)$

12. $(3x^4 - 6x - 5x^2 + 5) + (6x^2 - 4x^3 - 1 + 7x)$

13. $\left(\frac{1}{4}x^4 + \frac{2}{3}x^3 + \frac{5}{8}x^2 + 7\right) + \left(-\frac{3}{4}x^4 + \frac{3}{8}x^2 - 7\right)$

14. $\left(\frac{1}{3}x^9 + \frac{1}{5}x^5 - \frac{1}{2}x^2 + 7\right) +$
$\left(-\frac{1}{5}x^9 + \frac{1}{4}x^4 - \frac{3}{5}x^5 + \frac{3}{4}x^2 + \frac{1}{2}\right)$

15. $(0.02x^5 - 0.2x^3 + x + 0.08) +$
$(-0.01x^5 + x^4 - 0.8x - 0.02)$

16. $(0.03x^6 + 0.05x^3 + 0.22x + 0.05) +$
$\left(\frac{7}{100}x^6 - \frac{3}{100}x^3 + 0.5\right)$

17. $(9x^8 - 7x^4 + 2x^2 + 5) + (8x^7 + 4x^4 - 2x) +$
$(-3x^4 + 6x^2 + 2x - 1)$

18. $(4x^5 - 6x^3 - 9x + 1) + (6x^3 + 9x^2 + 9x) +$
$(-4x^3 + 8x^2 + 3x - 2)$

19.

$$\begin{array}{rrrrr}
0.15x^4 & + 0.10x^3 & - \;\; 0.9x^2 & & \\
 & - 0.01x^3 & + 0.01x^2 & + x & \\
1.25x^4 & & + 0.11x^2 & & + 0.01 \\
 & 0.27x^3 & & & + 0.99 \\
-0.35x^4 & & + \;\; 15x^2 & & - 0.03 \\
\hline
\end{array}$$

20.

$$\begin{array}{rrrrr}
0.05x^4 & + 0.12x^3 & - \;\; 0.5x^2 & & \\
 & - 0.02x^3 & + 0.02x^2 & + 2x & \\
1.5x^4 & & + 0.01x^2 & & + 0.15 \\
 & 0.25x^3 & & & + 0.85 \\
-0.25x^4 & & + \;\; 10x^2 & & - 0.04 \\
\hline
\end{array}$$

b Simplify.

21. $-(-5x)$

22. $-(x^2 - 3x)$

23. $-\left(-x^2 + \frac{3}{2}x - 2\right)$

24. $-\left(-4x^3 - x^2 - \frac{1}{4}x\right)$

25. $-(12x^4 - 3x^3 + 3)$

26. $-(4x^3 - 6x^2 - 8x + 1)$

27. $-(3x - 7)$

28. $-(-2x + 4)$

29. $-(4x^2 - 3x + 2)$

30. $-(-6a^3 + 2a^2 - 9a + 1)$

31. $-\left(-4x^4 + 6x^2 + \frac{3}{4}x - 8\right)$

32. $-(-5x^4 + 4x^3 - x^2 + 0.9)$

c Subtract.

33. $(3x + 2) - (-4x + 3)$

34. $(6x + 1) - (-7x + 2)$

35. $(-6x + 2) - (x^2 + x - 3)$

36. $(x^2 - 5x + 4) - (8x - 9)$

37. $(x^2 - 9) - (x^2 + 9)$

38. $(x^3 + x^2) - (2x^3 - 5x^2)$

39. $(6x^4 + 3x^3 - 1) - (4x^2 - 3x + 3)$

40. $(-4x^2 + 2x) - (3x^3 - 5x^2 + 3)$

41. $(1.2x^3 + 4.5x^2 - 3.8x) - (-3.4x^3 - 4.7x^2 + 23)$

42. $(0.5x^4 - 0.6x^2 + 0.7) - (2.3x^4 + 1.8x - 3.9)$

43. $\left(\frac{5}{8}x^3 - \frac{1}{4}x - \frac{1}{3}\right) - \left(-\frac{1}{8}x^3 + \frac{1}{4}x - \frac{1}{3}\right)$

44. $\left(\frac{1}{5}x^3 + 2x^2 - 0.1\right) - \left(-\frac{2}{5}x^3 + 2x^2 + 0.01\right)$

45. $(0.08x^3 - 0.02x^2 + 0.01x) - (0.02x^3 + 0.03x^2 - 1)$

46. $(0.8x^4 + 0.2x - 1) - \left(\frac{7}{10}x^4 + \frac{1}{5}x - 0.1\right)$

Subtract.

47.
$$\begin{array}{r} x^2 + 5x + 6 \\ \underline{-(x^2 + 2x)\phantom{{}+6}} \end{array}$$

48.
$$\begin{array}{r} x^3 \qquad\quad + 1 \\ \underline{-(x^3 + x^2 \qquad)} \end{array}$$

49.
$$\begin{array}{r} 5x^4 + 6x^3 - 9x^2 \qquad\qquad \\ \underline{-(-6x^4 - 6x^3 \qquad\qquad + 8x + 9)} \end{array}$$

50.
$$\begin{array}{r} 5x^4 \qquad + 6x^2 - 3x + 6 \\ \underline{-(\qquad 6x^3 + 7x^2 - 8x - 9)} \end{array}$$

51.
$$\begin{array}{r} x^5 \qquad\qquad\qquad\qquad\qquad - 1 \\ \underline{-(x^5 - x^4 + x^3 - x^2 + x - 1)} \end{array}$$

52.
$$\begin{array}{r} x^5 + x^4 - x^3 + x^2 - x + 2 \\ \underline{-(x^5 - x^4 + x^3 - x^2 - x + 2)} \end{array}$$

d Solve.

Find a polynomial for the perimeter of each figure.

53.

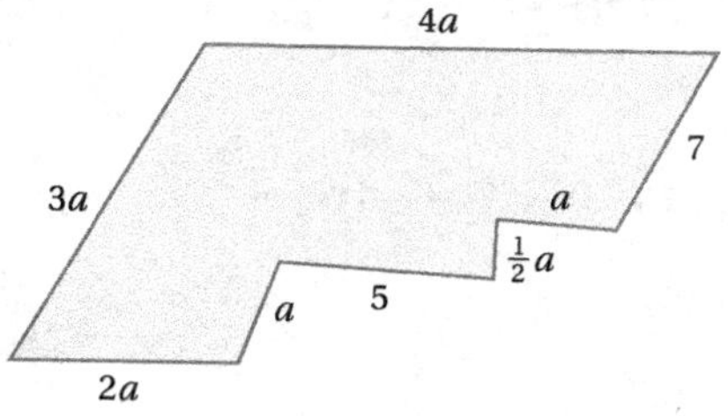

54.

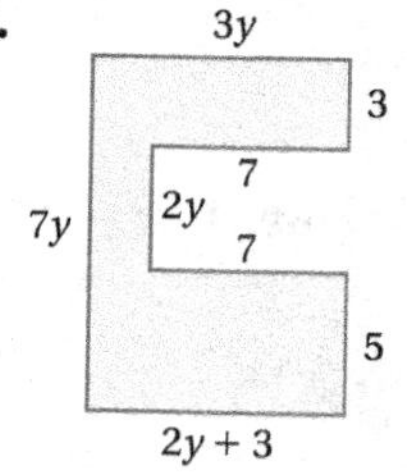

55. Find a polynomial for the sum of the areas of these rectangles.

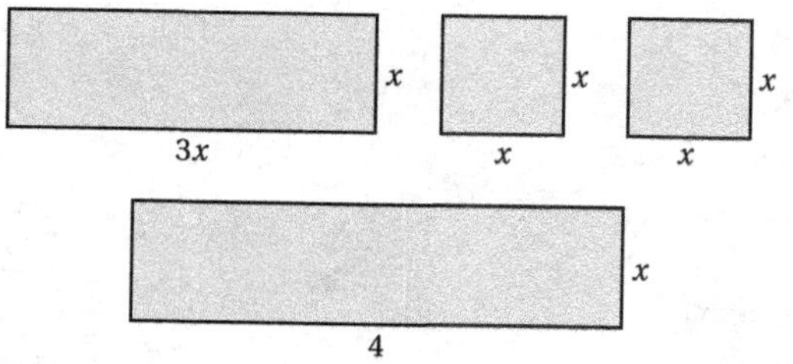

56. Find a polynomial for the sum of the areas of these circles.

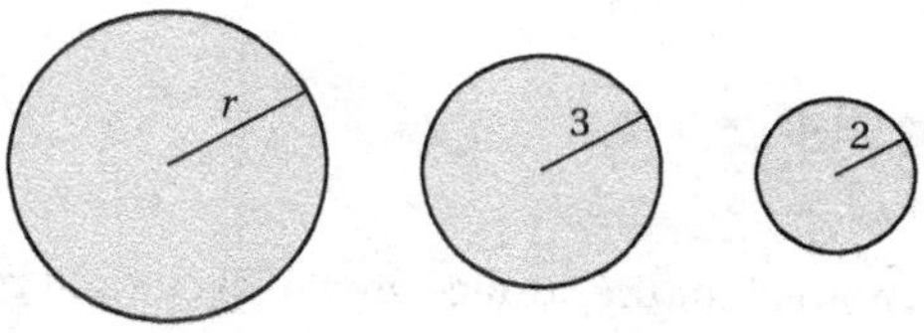

Find two algebraic expressions for the area of each figure. First, regard the figure as one large rectangle, and then regard the figure as a sum of four smaller rectangles.

57.

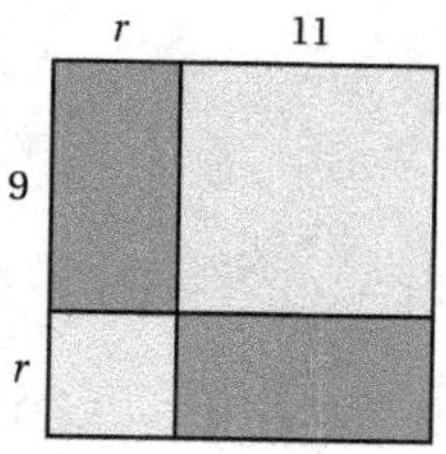

58.

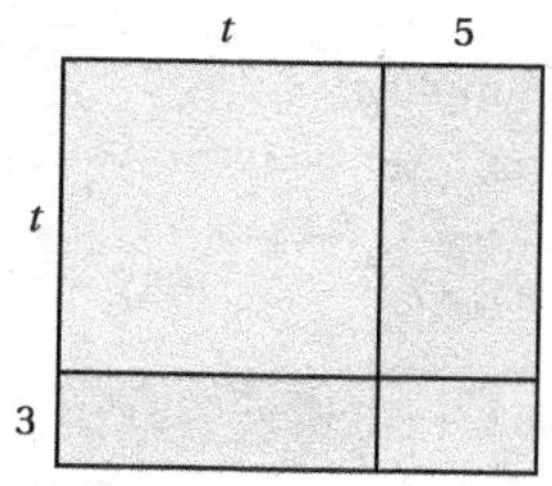

59.

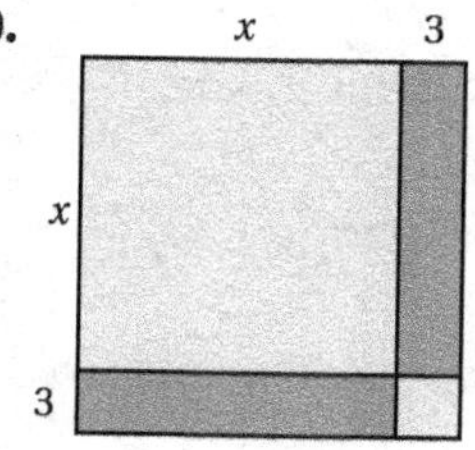

60.

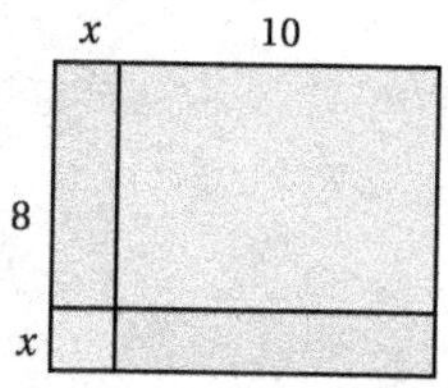

Find a polynomial for the shaded area of each figure.

61.

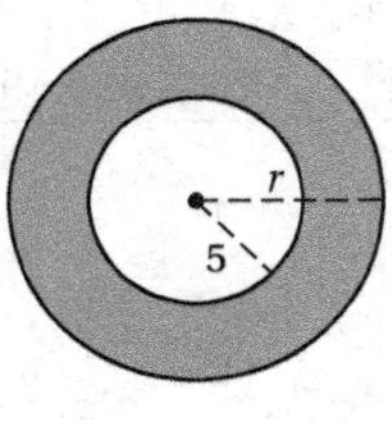

62.

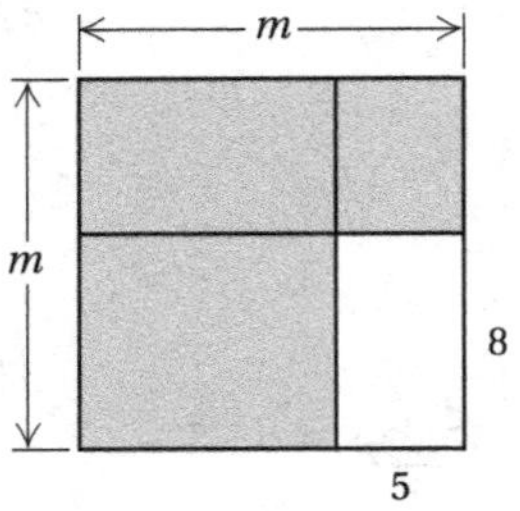

63.

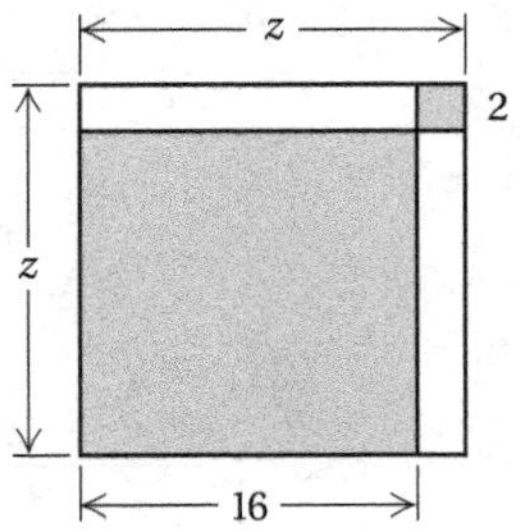

64.

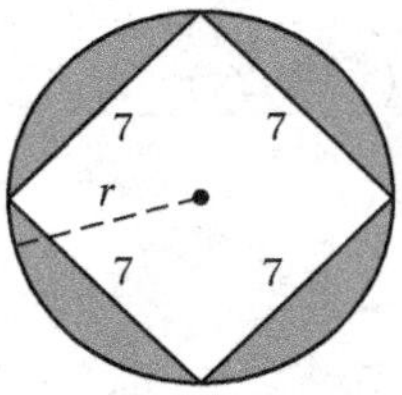

Skill Maintenance

Solve. [2.3b]

65. $8x + 3x = 66$

66. $5x - 7x = 38$

67. $\frac{3}{8}x + \frac{1}{4} - \frac{3}{4}x = \frac{11}{16} + x$

68. $5x - 4 = 26 - x$

69. $1.5x - 2.7x = 22 - 5.6x$

70. $3x - 3 = -4x + 4$

Solve. [2.3c]

71. $6(y - 3) - 8 = 4(y + 2) + 5$

72. $8(5x + 2) = 7(6x - 3)$

Solve. [2.7e]

73. $3x - 7 \leq 5x + 13$

74. $2(x - 4) > 5(x - 3) + 7$

Synthesis

Find a polynomial for the surface area of each right rectangular solid.

75.

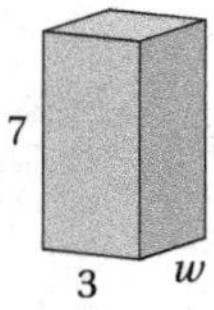

76.

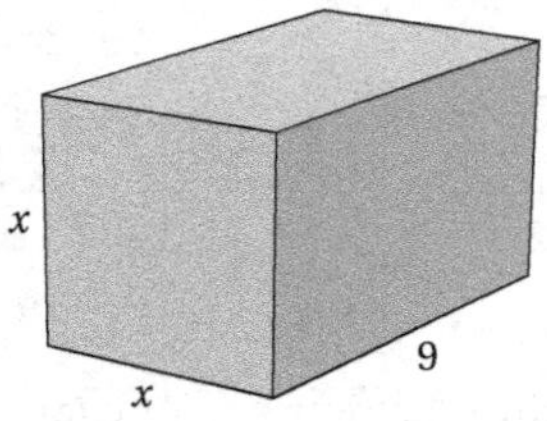

77.

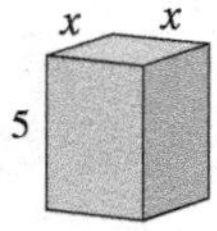

78.

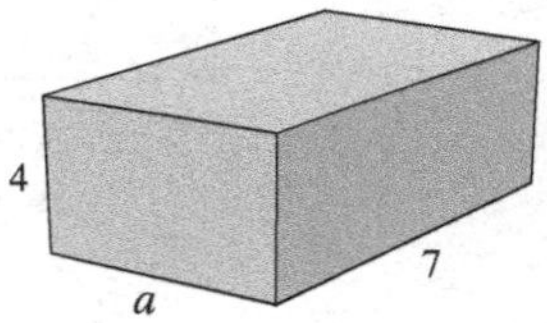

79. Find $(y - 2)^2$ using the four parts of this square.

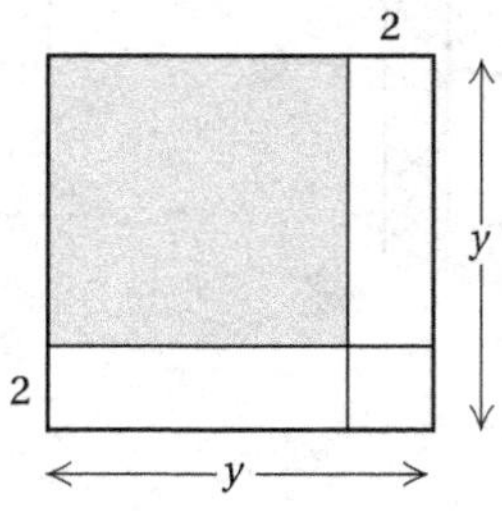

Simplify.

80. $(3x^2 - 4x + 6) - (-2x^2 + 4) + (-5x - 3)$

81. $(7y^2 - 5y + 6) - (3y^2 + 8y - 12) + (8y^2 - 10y + 3)$

82. $(-4 + x^2 + 2x^3) - (-6 - x + 3x^3) - (-x^2 - 5x^3)$

83. $(-y^4 - 7y^3 + y^2) + (-2y^4 + 5y - 2) - (-6y^3 + y^2)$

Mid-Chapter Review

Concept Reinforcement

Determine whether each statement is true or false.

______________ 1. a^n and a^{-n} are reciprocals. [3.1f]

______________ 2. $x^2 \cdot x^3 = x^6$ [3.1d]

______________ 3. $-5y^4$ and $-5y^2$ are like terms. [3.3c]

______________ 4. $4920^0 = 1$ [3.1b]

Guided Solutions

Fill in each blank with the number or variable that creates a correct statement or solution.

5. Collect like terms: $4w^3 + 6w - 8w^3 - 3w$. [3.3e]

$$4w^3 + 6w - 8w^3 - 3w = (4 - 8)\square + (6 - 3)\square$$
$$= \square w^3 + \square w$$

6. Subtract: $(3y^4 - y^2 + 11) - (y^4 - 4y^2 + 5)$. [3.4c]

$$(3y^4 - y^2 + 11) - (y^4 - 4y^2 + 5) = 3y^4 - y^2 + 11\square y^4 \square 4y^2 \square 5$$
$$= \square y^4 + \square y^2 + \square$$

Mixed Review

Evaluate. [3.1b, c]

7. z^1

8. 4.56^0

9. a^5, when $a = -2$

10. $-x^3$, when $x = -1$

Multiply and simplify. [3.1d, f]

11. $5^3 \cdot 5^4$

12. $(3a)^2\,(3a)^7$

13. $x^{-8} \cdot x^5$

14. $t^4 \cdot t^{-4}$

Divide and simplify. [3.1e, f]

15. $\frac{7^8}{7^4}$

16. $\frac{x}{x^3}$

17. $\frac{w^5}{w^{-3}}$

18. $\frac{y^{-6}}{y^{-2}}$

Simplify. [3.2a, b]

19. $(3^5)^3$

20. $(x^{-3}y^2)^{-6}$

21. $\left(\frac{a^4}{5}\right)^6$

22. $\left(\frac{2y^3}{xz^2}\right)^{-2}$

Convert to scientific notation. [3.2c]

23. 25,430,000

24. 0.00012

Convert to decimal notation. [3.2c]

25. 3.6×10^{-5}

26. 1.44×10^8

Multiply or divide and write scientific notation for the result. [3.2d]

27. $(3 \times 10^6)(2 \times 10^{-3})$

28. $\dfrac{1.2 \times 10^{-4}}{2.4 \times 10^2}$

Evaluate the polynomial when $x = -3$ and when $x = 2$. [3.3a]

29. $-3x + 7$

30. $x^3 - 2x + 5$

Collect like terms and then arrange in descending order. [3.3f]

31. $3x - 2x^5 + x - 5x^2 + 2$

32. $4x^3 - 9x^2 - 2x^3 + x^2 + 8x^6$

Identify the degree of each term of the polynomial and the degree of the polynomial. [3.3g]

33. $5x^3 - x + 4$

34. $2x - x^4 + 3x^6$

Classify the polynomial as a monomial, a binomial, a trinomial, or none of these. [3.3i]

35. $x - 9$

36. $x^5 - 2x^3 + 6x^2$

Add or subtract. [3.4a, c]

37. $(3x^2 - 1) + (5x^2 + 6)$

38. $(x^3 + 2x - 5) + (4x^3 - 2x^2 - 6)$

39. $(5x - 8) - (9x + 2)$

40. $(0.1x^2 - 2.4x + 3.6) - (0.5x^2 + x - 5.4)$

41. Find a polynomial for the sum of the areas of these rectangles. [3.4d]

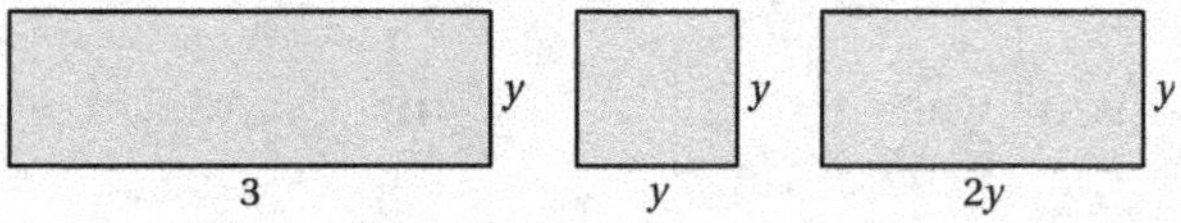

Understanding Through Discussion and Writing

42. Suppose that the length of a side of a square is three times the length of a side of a second square. How do the areas of the squares compare? Why? [3.1d]

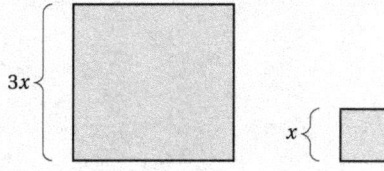

43. Suppose that the length of a side of a cube is twice the length of a side of a second cube. How do the volumes of the cubes compare? Why? [3.1d]

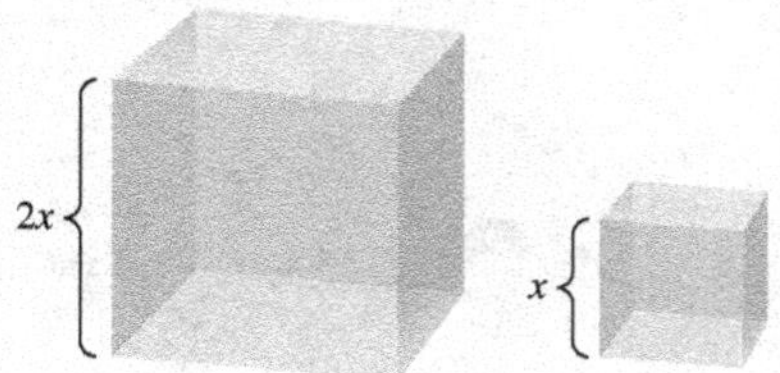

44. Explain in your own words when exponents should be added and when they should be multiplied. [3.1d], [3.2a]

45. Without performing actual computations, explain why 3^{-29} is smaller than 2^{-29}. [3.1f]

46. Is it better to evaluate a polynomial before or after like terms have been collected? Why? [3.3a, e]

47. Is the sum of two binomials ever a trinomial? Why or why not? [3.3i], [3.4a]

3.5 Multiplication of Polynomials

We now multiply polynomials using techniques based, for the most part, on the distributive laws, but also on the associative and commutative laws. As we proceed in this chapter, we will develop special ways to find certain products.

OBJECTIVES

a Multiply monomials.

b Multiply a monomial and any polynomial.

c Multiply two binomials.

d Multiply any two polynomials.

SKILL TO REVIEW
Objective 1.7c: Use the distributive laws to multiply expressions like 8 and $x - y$.

Multiply.

1. $3(x - 5)$
2. $2(3y + 4z - 1)$

a Multiplying Monomials

Consider $(3x)(4x)$. We multiply as follows:

$(3x)(4x)$	$= 3 \cdot x \cdot 4 \cdot x$	By the associative law of multiplication
	$= 3 \cdot 4 \cdot x \cdot x$	By the commutative law of multiplication
	$= (3 \cdot 4)(x \cdot x)$	By the associative law
	$= 12x^2.$	Using the product rule for exponents

MULTIPLYING MONOMIALS

To find an equivalent expression for the product of two monomials, multiply the coefficients and then multiply the variables using the product rule for exponents.

EXAMPLES Multiply.

1. $5x \cdot 6x = (5 \cdot 6)(x \cdot x)$ — By the associative and commutative laws
$= 30x^2$ — Multiplying the coefficients and multiplying the variables

2. $(3x)(-x) = (3x)(-1x)$
$= (3)(-1)(x \cdot x) = -3x^2$

3. $(-7x^5)(4x^3) = (-7 \cdot 4)(x^5 \cdot x^3)$
$= -28x^{5+3}$ — Adding the exponents
$= -28x^8$ — Simplifying

After some practice, you will be able to multiply mentally. Multiply the coefficients and then the variables by keeping the base and adding the exponents. Write only the answer.

Do Margin Exercises 1–8.

Multiply.

1. $(3x)(-5)$
2. $(-x) \cdot x$
3. $(-x)(-x)$
4. $(-x^2)(x^3)$
5. $3x^5 \cdot 4x^2$
6. $(4y^5)(-2y^6)$
7. $(-7y^4)(-y)$
8. $7x^5 \cdot 0$

b Multiplying a Monomial and Any Polynomial

To find an equivalent expression for the product of a monomial, such as $2x$, and a binomial, such as $5x + 3$, we use a distributive law and multiply each term of $5x + 3$ by $2x$.

EXAMPLE 4 Multiply: $2x(5x + 3)$.

$2x(5x + 3) = (2x)(5x) + (2x)(3)$ — Using a distributive law
$= 10x^2 + 6x$ — Multiplying the monomials

Answers

Skill to Review:
1. $3x - 15$ **2.** $6y + 8z - 2$

Margin Exercises:
1. $-15x$ **2.** $-x^2$ **3.** x^2 **4.** $-x^5$
5. $12x^7$ **6.** $-8y^{11}$ **7.** $7y^5$ **8.** 0

EXAMPLE 5 Multiply: $5x(2x^2 - 3x + 4)$.

$$5x(2x^2 - 3x + 4) = (5x)(2x^2) - (5x)(3x) + (5x)(4)$$
$$= 10x^3 - 15x^2 + 20x$$

MULTIPLYING A MONOMIAL AND A POLYNOMIAL

To multiply a monomial and a polynomial, multiply each term of the polynomial by the monomial.

EXAMPLE 6 Multiply: $-2x^2(x^3 - 7x^2 + 10x - 4)$.

$$-2x^2(x^3 - 7x^2 + 10x - 4)$$
$$= (-2x^2)(x^3) - (-2x^2)(7x^2) + (-2x^2)(10x) - (-2x^2)(4)$$
$$= -2x^5 + 14x^4 - 20x^3 + 8x^2$$

Do Exercises 9–11.

c Multiplying Two Binomials

To find an equivalent expression for the product of two binomials, we use the distributive laws more than once. In Example 7, we use a distributive law three times.

EXAMPLE 7 Multiply: $(x + 5)(x + 4)$.

$(x + 5)(x + 4) = x(x + 4) + 5(x + 4)$	Using a distributive law
$= x \cdot x + x \cdot 4 + 5 \cdot x + 5 \cdot 4$	Using a distributive law on each part
$= x^2 + 4x + 5x + 20$	Multiplying the monomials
$= x^2 + 9x + 20$	Collecting like terms

To visualize the product in Example 7, consider a rectangle of length $x + 5$ and width $x + 4$.

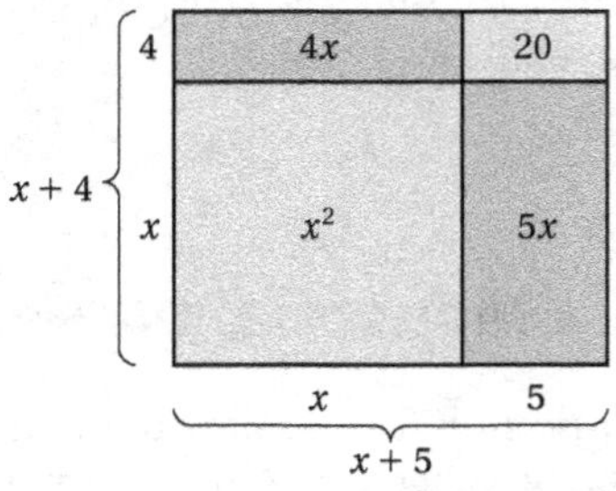

The total area can be expressed as $(x + 5)(x + 4)$ or, by adding the four smaller areas, $x^2 + 4x + 5x + 20$, or $x^2 + 9x + 20$.

Do Exercises 12–14.

Multiply.

9. $4x(2x + 4)$

10. $3t^2(-5t + 2)$

11. $-5x^3(x^3 + 5x^2 - 6x + 8)$

12. Multiply: $(y + 2)(y + 7)$.

a) Fill in the blanks in the steps of the solution below.

$(y + 2)(y + 7)$
$= y \cdot \_\_\_ + 2 \cdot \_\_\_$
$= y \cdot \_\_\_ + y \cdot \_\_\_$
$+ 2 \cdot \_\_\_ + 2 \cdot \_\_\_$
$= \_\_\_ + \_\_\_$
$+ \_\_\_ + \_\_\_$
$= y^2 + \_\_\_ + 14$

b) Write an algebraic expression that represents the total area of the four smaller rectangles in the figure shown here.

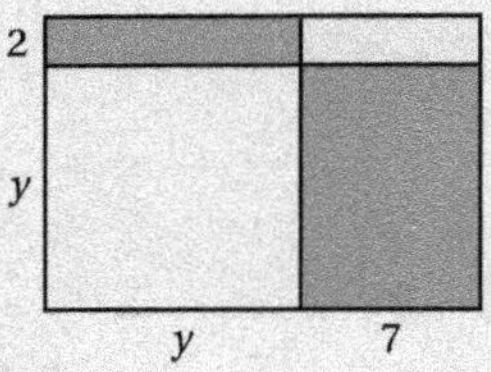

Multiply.

13. $(x + 8)(x + 5)$

14. $(x + 5)(x - 4)$

Answers

9. $8x^2 + 16x$ **10.** $-15t^3 + 6t^2$
11. $-5x^6 - 25x^5 + 30x^4 - 40x^3$
12. (a) $(y + 2)(y + 7)$
$= y \cdot (y + 7) + 2 \cdot (y + 7)$
$= y \cdot y + y \cdot 7$
$+ 2 \cdot y + 2 \cdot 7$
$= y^2 + 7y$
$+ 2y + 14$
$= y^2 + 9y + 14$
(b) $(y + 2)(y + 7)$, or $y^2 + 2y + 7y + 14$, or $y^2 + 9y + 14$ **13.** $x^2 + 13x + 40$
14. $x^2 + x - 20$

EXAMPLE 8 Multiply: $(4x + 3)(x - 2)$.

$$(4x + 3)(x - 2) = 4x(x - 2) + 3(x - 2)$$ Using a distributive law

$$= 4x \cdot x - 4x \cdot 2 + 3 \cdot x - 3 \cdot 2$$ Using a distributive law on each part

$$= 4x^2 - 8x + 3x - 6$$ Multiplying the monomials

$$= 4x^2 - 5x - 6$$ Collecting like terms

Do Exercises 15 and 16.

Multiply.

15. $(5x + 3)(x - 4)$

16. $(2x - 3)(3x - 5)$

d Multiplying Any Two Polynomials

Let's consider the product of a binomial and a trinomial. We use a distributive law four times. You may see ways to skip some steps and do the work mentally.

EXAMPLE 9 Multiply: $(x^2 + 2x - 3)(x^2 + 4)$.

$$(x^2 + 2x - 3)(x^2 + 4) = x^2(x^2 + 4) + 2x(x^2 + 4) - 3(x^2 + 4)$$

$$= x^2 \cdot x^2 + x^2 \cdot 4 + 2x \cdot x^2 + 2x \cdot 4 - 3 \cdot x^2 - 3 \cdot 4$$

$$= x^4 + 4x^2 + 2x^3 + 8x - 3x^2 - 12$$

$$= x^4 + 2x^3 + x^2 + 8x - 12$$

Do Exercises 17 and 18.

Multiply.

17. $(x^2 + 3x - 4)(x^2 + 5)$

18. $(3y^2 - 7)(2y^3 - 2y + 5)$

PRODUCT OF TWO POLYNOMIALS

To multiply two polynomials P and Q, select one of the polynomials—say, P. Then multiply each term of P by every term of Q and collect like terms.

To use columns for long multiplication, multiply each term in the top row by every term in the bottom row. We write like terms in columns, and then add the results. Such multiplication is like multiplying with whole numbers.

3 2 1	300 + 20 + 1	
× 1 2	× 10 + 2	
6 4 2	600 + 40 + 2	Multiplying the top row by 2
3 2 1	3000 + 200 + 10	Multiplying the top row by 10
3 8 5 2	3000 + 800 + 50 + 2	Adding

EXAMPLE 10 Multiply: $(4x^3 - 2x^2 + 3x)(x^2 + 2x)$.

$4x^3 - 2x^2 + 3x$	
$x^2 + 2x$	
$8x^4 - 4x^3 + 6x^2$	Multiplying the top row by $2x$
$4x^5 - 2x^4 + 3x^3$	Multiplying the top row by x^2
$4x^5 + 6x^4 - x^3 + 6x^2$	Collecting like terms
↑ ↑ ↑ ↑	Line up like terms in columns.

Answers

15. $5x^2 - 17x - 12$ **16.** $6x^2 - 19x + 15$
17. $x^4 + 3x^3 + x^2 + 15x - 20$
18. $6y^5 - 20y^3 + 15y^2 + 14y - 35$

EXAMPLE 11 Multiply: $(2x^2 + 3x - 4)(2x^2 - x + 3)$.

$$
\begin{array}{rrrrrl}
 & & 2x^2 & + 3x & - 4 & \\
 & & 2x^2 & - x & + 3 & \\
\hline
 & & 6x^2 & + 9x & - 12 & \text{Multiplying by } 3 \\
 & -2x^3 & - 3x^2 & + 4x & & \text{Multiplying by } -x \\
4x^4 & + 6x^3 & - 8x^2 & & & \text{Multiplying by } 2x^2 \\
\hline
4x^4 & + 4x^3 & - 5x^2 & + 13x & - 12 & \text{Collecting like terms}
\end{array}
$$

Do Exercise 19.

19. Multiply.

$$
\begin{array}{r}
3x^2 - 2x - 5 \\
2x^2 + x - 2 \\
\hline
\end{array}
$$

EXAMPLE 12 Multiply: $(5x^3 - 3x + 4)(-2x^2 - 3)$.

When missing terms occur, it helps to leave spaces for them and align like terms as we multiply.

$$
\begin{array}{rrrrrl}
 & 5x^3 & & - 3x & + 4 & \\
 & & -2x^2 & & - 3 & \\
\hline
 & -15x^3 & & + 9x & - 12 & \text{Multiplying by } -3 \\
-10x^5 & + 6x^3 & - 8x^2 & & & \text{Multiplying by } -2x^2 \\
\hline
-10x^5 & - 9x^3 & - 8x^2 & + 9x & - 12 & \text{Collecting like terms}
\end{array}
$$

Do Exercises 20 and 21.

Multiply.

20.
$$
\begin{array}{r}
3x^2 - 2x + 4 \\
x + 5 \\
\hline
\end{array}
$$

21.
$$
\begin{array}{r}
-5x^2 + 4x + 2 \\
-4x^2 - 8 \\
\hline
\end{array}
$$

Calculator Corner

Checking Multiplication of Polynomials A partial check of multiplication of polynomials can be performed graphically. Consider the product $(x + 3)(x - 2) = x^2 + x - 6$. We will use two graph styles to determine whether this product is correct. First, we press MODE to determine whether SEQUENTIAL mode is selected. If it is not, we position the blinking cursor over SEQUENTIAL and then press ENTER. Next, on the Y= screen, we enter $y_1 = (x + 3)(x - 2)$ and $y_2 = x^2 + x - 6$. We will select the line-graph style for y_1 and the path style for y_2. To select these graph styles, we use ◀ to position the cursor over the icon to the left of the equation and press ENTER repeatedly until the desired style of icon appears, as shown below. Then we graph the equations.

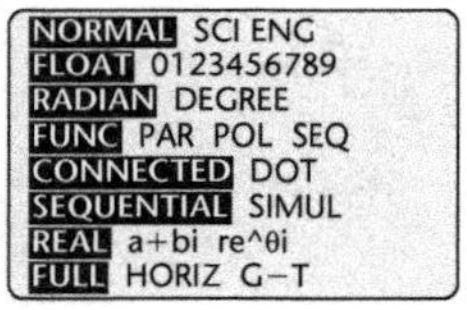

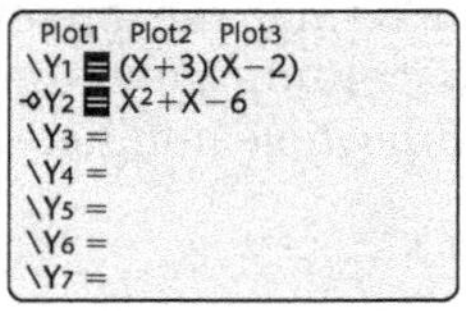

$y_1 = (x + 3)(x - 2)$,
$y_2 = x^2 + x - 6$

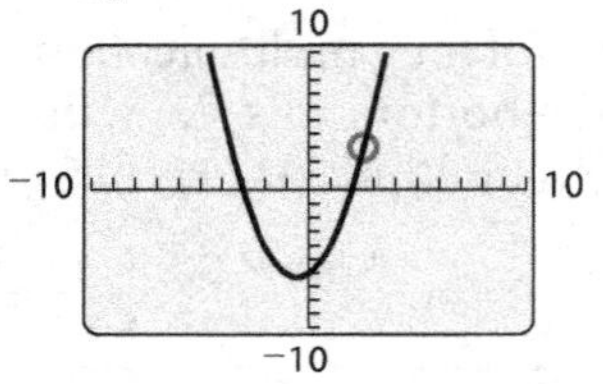

The graphing calculator will graph y_1 first as a solid line. Then it will graph y_2 as the circular cursor traces the leading edge of the graph, allowing us to determine visually whether the graphs coincide. In this case, the graphs appear to coincide, so the factorization is probably correct.

A table can also be used to perform a partial check of a product. See the Calculator Corner on p. 252 for the procedure.

Exercises Determine graphically whether each product is correct.

1. $(x + 5)(x + 4) = x^2 + 9x + 20$

2. $(4x + 3)(x - 2) = 4x^2 - 5x - 6$

3. $(5x + 3)(x - 4) = 5x^2 + 17x - 12$

4. $(2x - 3)(3x - 5) = 6x^2 - 19x - 15$

Answers

19. $6x^4 - x^3 - 18x^2 - x + 10$
20. $3x^3 + 13x^2 - 6x + 20$
21. $20x^4 - 16x^3 + 32x^2 - 32x - 16$

a Multiply.

1. $(8x^2)(5)$

2. $(4x^2)(-2)$

3. $(-x^2)(-x)$

4. $(-x^3)(x^2)$

5. $(8x^5)(4x^3)$

6. $(10a^2)(2a^2)$

7. $(0.1x^6)(0.3x^5)$

8. $(0.3x^4)(-0.8x^6)$

9. $\left(-\frac{1}{5}x^3\right)\left(-\frac{1}{3}x\right)$

10. $\left(-\frac{1}{4}x^4\right)\left(\frac{1}{5}x^8\right)$

11. $(-4x^2)(0)$

12. $(-4m^5)(-1)$

13. $(3x^2)(-4x^3)(2x^6)$

14. $(-2y^5)(10y^4)(-3y^3)$

b Multiply.

15. $2x(-x + 5)$

16. $3x(4x - 6)$

17. $-5x(x - 1)$

18. $-3x(-x - 1)$

19. $x^2(x^3 + 1)$

20. $-2x^3(x^2 - 1)$

21. $3x(2x^2 - 6x + 1)$

22. $-4x(2x^3 - 6x^2 - 5x + 1)$

23. $(-6x^2)(x^2 + x)$

24. $(-4x^2)(x^2 - x)$

25. $(3y^2)(6y^4 + 8y^3)$

26. $(4y^4)(y^3 - 6y^2)$

c Multiply.

27. $(x + 6)(x + 3)$

28. $(x + 5)(x + 2)$

29. $(x + 5)(x - 2)$

30. $(x + 6)(x - 2)$

31. $(x - 1)(x + 4)$

32. $(x - 8)(x + 7)$

33. $(x - 4)(x - 3)$

34. $(x - 7)(x - 3)$

35. $(x + 3)(x - 3)$

36. $(x + 6)(x - 6)$

37. $(x - 4)(x + 4)$

38. $(x - 9)(x + 9)$

39. $(3x + 5)(x + 2)$

40. $(2x + 6)(x + 3)$

41. $(5 - x)(5 - 2x)$

42. $(3 - 4x)(2 - x)$

43. $(2x + 5)(2x + 5)$

44. $(3x + 4)(3x + 4)$

45. $(x - 3)(x - 3)$

46. $(x - 6)(x - 6)$

47. $\left(x - \frac{5}{2}\right)\left(x + \frac{2}{5}\right)$

48. $\left(x + \frac{4}{3}\right)\left(x + \frac{3}{2}\right)$

49. $(x - 2.3)(x + 4.7)$

50. $(2x + 0.13)(2x - 0.13)$

Write an algebraic expression that represents the total area of the four smaller rectangles.

51.

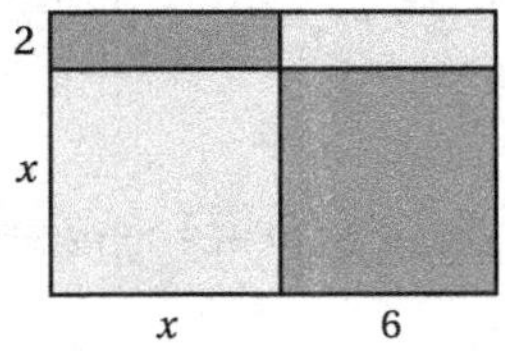

52.

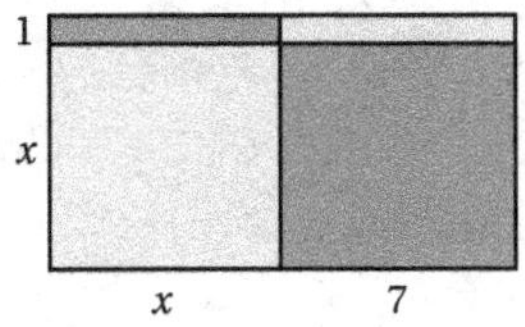

53.

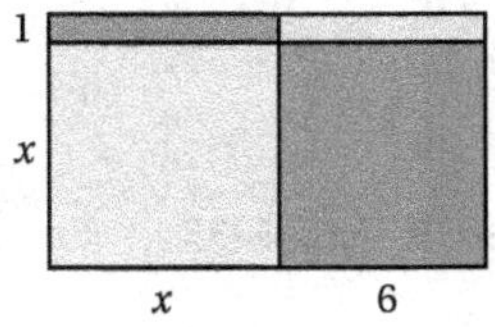

54.

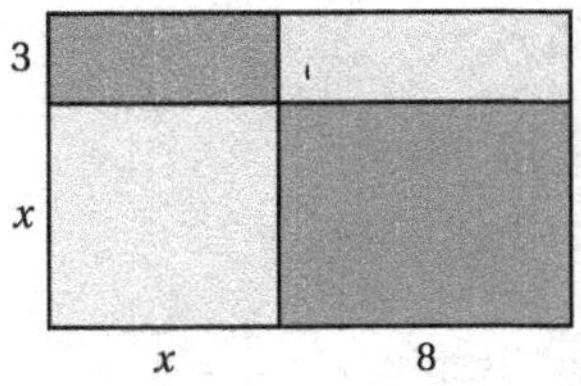

Draw and label rectangles similar to the one following Example 7 to illustrate each product.

55. $x(x + 5)$

56. $x(x + 2)$

57. $(x + 1)(x + 2)$

58. $(x + 3)(x + 1)$

59. $(x + 5)(x + 3)$

60. $(x + 4)(x + 6)$

d Multiply.

61. $(x^2 + x + 1)(x - 1)$

62. $(x^2 + x - 2)(x + 2)$

63. $(2x + 1)(2x^2 + 6x + 1)$

64. $(3x - 1)(4x^2 - 2x - 1)$

65. $(y^2 - 3)(3y^2 - 6y + 2)$

66. $(3y^2 - 3)(y^2 + 6y + 1)$

67. $(x^3 + x^2)(x^3 + x^2 - x)$

68. $(x^3 - x^2)(x^3 - x^2 + x)$

69. $(-5x^3 - 7x^2 + 1)(2x^2 - x)$

70. $(-4x^3 + 5x^2 - 2)(5x^2 + 1)$

71. $(1 + x + x^2)(-1 - x + x^2)$

72. $(1 - x + x^2)(1 - x + x^2)$

73. $(2t^2 - t - 4)(3t^2 + 2t - 1)$

74. $(3a^2 - 5a + 2)(2a^2 - 3a + 4)$

75. $(x - x^3 + x^5)(x^2 - 1 + x^4)$

76. $(x - x^3 + x^5)(3x^2 + 3x^6 + 3x^4)$

77. $(x^3 + x^2 + x + 1)(x - 1)$

78. $(x + 2)(x^3 - x^2 + x - 2)$

79. $(x + 1)(x^3 + 7x^2 + 5x + 4)$

80. $(x + 2)(x^3 + 5x^2 + 9x + 3)$

81. $\left(x - \frac{1}{2}\right)\left(2x^3 - 4x^2 + 3x - \frac{2}{5}\right)$

82. $\left(x + \frac{1}{3}\right)\left(6x^3 - 12x^2 - 5x + \frac{1}{2}\right)$

Skill Maintenance

Simplify.

83. $-\frac{1}{4} - \frac{1}{2}$ [1.4a]

84. $-3.8 - (-10.2)$ [1.4a]

85. $(10 - 2)(10 + 2)$ [1.8d]

86. $10 - 2 + (-6)^2 \div 3 \cdot 2$ [1.8d]

Factor. [1.7d]

87. $15x - 18y + 12$

88. $16x - 24y + 36$

89. $-9x - 45y + 15$

90. $100x - 100y + 1000a$

91. Graph: $y = \frac{1}{2}x - 3$.

92. Solve: $4(x - 3) = 5(2 - 3x) + 1$. [2.3c]

Synthesis

Find a polynomial for the shaded area of each figure.

93.

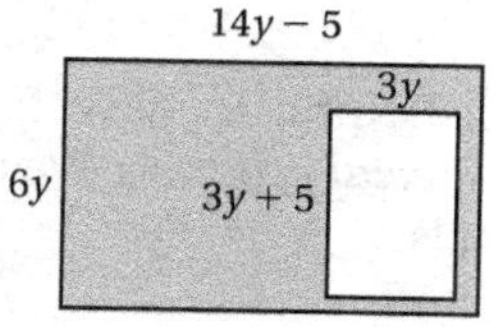

94.

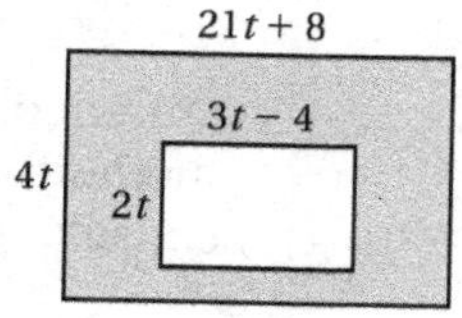

95. A box with a square bottom is to be made from a 12-in.-square piece of cardboard. Squares with side x are cut out of the corners and the sides are folded up. Find the polynomials for the volume and the outside surface area of the box.

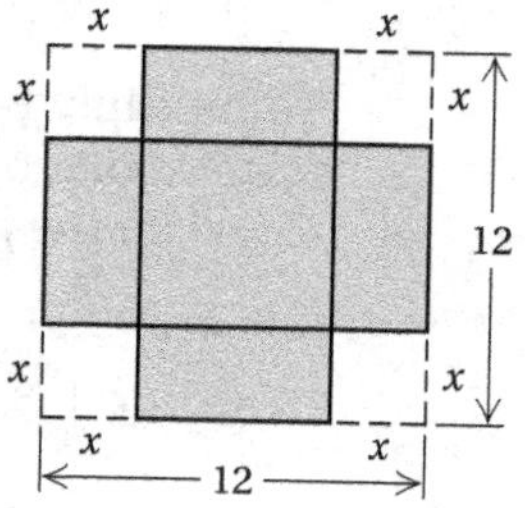

For each figure, determine what the missing number must be in order for the figure to have the given area.

96. Area $= x^2 + 7x + 10$

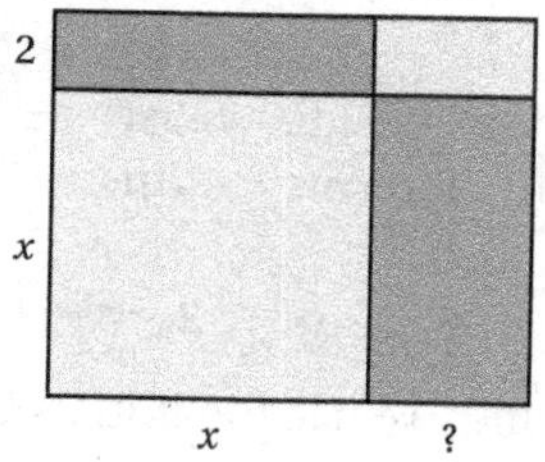

97. Area $= x^2 + 8x + 15$

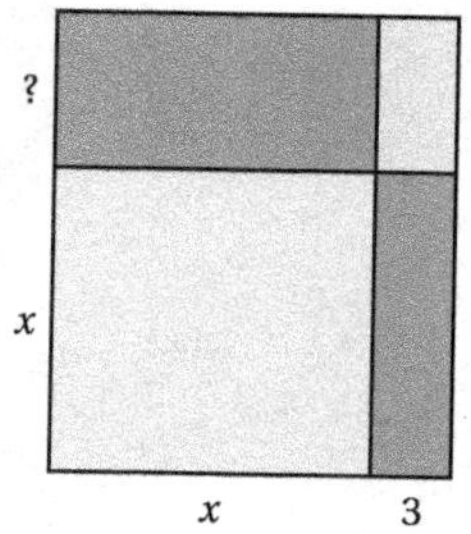

98. An open wooden box is a cube with side x cm. The box, including its bottom, is made of wood that is 1 cm thick. Find a polynomial for the interior volume of the cube.

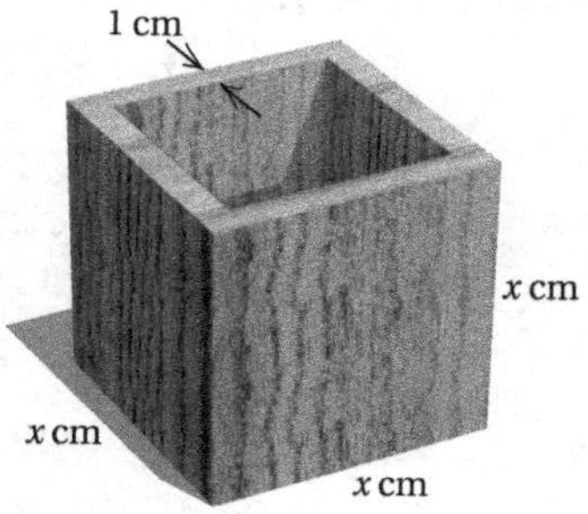

99. Find a polynomial for the volume of the solid shown below.

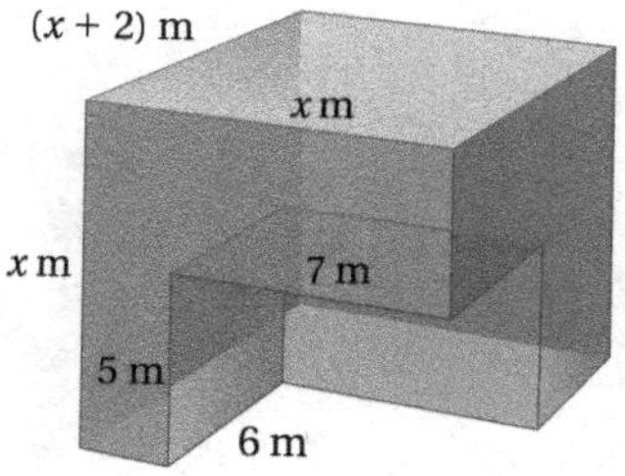

Compute and simplify.

100. $(x + 3)(x + 6) + (x + 3)(x + 6)$

101. $(x - 2)(x - 7) - (x - 7)(x - 2)$

102. $(x + 5)^2 - (x - 3)^2$

103. Extend the pattern and simplify:

$$(x - a)(x - b)(x - c)(x - d) \cdots (x - z).$$

104. Use a graphing calculator to check your answers to Exercises 15, 29, and 61. Use graphs, tables, or both, as directed by your instructor.

3.6 Special Products

OBJECTIVES

a Multiply two binomials mentally using the FOIL method.

b Multiply the sum and the difference of two terms mentally.

c Square a binomial mentally.

d Find special products when polynomial products are mixed together.

We encounter certain products so often that it is helpful to have faster methods of computing. Such techniques are called *special products*. We now consider special ways of multiplying any two binomials.

a Products of Two Binomials Using FOIL

To multiply two binomials, we can select one binomial and multiply each term of that binomial by every term of the other. Then we collect like terms. Consider the product $(x + 3)(x + 7)$:

$$\begin{aligned}(x + 3)(x + 7) &= x(x + 7) + 3(x + 7)\\ &= x \cdot x + x \cdot 7 + 3 \cdot x + 3 \cdot 7\\ &= x^2 + 7x + 3x + 21\\ &= x^2 + 10x + 21.\end{aligned}$$

This example illustrates a special technique for finding the product of two binomials:

First terms	Outside terms	Inside terms	Last terms

$$(x + 3)(x + 7) = x \cdot x + 7 \cdot x + 3 \cdot x + 3 \cdot 7.$$

To remember this method of multiplying, we use the initials **FOIL**.

THE FOIL METHOD

To multiply two binomials, $A + B$ and $C + D$, multiply the First terms AC, the Outside terms AD, the Inside terms BC, and then the Last terms BD. Then collect like terms, if possible.

$$(A + B)(C + D) = AC + AD + BC + BD$$

1. Multiply First terms: AC.
2. Multiply Outside terms: AD.
3. Multiply Inside terms: BC.
4. Multiply Last terms: BD.

↓

FOIL

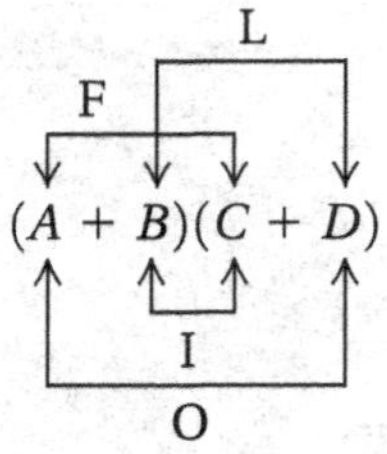

STUDY TIPS

MEMORIZING FORMULAS

Memorizing can be a very helpful tool in the study of mathematics. Don't underestimate its power as you consider the special products. Consider putting the rules, in words and in math symbols, on index cards and reviewing them many times.

EXAMPLE 1 Multiply: $(x + 8)(x^2 - 5)$.

We have

$$\begin{aligned}&\qquad\quad\ \text{F} \qquad\quad \text{O} \qquad\quad \text{I} \qquad\quad \text{L}\\ (x + 8)(x^2 - 5) &= x \cdot x^2 + x \cdot (-5) + 8 \cdot x^2 + 8(-5)\\ &= x^3 - 5x + 8x^2 - 40\\ &= x^3 + 8x^2 - 5x - 40.\end{aligned}$$

Since each of the original binomials is in descending order, we write the product in descending order, as is customary, but this is not a "must."

Often we can collect like terms after we have multiplied.

EXAMPLES Multiply.

2. $(x + 6)(x - 6) = x^2 - 6x + 6x - 36$ Using FOIL
$= x^2 - 36$ Collecting like terms

3. $(x + 7)(x + 4) = x^2 + 4x + 7x + 28$
$= x^2 + 11x + 28$

4. $(y - 3)(y - 2) = y^2 - 2y - 3y + 6$
$= y^2 - 5y + 6$

5. $(x^3 - 5)(x^3 + 5) = x^6 + 5x^3 - 5x^3 - 25$
$= x^6 - 25$

6. $(4t^3 + 5)(3t^2 - 2) = 12t^5 - 8t^3 + 15t^2 - 10$

Do Exercises 1–8.

Multiply mentally, if possible. If you need extra steps, be sure to use them.

1. $(x + 3)(x + 4)$
2. $(x + 3)(x - 5)$
3. $(2x - 1)(x - 4)$
4. $(2x^2 - 3)(x - 2)$
5. $(6x^2 + 5)(2x^3 + 1)$
6. $(y^3 + 7)(y^3 - 7)$
7. $(t + 2)(t + 3)$
8. $(2x^4 + x^2)(-x^3 + x)$

EXAMPLES Multiply.

7. $\left(x - \frac{2}{3}\right)\left(x + \frac{2}{3}\right) = x^2 + \frac{2}{3}x - \frac{2}{3}x - \frac{4}{9}$
$= x^2 - \frac{4}{9}$

8. $(x^2 - 0.3)(x^2 - 0.3) = x^4 - 0.3x^2 - 0.3x^2 + 0.09$
$= x^4 - 0.6x^2 + 0.09$

9. $(3 - 4x)(7 - 5x^3) = 21 - 15x^3 - 28x + 20x^4$
$= 21 - 28x - 15x^3 + 20x^4$

(*Note*: If the original polynomials are in ascending order, it is natural to write the product in ascending order, but this is not a "must.")

10. $(5x^4 + 2x^3)(3x^2 - 7x) = 15x^6 - 35x^5 + 6x^5 - 14x^4$
$= 15x^6 - 29x^5 - 14x^4$

Do Exercises 9–12.

Multiply.

9. $\left(x + \frac{4}{5}\right)\left(x - \frac{4}{5}\right)$
10. $(x^3 - 0.5)(x^2 + 0.5)$
11. $(2 + 3x^2)(4 - 5x^2)$
12. $(6x^3 - 3x^2)(5x^2 - 2x)$

We can show the FOIL method geometrically as follows.

The area of the large rectangle is $(A + B)(C + D)$.

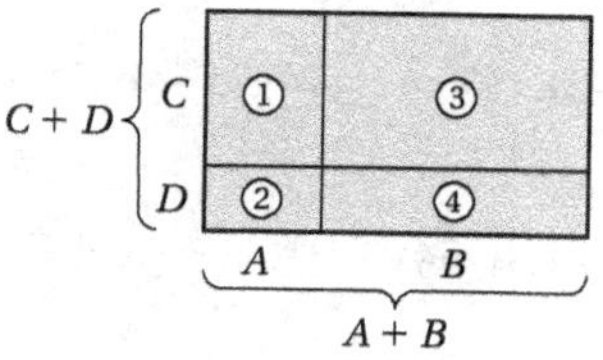

The area of rectangle ① is AC.
The area of rectangle ② is AD.
The area of rectangle ③ is BC.
The area of rectangle ④ is BD.

The area of the large rectangle is the sum of the areas of the smaller rectangles. Thus,

$$(A + B)(C + D) = AC + AD + BC + BD.$$

b Multiplying Sums and Differences of Two Terms

Consider the product of the sum and the difference of the same two terms, such as

$$(x + 2)(x - 2).$$

Answers

1. $x^2 + 7x + 12$ 2. $x^2 - 2x - 15$
3. $2x^2 - 9x + 4$ 4. $2x^3 - 4x^2 - 3x + 6$
5. $12x^5 + 10x^3 + 6x^2 + 5$ 6. $y^6 - 49$
7. $t^2 + 5t + 6$ 8. $-2x^7 + x^5 + x^3$
9. $x^2 - \frac{16}{25}$ 10. $x^5 + 0.5x^3 - 0.5x^2 - 0.25$
11. $8 + 2x^2 - 15x^4$ 12. $30x^5 - 27x^4 + 6x^3$

Since this is the product of two binomials, we can use FOIL. This type of product occurs so often, however, that it would be valuable if we could use an even faster method. To find a faster way to compute such a product, look for a pattern in the following:

a) $(x + 2)(x - 2) = x^2 - 2x + 2x - 4$ Using FOIL
$= x^2 - 4;$

b) $(3x - 5)(3x + 5) = 9x^2 + 15x - 15x - 25$
$= 9x^2 - 25.$

Multiply.

13. $(x + 5)(x - 5)$

14. $(2x - 3)(2x + 3)$

Do Exercises 13 and 14.

Perhaps you discovered in each case that when you multiply the two binomials, two terms are opposites, or additive inverses, which add to 0 and "drop out."

PRODUCT OF THE SUM AND THE DIFFERENCE OF TWO TERMS

The product of the sum and the difference of the same two terms is the square of the first term minus the square of the second term:

$$(A + B)(A - B) = A^2 - B^2.$$

It is helpful to memorize this rule in both words and symbols. (If you do forget it, you can, of course, use FOIL.)

EXAMPLES Multiply. (Carry out the rule and say the words as you go.)

$(A + B)(A - B) = A^2 - B^2$

11. $(x + 4)(x - 4) = x^2 - 4^2$ "The square of the first term, x^2, minus the square of the second, 4^2"
$= x^2 - 16$ Simplifying

12. $(5 + 2w)(5 - 2w) = 5^2 - (2w)^2$
$= 25 - 4w^2$

13. $(3x^2 - 7)(3x^2 + 7) = (3x^2)^2 - 7^2$
$= 9x^4 - 49$

14. $(-4x - 10)(-4x + 10) = (-4x)^2 - 10^2$
$= 16x^2 - 100$

15. $\left(x + \frac{3}{8}\right)\left(x - \frac{3}{8}\right) = x^2 - \left(\frac{3}{8}\right)^2 = x^2 - \frac{9}{64}$

Multiply.

15. $(x + 8)(x - 8)$

16. $(x - 7)(x + 7)$

17. $(6 - 4y)(6 + 4y)$

18. $(2x^3 - 1)(2x^3 + 1)$

19. $\left(x - \frac{2}{5}\right)\left(x + \frac{2}{5}\right)$

Do Exercises 15–19.

C Squaring Binomials

Consider the square of a binomial, such as $(x + 3)^2$. This can be expressed as $(x + 3)(x + 3)$. Since this is the product of two binomials, we can use FOIL. But again, this type of product occurs so often that we would like to use an even faster method. Look for a pattern in the following.

Answers

13. $x^2 - 25$ **14.** $4x^2 - 9$ **15.** $x^2 - 64$
16. $x^2 - 49$ **17.** $36 - 16y^2$ **18.** $4x^6 - 1$
19. $x^2 - \frac{4}{25}$

a) $(x + 3)^2 = (x + 3)(x + 3)$
$= x^2 + 3x + 3x + 9$
$= x^2 + 6x + 9;$

b) $(x - 3)^2 = (x - 3)(x - 3)$
$= x^2 - 3x - 3x + 9$
$= x^2 - 6x + 9;$

c) $(5 + 3p)^2 = (5 + 3p)(5 + 3p)$
$= 25 + 15p + 15p + 9p^2$
$= 25 + 30p + 9p^2;$

d) $(3x - 5)^2 = (3x - 5)(3x - 5)$
$= 9x^2 - 15x - 15x + 25$
$= 9x^2 - 30x + 25$

Do Exercises 20 and 21.

Multiply.

20. $(x + 8)(x + 8)$

21. $(x - 5)(x - 5)$

When squaring a binomial, we multiply a binomial by itself. Perhaps you noticed that two terms are the same and when added give twice the product of the terms in the binomial. The other two terms are squares.

SQUARE OF A BINOMIAL

The square of a sum or a difference of two terms is the square of the first term, plus twice the product of the two terms, plus the square of the last term:

$$(A + B)^2 = A^2 + 2AB + B^2; \quad (A - B)^2 = A^2 - 2AB + B^2.$$

It is helpful to memorize this rule in both words and symbols.

EXAMPLES Multiply. (Carry out the rule and say the words as you go.)

$(A + B)^2 = A^2 + 2 \cdot A \cdot B + B^2$

16. $(x + 3)^2 = x^2 + 2 \cdot x \cdot 3 + 3^2$ "x^2 plus 2 times x times 3 plus 3^2"
$= x^2 + 6x + 9$

$(A - B)^2 = A^2 - 2 \cdot A \cdot B + B^2$

17. $(t - 5)^2 = t^2 - 2 \cdot t \cdot 5 + 5^2$
$= t^2 - 10t + 25$

18. $(2x + 7)^2 = (2x)^2 + 2 \cdot 2x \cdot 7 + 7^2 = 4x^2 + 28x + 49$

19. $(5x - 3x^2)^2 = (5x)^2 - 2 \cdot 5x \cdot 3x^2 + (3x^2)^2 = 25x^2 - 30x^3 + 9x^4$

20. $(2.3 - 5.4m)^2 = 2.3^2 - 2(2.3)(5.4m) + (5.4m)^2$
$= 5.29 - 24.84m + 29.16m^2$

Do Exercises 22–27.

Multiply.

22. $(x + 2)^2$

23. $(a - 4)^2$

24. $(2x + 5)^2$

25. $(4x^2 - 3x)^2$

26. $(7.8 + 1.2y)(7.8 + 1.2y)$

27. $(3x^2 - 5)(3x^2 - 5)$

Caution!

Although the square of a product is the product of the squares, the square of a sum is *not* the sum of the squares. That is, $(AB)^2 = A^2B^2$, but

The term $2AB$ is missing.

$$(A + B)^2 \neq A^2 + B^2.$$

To illustrate this inequality, note, using the rules for order of operations, that

$$(7 + 5)^2 = 12^2 = 144,$$

whereas

$$7^2 + 5^2 = 49 + 25 = 74, \quad \text{and} \quad 74 \neq 144.$$

Answers

20. $x^2 + 16x + 64$ **21.** $x^2 - 10x + 25$
22. $x^2 + 4x + 4$ **23.** $a^2 - 8a + 16$
24. $4x^2 + 20x + 25$ **25.** $16x^4 - 24x^3 + 9x^2$
26. $60.84 + 18.72y + 1.44y^2$
27. $9x^4 - 30x^2 + 25$

We can look at the rule for finding $(A + B)^2$ geometrically as follows. The area of the large square is

$$(A + B)(A + B) = (A + B)^2.$$

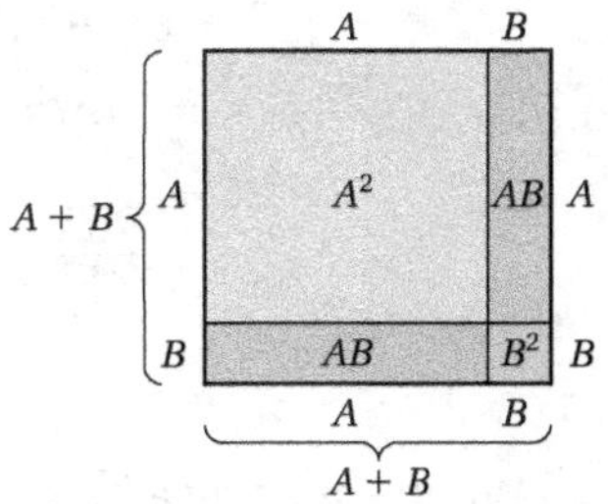

This is equal to the sum of the areas of the smaller rectangles:

$$A^2 + AB + AB + B^2 = A^2 + 2AB + B^2.$$

Thus, $(A + B)^2 = A^2 + 2AB + B^2$.

Do Exercise 28.

28. In the figure at right, describe in terms of area the sum $A^2 + B^2$. How can the figure be used to verify that $(A + B)^2 \neq A^2 + B^2$?

d Multiplication of Various Types

Let's now try several types of multiplications mixed together so that we can learn to sort them out. When you multiply, first see what kind of multiplication you have. Then use the best method.

MULTIPLYING TWO POLYNOMIALS

1. Is it the product of a monomial and a polynomial? If so, multiply each term of the polynomial by the monomial.
   Example: $5x(x + 7) = 5x \cdot x + 5x \cdot 7 = 5x^2 + 35x$
2. Is it the product of the sum and the difference of the *same* two terms? If so, use the following:
   $$(A + B)(A - B) = A^2 - B^2.$$
   The product of the sum and the difference of the same two terms is the difference of the squares. [The answer has 2 terms.]
   Example: $(x + 7)(x - 7) = x^2 - 7^2 = x^2 - 49$
3. Is the product the square of a binomial? If so, use the following:
   $$(A + B)(A + B) = (A + B)^2 = A^2 + 2AB + B^2,$$
   or $$(A - B)(A - B) = (A - B)^2 = A^2 - 2AB + B^2.$$
   The square of a binomial is the square of the first term, plus *twice* the product of the two terms, plus the square of the last term. [The answer has 3 terms.]
   Example: $(x + 7)(x + 7) = (x + 7)^2$
   $= x^2 + 2 \cdot x \cdot 7 + 7^2 = x^2 + 14x + 49$
4. Is it the product of two binomials other than those above? If so, use FOIL. [The answer will have 3 or 4 terms.]
   Example: $(x + 7)(x - 4) = x^2 - 4x + 7x - 28 = x^2 + 3x - 28$
5. Is it the product of two polynomials other than those above? If so, multiply each term of one by every term of the other. Use columns if you wish. [The answer will have 2 or more terms, usually more than 2 terms.]
   Example:
   $$\begin{aligned}(x^2 - 3x + 2)(x + 7) &= x^2(x + 7) - 3x(x + 7) + 2(x + 7)\\ &= x^2 \cdot x + x^2 \cdot 7 - 3x \cdot x - 3x \cdot 7\\ &\quad + 2 \cdot x + 2 \cdot 7\\ &= x^3 + 7x^2 - 3x^2 - 21x + 2x + 14\\ &= x^3 + 4x^2 - 19x + 14\end{aligned}$$

STUDY TIPS

CHECKLIST

The foundation of all your study skills is TIME!

- Are you taking the time to include all the steps when doing your homework and taking tests?
- Are you using the time-management suggestions we have given so that you have the proper amount of time to study mathematics?
- Have you been using the supplements for the text such as the *Student's Solutions Manual*?
- Have you memorized the rules for special products of polynomials and for manipulating expressions with exponents?

Answer

28. $(A + B)^2$ represents the area of the large square. This includes all four sections. $A^2 + B^2$ represents the area of only two of the sections.

Remember that FOIL will *always* work for two binomials. You can use it instead of either of rules 2 and 3, but those rules will make your work go faster.

EXAMPLE 21 Multiply: $(x + 3)(x - 3)$.

$(x + 3)(x - 3) = x^2 - 9$ Using method 2 (the product of the sum and the difference of two terms)

EXAMPLE 22 Multiply: $(t + 7)(t - 5)$.

$(t + 7)(t - 5) = t^2 + 2t - 35$ Using method 4, FOIL (the product of two binomials, but neither the square of a binomial nor the product of the sum and the difference of two terms)

EXAMPLE 23 Multiply: $(x + 6)(x + 6)$.

$(x + 6)(x + 6) = x^2 + 2(6)x + 36$ Using method 3 (the square of a binomial sum)

$= x^2 + 12x + 36$

EXAMPLE 24 Multiply: $2x^3(9x^2 + x - 7)$.

$2x^3(9x^2 + x - 7) = 18x^5 + 2x^4 - 14x^3$ Using method 1 (the product of a monomial and a trinomial; multiplying each term of the trinomial by the monomial)

EXAMPLE 25 Multiply: $(5x^3 - 7x)^2$.

$(5x^3 - 7x)^2 = 25x^6 - 2(5x^3)(7x) + 49x^2$ Using method 3 (the square of a binomial)

$= 25x^6 - 70x^4 + 49x^2$

EXAMPLE 26 Multiply: $\left(3x + \frac{1}{4}\right)^2$.

$\left(3x + \frac{1}{4}\right)^2 = 9x^2 + 2(3x)\left(\frac{1}{4}\right) + \frac{1}{16}$ Using method 3 (the square of a binomial. To get the middle term, we find twice the product of $3x$ and $\frac{1}{4}$.)

$= 9x^2 + \frac{3}{2}x + \frac{1}{16}$

EXAMPLE 27 Multiply: $\left(4x - \frac{3}{4}\right)^2$.

$\left(4x - \frac{3}{4}\right)^2 = 16x^2 - 2(4x)\left(\frac{3}{4}\right) + \frac{9}{16}$ Using method 3 (the square of a binomial)

$= 16x^2 - 6x + \frac{9}{16}$

EXAMPLE 28 Multiply: $(p + 3)(p^2 + 2p - 1)$.

$$\begin{array}{r} p^2 + 2p - 1 \\ p + 3 \\ \hline 3p^2 + 6p - 3 \\ p^3 + 2p^2 - p \quad \\ \hline p^3 + 5p^2 + 5p - 3 \end{array}$$

Using method 5 (the product of two polynomials)

Multiplying by 3

Multiplying by p

Do Exercises 29–36.

Multiply.

29. $(x + 5)(x + 6)$

30. $(t - 4)(t + 4)$

31. $4x^2(-2x^3 + 5x^2 + 10)$

32. $(9x^2 + 1)^2$

33. $(2a - 5)(2a + 8)$

34. $\left(5x + \frac{1}{2}\right)^2$

35. $\left(2x - \frac{1}{2}\right)^2$

36. $(x^2 - x + 4)(x - 2)$

Answers

29. $x^2 + 11x + 30$ 30. $t^2 - 16$
31. $-8x^5 + 20x^4 + 40x^2$ 32. $81x^4 + 18x^2 + 1$
33. $4a^2 + 6a - 40$ 34. $25x^2 + 5x + \frac{1}{4}$
35. $4x^2 - 2x + \frac{1}{4}$ 36. $x^3 - 3x^2 + 6x - 8$

Visualizing for Success

In each of Exercises 1–10, find two algebraic expressions for the shaded area of the figure from the list below.

A. $9 - 4x^2$

B. $x^2 - (x - 6)^2$

C. $(x + 3)(x - 3)$

D. $10^2 + 2^2$

E. $x^2 + 8x + 15$

F. $(x + 5)(x + 3)$

G. $x^2 - 6x + 9$

H. $(3 - 2x)^2 + 4x(3 - 2x)$

I. $(x + 3)^2$

J. $(5x + 3)^2$

K. $(5 - 2x)^2 + 4x(5 - 2x)$

L. $x^2 - 9$

M. 104

N. $x^2 - 15$

O. $12x - 36$

P. $25x^2 + 30x + 9$

Q. $(x - 5)(x - 3)$
$+ 3(x - 5) + 5(x - 3)$

R. $(x - 3)^2$

S. $25 - 4x^2$

T. $x^2 + 6x + 9$

Answers on page A-8

1

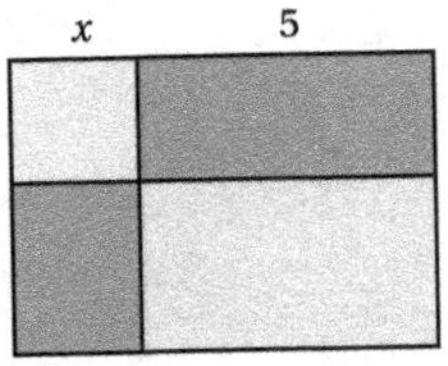

2

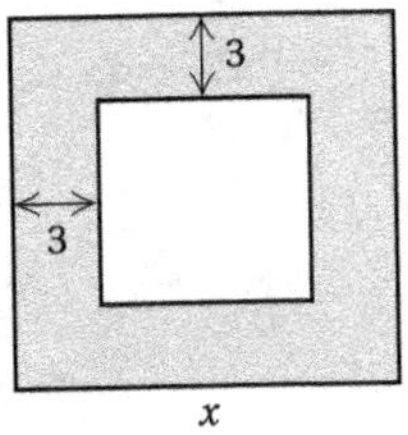

3

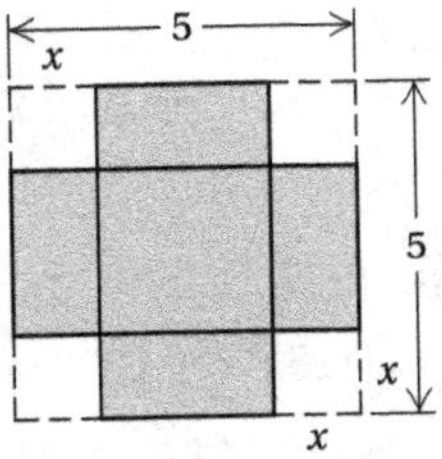

4

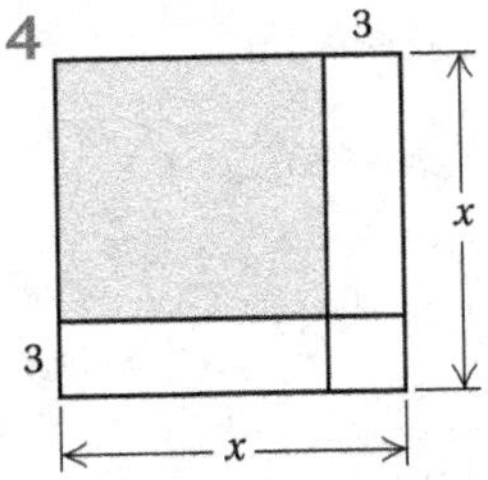

5

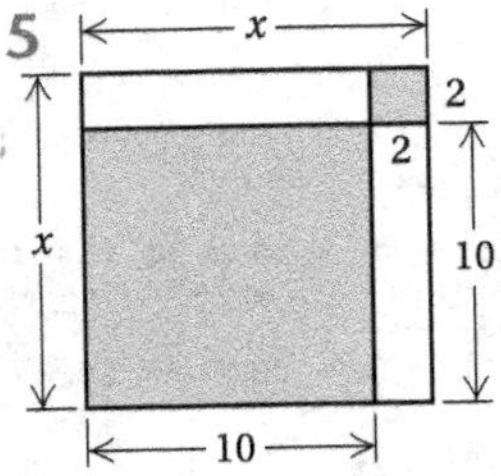

6

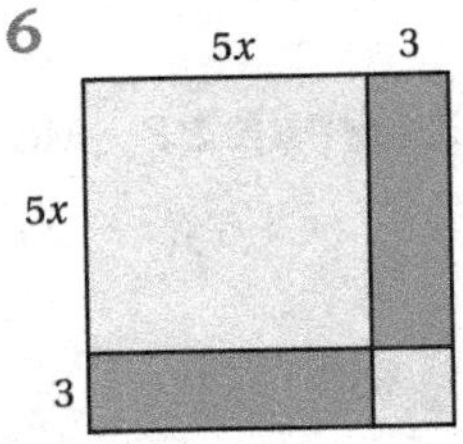

7

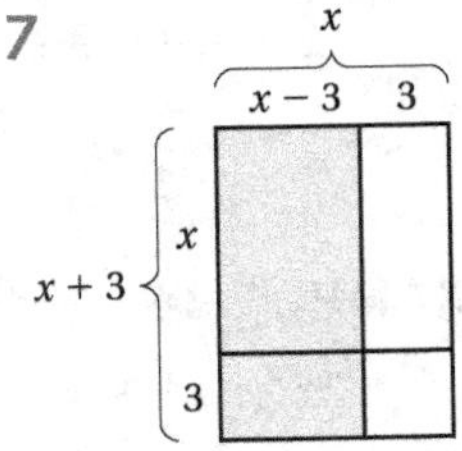

8

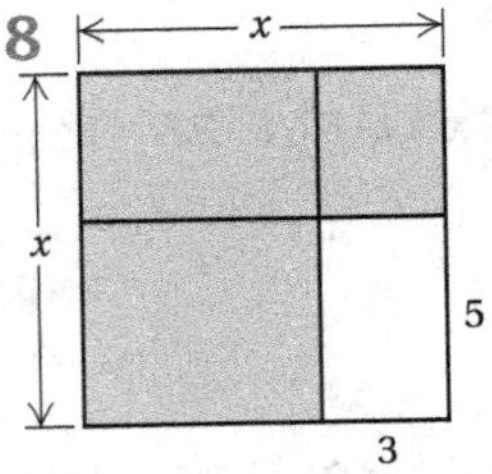

9

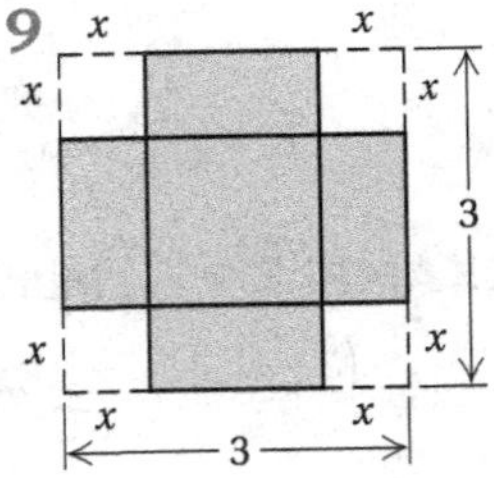

10

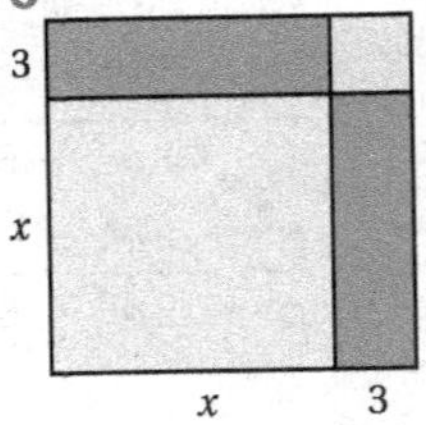

3.6 Exercise Set

For Extra Help
MyMathLab
Math XL PRACTICE | WATCH | DOWNLOAD | READ | REVIEW

a Multiply. Try to write only the answer. If you need more steps, be sure to use them.

1. $(x + 1)(x^2 + 3)$

2. $(x^2 - 3)(x - 1)$

3. $(x^3 + 2)(x + 1)$

4. $(x^4 + 2)(x + 10)$

5. $(y + 2)(y - 3)$

6. $(a + 2)(a + 3)$

7. $(3x + 2)(3x + 2)$

8. $(4x + 1)(4x + 1)$

9. $(5x - 6)(x + 2)$

10. $(x - 8)(x + 8)$

11. $(3t - 1)(3t + 1)$

12. $(2m + 3)(2m + 3)$

13. $(4x - 2)(x - 1)$

14. $(2x - 1)(3x + 1)$

15. $\left(p - \frac{1}{4}\right)\left(p + \frac{1}{4}\right)$

16. $\left(q + \frac{3}{4}\right)\left(q + \frac{3}{4}\right)$

17. $(x - 0.1)(x + 0.1)$

18. $(x + 0.3)(x - 0.4)$

19. $(2x^2 + 6)(x + 1)$

20. $(2x^2 + 3)(2x - 1)$

21. $(-2x + 1)(x + 6)$

22. $(3x + 4)(2x - 4)$

23. $(a + 7)(a + 7)$

24. $(2y + 5)(2y + 5)$

25. $(1 + 2x)(1 - 3x)$

26. $(-3x - 2)(x + 1)$

27. $\left(\frac{3}{8}y - \frac{5}{6}\right)\left(\frac{3}{8}y - \frac{5}{6}\right)$

28. $\left(\frac{1}{5}x - \frac{2}{7}\right)\left(\frac{1}{5}x + \frac{2}{7}\right)$

29. $(x^2 + 3)(x^3 - 1)$

30. $(x^4 - 3)(2x + 1)$

31. $(3x^2 - 2)(x^4 - 2)$

32. $(x^{10} + 3)(x^{10} - 3)$

33. $(2.8x - 1.5)(4.7x + 9.3)$

34. $\left(x - \frac{3}{8}\right)\left(x + \frac{4}{7}\right)$

35. $(3x^5 + 2)(2x^2 + 6)$

36. $(1 - 2x)(1 + 3x^2)$

37. $(8x^3 + 1)(x^3 + 8)$

38. $(4 - 2x)(5 - 2x^2)$

39. $(4x^2 + 3)(x - 3)$

40. $(7x - 2)(2x - 7)$

41. $(4y^4 + y^2)(y^2 + y)$

42. $(5y^6 + 3y^3)(2y^6 + 2y^3)$

b Multiply mentally, if possible. If you need extra steps, be sure to use them.

43. $(x + 4)(x - 4)$

44. $(x + 1)(x - 1)$

45. $(2x + 1)(2x - 1)$

46. $(x^2 + 1)(x^2 - 1)$

47. $(5m - 2)(5m + 2)$

48. $(3x^4 + 2)(3x^4 - 2)$

49. $(2x^2 + 3)(2x^2 - 3)$

50. $(6x^5 - 5)(6x^5 + 5)$

51. $(3x^4 - 4)(3x^4 + 4)$

52. $(t^2 - 0.2)(t^2 + 0.2)$

53. $(x^6 - x^2)(x^6 + x^2)$

54. $(2x^3 - 0.3)(2x^3 + 0.3)$

55. $(x^4 + 3x)(x^4 - 3x)$

56. $\left(\frac{3}{4} + 2x^3\right)\left(\frac{3}{4} - 2x^3\right)$

57. $(x^{12} - 3)(x^{12} + 3)$

58. $(12 - 3x^2)(12 + 3x^2)$

59. $(2y^8 + 3)(2y^8 - 3)$

60. $\left(m - \frac{2}{3}\right)\left(m + \frac{2}{3}\right)$

61. $\left(\frac{5}{8}x - 4.3\right)\left(\frac{5}{8}x + 4.3\right)$

62. $(10.7 - x^3)(10.7 + x^3)$

c Multiply mentally, if possible. If you need extra steps, be sure to use them.

63. $(x + 2)^2$

64. $(2x - 1)^2$

65. $(3x^2 + 1)^2$

66. $\left(3x + \frac{3}{4}\right)^2$

67. $\left(a - \frac{1}{2}\right)^2$

68. $\left(2a - \frac{1}{5}\right)^2$

69. $(3 + x)^2$

70. $(x^3 - 1)^2$

71. $(x^2 + 1)^2$

72. $(8x - x^2)^2$

73. $(2 - 3x^4)^2$

74. $(6x^3 - 2)^2$

75. $(5 + 6t^2)^2$

76. $(3p^2 - p)^2$

77. $\left(x - \frac{5}{8}\right)^2$

78. $(0.3y + 2.4)^2$

d Multiply mentally, if possible.

79. $(3 - 2x^3)^2$

80. $(x - 4x^3)^2$

81. $4x(x^2 + 6x - 3)$

82. $8x(-x^5 + 6x^2 + 9)$

83. $\left(2x^2 - \frac{1}{2}\right)\left(2x^2 - \frac{1}{2}\right)$

84. $(-x^2 + 1)^2$

85. $(-1 + 3p)(1 + 3p)$

86. $(-3q + 2)(3q + 2)$

87. $3t^2(5t^3 - t^2 + t)$

88. $-6x^2(x^3 + 8x - 9)$

89. $(6x^4 + 4)^2$

90. $(8a + 5)^2$

91. $(3x + 2)(4x^2 + 5)$

92. $(2x^2 - 7)(3x^2 + 9)$

93. $(8 - 6x^4)^2$

94. $\left(\frac{1}{5}x^2 + 9\right)\left(\frac{3}{5}x^2 - 7\right)$

95. $(t - 1)(t^2 + t + 1)$

96. $(y + 5)(y^2 - 5y + 25)$

Compute each of the following and compare.

97. $3^2 + 4^2$; $(3 + 4)^2$

98. $6^2 + 7^2$; $(6 + 7)^2$

99. $9^2 - 5^2$; $(9 - 5)^2$

100. $11^2 - 4^2$; $(11 - 4)^2$

Find the total area of all the shaded rectangles.

101.
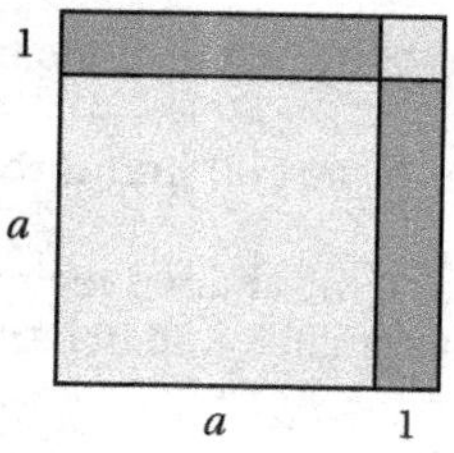

102.
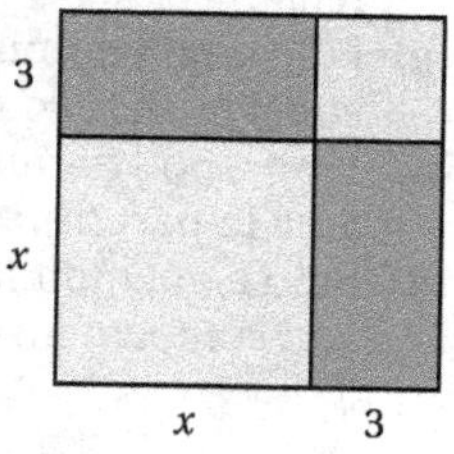

103.
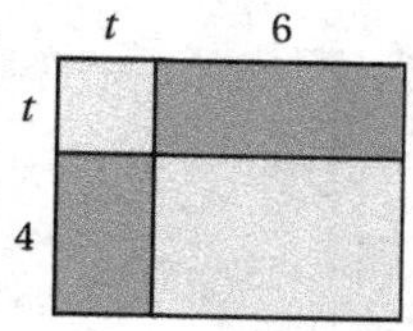

104.
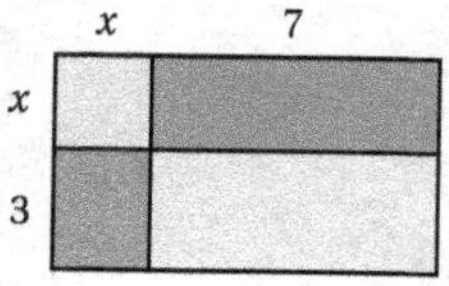

Skill Maintenance

105. *Electricity Usage.* In apartment 3B, lamps, an air conditioner, and a television set are all operating at the same time. The lamps use 10 times as many watts of electricity as the television set, and the air conditioner uses 40 times as many watts as the television set. The total wattage used in the apartment is 2550. How many watts are used by each appliance? [2.6a]

Solve. [2.3c]

106. $3x - 8x = 4(7 - 8x)$

107. $3(x - 2) = 5(2x + 7)$

108. $5(2x - 3) - 2(3x - 4) = 20$

Solve. [2.4b]

109. $3x - 2y = 12$, for y

110. $3a - 5d = 4$, for a

Synthesis

Multiply.

111. $5x(3x - 1)(2x + 3)$

112. $[(2x - 3)(2x + 3)](4x^2 + 9)$

113. $[(a - 5)(a + 5)]^2$

114. $(a - 3)^2(a + 3)^2$
(*Hint*: Examine Exercise 113.)

115. $(3t^4 - 2)^2(3t^4 + 2)^2$
(*Hint*: Examine Exercise 113.)

116. $[3a - (2a - 3)][3a + (2a - 3)]$

Solve.

117. $(x + 2)(x - 5) = (x + 1)(x - 3)$

118. $(2x + 5)(x - 4) = (x + 5)(2x - 4)$

119. *Factors and Sums.* To *factor* a number is to express it as a product. Since $12 = 4 \cdot 3$, we say that 12 is *factored* and that 4 and 3 are *factors* of 12. In the table below, the top number has been factored in such a way that the sum of the factors is the bottom number. For example, in the first column, 40 has been factored as $5 \cdot 8$, and $5 + 8 = 13$, the bottom number. Such thinking is important in algebra when we factor trinomials of the type $x^2 + bx + c$. Find the missing numbers in the table.

PRODUCT	40	63	36	72	−140	−96	48	168	110			
FACTOR	5									−9	−24	−3
FACTOR	8									−10	18	
SUM	13	16	−20	−38	−4	4	−14	−29	−21			18

120. Consider the rectangle below.

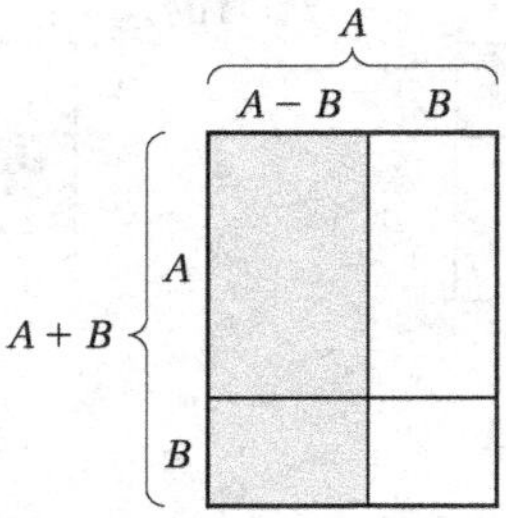

a) Find a polynomial for the area of the entire rectangle.
b) Find a polynomial for the sum of the areas of the two small unshaded rectangles.
c) Find a polynomial for the area in part (a) minus the area in part (b).
d) Find a polynomial for the area of the shaded region and compare this with the polynomial found in part (c).

Use the TABLE or GRAPH feature to check whether each of the following is correct.

121. $(x - 1)^2 = x^2 - 2x + 1$

122. $(x - 2)^2 = x^2 - 4x - 4$

123. $(x - 3)(x + 3) = x^2 - 6$

124. $(x - 3)(x + 2) = x^2 - x - 6$

3.7 Operations with Polynomials in Several Variables

The polynomials that we have been studying have only one variable. A **polynomial in several variables** is an expression like those you have already seen, but with more than one variable. Here are two examples:

$$3x + xy^2 + 5y + 4, \qquad 8xy^2z - 2x^3z - 13x^4y^2 + 15.$$

OBJECTIVES

- **a** Evaluate a polynomial in several variables for given values of the variables.
- **b** Identify the coefficients and the degrees of the terms of a polynomial and the degree of a polynomial.
- **c** Collect like terms of a polynomial.
- **d** Add polynomials.
- **e** Subtract polynomials.
- **f** Multiply polynomials.

a Evaluating Polynomials

EXAMPLE 1 Evaluate the polynomial $4 + 3x + xy^2 + 8x^3y^3$ when $x = -2$ and $y = 5$.

We replace x with -2 and y with 5:

$$\begin{aligned} 4 + 3x + xy^2 + 8x^3y^3 &= 4 + 3(-2) + (-2) \cdot 5^2 + 8(-2)^3 \cdot 5^3 \\ &= 4 + 3(-2) + (-2) \cdot 25 + 8(-8)(125) \\ &= 4 - 6 - 50 - 8000 \\ &= -8052. \end{aligned}$$

EXAMPLE 2 *Male Caloric Needs.* The number of calories needed each day by a moderately active man who weighs w kilograms, is h centimeters tall, and is a years old can be estimated by the polynomial

$$19.18w + 7h - 9.52a + 92.4.$$

Steve is moderately active, weighs 82 kg, is 185 cm tall, and is 67 yr old. What are his daily caloric needs?

Source: Parker, M., *She Does Math.* Mathematical Association of America

We evaluate the polynomial for $w = 82$, $h = 185$, and $a = 67$:

$$\begin{aligned} &19.18w + 7h - 9.52a + 92.4 \\ &\quad = 19.18(82) + 7(185) - 9.52(67) + 92.4 \qquad \text{Substituting} \\ &\quad = 2322.32. \end{aligned}$$

Steve's daily caloric need is about 2322 calories.

Do Exercises 1–3.

1. Evaluate the polynomial
$$4 + 3x + xy^2 + 8x^3y^3$$
when $x = 2$ and $y = -5$.

2. Evaluate the polynomial
$$8xy^2 - 2x^3z - 13x^4y^2 + 5$$
when $x = -1$, $y = 3$, and $z = 4$.

3. **Female Caloric Needs.** The number of calories needed each day by a moderately active woman who weighs w pounds, is h inches tall, and is a years old can be estimated by the polynomial
$$917 + 6w + 6h - 6a.$$
Christine is moderately active, weighs 125 lb, is 64 in. tall, and is 27 yr old. What are her daily caloric needs?
Source: Parker, M., *She Does Math.* Mathematical Association of America

Answers

1. -7940 2. -176 3. 1889 calories

b Coefficients and Degrees

The **degree** of a term is the sum of the exponents of the variables. The **degree of a polynomial** is the degree of the term of highest degree.

EXAMPLE 3 Identify the coefficient and the degree of each term and the degree of the polynomial

$$9x^2y^3 - 14xy^2z^3 + xy + 4y + 5x^2 + 7.$$

TERM	COEFFICIENT	DEGREE	DEGREE OF THE POLYNOMIAL
$9x^2y^3$	9	5	
$-14xy^2z^3$	-14	6	6
xy	1	2	
$4y$	4	1	Think: $4y = 4y^1$.
$5x^2$	5	2	
7	7	0	Think: $7 = 7x^0$, or $7x^0y^0z^0$.

Do Exercises 4 and 5.

4. Identify the coefficient of each term:
$-3xy^2 + 3x^2y - 2y^3 + xy + 2.$

5. Identify the degree of each term and the degree of the polynomial
$4xy^2 + 7x^2y^3z^2 - 5x + 2y + 4.$

c Collecting Like Terms

Like terms have exactly the same variables with exactly the same exponents. For example,

$3x^2y^3$ and $-7x^2y^3$ are like terms;
$9x^4z^7$ and $12x^4z^7$ are like terms.

But

$13xy^5$ and $-2x^2y^5$ are *not* like terms, because the x-factors have different exponents;

and

$3xyz^2$ and $4xy$ are *not* like terms, because there is no factor of z^2 in the second expression.

Collecting like terms is based on the distributive laws.

EXAMPLES Collect like terms.

4. $5x^2y + 3xy^2 - 5x^2y - xy^2 = (5 - 5)x^2y + (3 - 1)xy^2 = 2xy^2$

5. $8a^2 - 2ab + 7b^2 + 4a^2 - 9ab - 17b^2 = 12a^2 - 11ab - 10b^2$

6. $7xy - 5xy^2 + 3xy^2 - 7 + 6x^3 + 9xy - 11x^3 + y - 1$
$= 16xy - 2xy^2 - 5x^3 + y - 8$

Do Exercises 6 and 7.

Collect like terms.

6. $4x^2y + 3xy - 2x^2y$

7. $-3pq - 5pqr^3 - 12 + 8pq + 5pqr^3 + 4$

Answers

4. $-3, 3, -2, 1, 2$ **5.** $3, 7, 1, 1, 0; 7$
6. $2x^2y + 3xy$ **7.** $5pq - 8$

d Addition

We can find the sum of two polynomials in several variables by writing a plus sign between them and then collecting like terms.

EXAMPLE 7 Add: $(-5x^3 + 3y - 5y^2) + (8x^3 + 4x^2 + 7y^2)$.

$$(-5x^3 + 3y - 5y^2) + (8x^3 + 4x^2 + 7y^2)$$
$$= (-5 + 8)x^3 + 4x^2 + 3y + (-5 + 7)y^2$$
$$= 3x^3 + 4x^2 + 3y + 2y^2$$

EXAMPLE 8 Add:

$$(5xy^2 - 4x^2y + 5x^3 + 2) + (3xy^2 - 2x^2y + 3x^3y - 5).$$

We have

$$(5xy^2 - 4x^2y + 5x^3 + 2) + (3xy^2 - 2x^2y + 3x^3y - 5)$$
$$= (5 + 3)xy^2 + (-4 - 2)x^2y + 5x^3 + 3x^3y + (2 - 5)$$
$$= 8xy^2 - 6x^2y + 5x^3 + 3x^3y - 3.$$

Do Exercises 8–10.

Add.

8. $(4x^3 + 4x^2 - 8y - 3) + (-8x^3 - 2x^2 + 4y + 5)$

9. $(13x^3y + 3x^2y - 5y) + (x^3y + 4x^2y - 3xy + 3y)$

10. $(-5p^2q^4 + 2p^2q^2 + 3q) + (6pq^2 + 3p^2q + 5)$

e Subtraction

We subtract a polynomial by adding its opposite, or additive inverse. The opposite of the polynomial $4x^2y - 6x^3y^2 + x^2y^2 - 5y$ is

$$-(4x^2y - 6x^3y^2 + x^2y^2 - 5y) = -4x^2y + 6x^3y^2 - x^2y^2 + 5y.$$

EXAMPLE 9 Subtract:

$$(4x^2y + x^3y^2 + 3x^2y^3 + 6y + 10) - (4x^2y - 6x^3y^2 + x^2y^2 - 5y - 8).$$

We have

$$(4x^2y + x^3y^2 + 3x^2y^3 + 6y + 10) - (4x^2y - 6x^3y^2 + x^2y^2 - 5y - 8)$$
$$= 4x^2y + x^3y^2 + 3x^2y^3 + 6y + 10 - 4x^2y + 6x^3y^2 - x^2y^2 + 5y + 8$$

Finding the opposite by changing the sign of each term

$$= 7x^3y^2 + 3x^2y^3 - x^2y^2 + 11y + 18.$$

Collecting like terms. (Try to write just the answer!)

Caution!

Do *not* add exponents when collecting like terms—that is,

$7x^3 + 8x^3 \neq 15x^6$; ← Wrong

$7x^3 + 8x^3 = 15x^3$. ← Correct

Do Exercises 11 and 12.

Subtract.

11. $(-4s^4t + s^3t^2 + 2s^2t^3) - (4s^4t - 5s^3t^2 + s^2t^2)$

12. $(-5p^4q + 5p^3q^2 - 3p^2q^3 - 7q^4 - 2) - (4p^4q - 4p^3q^2 + p^2q^3 + 2q^4 - 7)$

Answers

8. $-4x^3 + 2x^2 - 4y + 2$
9. $14x^3y + 7x^2y - 3xy - 2y$
10. $-5p^2q^4 + 2p^2q^2 + 3p^2q + 6pq^2 + 3q + 5$
11. $-8s^4t + 6s^3t^2 + 2s^2t^3 - s^2t^2$
12. $-9p^4q + 9p^3q^2 - 4p^2q^3 - 9q^4 + 5$

f Multiplication

To multiply polynomials in several variables, we can multiply each term of one by every term of the other. We can use columns for long multiplications as with polynomials in one variable. We multiply each term at the top by every term at the bottom. We write like terms in columns, and then we add.

EXAMPLE 10 Multiply: $(3x^2y - 2xy + 3y)(xy + 2y)$.

$$\begin{array}{rrrrl} & 3x^2y & - 2xy & + 3y & \\ & & xy & + 2y & \\ \hline & 6x^2y^2 & - 4xy^2 & + 6y^2 & \text{Multiplying by } 2y \\ 3x^3y^2 & - 2x^2y^2 & + 3xy^2 & & \text{Multiplying by } xy \\ \hline 3x^3y^2 & + 4x^2y^2 & - xy^2 & + 6y^2 & \text{Adding} \end{array}$$

Do Exercises 13 and 14.

Multiply.

13. $(x^2y^3 + 2x)(x^3y^2 + 3x)$

14. $(p^4q - 2p^3q^2 + 3q^3)(p + 2q)$

Where appropriate, we use the special products that we have learned.

EXAMPLES Multiply.

11. $(x^2y + 2x)(xy^2 + y^2) = x^3y^3 + x^2y^3 + 2x^2y^2 + 2xy^2$ Using FOIL

12. $(p + 5q)(2p - 3q) = 2p^2 - 3pq + 10pq - 15q^2$ Using FOIL
$= 2p^2 + 7pq - 15q^2$

$(A + B)^2 = A^2 + 2 \cdot A \cdot B + B^2$

13. $(3x + 2y)^2 = (3x)^2 + 2(3x)(2y) + (2y)^2 = 9x^2 + 12xy + 4y^2$

$(A - B)^2 = A^2 - 2 \cdot A \cdot B + B^2$

14. $(2y^2 - 5x^2y)^2 = (2y^2)^2 - 2(2y^2)(5x^2y) + (5x^2y)^2$
$= 4y^4 - 20x^2y^3 + 25x^4y^2$

$(A + B)(A - B) = A^2 - B^2$

15. $(3x^2y + 2y)(3x^2y - 2y) = (3x^2y)^2 - (2y)^2 = 9x^4y^2 - 4y^2$

16. $(-2x^3y^2 + 5t)(2x^3y^2 + 5t) = (5t - 2x^3y^2)(5t + 2x^3y^2)$ The sum and the difference of the same two terms
$= (5t)^2 - (2x^3y^2)^2 = 25t^2 - 4x^6y^4$

$(A - B)(A + B) = A^2 - B^2$

17. $(2x + 3 - 2y)(2x + 3 + 2y) = (2x + 3)^2 - (2y)^2$
$= 4x^2 + 12x + 9 - 4y^2$

Remember that FOIL will always work when you are multiplying binomials. You can use it instead of the rules for special products, but those rules will make your work go faster.

Do Exercises 15–22.

Multiply.

15. $(3xy + 2x)(x^2 + 2xy^2)$

16. $(x - 3y)(2x - 5y)$

17. $(4x + 5y)^2$

18. $(3x^2 - 2xy^2)^2$

19. $(2xy^2 + 3x)(2xy^2 - 3x)$

20. $(3xy^2 + 4y)(-3xy^2 + 4y)$

21. $(3y + 4 - 3x)(3y + 4 + 3x)$

22. $(2a + 5b + c)(2a - 5b - c)$

Answers

13. $x^5y^5 + 2x^4y^2 + 3x^3y^3 + 6x^2$
14. $p^5q - 4p^3q^3 + 3pq^3 + 6q^4$
15. $3x^3y + 6x^2y^3 + 2x^3 + 4x^2y^2$
16. $2x^2 - 11xy + 15y^2$
17. $16x^2 + 40xy + 25y^2$
18. $9x^4 - 12x^3y^2 + 4x^2y^4$
19. $4x^2y^4 - 9x^2$ 20. $16y^2 - 9x^2y^4$
21. $9y^2 + 24y + 16 - 9x^2$
22. $4a^2 - 25b^2 - 10bc - c^2$

a Evaluate the polynomial when $x = 3$, $y = -2$, and $z = -5$.

1. $x^2 - y^2 + xy$

2. $x^2 + y^2 - xy$

3. $x^2 - 3y^2 + 2xy$

4. $x^2 - 4xy + 5y^2$

5. $8xyz$

6. $-3xyz^2$

7. $xyz^2 - z$

8. $xy - xz + yz$

Lung Capacity. The polynomial equation

$$C = 0.041h - 0.018A - 2.69$$

can be used to estimate the lung capacity C, in liters, of a person of height h, in centimeters, and age A, in years. Use this formula for Exercises 9 and 10.

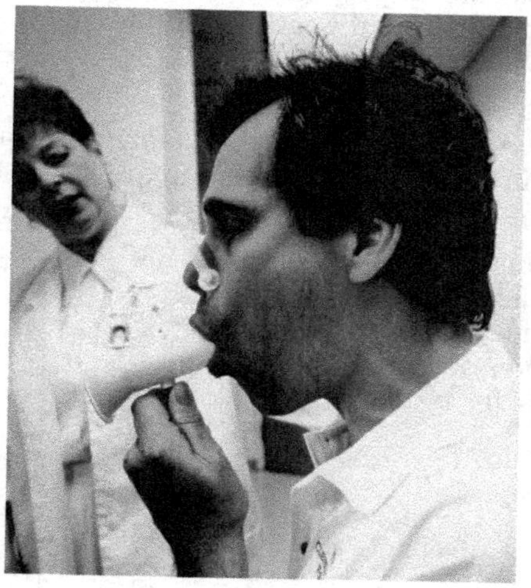

9. Find the lung capacity of a 20-year-old person who is 165 cm tall.

10. Find the lung capacity of a 50-year-old person who is 160 cm tall.

Altitude of a Launched Object. The altitude h, in meters, of a launched object is given by the polynomial equation

$$h = h_0 + vt - 4.9t^2,$$

where h_0 is the height, in meters, from which the launch occurs, v is the initial upward speed (or velocity), in meters per second (m/s), and t is the number of seconds for which the object is airborne. Use this formula for Exercises 11 and 12.

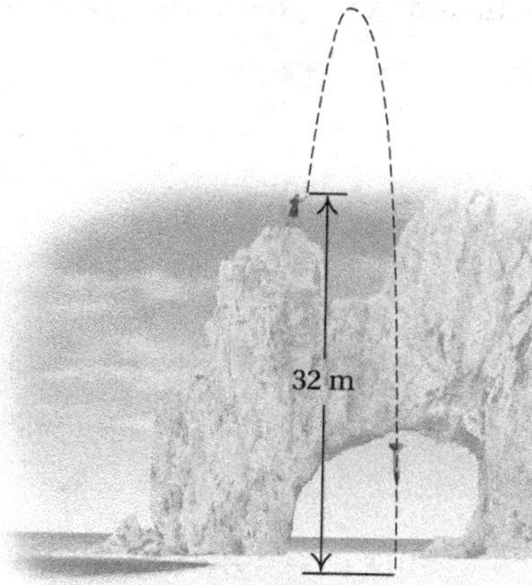

11. A golf ball is thrown upward with an initial speed of 30 m/s from the top of the Washington Monument, which is 160 m above the ground. How high above the ground will the ball be after 3 sec?

12. A model rocket is launched from the top of the Lands End Arch, near San Lucas, Baja, Mexico, 32 m above the ground. The upward speed is 40 m/s. How high will the rocket be 2 sec after the blastoff?

Surface Area of a Right Circular Cylinder. The surface area S of a right circular cylinder is given by the polynomial equation

$$S = 2\pi rh + 2\pi r^2,$$

where h is the height and r is the radius of the base. Use this formula for Exercises 13 and 14.

13. A 12-oz beverage can has a height of 4.7 in. and a radius of 1.2 in. Evaluate the polynomial when $h = 4.7$ and $r = 1.2$ to find the area of the can. Use 3.14 for π.

14. A 26-oz coffee can has a height of 6.5 in. and a radius of 2.5 in. Evaluate the polynomial when $h = 6.5$ and $r = 2.5$ to find the area of the can. Use 3.14 for π.

Surface Area of a Silo. A silo is a structure that is shaped like a right circular cylinder with a half sphere on top. The surface area S of a silo of height h and radius r (including the area of the base) is given by the polynomial equation $S = 2\pi rh + \pi r^2$. Note that h is the height of the entire silo.

15. A container of tennis balls is silo-shaped, with a height of $7\frac{1}{2}$ in. and a radius of $1\frac{1}{4}$ in. Find the surface area of the container. Use 3.14 for π.

16. A $1\frac{1}{2}$-oz bottle of roll-on deodorant has a height of 4 in. and a radius of $\frac{3}{4}$ in. Find the surface area of the bottle if the bottle is shaped like a silo. Use 3.14 for π.

b Identify the coefficient and the degree of each term of the polynomial. Then find the degree of the polynomial.

17. $x^3y - 2xy + 3x^2 - 5$

18. $5x^2y^2 - y^2 + 15xy + 1$

19. $17x^2y^3 - 3x^3yz - 7$

20. $6 - xy + 8x^2y^2 - y^5$

c Collect like terms.

21. $a + b - 2a - 3b$

22. $xy^2 - 1 + y - 6 - xy^2$

23. $3x^2y - 2xy^2 + x^2$

24. $m^3 + 2m^2n - 3m^2 + 3mn^2$

25. $6au + 3av + 14au + 7av$

26. $3x^2y - 2z^2y + 3xy^2 + 5z^2y$

27. $2u^2v - 3uv^2 + 6u^2v - 2uv^2$

28. $3x^2 + 6xy + 3y^2 - 5x^2 - 10xy - 5y^2$

d Add.

29. $(2x^2 - xy + y^2) + (-x^2 - 3xy + 2y^2)$

30. $(2zt - z^2 + 5t^2) + (z^2 - 3zt + t^2)$

31. $(r - 2s + 3) + (2r + s) + (s + 4)$

32. $(ab - 2a + 3b) + (5a - 4b) + (3a + 7ab - 8b)$

33. $(b^3a^2 - 2b^2a^3 + 3ba + 4) + (b^2a^3 - 4b^3a^2 + 2ba - 1)$

34. $(2x^2 - 3xy + y^2) + (-4x^2 - 6xy - y^2)$
$+ (x^2 + xy - y^2)$

e Subtract.

35. $(a^3 + b^3) - (a^2b - ab^2 + b^3 + a^3)$

36. $(x^3 - y^3) - (-2x^3 + x^2y - xy^2 + 2y^3)$

37. $(xy - ab - 8) - (xy - 3ab - 6)$

38. $(3y^4x^2 + 2y^3x - 3y - 7)$
$- (2y^4x^2 + 2y^3x - 4y - 2x + 5)$

39. $(-2a + 7b - c) - (-3b + 4c - 8d)$

40. Subtract $5a + 2b$ from the sum of $2a + b$ and $3a - b$.

f Multiply.

41. $(3z - u)(2z + 3u)$

42. $(a - b)(a^2 + b^2 + 2ab)$

43. $(a^2b - 2)(a^2b - 5)$

44. $(xy + 7)(xy - 4)$

45. $(a^3 + bc)(a^3 - bc)$

46. $(m^2 + n^2 - mn)(m^2 + mn + n^2)$

47. $(y^4x + y^2 + 1)(y^2 + 1)$

48. $(a - b)(a^2 + ab + b^2)$

49. $(3xy - 1)(4xy + 2)$

50. $(m^3n + 8)(m^3n - 6)$

51. $(3 - c^2d^2)(4 + c^2d^2)$

52. $(6x - 2y)(5x - 3y)$

53. $(m^2 - n^2)(m + n)$

54. $(pq + 0.2)(0.4pq - 0.1)$

55. $(xy + x^5y^5)(x^4y^4 - xy)$

56. $(x - y^3)(2y^3 + x)$

57. $(x + h)^2$

58. $(y - a)^2$

59. $(3a + 2b)^2$

60. $(2ab - cd)^2$

61. $(r^3t^2 - 4)^2$

62. $(3a^2b - b^2)^2$

63. $(p^4 + m^2n^2)^2$

64. $\left(2a^3 - \frac{1}{2}b^3\right)^2$

65. $3a(a - 2b)^2$

66. $-3x(x + 8y)^2$

67. $(m + n - 3)^2$

68. $(a^2 + b + 2)^2$

69. $(a + b)(a - b)$

70. $(x - y)(x + y)$

71. $(2a - b)(2a + b)$

72. $(w + 3z)(w - 3z)$

73. $(c^2 - d)(c^2 + d)$

74. $(p^3 - 5q)(p^3 + 5q)$

75. $(ab + cd^2)(ab - cd^2)$

76. $(xy + pq)(xy - pq)$

77. $(x + y - 3)(x + y + 3)$

78. $(p + q + 4)(p + q - 4)$

79. $[x + y + z][x - (y + z)]$

80. $[a + b + c][a - (b + c)]$

81. $(a + b + c)(a + b - c)$

82. $(3x + 2 - 5y)(3x + 2 + 5y)$

83. $(x^2 - 4y + 2)(3x^2 + 5y - 3)$

84. $(2x^2 - 7y + 4)(x^2 + y - 3)$

Skill Maintenance

In which quadrant is each point located? [3.1a]

85. $(2, -5)$

86. $(-8, -9)$

87. $(16, 23)$

88. $(-3, 2)$

Graph. [3.2b]

89. $2x = -10$

90. $y = -4$

91. $8y - 16 = 0$

92. $x = 4$

Synthesis

Find a polynomial for each shaded area. (Leave results in terms of π where appropriate.)

93.

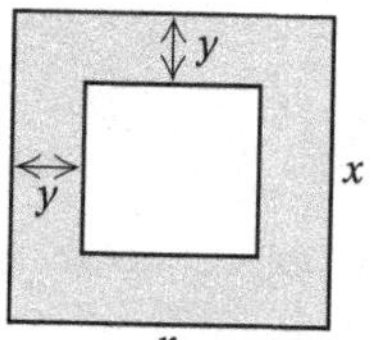

94.

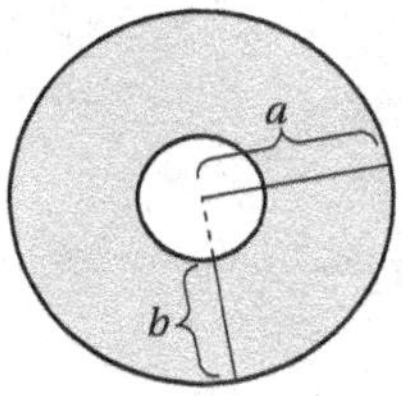

95.

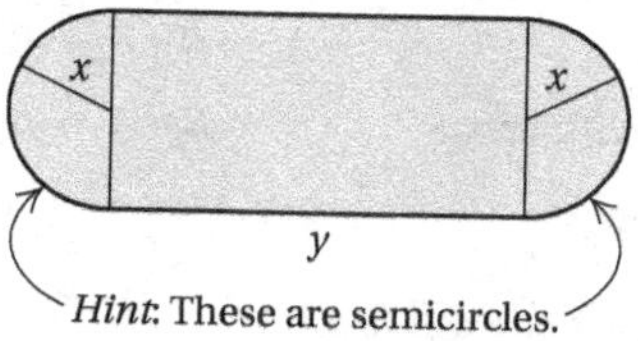

96.

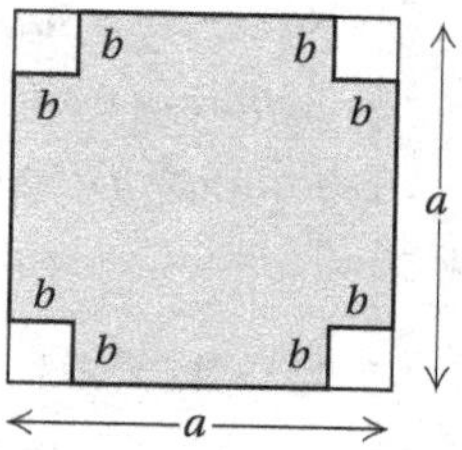

Find a formula for the surface area of each solid object. Leave results in terms of π.

97.

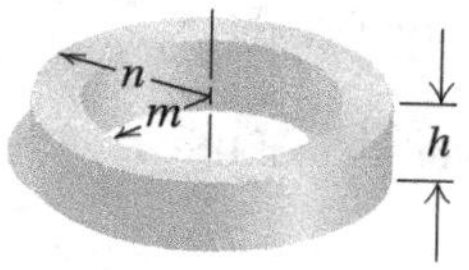

98.

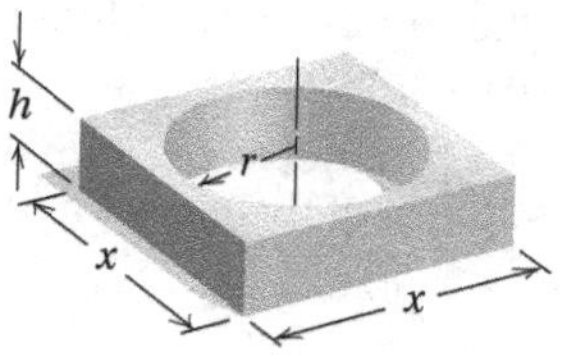

99. *Observatory Paint Costs.* The observatory at Danville University is shaped like a silo that is 40 ft high and 30 ft wide (see Exercise 15). The Heavenly Bodies Astronomy Club is to paint the exterior of the observatory using paint that covers 250 ft^2 per gallon. How many gallons should they purchase?

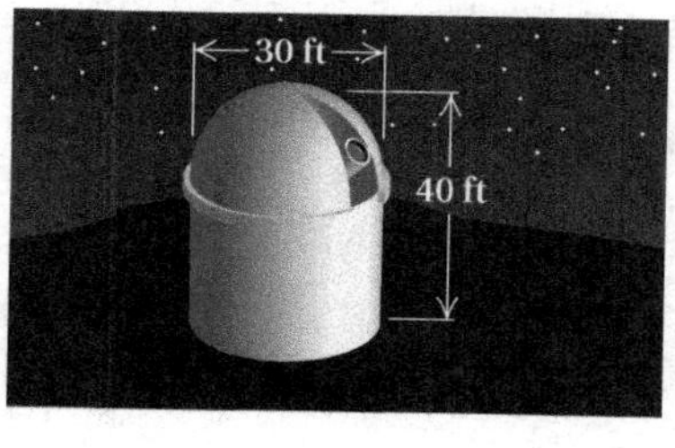

100. *Interest Compounded Annually.* An amount of money P that is invested at the yearly interest rate r grows to the amount

$$P(1 + r)^t$$

after t years. Find a polynomial that can be used to determine the amount to which P will grow after 2 yr.

101. Suppose that \$10,400 is invested at 3.5%, compounded annually. How much is in the account at the end of 5 yr? (See Exercise 100.)

102. Multiply: $(x + a)(x - b)(x - a)(x + b)$.

CHAPTER 3

Summary and Review

Key Terms and Properties

Definitions and Rules for Exponents:	See p. 230.
FOIL:	$(A + B)(C + D) = AC + AD + BC + BD$
Square of a Sum:	$(A + B)(A + B) = (A + B)^2 = A^2 + 2AB + B^2$
Square of a Difference:	$(A - B)(A - B) = (A - B)^2 = A^2 - 2AB + B^2$
Product of a Sum and a Difference:	$(A + B)(A - B) = A^2 - B^2$

Concept Reinforcement

Determine whether each statement is true or false.

______________ **1.** All trinomials are polynomials. [3.3i]

______________ **2.** $(x + y)^2 = x^2 + y^2$ [3.6c]

______________ **3.** The square of the difference of two expressions is the difference of the squares of the two expressions. [3.6c]

______________ **4.** The product of the sum and the difference of two expressions is the difference of the squares of the expressions. [3.6b]

Important Concepts

Objective 3.1d Use the product rule to multiply exponential expressions with like bases.

Example Multiply and simplify: $x^3 \cdot x^4$.

$$x^3 \cdot x^4 = x^{3+4} = x^7$$

Practice Exercise

1. Multiply and simplify: $z^5 \cdot z^3$.

Objective 3.1e Use the quotient rule to divide exponential expressions with like bases.

Example Divide and simplify: $\dfrac{x^6y^5}{xy^3}$.

$$\frac{x^6y^5}{xy^3} = \frac{x^6}{x} \cdot \frac{y^5}{y^3} = x^{6-1}y^{5-3} = x^5y^2$$

Practice Exercise

2. Divide and simplify: $\dfrac{a^4b^7}{a^2b}$.

Objective 3.1f Express an exponential expression involving negative exponents with positive exponents.

Objective 3.2a Use the power rule to raise powers to powers.

Objective 3.2b Raise a product to a power and a quotient to a power.

Example Simplify: $\left(\frac{2a^3b^{-2}}{c^4}\right)^5$.

$$\left(\frac{2a^3b^{-2}}{c^4}\right)^5 = \frac{(2a^3b^{-2})^5}{(c^4)^5}$$
$$= \frac{2^5(a^3)^5(b^{-2})^5}{(c^4)^5}$$
$$= \frac{32a^{3\cdot 5}b^{-2\cdot 5}}{c^{4\cdot 5}}$$
$$= \frac{32a^{15}b^{-10}}{c^{20}}$$
$$= \frac{32a^{15}}{b^{10}c^{20}}$$

Practice Exercise

3. Simplify: $\left(\frac{x^{-4}y^2}{3z^3}\right)^3$.

Objective 3.2c Convert between scientific notation and decimal notation.

Example Convert 0.00095 to scientific notation.

0.0009.5 (4 places)

The number is small, so the exponent is negative. (If the number were large, the exponent would be positive.)

$0.00095 = 9.5 \times 10^{-4}$

Example Convert 3.409×10^6 to decimal notation.

3.409000. (6 places)

The exponent is positive, so the number is large. (If the exponent were negative, the number would be small.)

$3.409 \times 10^6 = 3{,}409{,}000$

Practice Exercises

4. Convert to scientific notation: 763,000.

5. Convert to decimal notation: 3×10^{-4}.

Objective 3.2d Multiply and divide using scientific notation.

Example Multiply and express the result in scientific notation: $(5.3 \times 10^9) \cdot (2.4 \times 10^{-5})$.

$$(5.3 \times 10^9) \cdot (2.4 \times 10^{-5}) = (5.3 \cdot 2.4) \times (10^9 \cdot 10^{-5})$$
$$= 12.72 \times 10^4$$

The answer at this stage is not in scientific notation, because 12.72 is not a number between 1 and 10. We convert 12.72 to scientific notation and simplify:

$$12.72 \times 10^4 = (1.272 \times 10) \times 10^4$$
$$= 1.272 \times (10 \times 10^4)$$
$$= 1.272 \times 10^5.$$

Practice Exercise

6. Divide and express the result in scientific notation: $\frac{3.6 \times 10^3}{6.0 \times 10^{-2}}$.

Objective 3.3e Collect the like terms of a polynomial.

Example Collect like terms: $4x^3 - 2x^2 + 5 + 3x^2 - 12$.

$$4x^3 - 2x^2 + 5 + 3x^2 - 12$$
$$= 4x^3 + (-2 + 3)x^2 + (5 - 12)$$
$$= 4x^3 + x^2 - 7$$

Practice Exercise

7. Collect like terms: $5x^4 - 6x^2 - 3x^4 + 2x^2 - 3$.

Objective 3.4a Add polynomials.

Example Add: $(4x^3 + x^2 - 8) + (2x^3 - 5x + 1)$.

$$(4x^3 + x^2 - 8) + (2x^3 - 5x + 1)$$
$$= (4 + 2)x^3 + x^2 - 5x + (-8 + 1)$$
$$= 6x^3 + x^2 - 5x - 7$$

Practice Exercise

8. Add: $(3x^4 - 5x^2 - 4) + (x^3 + 3x^2 + 6)$.

Objective 3.5d Multiply any two polynomials.

Example Multiply: $(z^2 - 2z + 3)(z - 1)$.

We use columns. First, we multiply the top row by -1 and then by z, placing like terms of the product in the same column. Finally, we collect like terms.

$$\begin{array}{r} z^2 - 2z + 3 \\ z - 1 \\ \hline -z^2 + 2z - 3 \\ z^3 - 2z^2 + 3z \phantom{{}-3} \\ \hline z^3 - 3z^2 + 5z - 3 \end{array}$$

Practice Exercise

9. Multiply: $(x^4 - 3x^2 + 2)(x^2 - 3)$.

Objective 3.6a Multiply two binomials mentally using the FOIL method.

Example Multiply: $(3x + 5)(x - 1)$.

$$\begin{aligned} & \qquad\quad \text{F} \qquad\quad \text{O} \qquad\quad \text{I} \qquad\quad \text{L} \\ (3x + 5)(x - 1) &= 3x \cdot x + 3x \cdot (-1) + 5 \cdot x + 5 \cdot (-1) \\ &= 3x^2 - 3x + 5x - 5 \\ &= 3x^2 + 2x - 5 \end{aligned}$$

Practice Exercise

10. Multiply: $(y + 4)(2y + 3)$.

Objective 3.6b Multiply the sum and the difference of two terms mentally.

Example Multiply: $(3y + 2)(3y - 2)$.

$$(3y + 2)(3y - 2) = (3y)^2 - 2^2$$
$$= 9y^2 - 4$$

Practice Exercise

11. Multiply: $(x + 5)(x - 5)$.

Objective 3.6c Square a binomial mentally.

Example Multiply: $(2x - 3)^2$.

$$(2x - 3)^2 = (2x)^2 - 2 \cdot 2x \cdot 3 + 3^2$$
$$= 4x^2 - 12x + 9$$

Practice Exercise

12. Multiply: $(3w + 4)^2$.

Objective 3.7e Subtract polynomials.

Example Subtract:
$(m^4n + 2m^3n^2 - m^2n^3) - (3m^4n + 2m^3n^2 - 4m^2n^2)$.

$$(m^4n + 2m^3n^2 - m^2n^3) - (3m^4n + 2m^3n^2 - 4m^2n^2)$$
$$= m^4n + 2m^3n^2 - m^2n^3 - 3m^4n - 2m^3n^2 + 4m^2n^2$$
$$= -2m^4n - m^2n^3 + 4m^2n^2$$

Practice Exercise

13. Subtract:
$(a^3b^2 - 5a^2b + 2ab) - (3a^3b^2 - ab^2 + 4ab)$.

Objective 3.8a Divide a polynomial by a monomial.

Example Divide: $(6x^3 - 8x^2 + 15x) \div (3x)$.

$$\frac{6x^3 - 8x^2 + 15x}{3x} = \frac{6x^3}{3x} - \frac{8x^2}{3x} + \frac{15x}{3x}$$
$$= \frac{6}{3}x^{3-1} - \frac{8}{3}x^{2-1} + \frac{15}{3}x^{1-1}$$
$$= 2x^2 - \frac{8}{3}x + 5$$

Practice Exercise

14. Divide: $(5y^2 - 20y + 8) \div 5$.

Review Exercises

Multiply and simplify. [3.1d, f]

1. $7^2 \cdot 7^{-4}$

2. $y^7 \cdot y^3 \cdot y$

3. $(3x)^5 \cdot (3x)^9$

4. $t^8 \cdot t^0$

Divide and simplify. [3.1e, f]

5. $\frac{4^5}{4^2}$

6. $\frac{a^5}{a^8}$

7. $\frac{(7x)^4}{(7x)^4}$

Simplify.

8. $(3t^4)^2$ [3.2a, b]

9. $(2x^3)^2(-3x)^2$ [3.1d], [3.2a, b]

10. $\left(\frac{2x}{y}\right)^{-3}$ [3.2b]

11. Express using a negative exponent: $\frac{1}{t^5}$. [3.1f]

12. Express using a positive exponent: y^{-4}. [3.1f]

13. Convert to scientific notation: 0.0000328. [3.2c]

14. Convert to decimal notation: 8.3×10^6. [3.2c]

Multiply or divide and write scientific notation for the result. [3.2d]

15. $(3.8 \times 10^4)(5.5 \times 10^{-1})$

16. $\frac{1.28 \times 10^{-8}}{2.5 \times 10^{-4}}$

17. *Pizza Consumption.* Each man, woman, and child in the United States eats an average of 46 slices of pizza per year. The U.S. population is projected to be about 335.8 million in 2020. At this rate, how many slices of pizza would be consumed in 2020? Express the answer in scientific notation. [3.2e]

Sources: Packaged Facts; U.S. Census Bureau

18. Evaluate the polynomial $x^2 - 3x + 6$ when $x = -1$. [3.3a]

19. Identify the terms of the polynomial $-4y^5 + 7y^2 - 3y - 2$. [3.3b]

20. Identify the missing terms in $x^3 + x$. [3.3h]

21. Identify the degree of each term and the degree of the polynomial $4x^3 + 6x^2 - 5x + \frac{5}{3}$. [3.3g]

Classify the polynomial as a monomial, a binomial, a trinomial, or none of these. [3.3i]

22. $4x^3 - 1$

23. $4 - 9t^3 - 7t^4 + 10t^2$

24. $7y^2$

Collect like terms and then arrange in descending order. [3.3f]

25. $3x^2 - 2x + 3 - 5x^2 - 1 - x$

26. $-x + \frac{1}{2} + 14x^4 - 7x^2 - 1 - 4x^4$

Add. [3.4a]

27. $(3x^4 - x^3 + x - 4) + (x^5 + 7x^3 - 3x^2 - 5) + (-5x^4 + 6x^2 - x)$

28. $(3x^5 - 4x^4 + x^3 - 3) + (3x^4 - 5x^3 + 3x^2) + (-5x^5 - 5x^2) + (-5x^4 + 2x^3 + 5)$

Subtract. [3.4c]

29. $(5x^2 - 4x + 1) - (3x^2 + 1)$

30. $(3x^5 - 4x^4 + 3x^2 + 3) - (2x^5 - 4x^4 + 3x^3 + 4x^2 - 5)$

31. Find a polynomial for the perimeter and for the area. [3.4d], [3.5b]

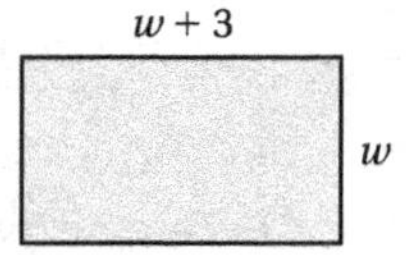

32. Find two algebraic expressions for the area of this figure. First, regard the figure as one large rectangle, and then regard the figure as a sum of four smaller rectangles. [3.4d]

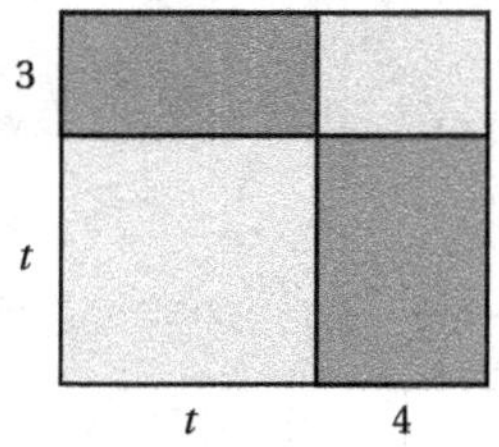

Multiply.

33. $\left(x + \frac{2}{3}\right)\left(x + \frac{1}{2}\right)$ [3.6a]

34. $(7x + 1)^2$ [3.6c]

35. $(4x^2 - 5x + 1)(3x - 2)$ [3.5d]

36. $(3x^2 + 4)(3x^2 - 4)$ [3.6b]

37. $5x^4(3x^3 - 8x^2 + 10x + 2)$ [3.5b]

38. $(x + 4)(x - 7)$ [3.6a]

39. $(3y^2 - 2y)^2$ [3.6c]

40. $(2t^2 + 3)(t^2 - 7)$ [3.6a]

41. Evaluate the polynomial

$$2 - 5xy + y^2 - 4xy^3 + x^6$$

when $x = -1$ and $y = 2$. [3.7a]

42. Identify the coefficient and the degree of each term of the polynomial

$$x^5y - 7xy + 9x^2 - 8.$$

Then find the degree of the polynomial. [3.7b]

Collect like terms. [3.7c]

43. $y + w - 2y + 8w - 5$

44. $m^6 - 2m^2n + m^2n^2 + n^2m - 6m^3 + m^2n^2 + 7n^2m$

45. Add: [3.7d]

$(5x^2 - 7xy + y^2) + (-6x^2 - 3xy - y^2) + (x^2 + xy - 2y^2)$.

46. Subtract: [3.7e]

$(6x^3y^2 - 4x^2y - 6x) - (-5x^3y^2 + 4x^2y + 6x^2 - 6)$.

Multiply. [3.7f]

47. $(p - q)(p^2 + pq + q^2)$

48. $\left(3a^4 - \frac{1}{3}b^3\right)^2$

Divide.

49. $(10x^3 - x^2 + 6x) \div (2x)$ [3.8a]

50. Subtract: $(2x^2 - 3x + 4) - (x^2 + 2x)$. [3.4c]

A. $x^2 - 3x - 2$
B. $x^2 - 5x + 4$
C. $x^2 - x + 4$
D. $3x^2 - x + 4$

51. Multiply: $(x - 1)^2$. [3.6c]

A. $x^2 - 1$
B. $x^2 + 1$
C. $x^2 - 2x - 1$
D. $x^2 - 2x + 1$

Synthesis

52. Collect like terms: [3.1d], [3.2a], [3.3e]

$-3x^5 \cdot 3x^3 - x^6(2x)^2 + (3x^4)^2 + (2x^2)^4 - 40x^2(x^3)^2$.

53. Solve: [2.3b], [3.6a]

$$(x - 7)(x + 10) = (x - 4)(x - 6).$$

54. The product of two polynomials is $x^5 - 1$. One of the polynomials is $x - 1$. Find the other.

55. A rectangular garden is twice as long as it is wide and is surrounded by a sidewalk that is 4 ft wide (see the figure below). The area of the sidewalk is 1024 ft^2. Find the dimensions of the garden. [3.3b], [3.4d], [3.5a], [3.6a]

Understanding Through Discussion and Writing

1. Explain why the expression 578.6×10^{-7} is not in scientific notation. [3.2c]

2. Explain why an understanding of the rules for order of operations is essential when evaluating polynomials. [3.3a]

3. How can the following figure be used to show that $(x + 3)^2 \neq x^2 + 9$? [3.5c]

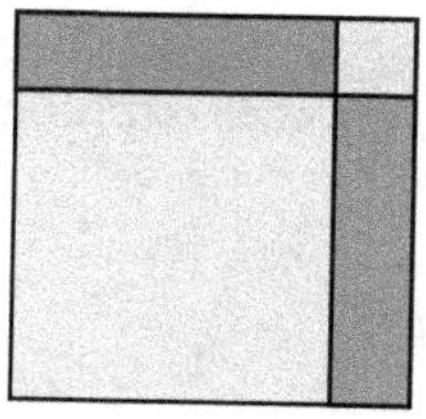

4. On an assignment, Emma *incorrectly* writes

$$\frac{12x^3 - 6x}{3x} = 4x^2 - 6x.$$

What mistake do you think she is making and how might you convince her that a mistake has been made?

5. Can the sum of two trinomials in several variables be a trinomial in one variable? Why or why not? [3.7d]

6. Is it possible for a polynomial in four variables to have a degree less than 4? Why or why not? [3.7b]

CHAPTER 3

Test

For Extra Help
CHAPTER Test Prep VIDEOS

Step-by-step test solutions are found on the Chapter Test Prep Videos available via the Video Resources on DVD, in MyMathLab, and on YouTube (search "BittingerIntroAlg" and click on "Channels").

Multiply and simplify.

1. $6^{-2} \cdot 6^{-3}$

2. $x^6 \cdot x^2 \cdot x$

3. $(4a)^3 \cdot (4a)^8$

Divide and simplify.

4. $\dfrac{3^5}{3^2}$

5. $\dfrac{x^3}{x^8}$

6. $\dfrac{(2x)^5}{(2x)^5}$

Simplify.

7. $(x^3)^2$

8. $(-3y^2)^3$

9. $(2a^3b)^4$

10. $\left(\dfrac{ab}{c}\right)^3$

11. $(3x^2)^3(-2x^5)^3$

12. $3(x^2)^3(-2x^5)^3$

13. $2x^2(-3x^2)^4$

14. $(2x)^2(-3x^2)^4$

15. Express using a positive exponent: 5^{-3}.

16. Express using a negative exponent: $\dfrac{1}{y^8}$.

17. Convert to scientific notation: 3,900,000,000.

18. Convert to decimal notation: 5×10^{-8}.

Multiply or divide and write scientific notation for the answer.

19. $\dfrac{5.6 \times 10^6}{3.2 \times 10^{-11}}$

20. $(2.4 \times 10^5)(5.4 \times 10^{16})$

21. *CD-ROM Memory.* A CD-ROM can contain about 600 million pieces of information (bytes). How many sound files, each containing 40,000 bytes, can a CD-ROM hold? Express the answer in scientific notation.

22. Evaluate the polynomial $x^5 + 5x - 1$ when $x = -2$.

23. Identify the coefficient of each term of the polynomial $\frac{1}{3}x^5 - x + 7$.

24. Identify the degree of each term and the degree of the polynomial $2x^3 - 4 + 5x + 3x^6$.

25. Classify the polynomial $7 - x$ as a monomial, a binomial, a trinomial, or none of these.

Collect like terms.

26. $4a^2 - 6 + a^2$

27. $y^2 - 3y - y + \dfrac{3}{4}y^2$

28. Collect like terms and then arrange in descending order:

$$3 - x^2 + 2x^3 + 5x^2 - 6x - 2x + x^5.$$

Add.

29. $(3x^5 + 5x^3 - 5x^2 - 3) +$
$(x^5 + x^4 - 3x^3 - 3x^2 + 2x - 4)$

30. $\left(x^4 + \dfrac{2}{3}x + 5\right) + \left(4x^4 + 5x^2 + \dfrac{1}{3}x\right)$

Subtract.

31. $(2x^4 + x^3 - 8x^2 - 6x - 3) - (6x^4 - 8x^2 + 2x)$

32. $(x^3 - 0.4x^2 - 12) - (x^5 + 0.3x^3 + 0.4x^2 + 9)$

Multiply.

33. $-3x^2(4x^2 - 3x - 5)$

34. $\left(x - \frac{1}{3}\right)^2$

35. $(3x + 10)(3x - 10)$

36. $(3b + 5)(b - 3)$

37. $(x^6 - 4)(x^8 + 4)$

38. $(8 - y)(6 + 5y)$

39. $(2x + 1)(3x^2 - 5x - 3)$

40. $(5t + 2)^2$

41. Collect like terms:

$$x^3y - y^3 + xy^3 + 8 - 6x^3y - x^2y^2 + 11.$$

42. Subtract:

$$(8a^2b^2 - ab + b^3) - (-6ab^2 - 7ab - ab^3 + 5b^3).$$

43. Multiply: $(3x^5 - 4y^5)(3x^5 + 4y^5)$.

Divide.

44. $(12x^4 + 9x^3 - 15x^2) \div (3x^2)$

CHAPTERS

1–3

Cumulative Review

1. Evaluate $\frac{x}{2y}$ when $x = 10$ and $y = 2$.

2. Evaluate $2x^3 + x^2 - 3$ when $x = -1$.

3. Evaluate $x^3y^2 + xy + 2xy^2$ when $x = -1$ and $y = 2$.

4. Find the absolute value: $|-4|$.

5. Find the reciprocal of 5.

Compute and simplify.

6. $-\frac{3}{5} + \frac{5}{12}$

7. $3.4 - (-0.8)$

8. $(-2)(-1.4)(2.6)$

9. $\frac{3}{8} \div \left(-\frac{9}{10}\right)$

10. $(1.1 \times 10^{10})(2 \times 10^{12})$

11. $(3.2 \times 10^{-10}) \div (8 \times 10^{-6})$

Simplify.

12. $\frac{-9x}{3x}$

13. $y - (3y + 7)$

14. $3(x - 1) - 2[x - (2x + 7)]$

15. $2 - [32 \div (4 + 2^2)]$

Add.

16. $(x^4 + 3x^3 - x + 7) + (2x^5 - 3x^4 + x - 5)$

17. $(x^2 + 2xy) + (y^2 - xy) + (2x^2 - 3y^2)$

Subtract.

18. $(x^3 + 3x^2 - 4) - (-2x^2 + x + 3)$

19. $\left(\frac{1}{3}x^2 - \frac{1}{4}x - \frac{1}{5}\right) - \left(\frac{2}{3}x^2 + \frac{1}{2}x - \frac{1}{5}\right)$

Multiply.

20. $3(4x - 5y + 7)$

21. $(-2x^3)(-3x^5)$

22. $2x^2(x^3 - 2x^2 + 4x - 5)$

23. $(y^2 - 2)(3y^2 + 5y + 6)$

24. $(2p^3 + p^2q + pq^2)(p - pq + q)$

25. $(2x + 3)(3x + 2)$

26. $(3x^2 + 1)^2$

27. $\left(t + \frac{1}{2}\right)\left(t - \frac{1}{2}\right)$

28. $(2y^2 + 5)(2y^2 - 5)$

29. $(2x^4 - 3)(2x^2 + 3)$

30. $(t - 2t^2)^2$

31. $(3p + q)(5p - 2q)$

Divide.

32. $(18x^3 + 6x^2 - 9x) \div (3x)$

Solve.

33. $1.5 = 2.7 + x$

34. $\frac{2}{7}x = -6$

35. $5x - 9 = 36$

36. $\frac{2}{3} = \frac{-m}{10}$

37. $5.4 - 1.9x = 0.8x$

38. $x - \frac{7}{8} = \frac{3}{4}$

39. $2(2 - 3x) = 3(5x + 7)$

40. $\frac{1}{4}x - \frac{2}{3} = \frac{3}{4} + \frac{1}{3}x$

41. $y + 5 - 3y = 5y - 9$

42. $\frac{1}{4}x - 7 < 5 - \frac{1}{2}x$

43. $2(x + 2) \geq 5(2x + 3)$

44. $A = Qx + P$, for x

Solve.

45. *Markup.* A bookstore sells books at a price that is 80% higher than the price the store pays for the books. A book is priced for sale at $6.30. How much did the store pay for the book?

46. *Consecutive Page Numbers.* The sum of the page numbers on the facing pages of a book is 37. What are the page numbers?

47. *Room Perimeter.* The perimeter of a room is 88 ft. The width is 4 ft less than the length. Find the width and the length.

48. The second angle of a triangle is five times as large as the first. The third angle is twice the sum of the other two angles. Find the measure of the first angle.

Simplify.

49. $y^2 \cdot y^{-6} \cdot y^8$

50. $\dfrac{x^6}{x^7}$

51. $(-3x^3y^{-2})^3$

52. $\dfrac{x^3x^{-4}}{x^{-5}x}$

53. *Matching.* Match each item in the first column with the appropriate item in the second column by drawing connecting lines.

3^2	$\frac{1}{6}$
3^{-2}	$-\frac{1}{9}$
$\left(\frac{1}{3}\right)^2$	6
$\left(\frac{1}{3}\right)^{-2}$	9
-3^2	-9
$(-3)^2$	$\frac{1}{9}$
$\left(-\frac{1}{3}\right)^2$	-6
$\left(-\frac{1}{3}\right)^{-2}$	12

Synthesis

Add.

54. $[(2x)^2 - (3x)^3 + 2x^2x^3 + (x^2)^2] + [5x^2(2x^3) - ((2x)^2)^2]$

55. $(x - 3)^2 + (2x + 1)^2$

Solve.

56. $(x + 3)(2x - 5) + (x - 1)^2 = (3x + 1)(x - 3)$

57. $20 - 3|x| = 5$

Polynomials: Factoring

CHAPTER

4

Real-World Application

Dr. Benton wants to investigate the potential spread of germs by contact. She knows that the number of possible handshakes within a group of x people, assuming each person shakes every other person's hand only once, is given by $N = \frac{1}{2}(x^2 - x)$. There are 40 people at a meeting. How many handshakes are possible?

4.1 Introduction to Factoring

OBJECTIVES

a Find the greatest common factor, the GCF, of monomials.

b Factor polynomials when the terms have a common factor, factoring out the greatest common factor.

c Factor certain expressions with four terms using factoring by grouping.

SKILL TO REVIEW
Objective R.1a: Find all the factors of numbers and find prime factorizations of numbers.

Find the prime factorization of each number.

1. 60 **2.** 105

We introduce factoring with a review of factoring natural numbers. Consider the product $15 = 3 \cdot 5$. We say that 3 and 5 are **factors** of 15 and that $3 \cdot 5$ is a **factorization** of 15. Since $15 = 15 \cdot 1$, we also know that 15 and 1 are factors of 15 and that $15 \cdot 1$ is a factorization of 15.

a Finding the Greatest Common Factor

The numbers 20 and 30 have several factors in common, among them 2 and 5. The greatest of the common factors is called the **greatest common factor**, **GCF**. One way to find the GCF is by making a list of factors of each number.

List all the factors of 20: <u>1</u>, <u>2</u>, 4, <u>5</u>, <u>10</u>, and 20.

List all the factors of 30: <u>1</u>, <u>2</u>, 3, <u>5</u>, 6, <u>10</u>, 15, and 30.

We now list the numbers common to both lists, the common factors:

1, 2, 5, and 10.

The greatest common factor, the GCF, is 10, the largest number in the common list.

The preceding procedure gives meaning to the notion of a GCF, but the following method, using prime factorizations, is generally faster.

EXAMPLE 1 Find the GCF of 20 and 30.

We find the prime factorization of each number. Then we draw lines between the common factors.

$$20 = 2 \cdot 2 \cdot 5$$
$$30 = 2 \cdot 3 \cdot 5$$

The GCF $= 2 \cdot 5 = 10$.

EXAMPLE 2 Find the GCF of 180 and 420.

We find the prime factorization of each number. Then we draw lines between the common factors.

$$180 = 2 \cdot 2 \cdot 3 \cdot 3 \cdot 5 = 2^2 \cdot 3^2 \cdot 5^1$$
$$420 = 2 \cdot 2 \cdot 3 \cdot 5 \cdot 7 = 2^2 \cdot 3^1 \cdot 5^1 \cdot 7^1$$

The GCF $= 2 \cdot 2 \cdot 3 \cdot 5 = 2^2 \cdot 3^1 \cdot 5^1 = 60$. Note how we can use the exponents to determine the GCF. There are 2 lines for the 2's, 1 line for the 3, 1 line for the 5, and no line for the 7.

EXAMPLE 3 Find the GCF of 30 and 77.

We find the prime factorization of each number. Then we draw lines between the common factors, if any exist.

$$30 = 2 \cdot 3 \cdot 5 = 2^1 \cdot 3^1 \cdot 5^1$$
$$77 = 7 \cdot 11 = 7^1 \cdot 11^1$$

Since there is no common prime factor, the GCF is 1.

Answers

Skill to Review:
1. $2 \cdot 2 \cdot 3 \cdot 5$ **2.** $3 \cdot 5 \cdot 7$

EXAMPLE 4 Find the GCF of 54, 90, and 252.

We find the prime factorization of each number. Then we draw lines between the common factors.

$$54 = 2 \cdot 3 \cdot 3 \cdot 3 = 2^1 \cdot 3^3,$$

$$90 = 2 \cdot 3 \cdot 3 \cdot 5 = 2^1 \cdot 3^2 \cdot 5^1,$$

$$252 = 2 \cdot 2 \cdot 3 \cdot 3 \cdot 7 = 2^2 \cdot 3^2 \cdot 7^1$$

The GCF $= 2^1 \cdot 3^2 = 18.$

Do Exercises 1–4.

Find the GCF.

1. 40, 100
2. 7, 21
3. 72, 360, 432
4. 3, 5, 22

Consider the product

$$12x^3(x^2 - 6x + 2) = 12x^5 - 72x^4 + 24x^3.$$

To factor the polynomial on the right, we reverse the process of multiplication:

$$12x^5 - 72x^4 + 24x^3 = \underbrace{12x^3(x^2 - 6x + 2)}.$$

This is a *factorization*. The *factors* are $(12x^3)$ and $(x^2 - 6x + 2)$.

FACTOR; FACTORIZATION

To **factor** a polynomial is to express it as a product.

A **factor** of a polynomial P is a polynomial that can be used to express P as a product.

A **factorization** of a polynomial is an expression that names that polynomial as a product.

In the factorization

$$12x^5 - 72x^4 + 24x^3 = 12x^3(x^2 - 6x + 2),$$

the monomial $12x^3$ is called the GCF of the terms, $12x^5$, $-72x^4$, and $24x^3$. The first step in factoring polynomials is to find the GCF of the terms.

Consider the monomials

$$x^3,\ x^4,\ x^6,\ \text{and}\ x^7.$$

The GCF of these monomials is x^3, found by noting that the smallest exponent of x is 3.

Consider

$$20x^2 \text{ and } 30x^5.$$

The GCF of 20 and 30 is 10. The GCF of x^2 and x^5 is x^2. Then the GCF of $20x^2$ and $30x^5$ is the product of the individual GCFs, $10x^2$.

Answers

1. 20 2. 7 3. 72 4. 1

EXAMPLE 5 Find the GCF of $15x^5$, $-12x^4$, $27x^3$, and $-3x^2$.

First, we find a prime factorization of the coefficients, including a factor of -1 for the negative coefficients.

$$\begin{aligned} 15x^5 &= 3 \cdot 5 \cdot x^5, \\ -12x^4 &= -1 \cdot 2 \cdot 2 \cdot 3 \cdot x^4, \\ 27x^3 &= 3 \cdot 3 \cdot 3 \cdot x^3, \\ -3x^2 &= -1 \cdot 3 \cdot x^2 \end{aligned}$$

The greatest *positive* common factor of the coefficients is 3.

Next, we find the GCF of the powers of x. That GCF is x^2, because 2 is the smallest exponent of x. Thus the GCF of the set of monomials is $3x^2$.

What about the factors of -1 in Example 5? Strictly speaking, both 1 and -1 are factors of any number or expression. We see this as follows:

$$3x^2 = 1 \cdot 3x^2 = (-1)(-3x^2).$$

Because the coefficient -3 is less than the coefficient 3, we consider $3x^2$, and not $-3x^2$, the GCF.

EXAMPLE 6 Find the GCF of $14p^2y^3$, $-8py^2$, $2py$, and $4p^3$.

We have

$$\begin{aligned} 14p^2y^3 &= 2 \cdot 7 \cdot p^2 \cdot y^3, \\ -8py^2 &= -1 \cdot 2 \cdot 2 \cdot 2 \cdot p \cdot y^2, \\ 2py &= 2 \cdot p \cdot y, \\ 4p^3 &= 2 \cdot 2 \cdot p^3. \end{aligned}$$

The greatest positive common factor of the coefficients is 2, the GCF of the powers of p is p, and the GCF of the powers of y is 1 since there is no y-factor in the last monomial. Thus the GCF is $2p$.

TO FIND THE GCF OF TWO OR MORE MONOMIALS

1. Find the prime factorization of the coefficients, including -1 as a factor if any coefficient is negative.
2. Determine any common prime factors of the coefficients. For each one that occurs, include it as a factor of the GCF. If none occurs, use 1 as a factor.
3. Examine each of the variables as factors. If any appear as a factor of all the monomials, include it as a factor, using the smallest exponent of the variable. If none occurs in all the monomials, use 1 as a factor.
4. The GCF is the product of the results of steps (2) and (3).

Do Exercises 5–8.

Find the GCF.

5. $12x^2$, $-16x^3$

6. $3y^6$, $-5y^3$, $2y^2$

7. $-24m^5n^6$, $12mn^3$, $-16m^2n^2$, $8m^4n^4$

8. $-35x^7$, $-49x^6$, $-14x^5$, $-63x^3$

Answers

5. $4x^2$ **6.** y^2 **7.** $4mn^2$ **8.** $7x^3$

b Factoring When Terms Have a Common Factor

The polynomials we consider most when factoring are those with more than one term. To multiply a monomial and a polynomial with more than one term, we multiply each term of the polynomial by the monomial using the distributive laws:

$$a(b + c) = ab + ac \quad \text{and} \quad a(b - c) = ab - ac.$$

To factor, we do the reverse. We express a polynomial as a product using the distributive laws in reverse:

$$ab + ac = a(b + c) \quad \text{and} \quad ab - ac = a(b - c).$$

Compare.

Multiply	*Factor*
$3x(x^2 + 2x - 4)$	$3x^3 + 6x^2 - 12x$
$= 3x \cdot x^2 + 3x \cdot 2x - 3x \cdot 4$	$= 3x \cdot x^2 + 3x \cdot 2x - 3x \cdot 4$
$= 3x^3 + 6x^2 - 12x$	$= 3x(x^2 + 2x - 4)$

Caution!

Consider the following:

$$3x^3 + 6x^2 - 12x = 3 \cdot x \cdot x \cdot x + 2 \cdot 3 \cdot x \cdot x - 2 \cdot 2 \cdot 3 \cdot x.$$

The terms of the polynomial, $3x^3$, $6x^2$, and $-12x$, have been factored but the polynomial itself has not been factored. This is not what we mean by a factorization of the polynomial. The *factorization* is

$3x(x^2 + 2x - 4)$. ← A product

The expressions $3x$ and $x^2 + 2x - 4$ are *factors* of $3x^3 + 6x^2 - 12x$.

Do Exercises 9 and 10.

9. a) Multiply: $3(x + 2)$.

b) Factor: $3x + 6$.

10. a) Multiply: $2x(x^2 + 5x + 4)$.

b) Factor: $2x^3 + 10x^2 + 8x$.

To factor, we first find the GCF of all terms. It may be 1.

EXAMPLE 7 Factor: $7x^2 + 14$.

We have

$$7x^2 + 14 = 7 \cdot x^2 + 7 \cdot 2 \qquad \text{Factoring each term}$$
$$= 7(x^2 + 2). \qquad \text{Factoring out the GCF, 7}$$

Check: We multiply to check:

$$7(x^2 + 2) = 7 \cdot x^2 + 7 \cdot 2 = 7x^2 + 14.$$

Answers

9. **(a)** $3x + 6$; **(b)** $3(x + 2)$
10. **(a)** $2x^3 + 10x^2 + 8x$; **(b)** $2x(x^2 + 5x + 4)$

EXAMPLE 8 Factor: $16x^3 + 20x^2$.

$$16x^3 + 20x^2 = (4x^2)(4x) + (4x^2)(5) \quad \text{Factoring each term}$$
$$= 4x^2(4x + 5) \quad \text{Factoring out the GCF, } 4x^2$$

Although it is always more efficient to begin by finding the GCF, suppose in Example 8 that you had not recognized the GCF and removed only part of it, as follows:

$$16x^3 + 20x^2 = (2x^2)(8x) + (2x^2)(10)$$
$$= 2x^2(8x + 10).$$

Note that $8x + 10$ still has a common factor of 2. You need not begin again. Just continue factoring out common factors, as follows, until finished:

$$= 2x^2(2 \cdot 4x + 2 \cdot 5)$$
$$= 2x^2[2(4x + 5)]$$
$$= (2x^2 \cdot 2)(4x + 5)$$
$$= 4x^2(4x + 5).$$

EXAMPLE 9 Factor: $15x^5 - 12x^4 + 27x^3 - 3x^2$.

$$15x^5 - 12x^4 + 27x^3 - 3x^2 = (3x^2)(5x^3) - (3x^2)(4x^2) + (3x^2)(9x) - (3x^2)(1)$$
$$= 3x^2(5x^3 - 4x^2 + 9x - 1) \quad \text{Factoring out the GCF, } 3x^2$$

Caution!

Don't forget the term -1.

Check: We multiply to check:

$$3x^2(5x^3 - 4x^2 + 9x - 1)$$
$$= (3x^2)(5x^3) - (3x^2)(4x^2) + (3x^2)(9x) - (3x^2)(1)$$
$$= 15x^5 - 12x^4 + 27x^3 - 3x^2.$$

As you become more familiar with factoring, you will be able to spot the GCF without factoring each term. Then you can write just the answer.

EXAMPLES Factor.

10. $24x^2 + 12x - 36 = 12(2x^2 + x - 3)$

11. $8m^3 - 16m = 8m(m^2 - 2)$

12. $14p^2y^3 - 8py^2 + 2py = 2py(7py^2 - 4y + 1)$

13. $\frac{4}{5}x^2 + \frac{1}{5}x + \frac{2}{5} = \frac{1}{5}(4x^2 + x + 2)$

Do Exercises 11–16.

Factor. Check by multiplying.

11. $x^2 + 3x$

12. $3y^6 - 5y^3 + 2y^2$

13. $9x^4y^2 - 15x^3y + 3x^2y$

14. $\frac{3}{4}t^3 + \frac{5}{4}t^2 + \frac{7}{4}t + \frac{1}{4}$

15. $35x^7 - 49x^6 + 14x^5 - 63x^3$

16. $84x^2 - 56x + 28$

Answers

11. $x(x + 3)$ **12.** $y^2(3y^4 - 5y + 2)$
13. $3x^2y(3x^2y - 5x + 1)$
14. $\frac{1}{4}(3t^3 + 5t^2 + 7t + 1)$
15. $7x^3(5x^4 - 7x^3 + 2x^2 - 9)$
16. $28(3x^2 - 2x + 1)$

There are two important points to keep in mind as we study this chapter.

TIPS FOR FACTORING

- Before doing any other kind of factoring, first try to factor out the GCF.
- Always check the result of factoring by multiplying.

C Factoring by Grouping: Four Terms

Certain polynomials with four terms can be factored using a method called *factoring by grouping.*

EXAMPLE 14 Factor: $x^2(x + 1) + 2(x + 1)$.

The binomial $x + 1$ is a common factor. We factor it out:

$$x^2(x + 1) + 2(x + 1) = (x + 1)(x^2 + 2).$$

The factorization is $(x + 1)(x^2 + 2)$.

Do Exercises 17 and 18.

Factor.

17. $x^2(x + 7) + 3(x + 7)$

18. $x^3(a + b) - 5(a + b)$

Consider the four-term polynomial

$$x^3 + x^2 + 2x + 2.$$

There is no factor other than 1 that is common to all the terms. We can, however, factor $x^3 + x^2$ and $2x + 2$ separately:

$$x^3 + x^2 = x^2(x + 1); \quad \text{Factoring } x^3 + x^2$$
$$2x + 2 = 2(x + 1). \quad \text{Factoring } 2x + 2$$

When we group the terms as shown above and factor each polynomial separately, we see that $(x + 1)$ appears in *both* factorizations. Thus we can factor out the common binomial factor as in Example 14:

$$\begin{aligned} x^3 + x^2 + 2x + 2 &= (x^3 + x^2) + (2x + 2) \\ &= x^2(x + 1) + 2(x + 1) \\ &= (x + 1)(x^2 + 2). \end{aligned}$$

This method of factoring is called **factoring by grouping**. We began with a polynomial with four terms. After grouping and removing common factors, we obtained a polynomial with two parts, each having the common factor $x + 1$, which we then factored out. Not all polynomials with four terms can be factored by this procedure, but it does give us a method to try.

STUDY TIPS

CHECKLIST

The foundation of all your study skills is TIME!

- Are you staying on schedule, getting to class on time, and adapting your study time to your schedule?
- Do you study the examples in the text carefully?
- Are you asking questions at appropriate times in class and with your tutors?

Answers

17. $(x + 7)(x^2 + 3)$ **18.** $(a + b)(x^3 - 5)$

EXAMPLES Factor by grouping.

15. $6x^3 - 9x^2 + 4x - 6$

$= (6x^3 - 9x^2) + (4x - 6)$ Grouping the terms

$= 3x^2(2x - 3) + 2(2x - 3)$ Factoring each binomial

$= (2x - 3)(3x^2 + 2)$ Factoring out the common factor $2x - 3$

We think through this process as follows:

$$6x^3 - 9x^2 + 4x - 6 = 3x^2(2x - 3)\ \square\ (2x - 3)$$

(1) Factor the first two terms.

(2) The factor $2x - 3$ gives us a hint to the factorization of the last two terms.

(3) Now we ask ourselves, "What times $2x - 3$ is $4x - 6$?" The answer is $+ 2$.

Caution!

Don't forget the 1.

16. $x^3 + x^2 + x + 1 = (x^3 + x^2) + (x + 1)$

$= x^2(x + 1) + 1(x + 1)$ Factoring each binomial

$= (x + 1)(x^2 + 1)$ Factoring out the common factor $x + 1$

17. $2x^3 - 6x^2 - x + 3$

$= (2x^3 - 6x^2) + (-x + 3)$ Grouping as two binomials

$= 2x^2(x - 3) - 1(x - 3)$ *Check*: $-1(x - 3) = -x + 3$.

$= (x - 3)(2x^2 - 1)$ Factoring out the common factor $x - 3$

We can think through this process as follows.

(1) Factor the first two terms: $2x^3 - 6x^2 = 2x^2(x - 3)$.

(2) The factor $x - 3$ gives us a hint for factoring the last two terms:

$$2x^3 - 6x^2 - x + 3 = 2x^2(x - 3)\ \square\ (x - 3).$$

(3) Now we ask ourselves, "What times $x - 3$ is $-x + 3$?" The answer is -1.

18. $12x^5 + 20x^2 - 21x^3 - 35 = 4x^2(3x^3 + 5) - 7(3x^3 + 5)$

$= (3x^3 + 5)(4x^2 - 7)$

19. $x^3 + x^2 + 2x - 2 = x^2(x + 1) + 2(x - 1)$

This polynomial is not factorable using factoring by grouping. It may be factorable, but not by methods that we will consider in this text.

Do Exercises 19–24.

Factor by grouping.

19. $x^3 + 7x^2 + 3x + 21$

20. $8t^3 + 2t^2 + 12t + 3$

21. $3m^5 - 15m^3 + 2m^2 - 10$

22. $3x^3 - 6x^2 - x + 2$

23. $4x^3 - 6x^2 - 6x + 9$

24. $y^4 - 2y^3 - 2y - 10$

Answers

19. $(x + 7)(x^2 + 3)$ **20.** $(4t + 1)(2t^2 + 3)$
21. $(m^2 - 5)(3m^3 + 2)$
22. $(x - 2)(3x^2 - 1)$ **23.** $(2x - 3)(2x^2 - 3)$
24. Not factorable using factoring by grouping

a Find the GCF.

1. $x^2, \ -6x$
2. $x^2, \ 5x$
3. $3x^4, \ x^2$
4. $8x^4, \ -24x^2$
5. $2x^2, \ 2x, \ -8$
6. $8x^2, \ -4x, \ -20$
7. $-17x^5y^3, \ 34x^3y^2, \ 51xy$
8. $16p^6q^4, \ 32p^3q^3, \ -48pq^2$
9. $-x^2, \ -5x, \ -20x^3$
10. $-x^2, \ -6x, \ -24x^5$
11. $x^5y^5, \ x^4y^3, \ x^3y^3, \ -x^2y^2$
12. $-x^9y^6, \ -x^7y^5, \ x^4y^4, \ x^3y^3$

b Factor. Check by multiplying.

13. $x^2 - 6x$
14. $x^2 + 5x$
15. $2x^2 + 6x$
16. $8y^2 - 8y$
17. $x^3 + 6x^2$
18. $3x^4 - x^2$
19. $8x^4 - 24x^2$
20. $5x^5 + 10x^3$
21. $2x^2 + 2x - 8$
22. $8x^2 - 4x - 20$
23. $17x^5y^3 + 34x^3y^2 + 51xy$
24. $16p^6q^4 + 32p^5q^3 - 48pq^2$
25. $6x^4 - 10x^3 + 3x^2$
26. $5x^5 + 10x^2 - 8x$
27. $x^5y^5 + x^4y^3 + x^3y^3 - x^2y^2$
28. $x^9y^6 - x^7y^5 + x^4y^4 + x^3y^3$
29. $2x^7 - 2x^6 - 64x^5 + 4x^3$
30. $8y^3 - 20y^2 + 12y - 16$
31. $1.6x^4 - 2.4x^3 + 3.2x^2 + 6.4x$
32. $2.5x^6 - 0.5x^4 + 5x^3 + 10x^2$
33. $\frac{5}{3}x^6 + \frac{4}{3}x^5 + \frac{1}{3}x^4 + \frac{1}{3}x^3$
34. $\frac{5}{9}x^7 + \frac{2}{9}x^5 - \frac{4}{9}x^3 - \frac{1}{9}x$

c Factor.

35. $x^2(x + 3) + 2(x + 3)$
36. $y^2(y + 4) + 6(y + 4)$
37. $4z^2(3z - 1) + 7(3z - 1)$
38. $2x^2(4x - 3) + 5(4x - 3)$

39. $2x^2(3x + 2) + (3x + 2)$

40. $3z^2(2z + 7) + (2z + 7)$

41. $5a^3(2a - 7) - (2a - 7)$

42. $m^4(8 - 3m) - 3(8 - 3m)$

Factor by grouping.

43. $x^3 + 3x^2 + 2x + 6$

44. $6z^3 + 3z^2 + 2z + 1$

45. $2x^3 + 6x^2 + x + 3$

46. $3x^3 + 2x^2 + 3x + 2$

47. $8x^3 - 12x^2 + 6x - 9$

48. $10x^3 - 25x^2 + 4x - 10$

49. $12p^3 - 16p^2 + 3p - 4$

50. $18x^3 - 21x^2 + 30x - 35$

51. $5x^3 - 5x^2 - x + 1$

52. $7x^3 - 14x^2 - x + 2$

53. $x^3 + 8x^2 - 3x - 24$

54. $2x^3 + 12x^2 - 5x - 30$

55. $2x^3 - 8x^2 - 9x + 36$

56. $20g^3 - 4g^2 - 25g + 5$

Skill Maintenance

Solve.

57. $-2x < 48$ [2.7d]

58. $4x - 8x + 16 \geq 6(x - 2)$ [2.7e]

59. Divide: $\frac{-108}{-4}$. [1.6a]

60. Solve $A = \frac{p + q}{2}$ for p. [2.4b]

Multiply. [4.6d]

61. $(y + 5)(y + 7)$

62. $(y + 7)^2$

63. $(y + 7)(y - 7)$

64. $(y - 7)^2$

Find the intercepts of each equation. Then graph the equation.

65. $x + y = 4$

66. $x - y = 3$

67. $5x - 3y = 15$

68. $y - 3x = 6$

Synthesis

Factor.

69. $4x^5 + 6x^3 + 6x^2 + 9$

70. $x^6 + x^4 + x^2 + 1$

71. $x^{12} + x^7 + x^5 + 1$

72. $x^3 - x^2 - 2x + 5$

73. $p^3 + p^2 - 3p + 10$

4.2 Factoring Trinomials of the Type $x^2 + bx + c$

a Factoring $x^2 + bx + c$

We now begin a study of the factoring of trinomials. We first factor trinomials like

$$x^2 + 5x + 6 \quad \text{and} \quad x^2 + 3x - 10$$

by a refined *trial-and-error process*. In this section, we restrict our attention to trinomials of the type $ax^2 + bx + c$, where $a = 1$. The coefficient a is called the **leading coefficient**.

To understand the factoring that follows, compare the following multiplications:

$$\begin{aligned}
& \quad\quad\quad\quad\quad\ \ \text{F} \quad\ \ \text{O} \quad\ \ \text{I} \quad\ \ \text{L} \\
(x + 2)(x + 5) &= x^2 + 5x + 2x + 2 \cdot 5 \\
&= x^2 + \quad 7x \quad + \ 10; \\
(x - 2)(x - 5) &= x^2 - 5x - 2x + (-2)(-5) \\
&= x^2 - \quad 7x \quad + \ 10; \\
(x + 3)(x - 7) &= x^2 - 7x + 3x + 3(-7) \\
&= x^2 - \quad 4x \quad - \ 21; \\
(x - 3)(x + 7) &= x^2 + 7x - 3x + (-3)7 \\
&= x^2 + \quad 4x \quad - \ 21.
\end{aligned}$$

Note that for all four products:

- The product of the two binomials is a trinomial.
- The coefficient of x in the trinomial is the sum of the constant terms in the binomials.
- The constant term in the trinomial is the product of the constant terms in the binomials.

These observations lead to a method for factoring certain trinomials. The first type we consider has a positive constant term, just as in the first two multiplications above.

Constant Term Positive

To factor $x^2 + 7x + 10$, we think of FOIL in reverse. We multiplied x times x to get the first term of the trinomial, so we know that the first term of each binomial factor is x. Next, we look for numbers p and q such that

$$x^2 + 7x + 10 = (x + p)(x + q).$$

To get the middle term and the last term of the trinomial, we look for two numbers p and q whose product is 10 and whose sum is 7. Those numbers are 2 and 5. Thus the factorization is

$$(x + 2)(x + 5).$$

Check: $(x + 2)(x + 5) = x^2 + 5x + 2x + 10$
$\quad\quad\quad\quad\quad\quad\quad\quad\ = x^2 + 7x + 10.$

OBJECTIVE

a Factor trinomials of the type $x^2 + bx + c$ by examining the constant term c.

SKILL TO REVIEW

Objective 3.6a: Multiply two binomials mentally using the FOIL method.

Multiply.

1. $(x + 3)(x + 4)$

2. $(x - 1)(x + 2)$

Answers

Skill to Review:

1. $x^2 + 7x + 12$ **2.** $x^2 + x - 2$

EXAMPLE 1 Factor: $x^2 + 5x + 6$.

Think of FOIL in reverse. The first term of each factor is x: $(x + \square)(x + \square)$. Next, we look for two numbers whose product is 6 and whose sum is 5. All the pairs of factors of 6 are shown in the table on the left below. Since both the product, 6, and the sum, 5, of the pair of numbers must be positive, we need consider only the positive factors, listed in the table on the right.

PAIRS OF FACTORS	SUMS OF FACTORS
1, 6	7
−1, −6	−7
2, 3	5
−2, −3	−5

PAIRS OF FACTORS	SUMS OF FACTORS
1, 6	7
2, 3	5

The numbers we need are 2 and 3.

The factorization is $(x + 2)(x + 3)$. We can check by multiplying to see whether we get the original trinomial.

Check: $(x + 2)(x + 3) = x^2 + 3x + 2x + 6 = x^2 + 5x + 6$.

Do Exercises 1 and 2.

1. Consider the trinomial $x^2 + 7x + 12$.
   a) Complete the following table.

PAIRS OF FACTORS	SUMS OF FACTORS
1, 12	13
−1, −12	
2, 6	
−2, −6	
3, 4	
−3, −4	

   b) Explain why you need to consider only the positive factors in the table above.
   c) Factor: $x^2 + 7x + 12$.

2. Factor: $x^2 + 13x + 36$.

Compare these multiplications:

$$(x - 2)(x - 5) = x^2 - 5x - 2x + 10 = x^2 - 7x + 10;$$
$$(x + 2)(x + 5) = x^2 + 5x + 2x + 10 = x^2 + 7x + 10.$$

TO FACTOR $x^2 + bx + c$ WHEN c IS POSITIVE

When the constant term of a trinomial is positive, look for two numbers with the same sign. The sign is that of the middle term:

$$x^2 - 7x + 10 = (x - 2)(x - 5);$$

$$x^2 + 7x + 10 = (x + 2)(x + 5).$$

EXAMPLE 2 Factor: $y^2 - 8y + 12$.

Since the constant term, 12, is positive and the coefficient of the middle term, −8, is negative, we look for a factorization of 12 in which both factors are negative. Their sum must be −8.

PAIRS OF FACTORS	SUMS OF FACTORS
−1, −12	−13
−2, −6	−8
−3, −4	−7

The numbers we need are −2 and −6.

The factorization is $(y - 2)(y - 6)$. The student should check by multiplying.

Do Exercises 3–5.

3. Explain why you would *not* consider the pairs of factors listed below in factoring $y^2 - 8y + 12$.

PAIRS OF FACTORS	SUMS OF FACTORS
1, 12	
2, 6	
3, 4	

Factor.

4. $x^2 - 8x + 15$

5. $t^2 - 9t + 20$

Answers

1. (a) −13, 8, −8, 7, −7; (b) Both 7 and 12 are positive. (c) $(x + 3)(x + 4)$
2. $(x + 4)(x + 9)$ 3. The coefficient of the middle term, −8, is negative.
4. $(x - 5)(x - 3)$
5. $(t - 5)(t - 4)$

Constant Term Negative

As we saw in two of the multiplications earlier in this section, the product of two binomials can have a negative constant term:

$$(x + 3)(x - 7) = x^2 - 4x - 21$$

and

$$(x - 3)(x + 7) = x^2 + 4x - 21.$$

Note that when the signs of the constants in the binomials are reversed, only the sign of the middle term in the product changes.

EXAMPLE 3 Factor: $x^2 - 8x - 20$.

The constant term, -20, must be expressed as the product of a negative number and a positive number. Since the sum of these two numbers must be negative (specifically, -8), the negative number must have the greater absolute value.

PAIRS OF FACTORS	SUMS OF FACTORS
1, −20	−19
2, −10	−8 ←
4, −5	−1
5, −4	1
10, −2	8
20, −1	19

The numbers we need are 2 and −10.

Because these sums are all positive, for this problem all the corresponding pairs can be disregarded. Note that in all three pairs, the positive number has the greater absolute value.

The numbers that we are looking for are 2 and −10. The factorization is $(x + 2)(x - 10)$.

Check: $(x + 2)(x - 10) = x^2 - 10x + 2x - 20$
$= x^2 - 8x - 20.$

TO FACTOR $x^2 + bx + c$ WHEN c IS NEGATIVE

When the constant term of a trinomial is negative, look for two numbers whose product is negative. One must be positive and the other negative:

$$x^2 - 4x - 21 = (x + 3)(x - 7);$$

$$x^2 + 4x - 21 = (x - 3)(x + 7).$$

Consider pairs of numbers for which the number with the larger absolute value has the same sign as b, the coefficient of the middle term.

Do Exercises 6 and 7. (Exercise 7 is on the following page.)

6. Consider $x^2 - 5x - 24$.

a) Explain why you would *not* consider the pairs of factors listed below in factoring $x^2 - 5x - 24$.

PAIRS OF FACTORS	SUMS OF FACTORS
−1, 24	
−2, 12	
−3, 8	
−4, 6	

b) Explain why you *would* consider the pairs of factors listed below in factoring $x^2 - 5x - 24$.

PAIRS OF FACTORS	SUMS OF FACTORS
1, −24	
2, −12	
3, −8	
4, −6	

c) Factor: $x^2 - 5x - 24$.

Answers

6. (a) The positive factor has the larger absolute value. (b) The negative factor has the larger absolute value. (c) $(x + 3)(x - 8)$

7. Consider $x^2 + 10x - 24$.

a) Explain why you would *not* consider the pairs of factors listed below in factoring $x^2 + 10x - 24$.

PAIRS OF FACTORS	SUMS OF FACTORS
1, −24	
2, −12	
3, −8	
4, −6	

b) Explain why you *would* consider the pairs of factors listed below in factoring $x^2 + 10x - 24$.

PAIRS OF FACTORS	SUMS OF FACTORS
−1, 24	
−2, 12	
−3, 8	
−4, 6	

c) Factor: $x^2 + 10x - 24$.

Factor.

8. $a^2 - 40 + 3a$

9. $-18 - 3t + t^2$

Answers

7. (a) The negative factor has the larger absolute value. **(b)** The positive factor has the larger absolute value. **(c)** $(x - 2)(x + 12)$
8. $(a - 5)(a + 8)$ **9.** $(t - 6)(t + 3)$

EXAMPLE 4 Factor: $t^2 - 24 + 5t$.

It helps to first write the trinomial in descending order: $t^2 + 5t - 24$. Since the constant term, -24, is negative, we look for a factorization of -24 in which one factor is positive and one factor is negative. Their sum must be 5, so we consider only pairs of factors in which the positive factor has the larger absolute value.

PAIRS OF FACTORS	SUMS OF FACTORS
−1, 24	23
−2, 12	10
−3, 8	5 ← The numbers we need are −3 and 8.
−4, 6	2

The factorization is $(t - 3)(t + 8)$. The check is left to the student.

Do Exercises 8 and 9.

EXAMPLE 5 Factor: $x^4 - x^2 - 110$.

Consider this trinomial as $(x^2)^2 - x^2 - 110$. We look for numbers p and q such that

$$x^4 - x^2 - 110 = (x^2 + p)(x^2 + q).$$

Since the constant term, -110, is negative, we look for a factorization of -110 in which one factor is positive and one factor is negative. Their sum must be -1. The middle-term coefficient, -1, is small compared to -110. This tells us that the desired factors are close to each other in absolute value. The numbers we want are 10 and -11. The factorization is

$$(x^2 + 10)(x^2 - 11).$$

EXAMPLE 6 Factor: $a^2 + 4ab - 21b^2$.

We consider the trinomial in the equivalent form

$$a^2 + 4ba - 21b^2.$$

This way we think of $-21b^2$ as the "constant" term and $4b$ as the "coefficient" of the middle term. Then we try to express $-21b^2$ as a product of two factors whose sum is $4b$. Those factors are $-3b$ and $7b$. The factorization is $(a - 3b)(a + 7b)$.

Check: $(a - 3b)(a + 7b) = a^2 + 7ab - 3ba - 21b^2$
$= a^2 + 4ab - 21b^2.$

There are polynomials that are not factorable.

EXAMPLE 7 Factor: $x^2 - x + 5$.

Since 5 has very few factors, we can easily check all possibilities.

PAIRS OF FACTORS	SUMS OF FACTORS
5, 1	6
−5, −1	−6

There are no factors whose sum is -1. Thus the polynomial is *not* factorable into factors that are polynomials with rational-number coefficients.

In this text, a polynomial like $x^2 - x + 5$ that cannot be factored further is said to be **prime**. In more advanced courses, polynomials like $x^2 - x + 5$ can be factored and are not considered prime.

Do Exercises 10–12.

Factor.

10. $y^2 - 12 - 4y$

11. $t^4 + 5t^2 - 14$

12. $x^2 + 2x + 7$

Often factoring requires two or more steps. In general, when told to factor, we should *factor completely*. This means that the final factorization should not contain any factors that can be factored further.

EXAMPLE 8 Factor: $2x^3 - 20x^2 + 50x$.

Always look first for a common factor. This time there is one, $2x$, which we factor out first:

$$2x^3 - 20x^2 + 50x = 2x(x^2 - 10x + 25).$$

Now consider $x^2 - 10x + 25$. Since the constant term is positive and the coefficient of the middle term is negative, we look for a factorization of 25 in which both factors are negative. Their sum must be -10.

PAIRS OF FACTORS	SUMS OF FACTORS
$-25, -1$	-26
$-5, -5$	-10 ← The numbers we need are -5 and -5.

The factorization of $x^2 - 10x + 25$ is $(x - 5)(x - 5)$, or $(x - 5)^2$. The final factorization is $2x(x - 5)^2$. We check by multiplying:

$$\begin{aligned} 2x(x - 5)^2 &= 2x(x^2 - 10x + 25) \\ &= (2x)(x^2) - (2x)(10x) + (2x)(25) \\ &= 2x^3 - 20x^2 + 50x. \end{aligned}$$

Do Exercises 13–15.

Factor.

13. $x^3 + 4x^2 - 12x$

14. $p^2 - pq - 3pq^2$

15. $3x^3 + 24x^2 + 48x$

Once any common factors have been factored out, the following summary can be used to factor $x^2 + bx + c$.

TO FACTOR $x^2 + bx + c$

1. First arrange in descending order.
2. Use a trial-and-error process that looks for factors of c whose sum is b.
3. If c is positive, the signs of the factors are the same as the sign of b.
4. If c is negative, one factor is positive and the other is negative. If the sum of two factors is the opposite of b, changing the sign of each factor will give the desired factors whose sum is b.
5. Check by multiplying.

Answers

10. $(y - 6)(y + 2)$ **11.** $(t^2 + 7)(t^2 - 2)$
12. Prime **13.** $x(x + 6)(x - 2)$
14. $p(p - q - 3q^2)$ **15.** $3x(x + 4)^2$

Leading Coefficient −1

EXAMPLE 9 Factor: $10 - 3x - x^2$.

Note that the polynomial is written in ascending order. When we write it in descending order, we get

$$-x^2 - 3x + 10,$$

which has a leading coefficient of -1. Before factoring in such a case, we can factor out a -1, as follows:

$$\begin{aligned} -x^2 - 3x + 10 &= -1 \cdot x^2 + (-1)(3x) + (-1)(-10) \\ &= -1(x^2 + 3x - 10). \end{aligned}$$

Then we proceed to factor $x^2 + 3x - 10$. We get

$$-x^2 - 3x + 10 = -1(x^2 + 3x - 10) = -1(x + 5)(x - 2).$$

We can also express this answer in two other ways by multiplying either binomial by -1. Thus each of the following is a correct answer:

$$\begin{aligned} -x^2 - 3x + 10 &= -1(x + 5)(x - 2) \\ &= (-x - 5)(x - 2) && \text{Multiplying } x + 5 \text{ by } -1 \\ &= (x + 5)(-x + 2). && \text{Multiplying } x - 2 \text{ by } -1 \end{aligned}$$

Do Exercises 16 and 17.

Factor.

16. $14 + 5x - x^2$

17. $-x^2 + 3x + 18$

STUDY TIPS

TIME MANAGEMENT

- **Are you a morning or an evening person?** If you are an evening person, it might be best to avoid scheduling early-morning classes. If you are a morning person, you will probably want to schedule morning classes if your work schedule and family obligations will allow it. Nothing can drain your study time and effectiveness like fatigue.
- **Keep on schedule.** Your course syllabus provides a plan for the semester's schedule. Read the entire syllabus at the beginning of the semester. Use a write-on calendar, daily planner, PDA, or laptop computer to outline your time for the semester. Be sure to note deadlines involving writing assignments and exams so you can begin a big task early, breaking it down into smaller segments that will not overwhelm you.

Answers

16. $-1(x + 2)(x - 7)$, or $(-x - 2)(x - 7)$, or $(x + 2)(-x + 7)$
17. $-1(x + 3)(x - 6)$, or $(-x - 3)(x - 6)$, or $(x + 3)(-x + 6)$

For Extra Help

MyMathLab

Math XL PRACTICE | WATCH | DOWNLOAD | READ | REVIEW

a Factor. Remember that you can check by multiplying.

1. $x^2 + 8x + 15$

PAIRS OF FACTORS	SUMS OF FACTORS

2. $x^2 + 5x + 6$

PAIRS OF FACTORS	SUMS OF FACTORS

3. $x^2 + 7x + 12$

PAIRS OF FACTORS	SUMS OF FACTORS

4. $x^2 + 9x + 8$

PAIRS OF FACTORS	SUMS OF FACTORS

5. $x^2 - 6x + 9$

PAIRS OF FACTORS	SUMS OF FACTORS

6. $y^2 - 11y + 28$

PAIRS OF FACTORS	SUMS OF FACTORS

7. $x^2 - 5x - 14$

PAIRS OF FACTORS	SUMS OF FACTORS

8. $a^2 + 7a - 30$

PAIRS OF FACTORS	SUMS OF FACTORS

9. $b^2 + 5b + 4$

PAIRS OF FACTORS	SUMS OF FACTORS

10. $z^2 - 8z + 7$

PAIRS OF FACTORS	SUMS OF FACTORS

11. $x^2 + \frac{2}{3}x + \frac{1}{9}$

PAIRS OF FACTORS	SUMS OF FACTORS

12. $x^2 - \frac{2}{5}x + \frac{1}{25}$

PAIRS OF FACTORS	SUMS OF FACTORS

13. $d^2 - 7d + 10$

14. $t^2 - 12t + 35$

15. $y^2 - 11y + 10$

16. $x^2 - 4x - 21$

17. $x^2 + x + 1$

18. $x^2 + 5x + 3$

19. $x^2 - 7x - 18$

20. $y^2 - 3y - 28$

21. $x^3 - 6x^2 - 16x$

22. $x^3 - x^2 - 42x$

23. $y^3 - 4y^2 - 45y$

24. $x^3 - 7x^2 - 60x$

25. $-2x - 99 + x^2$

26. $x^2 - 72 + 6x$

27. $c^4 + c^2 - 56$

28. $b^4 + 5b^2 - 24$

29. $a^4 + 2a^2 - 35$

30. $x^4 - x^2 - 6$

31. $x^2 + x - 42$

32. $x^2 + 2x - 15$

33. $7 - 2p + p^2$

34. $11 - 3w + w^2$

35. $x^2 + 20x + 100$

36. $a^2 + 19a + 88$

37. $2z^3 - 2z^2 - 24z$

38. $5w^4 - 20w^3 - 25w^2$

39. $3t^4 + 3t^3 + 3t^2$

40. $4y^5 - 4y^4 - 4y^3$

41. $x^4 - 21x^3 - 100x^2$

42. $x^4 - 20x^3 + 96x^2$

43. $x^2 - 21x - 72$

44. $4x^2 + 40x + 100$

45. $x^2 - 25x + 144$

46. $y^2 - 21y + 108$

47. $a^2 + a - 132$

48. $a^2 + 9a - 90$

49. $3t^2 + 6t + 3$

50. $2y^2 + 24y + 72$

51. $w^4 - 8w^3 + 16w^2$

52. $z^5 - 6z^4 + 9z^3$

53. $30 + 7x - x^2$

54. $45 + 4x - x^2$

55. $24 - a^2 - 10a$

56. $-z^2 + 36 - 9z$

57. $120 - 23x + x^2$

58. $96 + 22d + d^2$

59. $108 - 3x - x^2$

60. $112 + 9y - y^2$

61. $y^2 - 0.2y - 0.08$

62. $t^2 - 0.3t - 0.10$

63. $p^2 + 3pq - 10q^2$

64. $a^2 + 2ab - 3b^2$

65. $84 - 8t - t^2$

66. $72 - 6m - m^2$

67. $m^2 + 5mn + 4n^2$

68. $x^2 + 11xy + 24y^2$

69. $s^2 - 2st - 15t^2$

70. $p^2 + 5pq - 24q^2$

71. $6a^{10} - 30a^9 - 84a^8$

72. $7x^9 - 28x^8 - 35x^7$

Skill Maintenance

Multiply. [3.5b], [3.6d]

73. $8x(2x^2 - 6x + 1)$

74. $(7w + 6)(4w - 11)$

75. $(7w + 6)^2$

76. $(4w - 11)^2$

77. $(4w - 11)(4w + 11)$

78. $-y(-y^2 + 3y - 5)$

79. $(3x - 5y)(2x + 7y)$

80. Simplify: $(3x^4)^3$. [3.2a, b]

Solve. [2.3a]

81. $3x - 8 = 0$

82. $2x + 7 = 0$

Solve.

83. *Arrests for Counterfeiting.* In 2008, the U.S. Secret Service made 2231 arrests for counterfeiting. This was an increase of 28% over the number of arrests in 2007. How many arrests for counterfeiting were made in 2007? [2.5a]

Source: U.S. Secret Service

84. The first angle of a triangle is four times as large as the second. The measure of the third angle is 30° greater than that of the second. Find the angle measures. [2.6a]

Synthesis

85. Find all integers m for which $y^2 + my + 50$ can be factored.

86. Find all integers b for which $a^2 + ba - 50$ can be factored.

Factor completely.

87. $x^2 - \frac{1}{2}x - \frac{3}{16}$

88. $x^2 - \frac{1}{4}x - \frac{1}{8}$

89. $x^2 + \frac{30}{7}x - \frac{25}{7}$

90. $\frac{1}{3}x^3 + \frac{1}{3}x^2 - 2x$

91. $b^{2n} + 7b^n + 10$

92. $a^{2m} - 11a^m + 28$

Find a polynomial in factored form for the shaded area in each figure. (Leave answers in terms of π.)

93.

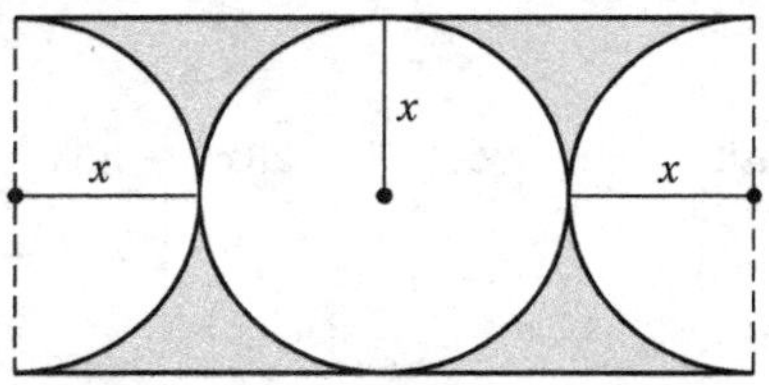

94.

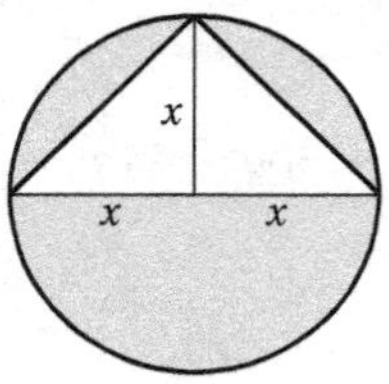

Mid-Chapter Review

Concept Reinforcement

Determine whether each statement is true or false.

_______________ **1.** The greatest common factor (GCF) of a set of natural numbers is at least 1 and always less than or equal to the smallest number in the set. [3.1a]

_______________ **2.** To factor $x^2 + bx + c$, we use a trial-and-error process that looks for factors of b whose sum is c. [3.2a]

_______________ **3.** A prime polynomial has no common factor other than 1 and -1. [3.2a]

_______________ **4.** When factoring $x^2 - 14x + 45$, we need consider only positive pairs of factors of 45. [3.2a]

Guided Solutions

Fill in each blank with the number, variable, or expression that creates a correct statement or solution.

5. Factor: $10y^3 - 18y^2 + 12y$. [3.1b]

$$10y^3 - 18y^2 + 12y = \square \cdot 5y^2 - \square \cdot 9y + \square \cdot 6$$
$$= 2y(\square)$$

6. Factor $2x^2 - x - 6$ using the ac-method. [3.4a]

$a \cdot c = \square \cdot \square = -12;$ Multiplying the leading coefficient and the constant

$-x = \square + 3x;$ Splitting the middle term

$$2x^2 - x - 6 = 2x^2 - 4x + \square - 6$$
$$= \square(x - 2) + \square(x - 2)$$
$$= (x - 2)(\square)$$

Mixed Review

Find the GCF. [3.1a]

7. $x^3,\ 3x$

8. $5x^4,\ x^2$

9. $6x^5,\ -12x^3$

10. $-8x,\ -12,\ 16x^2$

11. $15x^3y^2,\ 5x^2y,\ 40x^4y^3$

12. $x^2y^4,\ -x^3y^3,\ x^3y^2,\ x^5y^4$

Factor completely. [3.1b, c], [3.2a], [3.3a], [3.4a]

13. $x^3 - 8x$

14. $3x^2 + 12x$

15. $2y^2 + 8y - 4$

16. $3t^6 - 5t^4 - 2t^3$

17. $x^2 + 4x + 3$

18. $z^2 - 4z + 4$

19. $x^3 + 4x^2 + 3x + 12$

20. $8y^5 - 48y^3$

21. $z^2 + 4z - 5$

22. $15 - 8w + w^2$

23. $x^2 - 10xy + 24y^2$

24. $3x^3 + 21x^2 + 30x$

25. $y^2 + 6y + 8$

26. $x^3 - 7x^2 + 4x - 28$

27. $4 + 3y - y^2$

28. $y^3 + 9y^2 + 18y$

29. $y^2 + yz - 20z^2$

30. $m^2 - 6mn - 16n^2$

31. $2w^2 - 12w + 18$

32. $-14 + 5t + t^2$

33. $4t^2 - 20t + 25$

34. $t^2 + 4t - 12$

35. $12 + 4y - y^2$

4.3 Factoring Trinomial Squares and Differences of Squares

OBJECTIVES

- **a** Recognize trinomial squares.
- **b** Factor trinomial squares.
- **c** Recognize differences of squares.
- **d** Factor differences of squares, being careful to factor completely.

In this section, we first learn to factor trinomials that are squares of binomials. Then we factor binomials that are differences of squares.

a Recognizing Trinomial Squares

Some trinomials are squares of binomials. For example, the trinomial $x^2 + 10x + 25$ is the square of the binomial $x + 5$. To see this, we can calculate $(x + 5)^2$. It is $x^2 + 2 \cdot x \cdot 5 + 5^2$, or $x^2 + 10x + 25$. A trinomial that is the square of a binomial is called a **trinomial square**, or a **perfect-square trinomial**.

In Chapter 4, we considered squaring binomials as special-product rules:

$$(A + B)^2 = A^2 + 2AB + B^2;$$
$$(A - B)^2 = A^2 - 2AB + B^2.$$

We can use these equations in reverse to factor trinomial squares.

TRINOMIAL SQUARES

$$A^2 + 2AB + B^2 = (A + B)^2;$$
$$A^2 - 2AB + B^2 = (A - B)^2$$

It would be helpful to memorize this table of perfect squares.

NUMBER, N	PERFECT SQUARE, N^2
1	1
2	4
3	9
4	16
5	25
6	36
7	49
8	64
9	81
10	100
11	121
12	144
13	169
14	196
15	225
16	256
17	289
18	324
19	361
20	400
21	441
22	484
23	529
24	576
25	625

How can we recognize when an expression to be factored is a trinomial square? Look at $A^2 + 2AB + B^2$ and $A^2 - 2AB + B^2$. In order for an expression to be a trinomial square:

a) The two expressions A^2 and B^2 must be squares, such as

$$4, \quad x^2, \quad 25x^4, \quad 16t^2.$$

When the coefficient is a perfect square and the power(s) of the variable(s) is (are) even, then the expression is a perfect square.

b) There must be no minus sign before A^2 or B^2.

c) If we multiply A and B and double the result, $2 \cdot AB$, we get either the remaining term or its opposite.

EXAMPLE 1 Determine whether $x^2 + 6x + 9$ is a trinomial square.

a) We know that x^2 and 9 are squares.

b) There is no minus sign before x^2 or 9.

c) If we multiply the square roots, x and 3, and double the product, we get the remaining term: $2 \cdot x \cdot 3 = 6x$.

Thus, $x^2 + 6x + 9$ is the square of a binomial. In fact, $x^2 + 6x + 9 = (x + 3)^2$.

EXAMPLE 2 Determine whether $x^2 + 6x + 11$ is a trinomial square.

The answer is no, because only one term, x^2, is a square.

Determine whether each is a trinomial square. Write "yes" or "no."

1. $x^2 + 8x + 16$

2. $25 - x^2 + 10x$

3. $t^2 - 12t + 4$

4. $25 + 20y + 4y^2$

5. $5x^2 + 16 - 14x$

6. $16x^2 + 40x + 25$

7. $p^2 + 6p - 9$

8. $25a^2 + 9 - 30a$

EXAMPLE 3 Determine whether $16x^2 + 49 - 56x$ is a trinomial square.

It helps to first write the trinomial in descending order:

$$16x^2 - 56x + 49.$$

a) We know that $16x^2$ and 49 are squares.

b) There is no minus sign before $16x^2$ or 49.

c) If we multiply the square roots, $4x$ and 7, and double the product, we get the opposite of the remaining term: $2 \cdot 4x \cdot 7 = 56x$; $56x$ is the opposite of $-56x$.

Thus, $16x^2 + 49 - 56x$ is a trinomial square. In fact, $16x^2 - 56x + 49 = (4x - 7)^2$.

Do Exercises 1–8.

b Factoring Trinomial Squares

We can use the factoring methods from Sections 4.2–4.4 to factor trinomial squares, but there is a faster method using the following equations.

> **FACTORING TRINOMIAL SQUARES**
>
> $A^2 + 2AB + B^2 = (A + B)^2$;
>
> $A^2 - 2AB + B^2 = (A - B)^2$

We consider 3 to be a square root of 9 because $3^2 = 9$. Similarly, A is a square root of A^2. We use square roots of the squared terms and the sign of the remaining term to factor a trinomial square.

EXAMPLE 4 Factor: $x^2 + 6x + 9$.

$$x^2 + 6x + 9 = x^2 + 2 \cdot x \cdot 3 + 3^2 = (x + 3)^2$$

$$A^2 + 2\ A\ B + B^2 = (A + B)^2$$

The sign of the middle term is positive.

EXAMPLE 5 Factor: $x^2 + 49 - 14x$.

$x^2 + 49 - 14x = x^2 - 14x + 49$ Changing to descending order

$= x^2 - 2 \cdot x \cdot 7 + 7^2$ The sign of the middle term is negative.

$= (x - 7)^2$

EXAMPLE 6 Factor: $16x^2 - 40x + 25$.

$$16x^2 - 40x + 25 = (4x)^2 - 2 \cdot 4x \cdot 5 + 5^2 = (4x - 5)^2$$

$$A^2 - 2\ A\ B + B^2 = (A - B)^2$$

Do Exercises 9–13.

Factor.

9. $x^2 + 2x + 1$

10. $1 - 2x + x^2$

11. $4 + t^2 + 4t$

12. $25x^2 - 70x + 49$

13. $49 - 56y + 16y^2$

Answers

1. Yes 2. No 3. No 4. Yes 5. No 6. Yes 7. No 8. Yes 9. $(x + 1)^2$ 10. $(x - 1)^2$, or $(1 - x)^2$ 11. $(t + 2)^2$ 12. $(5x - 7)^2$ 13. $(4y - 7)^2$, or $(7 - 4y)^2$

EXAMPLE 7 Factor: $t^4 + 20t^2 + 100$.

$$t^4 + 20t^2 + 100 = (t^2)^2 + 2(t^2)(10) + 10^2$$
$$= (t^2 + 10)^2$$

EXAMPLE 8 Factor: $75m^3 + 210m^2 + 147m$.

Always look first for a common factor. This time there is one, $3m$:

$$75m^3 + 210m^2 + 147m = 3m(25m^2 + 70m + 49)$$
$$= 3m[(5m)^2 + 2(5m)(7) + 7^2]$$
$$= 3m(5m + 7)^2.$$

EXAMPLE 9 Factor: $4p^2 - 12pq + 9q^2$.

$$4p^2 - 12pq + 9q^2 = (2p)^2 - 2(2p)(3q) + (3q)^2$$
$$= (2p - 3q)^2$$

Do Exercises 14–17.

Factor.

14. $48m^2 + 75 + 120m$

15. $p^4 + 18p^2 + 81$

16. $4z^5 - 20z^4 + 25z^3$

17. $9a^2 + 30ab + 25b^2$

c Recognizing Differences of Squares

The following polynomials are *differences of squares:*

$$x^2 - 9, \quad 4t^2 - 49, \quad a^2 - 25b^2.$$

To factor a difference of squares such as $x^2 - 9$, think about the formula we used in Chapter 4:

$$(A + B)(A - B) = A^2 - B^2.$$

Equations are reversible, so we also know the following.

DIFFERENCE OF SQUARES

$$A^2 - B^2 = (A + B)(A - B)$$

Thus,

$$x^2 - 9 = (x + 3)(x - 3).$$

To use this formula, we must be able to recognize when it applies. A **difference of squares** is an expression like the following:

$$A^2 - B^2.$$

How can we recognize such expressions? Look at $A^2 - B^2$. In order for a binomial to be a difference of squares:

a) There must be two expressions, both squares, such as

$$4x^2, \quad 9, \quad 25t^4, \quad 1, \quad x^6, \quad 49y^8.$$

b) The terms must have different signs.

Answers

14. $3(4m + 5)^2$ **15.** $(p^2 + 9)^2$
16. $z^3(2z - 5)^2$ **17.** $(3a + 5b)^2$

EXAMPLE 10 Is $9x^2 - 64$ a difference of squares?

a) The first expression is a square: $9x^2 = (3x)^2$.
   The second expression is a square: $64 = 8^2$.

b) The terms have different signs, $+9x^2$ and -64.

Thus we have a difference of squares, $(3x)^2 - 8^2$.

EXAMPLE 11 Is $25 - t^3$ a difference of squares?

a) The expression t^3 is not a square.

The expression is not a difference of squares.

EXAMPLE 12 Is $-4x^2 + 16$ a difference of squares?

a) The expressions $4x^2$ and 16 are squares: $4x^2 = (2x)^2$ and $16 = 4^2$.

b) The terms have different signs, $-4x^2$ and $+16$.

Thus we have a difference of squares. We can also see this by rewriting in the equivalent form: $16 - 4x^2$.

Do Exercises 18–24.

Determine whether each is a difference of squares. Write "yes" or "no."

18. $x^2 - 25$

19. $t^2 - 24$

20. $y^2 + 36$

21. $4x^2 - 15$

22. $16x^4 - 49$

23. $9w^6 - 1$

24. $-49 + 25t^2$

d Factoring Differences of Squares

To factor a difference of squares, we use the following equation.

FACTORING A DIFFERENCE OF SQUARES

$A^2 - B^2 = (A + B)(A - B)$

To factor a difference of squares $A^2 - B^2$, we find A and B, which are square roots of the expressions A^2 and B^2. We then use A and B to form two factors. One is the sum $A + B$, and the other is the difference $A - B$.

EXAMPLE 13 Factor: $x^2 - 4$.

$$x^2 - 4 = \underset{A^2}{x^2} - \underset{B^2}{2^2} = (\underset{A}{x} + \underset{B}{2})(\underset{A}{x} - \underset{B}{2})$$

EXAMPLE 14 Factor: $9 - 16t^4$.

$$9 - 16t^4 = \underset{A^2}{3^2} - \underset{B^2}{(4t^2)^2} = (\underset{A}{3} + \underset{B}{4t^2})(\underset{A}{3} - \underset{B}{4t^2})$$

Answers

18. Yes 19. No 20. No 21. No
22. Yes 23. Yes 24. Yes

EXAMPLE 15 Factor: $m^2 - 4p^2$.

$$m^2 - 4p^2 = m^2 - (2p)^2 = (m + 2p)(m - 2p)$$

EXAMPLE 16 Factor: $x^2 - \frac{1}{9}$.

$$x^2 - \frac{1}{9} = x^2 - \left(\frac{1}{3}\right)^2 = \left(x + \frac{1}{3}\right)\left(x - \frac{1}{3}\right)$$

EXAMPLE 17 Factor: $18x^2 - 50x^6$.

Always look first for a factor common to all terms. This time there is one, $2x^2$.

$$\begin{aligned} 18x^2 - 50x^6 &= 2x^2(9 - 25x^4) \\ &= 2x^2[3^2 - (5x^2)^2] \\ &= 2x^2(3 + 5x^2)(3 - 5x^2) \end{aligned}$$

EXAMPLE 18 Factor: $49x^4 - 9x^6$.

$$\begin{aligned} 49x^4 - 9x^6 &= x^4(49 - 9x^2) \\ &= x^4[7^2 - (3x)^2] \\ &= x^4(7 + 3x)(7 - 3x) \end{aligned}$$

Do Exercises 25–29.

Factor.

25. $x^2 - 9$

26. $4t^2 - 64$

27. $a^2 - 25b^2$

28. $64x^4 - 25x^6$

29. $5 - 20t^6$
[*Hint*: $1 = 1^2$, $t^6 = (t^3)^2$.]

Caution!

Note carefully in these examples that a difference of squares is *not* the square of the difference; that is,

$$A^2 - B^2 \neq (A - B)^2.$$

For example,

$$(45 - 5)^2 = 40^2 = 1600,$$

but

$$45^2 - 5^2 = 2025 - 25 = 2000.$$

Similarly,

$$A^2 - 2AB + B^2 \neq (A - B)(A + B).$$

For example,

$$(10 - 3)(10 + 3) = 7 \cdot 13 = 91,$$

but

$$\begin{aligned} 10^2 - 2 \cdot 10 \cdot 3 + 3^2 &= 100 - 2 \cdot 10 \cdot 3 + 9 \\ &= 100 - 60 + 9 \\ &= 49. \end{aligned}$$

Answers

25. $(x + 3)(x - 3)$
26. $4(t + 4)(t - 4)$
27. $(a + 5b)(a - 5b)$
28. $x^4(8 + 5x)(8 - 5x)$
29. $5(1 + 2t^3)(1 - 2t^3)$

Factoring Completely

If a factor with more than one term can still be factored, you should do so. When no factor can be factored further, you have **factored completely**. Always factor completely whenever told to factor.

EXAMPLE 19 Factor: $p^4 - 16$.

$$p^4 - 16 = (p^2)^2 - 4^2$$
$$= (p^2 + 4)(p^2 - 4) \quad \text{Factoring a difference of squares}$$
$$= (p^2 + 4)(p + 2)(p - 2) \quad \text{Factoring further; } p^2 - 4 \text{ is a difference of squares.}$$

The polynomial $p^2 + 4$ cannot be factored further into polynomials with real coefficients.

Caution!

Apart from possibly removing a common factor, you cannot factor a sum of squares as a product of binomials. In particular,

$$A^2 + B^2 \neq (A + B)^2.$$

Consider $25x^2 + 100$. Here a sum of squares has a common factor, 25. Factoring, we get $25(x^2 + 4)$, where $x^2 + 4$ is prime. For example,

$$x^2 + 4 \neq (x + 2)^2.$$

EXAMPLE 20 Factor: $y^4 - 16x^{12}$.

$$y^4 - 16x^{12} = (y^2 + 4x^6)(y^2 - 4x^6) \quad \text{Factoring a difference of squares}$$
$$= (y^2 + 4x^6)(y + 2x^3)(y - 2x^3) \quad \text{Factoring further. The factor } y^2 - 4x^6 \text{ is a difference of squares.}$$

The polynomial $y^2 + 4x^6$ cannot be factored further into polynomials with real coefficients.

EXAMPLE 21 Factor: $\frac{1}{16}x^8 - 81$.

$$\frac{1}{16}x^8 - 81 = \left(\frac{1}{4}x^4 + 9\right)\left(\frac{1}{4}x^4 - 9\right) \quad \text{Factoring a difference of squares}$$
$$= \left(\frac{1}{4}x^4 + 9\right)\left(\frac{1}{2}x^2 + 3\right)\left(\frac{1}{2}x^2 - 3\right) \quad \text{Factoring further. The factor } \tfrac{1}{4}x^4 - 9 \text{ is a difference of squares.}$$

TIPS FOR FACTORING

- Always look first for a common factor. If there is one, factor it out.
- Be alert for trinomial squares and differences of squares. Once recognized, they can be factored without trial and error.
- Always factor completely.
- Check by multiplying.

Do Exercises 30–32.

Factor completely.

30. $81x^4 - 1$

31. $16 - \frac{1}{81}y^8$

32. $49p^4 - 25q^6$

Answers

30. $(9x^2 + 1)(3x + 1)(3x - 1)$
31. $\left(4 + \frac{1}{9}y^4\right)\left(2 + \frac{1}{3}y^2\right)\left(2 - \frac{1}{3}y^2\right)$
32. $(7p^2 + 5q^3)(7p^2 - 5q^3)$

4.3 Exercise Set

For Extra Help

MyMathLab | Math XL PRACTICE | WATCH | DOWNLOAD | READ | REVIEW

a Determine whether each of the following is a trinomial square. Answer "yes" or "no."

1. $x^2 - 14x + 49$

2. $x^2 - 16x + 64$

3. $x^2 + 16x - 64$

4. $x^2 - 14x - 49$

5. $x^2 - 2x + 4$

6. $x^2 + 3x + 9$

7. $9x^2 - 24x + 16$

8. $25x^2 + 30x + 9$

b Factor completely. Remember to look first for a common factor and to check by multiplying.

9. $x^2 - 14x + 49$

10. $x^2 - 20x + 100$

11. $x^2 + 16x + 64$

12. $x^2 + 20x + 100$

13. $x^2 - 2x + 1$

14. $x^2 + 2x + 1$

15. $4 + 4x + x^2$

16. $4 + x^2 - 4x$

17. $y^2 + 12y + 36$

18. $y^2 + 18y + 81$

19. $16 + t^2 - 8t$

20. $9 + t^2 - 6t$

21. $q^4 - 6q^2 + 9$

22. $64 + 16a^2 + a^4$

23. $49 + 56y + 16y^2$

24. $75 + 48a^2 - 120a$

25. $2x^2 - 4x + 2$

26. $2x^2 - 40x + 200$

27. $x^3 - 18x^2 + 81x$

28. $x^3 + 24x^2 + 144x$

29. $12q^2 - 36q + 27$

30. $20p^2 + 100p + 125$

31. $49 - 42x + 9x^2$

32. $64 - 112x + 49x^2$

33. $5y^4 + 10y^2 + 5$

34. $a^4 + 14a^2 + 49$

35. $1 + 4x^4 + 4x^2$

36. $1 - 2a^5 + a^{10}$

37. $4p^2 + 12pq + 9q^2$

38. $25m^2 + 20mn + 4n^2$

39. $a^2 - 6ab + 9b^2$

40. $x^2 - 14xy + 49y^2$

41. $81a^2 - 18ab + b^2$

42. $64p^2 + 16pq + q^2$

43. $36a^2 + 96ab + 64b^2$

44. $16m^2 - 40mn + 25n^2$

c Determine whether each of the following is a difference of squares. Answer “yes” or “no.”

45. $x^2 - 4$

46. $x^2 - 36$

47. $x^2 + 25$

48. $x^2 + 9$

49. $x^2 - 45$

50. $x^2 - 80y^2$

51. $-25y^2 + 16x^2$

52. $-1 + 36x^2$

d Factor completely. Remember to look first for a common factor.

53. $y^2 - 4$

54. $q^2 - 1$

55. $p^2 - 9$

56. $x^2 - 36$

57. $-49 + t^2$

58. $-64 + m^2$

59. $a^2 - b^2$

60. $p^2 - q^2$

61. $25t^2 - m^2$

62. $w^2 - 49z^2$

63. $100 - k^2$

64. $81 - w^2$

65. $16a^2 - 9$

66. $25x^2 - 4$

67. $4x^2 - 25y^2$

68. $9a^2 - 16b^2$

69. $8x^2 - 98$

70. $24x^2 - 54$

71. $36x - 49x^3$

72. $16x - 81x^3$

73. $\frac{1}{16} - 49x^8$

74. $\frac{1}{625}x^8 - 49$

75. $0.09y^2 - 0.0004$

76. $0.16p^2 - 0.0025$

77. $49a^4 - 81$

78. $25a^4 - 9$

79. $a^4 - 16$

80. $y^4 - 1$

81. $5x^4 - 405$

82. $4x^4 - 64$

83. $1 - y^8$

84. $x^8 - 1$

85. $x^{12} - 16$

86. $x^8 - 81$

87. $y^2 - \frac{1}{16}$

88. $x^2 - \frac{1}{25}$

89. $25 - \frac{1}{49}x^2$

90. $\frac{1}{4} - 9q^2$

91. $16m^4 - t^4$

92. $p^4q^4 - 1$

Skill Maintenance

Divide. [1.6a, c]

93. $(-110) \div 10$

94. $-1000 \div (-2.5)$

95. $\left(-\frac{2}{3}\right) \div \frac{4}{5}$

96. $8.1 \div (-9)$

97. $-64 \div (-32)$

98. $-256 \div 1.6$

Find a polynomial for the shaded area in each figure. (Leave results in terms of π where appropriate.) [4.4d]

99.

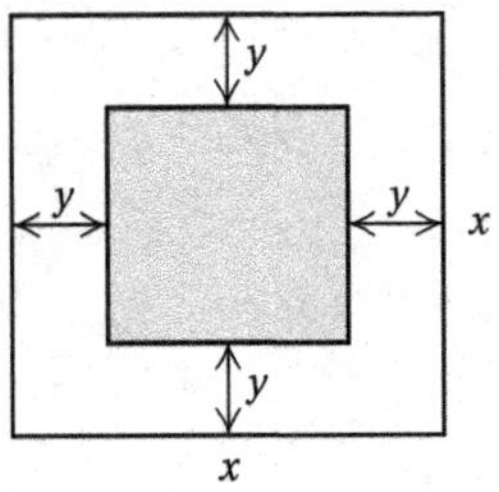

100.

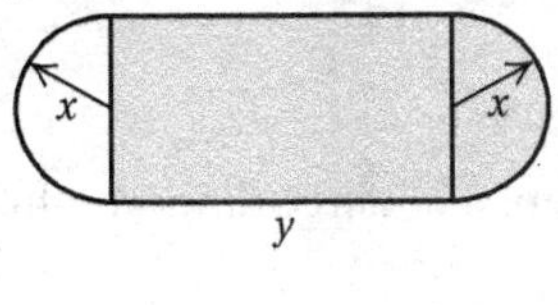

Simplify.

101. $y^5 \cdot y^7$ [3.1d]

102. $(5a^2b^3)^2$ [3.2a, b]

Find the intercepts. Then graph each equation.

103. $y - 6x = 6$

104. $3x - 5y = 15$

Synthesis

Factor completely, if possible.

105. $49x^2 - 216$

106. $27x^3 - 13x$

107. $x^2 + 22x + 121$

108. $x^2 - 5x + 25$

109. $18x^3 + 12x^2 + 2x$

110. $162x^2 - 82$

111. $x^8 - 2^8$

112. $4x^4 - 4x^2$

113. $3x^5 - 12x^3$

114. $3x^2 - \frac{1}{3}$

115. $18x^3 - \frac{8}{25}x$

116. $x^2 - 2.25$

117. $0.49p - p^3$

118. $3.24x^2 - 0.81$

119. $0.64x^2 - 1.21$

120. $1.28x^2 - 2$

121. $(x + 3)^2 - 9$

122. $(y - 5)^2 - 36q^2$

123. $x^2 - \left(\frac{1}{x}\right)^2$

124. $a^{2n} - 49b^{2n}$

125. $81 - b^{4k}$

126. $9x^{18} + 48x^9 + 64$

127. $9b^{2n} + 12b^n + 4$

128. $(x + 7)^2 - 4x - 24$

129. $(y + 3)^2 + 2(y + 3) + 1$

130. $49(x + 1)^2 - 42(x + 1) + 9$

Find c such that the polynomial is the square of a binomial.

131. $cy^2 + 6y + 1$

132. $cy^2 - 24y + 9$

Use the TABLE feature or graphs to determine whether each factorization is correct.

133. $x^2 + 9 = (x + 3)(x + 3)$

134. $x^2 - 49 = (x - 7)(x + 7)$

135. $x^2 + 9 = (x + 3)^2$

136. $x^2 - 49 = (x - 7)^2$

CHAPTER
4
Summary and Review

Key Terms and Properties

greatest common factor (GCF), p. 298
factor, p. 299
factorization, p. 299
factoring by grouping, p. 303
leading coefficient, p. 307
trinomial square, or perfect-square trinomial, p. 319
difference of squares, p. 321

Factoring Formulas:
$A^2 - B^2 = (A + B)(A - B)$,
$A^2 + 2AB + B^2 = (A + B)^2$,
$A^2 - 2AB + B^2 = (A - B)^2$

The Principle of Zero Products: An equation $ab = 0$ is true if and only if $a = 0$ is true or $b = 0$ is true, or both are true.

The Pythagorean Theorem: $a^2 + b^2 = c^2$

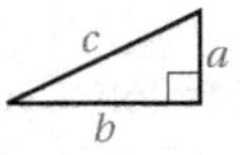

Concept Reinforcement

Determine whether each statement is true or false.

_______________ **1.** Every polynomial with four terms can be factored by grouping. [4.1c]

_______________ **2.** When factoring $x^2 + 5x + 6$, we need consider only positive pairs of factors of 6. [4.2a]

_______________ **3.** A product is 0 if and only if all the factors are 0. [4.7a]

_______________ **4.** If the principle of zero products is to be used, one side of the equation must be 0. [4.7b]

Important Concepts

Objective 4.1a Find the greatest common factor, the GCF, of monomials.

Example Find the GCF of $15x^4y^2$, $-18x$, and $12x^3y$.

$$15x^4y^2 = 3 \cdot 5 \cdot x^4 \cdot y^2;$$
$$-18x = -1 \cdot 2 \cdot 3 \cdot 3 \cdot x;$$
$$12x^3y = 2 \cdot 2 \cdot 3 \cdot x^3 \cdot y$$

Each coefficient has a factor of 3. There are no other common prime factors. The GCF of the powers of x is x because 1 is the smallest exponent of x. The GCF of the powers of y is 1 because $18x$ has no y-factor. Thus the GCF is $3 \cdot x \cdot 1$, or $3x$.

Practice Exercise

1. Find the GCF of $8x^3y^2$, $-20xy^3$, and $32x^2y$.

Objective 4.1b Factor polynomials when the terms have a common factor, factoring out the greatest common factor.

Example Factor: $16y^4 + 8y^3 - 24y^2$.

The *largest* common factor is $8y^2$.

$$16y^4 + 8y^3 - 24y^2 = (8y^2)(2y^2) + (8y^2)(y) - (8y^2)(3)$$
$$= 8y^2(2y^2 + y - 3)$$

Practice Exercise

2. Factor $27x^5 - 9x^3 + 18x^2$, factoring out the largest common factor.

Objective 4.1c Factor certain expressions with four terms using factoring by grouping.

Example Factor $6x^3 + 4x^2 - 15x - 10$ by grouping.

$$6x^3 + 4x^2 - 15x - 10 = (6x^3 + 4x^2) + (-15x - 10)$$
$$= 2x^2(3x + 2) - 5(3x + 2)$$
$$= (3x + 2)(2x^2 - 5)$$

Practice Exercise

3. Factor $z^3 - 3z^2 + 4z - 12$ by grouping.

Objective 4.2a Factor trinomials of the type $x^2 + bx + c$ by examining the constant term c.

Example Factor: $x^2 - x - 12$.

Since the constant term, -12, is negative, we look for a factorization of -12 in which one factor is positive and one factor is negative. The sum of the factors must be the coefficient of the middle term, -1, so the negative factor must have the larger absolute value. The possible pairs of factors that meet these criteria are $1, -12$ and $2, -6$ and $3, -4$. The numbers we need are 3 and -4:

$$x^2 - x - 12 = (x + 3)(x - 4).$$

Practice Exercise

4. Factor: $x^2 + 6x + 8$.

Objective 4.3b Factor trinomial squares.

Example Factor: $9x^2 - 12x + 4$.

$$9x^2 - 12x + 4 = (3x)^2 - 2 \cdot 3x \cdot 2 + 2^2$$
$$= (3x - 2)^2$$

Practice Exercise

5. Factor: $4x^2 + 4x + 1$.

Objective 4.3d Factor differences of squares, being careful to factor completely.

Example Factor: $b^6 - b^2$.

$$b^6 - b^2 = b^2(b^4 - 1)$$
$$= b^2(b^2 + 1)(b^2 - 1)$$
$$= b^2(b^2 + 1)(b + 1)(b - 1)$$

Practice Exercise

6. Factor $18x^2 - 8$ completely.

Review Exercises

Find the GCF. [4.1a]

1. $-15y^2,\ 25y^6$

2. $12x^3,\ -60x^2y,\ 36xy$

Factor completely. [4.6a]

3. $5 - 20x^6$

4. $x^2 - 3x$

5. $9x^2 - 4$

6. $x^2 + 4x - 12$

7. $x^2 + 14x + 49$

8. $x^3 + x^2 + 3x + 3$

9. $x^4 - 81$

10. $2x^2 - 50$

11. $16x^4 - 1$

12. $x^2 + 9$

13. $x^3 - x^2 - 30x$

14. $4x^2 - 25$

15. $x^2 - 6x + 9$

16. $3x^2 - 27$

17. $15 - 8x + x^2$

18. $25x^2 - 20x + 4$

19. $x^2y^2 + xy - 12$

20. $m^2 + 5m + mt + 5t$

21. $32x^4 - 128y^4z^4$

CHAPTER 4

Test

For Extra Help

CHAPTER Test Prep VIDEOS

Step-by-step test solutions are found on the Chapter Test Prep Videos available via the Video Resources on DVD, in MyMathLab, and on YouTube (search "BittingerIntroAlg" and click on "Channels").

1. Find the GCF: $28x^3, 48x^7$.

Factor completely.

2. $x^2 - 7x + 10$

3. $x^2 + 25 - 10x$

4. $x^3 + x^2 + 2x + 2$

5. $x^2 - 5x$

6. $x^3 + 2x^2 - 3x$

7. $4x^2 - 9$

8. $x^2 - x - 12$

9. $3w^2 - 75$

10. $3x^4 - 48$

11. $49x^2 - 84x + 36$

12. $80 - 5x^4$

CHAPTERS

1-4

Cumulative Review

Use either < or > for □ to write a true sentence.

1. $\frac{2}{3} \square \frac{5}{7}$

2. $-\frac{4}{7} \square -\frac{8}{11}$

Compute and simplify.

3. $2.06 + (-4.79) - (-3.08)$

4. $5.652 \div (-3.6)$

5. $\left(\frac{2}{9}\right)\left(-\frac{3}{8}\right)\left(\frac{6}{7}\right)$

6. $\frac{21}{5} \div \left(-\frac{7}{2}\right)$

Simplify.

7. $[3x + 2(x - 1)] - [2x - (x + 3)]$

8. $1 - [14 + 28 \div 7 - (6 + 9 \div 3)]$

9. $(2x^2y^{-1})^3$

10. $\frac{3x^5}{4x^3} \cdot \frac{-2x^{-3}}{9x^2}$

11. Add: $(2x^2 - 3x^3 + x - 4) + (x^4 - x - 5x^2)$.

12. Subtract: $(2x^2y^2 + xy - 2xy^2) - (2xy - 2xy^2 + x^2y)$.

Multiply.

13. $(2t - 3)^2$

14. $(x^2 - 3)(x^2 + 3)$

15. $(2x + 4)(3x - 4)$

16. $2x(x^3 + 3x^2 + 4x)$

17. $(2y - 1)(2y^2 + 3y + 4)$

18. $\left(x + \frac{2}{3}\right)\left(x - \frac{2}{3}\right)$

Factor.

19. $x^2 + 2x - 8$

20. $4x^2 - 25$

21. $x^2 - 26x + 169$

22. $3x^8 - 48y^8$

Solve.

23. $3x - 5 = 2x + 10$

24. $3y + 4 > 5y - 8$

25. $1.6 - 3.5x = 0.9$

26. $1.5x - 3.6 \leq 1.3x + 0.4$

27. $2x - [3x - (2x + 3)] = 3x + [4 - (2x + 1)]$

28. $y = mx + b$, for m

Solve.

29. The sum of two consecutive even integers is 102. Find the integers.

30. A 100-m wire is cut into three pieces. The second piece is twice as long as the first piece. The third piece is one-third as long as the first piece. How long is each piece?

31. After a 25% price reduction, a pair of shoes is on sale for $21.75. What was the price before reduction?

32. $\frac{x - 3}{2} - \frac{2x + 5}{26} = \frac{4x + 11}{13}$

APPENDIX

Sets

OBJECTIVES

a Name sets using the roster method.

b Classify statements regarding set membership and subsets as true or false.

c Find the intersection and the union of sets.

a Naming Sets

To name the set of whole numbers less than 6, we can use the **roster method**, as follows: $\{0, 1, 2, 3, 4, 5\}$.

The set of real numbers x such that x is less than 6 cannot be named by listing all its members because there are infinitely many. We name such a set using **set-builder notation**, as follows: $\{x|x < 6\}$. This is read "The set of all x such that x is less than 6." See Section 2.7 for more on this notation.

Do Exercises 1 and 2.

Name each set using the roster method.

1. The set of whole numbers 0 through 7
2. $\{x|$ the square of x is $25\}$

b Set Membership and Subsets

The symbol $\in$ means **is a member of** or **belongs to**, or **is an element of**. Thus, $x \in A$ means x is a member of A or x belongs to A or x is an element of A.

EXAMPLE 1 Classify each of the following as true or false.

a) $1 \in \{1, 2, 3\}$
b) $1 \in \{2, 3\}$
c) $4 \in \{x|x \text{ is an even whole number}\}$
d) $5 \in \{x|x \text{ is an even whole number}\}$

a) Since 1 *is* listed as a member of the set, $1 \in \{1, 2, 3\}$ is true.
b) Since 1 *is not* a member of $\{2, 3\}$, the statement $1 \in \{2, 3\}$ is false.
c) Since 4 *is* an even whole number, $4 \in \{x|x \text{ is an even whole number}\}$ is a true statement.
d) Since 5 *is not* even, $5 \in \{x|x \text{ is an even whole number}\}$ is false.

Set membership can be illustrated with a diagram, as shown here.

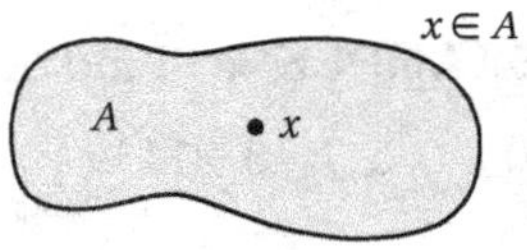

Do Exercises 3 and 4.

Determine whether each of the following is true or false.

3. $8 \in \{x|x \text{ is an even whole number}\}$
4. $2 \in \{x|x \text{ is a prime number}\}$

If every element of A is an element of B, then A is a **subset** of B. This is denoted $A \subseteq B$. The set of whole numbers is a subset of the set of integers. The set of rational numbers is a subset of the set of real numbers.

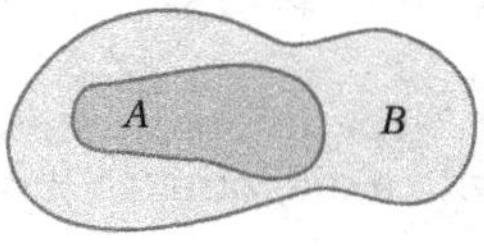

EXAMPLE 2 Classify each of the following as true or false.

a) $\{1, 2\} \subseteq \{1, 2, 3, 4\}$
b) $\{p, q, r, w\} \subseteq \{a, p, r, z\}$
c) $\{x|x < 6\} \subseteq \{x|x \leq 11\}$

a) Since every element of $\{1, 2\}$ is in the set $\{1, 2, 3, 4\}$, the statement $\{1, 2\} \subseteq \{1, 2, 3, 4\}$ is true.

Answers

1. $\{0, 1, 2, 3, 4, 5, 6, 7\}$ 2. $\{-5, 5\}$
3. True 4. True

b) Since $q \in \{p, q, r, w\}$, but $q \notin \{a, p, r, z\}$, the statement $\{p, q, r, w\} \subseteq \{a, p, r, z\}$ is false.

c) Since every number that is less than 6 is also less than or equal to 11, the statement $\{x|x < 6\} \subseteq \{x|x \le 11\}$ is true.

Do Exercises 5–7.

Determine whether each of the following is true or false.

5. $\{-2, -3, 4\} \subseteq \{-5, -4, -2, 7, -3, 5, 4\}$

6. $\{a, e, i, o, u\} \subseteq$ The set of all consonants

7. $\{x|x \le -8\} \subseteq \{x|x \le -7\}$

c Intersections and Unions

The **intersection** of sets A and B, denoted $A \cap B$, is the set of members that are common to both sets.

EXAMPLE 3 Find the intersection.

a) $\{0, 1, 3, 5, 25\} \cap \{2, 3, 4, 5, 6, 7, 9\}$ b) $\{a, p, q, w\} \cap \{p, q, t\}$

a) $\{0, 1, 3, 5, 25\} \cap \{2, 3, 4, 5, 6, 7, 9\} = \{3, 5\}$

b) $\{a, p, q, w\} \cap \{p, q, t\} = \{p, q\}$

Set intersection can be illustrated with a diagram, as shown here.

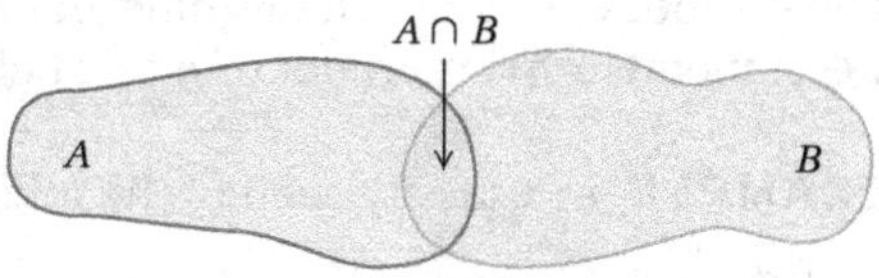

The set without members is known as the **empty set**, and is often named $\varnothing$, and sometimes $\{\ \}$. Each of the following is a description of the empty set:

$\{2, 3\} \cap \{5, 6, 7\}$;

$\{x|x \text{ is an even natural number}\} \cap \{x|x \text{ is an odd natural number}\}$.

Do Exercises 8–10.

Find the intersection.

8. $\{-2, -3, 4, -4, 8\} \cap \{-5, -4, -2, 7, -3, 5, 4\}$

9. $\{a, e, i, o, u\} \cap \{m, a, r, v, i, n\}$

10. $\{a, e, i, o, u\} \cap$ The set of all consonants

Two sets A and B can be combined to form a set that contains the members of A as well as those of B. The new set is called the **union** of A and B, denoted $A \cup B$.

EXAMPLE 4 Find the union.

a) $\{0, 5, 7, 13, 27\} \cup \{0, 2, 3, 4, 5\}$ b) $\{a, c, e, g\} \cup \{b, d, f\}$

a) $\{0, 5, 7, 13, 27\} \cup \{0, 2, 3, 4, 5\} = \{0, 2, 3, 4, 5, 7, 13, 27\}$

Note that the 0 and the 5 are *not* listed twice in the solution.

b) $\{a, c, e, g\} \cup \{b, d, f\} = \{a, b, c, d, e, f, g\}$

Set union can be illustrated with a diagram, as shown here.

$A \cup B$ is shaded.

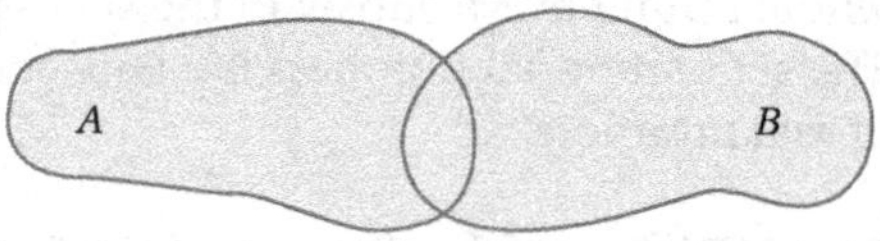

The solution set of the equation $(x - 3)(x + 2) = 0$ is $\{3, -2\}$. This set is the union of the solution sets of $x - 3 = 0$ and $x + 2 = 0$, which are $\{3\}$ and $\{-2\}$.

Do Exercises 11–13.

Find the union.

11. $\{-2, -3, 4, -4, 8\} \cup \{-5, -4, -2, 7, -3, 5, 4\}$

12. $\{a, e, i, o, u\} \cup \{m, a, r, v, i, n\}$

13. $\{a, e, i, o, u\} \cup$ The set of all consonants

Answers

5. True 6. False 7. True
8. $\{-2, -3, 4, -4\}$ 9. $\{a, i\}$
10. $\{\ \}$, or $\varnothing$ 11. $\{-2, -3, 4, -4, 8, -5, 7, 5\}$
12. $\{a, e, i, o, u, m, r, v, n\}$
13. $\{a, b, c, d, e, f, g, h, i, j, k, l, m, n, o, p, q, r, s, t, u, v, w, x, y, z\}$

Exercise Set

For Extra Help
MyMathLab
Math XL PRACTICE | WATCH | DOWNLOAD | READ | REVIEW

a Name each set using the roster method.

1. The set of whole numbers 3 through 8

2. The set of whole numbers 101 through 107

3. The set of odd numbers between 40 and 50

4. The set of multiples of 5 between 11 and 39

5. $\{x \mid \text{the square of } x \text{ is } 9\}$

6. $\{x \mid x \text{ is the cube of } 0.2\}$

b Classify each statement as true or false.

7. $2 \in \{x \mid x \text{ is an odd number}\}$

8. $7 \in \{x \mid x \text{ is an odd number}\}$

9. Kyle Busch $\in$ The set of all NASCAR drivers

10. Apple $\in$ The set of all fruit

11. $-3 \in \{-4, -3, 0, 1\}$

12. $0 \in \{-4, -3, 0, 1\}$

13. $\frac{2}{3} \in \{x \mid x \text{ is a rational number}\}$

14. Heads $\in$ The set of outcomes of flipping a penny

15. $\{4, 5, 8,\} \subseteq \{1, 3, 4, 5, 6, 7, 8, 9\}$

16. The set of vowels $\subseteq$ The set of consonants

17. $\{-1, -2, -3, -4, -5\} \subseteq \{-1, 2, 3, 4, 5\}$

18. The set of integers $\subseteq$ The set of rational numbers

c Find the intersection.

19. $\{a, b, c, d, e\} \cap \{c, d, e, f, g\}$

20. $\{a, e, i, o, u\} \cap \{q, u, i, c, k\}$

21. $\{1, 2, 5, 10\} \cap \{0, 1, 7, 10\}$

22. $\{0, 1, 7, 10\} \cap \{0, 1, 2, 5\}$

23. $\{1, 2, 5, 10\} \cap \{3, 4, 7, 8\}$

24. $\{\text{a, e, i, o, u}\} \cap \{\text{m, n, f, g, h}\}$

Find the union.

25. $\{\text{a, e, i, o, u}\} \cup \{\text{q, u, i, c, k}\}$

26. $\{\text{a, b, c, d, e}\} \cup \{\text{c, d, e, f, g}\}$

27. $\{0, 1, 7, 10\} \cup \{0, 1, 2, 5\}$

28. $\{1, 2, 5, 10\} \cup \{0, 1, 7, 10\}$

29. $\{\text{a, e, i, o, u}\} \cup \{\text{m, n, f, g, h}\}$

30. $\{1, 2, 5, 10\} \cup \{\text{a, b}\}$

Synthesis

31. Find the union of the set of integers and the set of whole numbers.

32. Find the intersection of the set of odd integers and the set of even integers.

33. Find the union of the set of rational numbers and the set of irrational numbers.

34. Find the intersection of the set of even integers and the set of positive rational numbers.

35. Find the intersection of the set of rational numbers and the set of irrational numbers.

36. Find the union of the set of negative integers, the set of positive integers, and the set containing 0.

37. For a set *A*, find each of the following.

a) $A \cup \varnothing$ **b)** $A \cup A$
c) $A \cap A$ **d)** $A \cap \varnothing$

38. A set is *closed* under an operation if, when the operation is performed on its members, the result is in the set. For example, the set of real numbers is closed under the operation of addition since the sum of any two real numbers is a real number.

a) Is the set of even numbers closed under addition?
b) Is the set of odd numbers closed under addition?
c) Is the set $\{0, 1\}$ closed under addition?
d) Is the set $\{0, 1\}$ closed under multiplication?
e) Is the set of real numbers closed under multiplication?
f) Is the set of integers closed under division?

39. Experiment with sets of various types and determine whether the following distributive law for sets is true:

$$A \cap (B \cup C) = (A \cap B) \cup (A \cap C).$$

Photo Credits

1, © George Steinmetz/Corbis **7,** Dr. Paulus Gerdes, Professor of Mathematics, Research Center for Mathematics, Culture, and Education. C. P. 915, maputo, Mozambique **28,** © Brand X/SuperStock **29 (left),** NASA **29 (right),** © James W. Porter/Corbis **31 (left),** © David Arky/Corbis **31 (right),** © Tom Grill/Corbis **47,** © George Steinmetz/Corbis **51,** © Jeffrey Markowitz/Sygma/Corbis **55,** © Roger Ressmeyer/CORBIS **58,** © Fancy/Veer/Corbis **72 (left),** Raymond Gehman/National Geographic/Getty Images **72 (right),** Melissa Farlow/National Geographic/Getty Images **81,** © Roger Ressmeyer/CORBIS **85,** Purestock/Getty Images **135,** Thinkstock/Getty Images **139,**© age fotostock/SuperStock **175,** © Glow Images/SuperStock **176,** Medioimages/Photodisc/ Getty Images **178 (left),** Jochen Sand, Digital Vision/Getty Images **178 (right),** © Don Mason/Blend Images/Corbis **179,** © Tetra Images/Tetra Images/Corbis **180 (left),** © Fancy/Veer/Corbis **180 (right),** © age fotostock/SuperStock **187,** Corbis/Jupiter Images **189,** AFP/Getty Images **190,** Visual Ideas/Camilo Morales/Jupiter Images **193 (left),** © age fotostock/SuperStock **193 (right),** © Photodisc/SuperStock **196,** © Glow Images/SuperStock **211,** © Aladdin Color, Inc./Corbis **214,** © Charles O'Rear/CORBIS **215,** Tetra Images/Jupiter Images **216 (left),** Copyright © A. Ramey/PhotoEd **216 (right),** © Mark Karrass/Corbis **222,** Rob Van Petten, Digital Vision/Getty Images **227,** © David Sailors/CORBIS **261,** Digital Vision/Getty Images **265 (left),** © David Sailors/ CORBIS **265 (right),** © D. Robert & Lorri Franz/CORBIS **266 (left),** Copyright © Jim West/PhotoEdit **266 (right),** © Photodisc/ SuperStock **298,** Federal Highway Administration and Washington Infrastructure Services, Inc. **306,** Peter Dazeley, Photographer's Choice/Getty Images **307,** © Larry W. Smith/epa/Corbis **320,** Francesca Yorke © Dorling Kindersley **321 (top),** NASA **321 (bottom),** Eyewire Collection **324 (left),** Phototake **324 (right),** Alfred Pasieka/Peter Arnold Inc. **326,** © Larry W. Smith/epa/Corbis **327 (left),** Copyright © Dennis MacDonald/PhotoEdit **327 (right),** NASA **328,** © Creatas/SuperStock **375,** Time&Life Pictures/ Getty Images **397,** © Stockbyte/SuperStock **430,** GSFC/NASA **462,** © SW Productions/Brand X/Corbis **465,** Fredrik Nyman, Johner Images Royalty-Free/Getty Images **468 (top),** Shaffer Smith Photo LLC/Jupiter Images **468 (bottom),** Jupiter Images **469 (left),** © Corbis **469 (right),** Hans Neleman, Taxi/Getty Images **483,** © age fotostock/SuperStock **502,** © Tetra Images/SuperStock **530,** Alamy Images **534,** Associated Press **535 (top),** Joel Sartore, National Geographic/Getty Images **535 (bottom),** Pacific Stock **536,** © age fotostock/SuperStock **541,** © Tim Pannell/Corbis **542 (left),** PEARSON STUDENT PHOTO ARCHIVE **542 (right),** Tom Turpin, Purdue University **543 (left),** © MATTHEW CAVANAUGH/epa/Corbis **543 (right),** © Noah K. Murray/Star Ledger/ Corbis **544,** Axiom Photographic Agency/Getty Images **554,** U. S. Mint **557,** Heather Charles/The Indianapolis Star **558,** PhotoEdit, Inc. **559 (left),** © Anthony West/Corbis **559 (right),** © Fancy/Veer/Corbis **562,** © Kevin Burke/Corbis **567 (left),** PhotoEdit, Inc. **567 (right),** PhotoLink/Getty Images **571,** Monty Rakusen/Jupiter Images **573,** © Alan Carey/Corbis **598,** Comstock/Getty Images **599,** Aurora/Getty Images **603,** PhotoEdit, Inc. **605 (left),** © Alan Carey/Corbis **605 (right),** PhotoEdit, Inc. **607 (top),** © Rick D'Elia/Corbis/Corbis **607 (bottom),** © Jeff Smith/Getty Images **609,** © Car Culture/Corbis **617,** Corbis/Bettmann **626,** © moodboard/Corbis **627,** © Fancy Collection/SuperStock **629,** Copyright © David Frazier/PhotoEdit **633 (left),** Photodisc/Getty Images **633 (right),** Copyright © Michael Newman/PhotoEdit **643,** Getty Images—Photodisc—Royalty Free **660,** © Steve Smith/ SuperStock **667,** National Geographic/Photolibrary.com **671,** LandWave Products, Inc. **674,** Indianapolis Museum of Art, Ann M. Stack Fund for Contemporary Art © Estate of Fred Sandback **685,** Frederick Mckinney/Getty Images **699,** David McNew/Staff/ Getty Images **722,** Johner Images Royalty-Free/Getty Images **723,** Image Source/Jupiter Images **739,** Doug Menuez/Photodisc/ Getty Images **741,** MedicalRF/The Medical File/Peter Arnold, Inc. **754 (left),** © Thinkstock/Corbis **754 (right),** © Design Pics/ SuperStock **774,** Copyright © Tom Carter/PhotoEdit **777 (left),** © George D. Lepp/CORBIS **777 (right),** © Markus Moellenberg/ zefa/Corbis

Answers

CHAPTER R

Exercise Set R.1, p. 6

1. 1, 2, 4, 5, 10, 20 **3.** 1, 2, 3, 4, 6, 8, 9, 12, 18, 24, 36, 72 **5.** $3 \cdot 5$ **7.** $2 \cdot 11$ **9.** $3 \cdot 3$ **11.** $7 \cdot 7$ **13.** $2 \cdot 3 \cdot 3$ **15.** $2 \cdot 2 \cdot 2 \cdot 5$ **17.** $2 \cdot 3 \cdot 3 \cdot 5$ **19.** $2 \cdot 3 \cdot 5 \cdot 7$ **21.** $7 \cdot 13$ **23.** $7 \cdot 17$ **25.** $2 \cdot 2$; 5; 20 **27.** $2 \cdot 2 \cdot 2 \cdot 3$; $2 \cdot 2 \cdot 3 \cdot 3$; 72 **29.** 3; $3 \cdot 5$; 15 **31.** $2 \cdot 3 \cdot 5$; $2 \cdot 2 \cdot 2 \cdot 5$; 120 **33.** 13; 23; 299 **35.** $2 \cdot 3 \cdot 3$; $2 \cdot 3 \cdot 5$; 90 **37.** $2 \cdot 3 \cdot 5$; $2 \cdot 2 \cdot 3 \cdot 3$; 180 **39.** $2 \cdot 2 \cdot 2 \cdot 3$; $2 \cdot 3 \cdot 5$; 120 **41.** $2 \cdot 2 \cdot 3$; $2 \cdot 3 \cdot 3$; 36 **43.** $2 \cdot 2 \cdot 3$; $2 \cdot 2 \cdot 7$; 84 **45.** 2; 3; 5; 30 **47.** $2 \cdot 2 \cdot 2 \cdot 3$; $2 \cdot 2 \cdot 3 \cdot 3$; $2 \cdot 2 \cdot 3$; 72 **49.** 5; $2 \cdot 2 \cdot 3$; $3 \cdot 5$; 60 **51.** $2 \cdot 3$; $2 \cdot 2 \cdot 3$; $2 \cdot 3 \cdot 3$; 36 **53.** Every 60 yr **55.** Every 420 yr **57.** 30 strands **59.** **(a)** No; not a multiple of 8; **(b)** no; it is a multiple of both 8 and 12, but it is not the least common multiple; **(c)** no; not a multiple of 8 or 12; **(d)** yes; it is a multiple of both 8 and 12 and is the smallest such multiple. **61.** 70,200

Calculator Corner, p. 15

1. $\frac{41}{24}$ **2.** $\frac{27}{112}$ **3.** $\frac{35}{16}$ **4.** $\frac{3}{10}$

Exercise Set R.2, p. 16

1. $\frac{9}{12}$ **3.** $\frac{60}{100}$ **5.** $\frac{104}{160}$ **7.** $\frac{21}{24}$ **9.** $\frac{20}{16}$ **11.** $\frac{391}{437}$ **13.** $\frac{2}{3}$ **15.** 4 **17.** $\frac{1}{7}$ **19.** 8 **21.** $\frac{1}{4}$ **23.** 5 **25.** $\frac{17}{21}$ **27.** $\frac{13}{7}$ **29.** $\frac{4}{3}$ **31.** $\frac{1}{12}$ **33.** $\frac{45}{16}$ **35.** $\frac{2}{3}$ **37.** $\frac{7}{6}$ **39.** $\frac{5}{6}$ **41.** $\frac{13}{20}$ **43.** $\frac{1}{2}$ **45.** $\frac{13}{24}$ **47.** $\frac{31}{60}$ **49.** $\frac{35}{18}$ **51.** $\frac{10}{3}$ **53.** $\frac{1}{2}$ **55.** $\frac{5}{36}$ **57.** 500 **59.** $\frac{3}{40}$ **61.** $\frac{99,999}{100}$ **63.** 900 **65.** $2 \cdot 2 \cdot 7$ **66.** $2 \cdot 2 \cdot 2 \cdot 7$ **67.** $2 \cdot 2 \cdot 2 \cdot 5 \cdot 5 \cdot 5$ **68.** $2 \cdot 2 \cdot 2 \cdot 2 \cdot 2 \cdot 2 \cdot 3$ **69.** $3 \cdot 23 \cdot 29$ **70.** 126 **71.** 48 **72.** 392 **73.** 192 **74.** 150 **75.** $\frac{3}{4}$ **77.** 4 **79.** 1

Calculator Corner, p. 21

1. 40.42 **2.** 3.33 **3.** 0.69324 **4.** 2.38

Exercise Set R.3, p. 24

1. $\frac{53}{10}$ **3.** $\frac{67}{100}$ **5.** $\frac{20,007}{10,000}$ **7.** $\frac{78,898}{10}$ **9.** 0.1 **11.** 0.0001 **13.** 9.999 **15.** 0.4578 **17.** 444.94 **19.** 390.617 **21.** 155.724 **23.** 63.79 **25.** 32.234 **27.** 26.835 **29.** 47.91 **31.** 1.9193 **33.** 13.212 **35.** 0.7998 **37.** 179.5 **39.** 1.40756 **41.** 3.60558 **43.** 2.3 **45.** 5.2 **47.** 0.023 **49.** 18.75 **51.** 660 **53.** 0.68 **55.** 0.34375 **57.** $1.\overline{18}$ **59.** $0.\overline{5}$ **61.** $2.\overline{1}$ **63.** 745.07; 745.1; 745; 750; 700 **65.** 6780.51; 6780.5; 6781; 6780; 6800 **67.** \$17.99; \$18 **69.** \$346.08; \$346 **71.** \$17 **73.** \$190 **75.** 0.2857; 0.286; 0.29; 0.3; 0 **77.** 0.5897; 0.590; 0.59; 0.6; 1 **79.** $\frac{33}{32}$ **80.** $\frac{1}{48}$ **81.** $\frac{55}{64}$ **82.** $\frac{5}{4}$ **83.** $\frac{139}{210}$ **84.** $\frac{449}{336}$ **85.** $\frac{1023}{1000}$ **86.** $\frac{259}{210}$, or $\frac{37}{30}$ **87.** $2 \cdot 2 \cdot 2 \cdot 2 \cdot 13$ **88.** $2 \cdot 2 \cdot 2 \cdot 2 \cdot 2 \cdot 2 \cdot 2$ **89.** $2 \cdot 5 \cdot 5 \cdot 5 \cdot 5$ **90.** $2 \cdot 2 \cdot 2 \cdot 2 \cdot 2 \cdot 2 \cdot 2 \cdot 2 \cdot 2 \cdot 5$ **91.** $0.\overline{714285}$ **93.** $0.6\overline{428571}$

Exercise Set R.4, p. 29

1. 0.13 **3.** 0.351; 0.2 **5.** 0.63 **7.** 0.941 **9.** 0.01 **11.** 0.0061 **13.** 2.4 **15.** 0.0325 **17.** $\frac{39}{100}$ **19.** $\frac{105}{1000}$ **21.** $\frac{88}{100}$ **23.** $\frac{60}{100}$ **25.** $\frac{289}{1000}$ **27.** $\frac{110}{100}$ **29.** $\frac{42}{100,000}$ **31.** $\frac{250}{100}$ **33.** $\frac{347}{10,000}$ **35.** 10.7% **37.** 14% **39.** 99% **41.** 100% **43.** 0.47% **45.** 7.2% **47.** 920% **49.** 0.68% **51.** $16.\overline{6}\%$, or $16\frac{2}{3}\%$ **53.** 65% **55.** 29% **57.** 80% **59.** 60% **61.** $66.\overline{6}\%$, or $66\frac{2}{3}\%$ **63.** 175% **65.** 75% **67.** 40% **69.** 0.04; $\frac{4}{100}$, or $\frac{1}{25}$ **71.** $\frac{69}{100}$; 69% **73.** 0.49; 49% **75.** 0.36; $\frac{36}{100}$, or $\frac{9}{25}$ **77.** 2.25 **78.** $1.\overline{54}$ **79.** 164.90974 **80.** 56.43 **81.** 32% **83.** 70% **85.** 105% **87.** 345% **89.** 2.5%

Calculator Corner, p. 33

1. 40,353,607 **2.** 10.4976 **3.** 12,812.904 **4.** $\frac{64}{729}$

Calculator Corner, p. 34

1. 81 **2.** 2 **3.** 5932 **4.** 743.027 **5.** 783 **6.** 228,112.96

Exercise Set R.5, p. 35

1. 5^4 **3.** 10^3 **5.** 10^6 **7.** 49 **9.** 59,049 **11.** 100 **13.** 1 **15.** 5.29 **17.** 0.008 **19.** 416.16 **21.** $\frac{9}{64}$ **23.** 125 **25.** 1061.208 **27.** 25 **29.** 114 **31.** 33 **33.** 5 **35.** 12 **37.** 324 **39.** 100 **41.** 1000 **43.** 22 **45.** 1 **47.** 4 **49.** 102 **51.** 96 **53.** 24 **55.** 90 **57.** 8 **59.** 1 **61.** 50,000 **63.** 5 **65.** 27 **67.** $\frac{22}{45}$ **69.** $\frac{19}{66}$ **71.** 9 **73.** 31.25% **74.** $183.\overline{3}\%$, or $183\frac{1}{3}\%$ **75.** $\frac{3}{667}$ **76.** $\frac{401}{728}$ **77.** $2 \cdot 2 \cdot 2 \cdot 2 \cdot 3$ **78.** 168 **79.** 10^2 **81.** 5^6

83. $3 = \dfrac{5+5}{5} + \dfrac{5}{5}$; $4 = \dfrac{5+5+5+5}{5}$; $5 = \dfrac{5(5+5)}{5} - 5$;

$6 = \dfrac{5}{5} + \dfrac{5 \cdot 5}{5}$; $7 = \dfrac{5}{5} + \dfrac{5}{5} + 5$; $8 = 5 + \dfrac{5+5+5}{5}$;

$9 = \dfrac{5 \cdot 5 - 5}{5} + 5$; $10 = \dfrac{5 \cdot 5 + 5 \cdot 5}{5}$

Summary and Review: Chapter R, p. 37

Concept Reinforcement

1. True **2.** False **3.** True

Review Exercises

1. $2 \cdot 2 \cdot 23$ **2.** $2 \cdot 2 \cdot 2 \cdot 5 \cdot 5 \cdot 7$ **3.** 416 **4.** 90 **5.** $\frac{12}{30}$

6. $\frac{96}{184}$ **7.** $\frac{40}{64}$ **8.** $\frac{91}{84}$ **9.** $\frac{5}{12}$ **10.** $\frac{51}{91}$ **11.** $\frac{31}{36}$ **12.** $\frac{1}{4}$ **13.** $\frac{3}{5}$
14. $\frac{72}{25}$ **15.** $\frac{205}{144}$ **16.** $\frac{139}{72}$ **17.** $\frac{101}{54}$ **18.** $\frac{109}{84}$ **19.** $\frac{13}{72}$
20. $\frac{29}{144}$ **21.** $\frac{1}{12}$ **22.** $\frac{23}{90}$ **23.** $\frac{1797}{100}$ **24.** 0.2337
25. 2442.905 **26.** 86.0298 **27.** 9.342 **28.** 133.264
29. 430.8 **30.** 110.483 **31.** 55.6 **32.** 0.45 **33.** $1.58\overline{3}$
34. 34.1 **35.** 0.142 **36.** 5.02% **37.** $\frac{357}{1000}$ **38.** 39.6%
39. 62.5%, or $62\frac{1}{2}\%$ **40.** 116% **41.** 6^3 **42.** 1.1236
43. 119 **44.** 4 **45.** 29 **46.** 1 **47.** 7 **48.** 64 **49.** $\frac{103}{17}$

Test: Chapter R, p. 40

1. [R.1a] $2 \cdot 2 \cdot 3 \cdot 5 \cdot 5$ **2.** [R.1b] 120 **3.** [R.2a] $\frac{21}{49}$
4. [R.2a] $\frac{33}{48}$ **5.** [R.2b] $\frac{2}{3}$ **6.** [R.2b] $\frac{37}{61}$ **7.** [R.2c] $\frac{5}{36}$
8. [R.2c] $\frac{11}{40}$ **9.** [R.2c] $\frac{67}{36}$ **10.** [R.2c] $\frac{5}{36}$ **11.** [R.3a] $\frac{678}{100}$
12. [R.3a] 1.895 **13.** [R.3b] 99.0187 **14.** [R.3b] 1796.58
15. [R.3b] 435.072 **16.** [R.3b] 1.6 **17.** [R.3b] $2.\overline{09}$
18. [R.3c] 234.7 **19.** [R.3c] 234.728 **20.** [R.4a] 0.007
21. [R.4b] $\frac{91}{100}$ **22.** [R.4d] 44% **23.** [R.5b] 625
24. [R.5b] 1.44 **25.** [R.5c] 242 **26.** [R.5c] 20,000
27. [R.4a] 0.054 **28.** [R.4d] 1.2%

CHAPTER 1

Exercise Set 1.1, p. 46

1. 32 min; 69 min; 81 min **3.** $1935\ m^2$ **5.** 260 mi
7. $24\ ft^2$ **9.** 56 **11.** 8 **13.** 1 **15.** 6 **17.** 2
19. $b + 7$, or $7 + b$ **21.** $c - 12$ **23.** $q + 4$, or $4 + q$
25. $a + b$, or $b + a$ **27.** $x \div y$, or $\frac{x}{y}$, or x/y, or $x \cdot \frac{1}{y}$
29. $x + w$, or $w + x$ **31.** $n - m$ **33.** $x + y$, or $y + x$
35. $2z$ **37.** $3m$ **39.** $4a + 6$, or $6 + 4a$ **41.** $xy - 8$
43. $2t - 5$ **45.** $3n + 11$, or $11 + 3n$ **47.** $4x + 3y$, or $3y + 4x$ **49.** 89%s, or 0.89s, where s is the salary
51. $s + 0.05s$ **53.** $65t$ miles **55.** $\$50 - x$ **57.** $\$8.50n$
59. $2 \cdot 3 \cdot 3 \cdot 3$ **60.** $2 \cdot 2 \cdot 2 \cdot 2 \cdot 2$ **61.** $2 \cdot 2 \cdot 3 \cdot 3 \cdot 3$
62. $2 \cdot 2 \cdot 2 \cdot 2 \cdot 2 \cdot 2 \cdot 3$ **63.** $3 \cdot 11 \cdot 31$ **64.** 18
65. 96 **66.** 60 **67.** 96 **68.** 396 **69.** $\frac{1}{4}$ **71.** 0

Calculator Corner, p. 53

1. 8.717797887 **2.** 17.80449381 **3.** 67.08203932
4. 35.4807407 **5.** 3.141592654 **6.** 91.10618695
7. 530.9291585 **8.** 138.8663978

Calculator Corner, p. 54

1. −0.75 **2.** −0.45 **3.** −0.125 **4.** −1.8 **5.** −0.675
6. −0.6875 **7.** −3.5 **8.** −0.76

Calculator Corner, p. 56

1. 5 **2.** 17 **3.** 0 **4.** 6.48 **5.** 12.7 **6.** 0.9 **7.** $\frac{5}{7}$ **8.** $\frac{4}{3}$

Exercise Set 1.2, p. 58

1. −282 **3.** 24; −2 **5.** 3,600,000,000; −460
7. Alley Cats: −34; Strikers: 34
9.
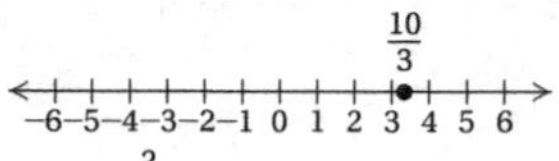

11.
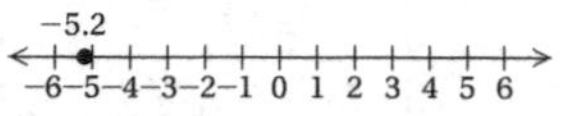

13.
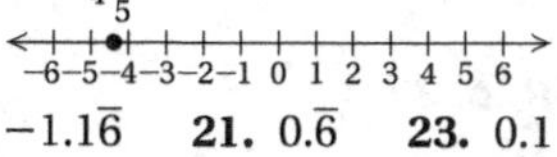

15. −0.875 **17.** $0.8\overline{3}$
19. $-1.1\overline{6}$ **21.** $0.\overline{6}$ **23.** 0.1 **25.** −0.5 **27.** 0.16
29. > **31.** < **33.** < **35.** < **37.** > **39.** < **41.** >
43. < **45.** < **47.** > **49.** < **51.** < **53.** $x < -6$
55. $y \geq -10$ **57.** False **59.** True **61.** True
63. False **65.** 3 **67.** 10 **69.** 0 **71.** 30.4 **73.** $\frac{2}{3}$
75. 0 **77.** 2.65 **79.** $7\frac{4}{5}$ **80.** 0.238 **81.** 0.63
82. 0.2276 **83.** 1.1 **84.** 125% **85.** 52% **86.** 59.375%, or $59\frac{3}{8}\%$ **87.** $83.\overline{3}\%$, or $83\frac{1}{3}\%$ **89.** $-\frac{2}{3}, -\frac{2}{5}, -\frac{1}{3}, -\frac{2}{7}, -\frac{1}{7}, \frac{1}{3}, \frac{2}{5}, \frac{2}{3}, \frac{9}{8}$
91. $-100, -8\frac{7}{8}, -8\frac{5}{8}, -\frac{67}{8}, -5, 0, 1^7, |3|, \frac{14}{4}, 4, |-6|, 7^1$ **93.** $\frac{1}{1}$

Exercise Set 1.3, p. 66

1. −7 **3.** −6 **5.** 0 **7.** −8 **9.** −7 **11.** −27
13. 0 **15.** −42 **17.** 0 **19.** 0 **21.** 3 **23.** −9
25. 7 **27.** 0 **29.** 35 **31.** −3.8 **33.** −8.1 **35.** $-\frac{1}{5}$
37. $-\frac{7}{9}$ **39.** $-\frac{3}{8}$ **41.** $-\frac{19}{24}$ **43.** $\frac{1}{24}$ **45.** $\frac{8}{15}$ **47.** $\frac{16}{45}$
49. 37 **51.** 50 **53.** −1409 **55.** −24 **57.** 26.9
59. −8 **61.** $\frac{13}{8}$ **63.** −43 **65.** $\frac{4}{3}$ **67.** 24 **69.** $\frac{3}{8}$
71. 13,796 ft **73.** −3°F **75.** −$20,300 **77.** He owes $85.
79. 0.713 **80.** 0.92875 **81.** 12.5% **82.** 40.625% **83.** $\frac{8}{5}$
84. $\frac{1}{4}$ **85.** All positive numbers **87.** B

Exercise Set 1.4, p. 72

1. −7 **3.** −6 **5.** 0 **7.** −4 **9.** −7 **11.** −6 **13.** 0
15. 14 **17.** 11 **19.** −14 **21.** 5 **23.** −1 **25.** 18
27. −3 **29.** −21 **31.** 5 **33.** −8 **35.** 12 **37.** −23
39. −68 **41.** −73 **43.** 116 **45.** 0 **47.** −1 **49.** $\frac{1}{12}$
51. $-\frac{17}{12}$ **53.** $\frac{1}{8}$ **55.** 19.9 **57.** −8.6 **59.** −0.01
61. −193 **63.** 500 **65.** −2.8 **67.** −3.53 **69.** $-\frac{1}{2}$
71. $\frac{6}{7}$ **73.** $-\frac{41}{30}$ **75.** $-\frac{2}{15}$ **77.** $-\frac{1}{48}$ **79.** $-\frac{43}{60}$ **81.** 37
83. −62 **85.** −139 **87.** 6 **89.** 108.5 **91.** $\frac{1}{4}$
93. 2319 m **95.** $347.94 **97.** 5676 ft **99.** 381 ft
101. 1130°F **103.** 100.5 **104.** 226 **105.** 13
106. 50 **107.** $\frac{11}{12}$ **108.** $\frac{41}{64}$ **109.** False; $3 - 0 \neq 0 - 3$
111. True **113.** True

Mid-Chapter Review: Chapter 1, p. 76

1. True **2.** False **3.** True **4.** False
5. $-x = -(-4) = 4$;
$-(-x) = -(-(-4)) = -(4) = -4$
6. $5 - 13 = 5 + (-13) = -8$ **7.** $-6 - 7 = -6 + (-7) = -13$
8. 4 **9.** 11 **10.** $3y$ **11.** $n - 5$ **12.** 450; −79
13.
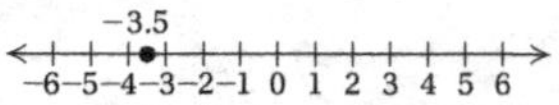

14. −0.8 **15.** $2.\overline{3}$ **16.** <
17. > **18.** False **19.** True **20.** $5 > y$ **21.** $t \leq -3$
22. 15.6 **23.** 18 **24.** 0 **25.** $\frac{12}{5}$ **26.** 5.6 **27.** $-\frac{7}{4}$
28. 0 **29.** 49 **30.** 19 **31.** 2.3 **32.** −2 **33.** $-\frac{1}{8}$
34. 0 **35.** −17 **36.** $-\frac{11}{24}$ **37.** −8.1 **38.** −9 **39.** −2
40. −10.4 **41.** 16 **42.** $\frac{7}{20}$ **43.** −12 **44.** −4 **45.** $-\frac{4}{3}$
46. −1.8 **47.** 13 **48.** 9 **49.** −23 **50.** 75 **51.** 14
52. 33°C **53.** $54.80 **54.** Answers may vary. Three examples are $\frac{6}{13}$, −23.8, and $\frac{43}{5}$. These are rational numbers because they can be named in the form $\frac{a}{b}$, where a and b are integers and b is not 0. They are not integers, however, because they are neither whole numbers nor the opposites of whole numbers. **55.** Answers may vary. Three examples are π, $-\sqrt{7}$, and 0.31311311131111. . . . Irrational numbers cannot be written as the quotient of two integers. Real numbers that are not rational are irrational. Decimal notation for rational numbers either terminates or repeats. Decimal notation for irrational numbers neither terminates nor repeats. **56.** Answers may vary. If we think of the addition on the number line, we start at 0, move to the left to a negative number, and then move to the left again. This always brings us to a point on the negative portion of the number line. **57.** Yes; consider $m - (-n)$, where both m and n are positive. Then $m - (-n) = m + n$. Now $m + n$, the sum of two positive numbers, is positive.

Exercise Set 1.5, p. 82

1. -8 **3.** -48 **5.** -24 **7.** -72 **9.** 16 **11.** 42 **13.** -120 **15.** -238 **17.** 1200 **19.** 98 **21.** -72 **23.** -12.4 **25.** 30 **27.** 21.7 **29.** $-\frac{2}{5}$ **31.** $\frac{1}{12}$ **33.** -17.01 **35.** $-\frac{5}{12}$ **37.** 420 **39.** $\frac{2}{7}$ **41.** -60 **43.** 150 **45.** $-\frac{2}{45}$ **47.** 1911 **49.** 50.4 **51.** $\frac{10}{189}$ **53.** -960 **55.** 17.64 **57.** $-\frac{5}{784}$ **59.** 0 **61.** -720 **63.** $-30{,}240$ **65.** 1 **67.** $16, -16; 16, -16$ **69.** $441; -147$ **71.** 20; 20 **73.** $-2; 2$ **75.** -20 lb **77.** -54°C **79.** \$12.71 **81.** -32 m **83.** 38°F **85.** 180 **86.** $2 \cdot 2 \cdot 2 \cdot 2 \cdot 2 \cdot 2 \cdot 2 \cdot 2 \cdot 2 \cdot 3 \cdot 3$ **87.** $\frac{2}{3}$ **88.** $\frac{8}{9}$ **89.** $\frac{6}{11}$ **90.** $\frac{41}{265}$ **91.** $\frac{11}{32}$ **92.** $\frac{37}{67}$ **93.** $\frac{1}{24}$ **94.** 6 **95.** A **97.**

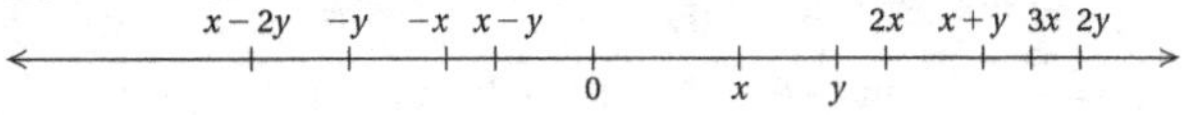

Calculator Corner, p. 90

1. -4 **2.** -0.3 **3.** -12 **4.** -9.5 **5.** -12 **6.** 2.7 **7.** -2 **8.** -5.7 **9.** -32 **10.** -1.8 **11.** 35 **12.** 14.44 **13.** -2 **14.** -0.8 **15.** 1.4 **16.** 4

Exercise Set 1.6, p. 91

1. -8 **3.** -14 **5.** -3 **7.** 3 **9.** -8 **11.** 2 **13.** -12 **15.** -8 **17.** Not defined **19.** 0 **21.** $\frac{7}{15}$ **23.** $-\frac{13}{47}$ **25.** $\frac{1}{13}$ **27.** $-\frac{1}{32}$ **29.** -7.1 **31.** 9 **33.** $4y$ **35.** $\frac{3b}{2a}$ **37.** $4 \cdot \left(\frac{1}{17}\right)$ **39.** $8 \cdot \left(-\frac{1}{13}\right)$ **41.** $13.9 \cdot \left(-\frac{1}{1.5}\right)$ **43.** $\frac{2}{3} \cdot \left(-\frac{5}{4}\right)$ **45.** $x \cdot y$ **47.** $(3x + 4)\left(\frac{1}{5}\right)$ **49.** $-\frac{9}{8}$ **51.** $\frac{5}{3}$ **53.** $\frac{9}{14}$ **55.** $\frac{9}{64}$ **57.** $-\frac{5}{4}$ **59.** $-\frac{27}{5}$ **61.** $\frac{11}{13}$ **63.** -2 **65.** -16.2 **67.** -2.5 **69.** -1.25 **71.** Not defined **73.** 23.5% **75.** -3.3% **77.** 33 **78.** 129 **79.** 1 **80.** 1296 **81.** $\frac{22}{39}$ **82.** 0.477 **83.** 87.5% **84.** $\frac{2}{3}$ **85.** $\frac{9}{8}$ **86.** $\frac{128}{625}$ **87.** $\frac{1}{-10.5}$; -10.5, the reciprocal of the reciprocal is the original number. **89.** Negative **91.** Positive **93.** Negative

Exercise Set 1.7, p. 103

1. $\frac{3y}{5y}$ **3.** $\frac{10x}{15x}$ **5.** $\frac{2x}{x^2}$ **7.** $-\frac{3}{2}$ **9.** $-\frac{7}{6}$ **11.** $\frac{4s}{3}$ **13.** $8 + y$ **15.** nm **17.** $xy + 9$, or $9 + yx$ **19.** $c + ab$, or $ba + c$ **21.** $(a + b) + 2$ **23.** $8(xy)$ **25.** $a + (b + 3)$ **27.** $(3a)b$ **29.** $2 + (b + a), (2 + a) + b, (b + 2) + a$; answers may vary **31.** $(5 + w) + v, (v + 5) + w, (w + v) + 5$; answers may vary **33.** $(3x)y, y(x \cdot 3), 3(yx)$; answers may vary **35.** $a(7b), b(7a), (7b)a$; answers may vary **37.** $2b + 10$ **39.** $7 + 7t$ **41.** $30x + 12$ **43.** $7x + 28 + 42y$ **45.** $7x - 21$ **47.** $-3x + 21$ **49.** $\frac{2}{3}b - 4$ **51.** $7.3x - 14.6$ **53.** $-\frac{3}{5}x + \frac{3}{5}y - 6$ **55.** $45x + 54y - 72$ **57.** $-4x + 12y + 8z$ **59.** $-3.72x + 9.92y - 3.41$ **61.** $4x, 3z$ **63.** $7x, 8y, -9z$ **65.** $2(x + 2)$ **67.** $5(6 + y)$ **69.** $7(2x + 3y)$ **71.** $7(2t - 1)$ **73.** $8(x - 3)$ **75.** $6(3a - 4b)$ **77.** $-4(y - 8)$, or $4(-y + 8)$ **79.** $5(x + 2 + 3y)$ **81.** $8(2m - 4n + 1)$ **83.** $4(3a + b - 6)$ **85.** $2(4x + 5y - 11)$ **87.** $a(x - 1)$ **89.** $a(x - y - z)$ **91.** $-6(3x - 2y - 1)$, or $6(-3x + 2y + 1)$ **93.** $\frac{1}{3}(2x - 5y + 1)$ **95.** $6(6x - y + 3z)$ **97.** $19a$ **99.** $9a$ **101.** $8x + 9z$ **103.** $7x + 15y^2$ **105.** $-19a + 88$ **107.** $4t + 6y - 4$ **109.** b **111.** $\frac{13}{4}y$ **113.** $8x$ **115.** $5n$ **117.** $-16y$ **119.** $17a - 12b - 1$ **121.** $4x + 2y$ **123.** $7x + y$ **125.** $0.8x + 0.5y$ **127.** $\frac{35}{6}a + \frac{3}{2}b - 42$ **129.** 144 **130.** 72 **131.** 144 **132.** 60 **133.** 32 **134.** 72 **135.** 90 **136.** 108 **137.** $\frac{89}{48}$ **138.** $\frac{5}{24}$ **139.** $-\frac{5}{24}$ **140.** 30% **141.** Not equivalent; $3 \cdot 2 + 5 \neq 3 \cdot 5 + 2$ **143.** Equivalent; commutative law of addition **145.** $q(1 + r + rs + rst)$

Calculator Corner, p. 112

1. -11 **2.** 9 **3.** 114 **4.** 117,649 **5.** $-1{,}419{,}857$ **6.** $-1{,}124{,}864$ **7.** $-117{,}649$ **8.** $-1{,}419{,}857$ **9.** $-1{,}124{,}864$ **10.** -4 **11.** -2 **12.** 787

Exercise Set 1.8, p. 113

1. $-2x - 7$ **3.** $-8 + x$ **5.** $-4a + 3b - 7c$ **7.** $-6x + 8y - 5$ **9.** $-3x + 5y + 6$ **11.** $8x + 6y + 43$ **13.** $5x - 3$ **15.** $-3a + 9$ **17.** $5x - 6$ **19.** $-19x + 2y$ **21.** $9y - 25z$ **23.** $-7x + 10y$ **25.** $37a - 23b + 35c$ **27.** 7 **29.** -40 **31.** 19 **33.** $12x + 30$ **35.** $3x + 30$ **37.** $9x - 18$ **39.** $-4x - 64$ **41.** -7 **43.** -7 **45.** -16 **47.** -334 **49.** 14 **51.** 1880 **53.** 12 **55.** 8 **57.** -86 **59.** 37 **61.** -1 **63.** -10 **65.** -67 **67.** -7988 **69.** -3000 **71.** 60 **73.** 1 **75.** 10 **77.** $-\frac{13}{45}$ **79.** $-\frac{23}{18}$ **81.** -122 **83.** Integers **84.** Additive inverses **85.** Commutative law **86.** Identity property of 1 **87.** Associative law **88.** Associative law **89.** Multiplicative inverses **90.** Identity property of 0 **91.** $6y - (-2x + 3a - c)$ **93.** $6m - (-3n + 5m - 4b)$ **95.** $-2x - f$ **97. (a)** 52; 52; 28.130169; **(b)** -24; -24; -108.307025 **99.** -6

Summary and Review: Chapter 1, p. 117

Concept Reinforcement

1. True **2.** True **3.** False **4.** False

Important Concepts

1. 14 **2.** $<$ **3.** $\frac{5}{4}$ **4.** -8.5 **5.** -2 **6.** 56 **7.** -8 **8.** $\frac{9}{20}$ **9.** $\frac{5}{3}$ **10.** $5x + 15y - 20z$ **11.** $9(3x + y - 4z)$ **12.** $5a - 2b$ **13.** $4a - 4b$ **14.** -2

Review Exercises

1. 4 **2.** $19\%x$, or $0.19x$ **3.** $-45, 72$ **4.** 38 **5.** 126 **6.**

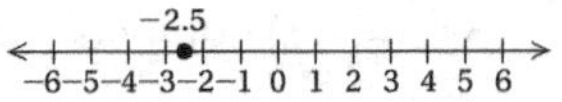

7.

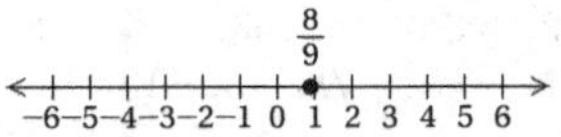

8. $<$ **9.** $>$ **10.** $>$ **11.** $<$ **12.** $x > -3$ **13.** True **14.** False **15.** -3.8 **16.** $\frac{3}{4}$ **17.** $\frac{8}{3}$ **18.** $-\frac{1}{7}$ **19.** 34 **20.** 5 **21.** -3 **22.** -4 **23.** -5 **24.** 1 **25.** $-\frac{7}{5}$ **26.** -7.9 **27.** 54 **28.** -9.18 **29.** $-\frac{2}{7}$ **30.** -210 **31.** -7 **32.** -3 **33.** $\frac{3}{4}$ **34.** 40.4 **35.** -2 **36.** 2 **37.** -2 **38.** 8-yd gain **39.** $-\$130$ **40.** \$4.64 **41.** \$18.95 **42.** $15x - 35$ **43.** $-8x + 10$ **44.** $4x + 15$ **45.** $-24 + 48x$ **46.** $2(x - 7)$ **47.** $-6(x - 1)$, or $6(-x + 1)$ **48.** $5(x + 2)$ **49.** $-3(x - 4y + 4)$, or $3(-x + 4y - 4)$ **50.** $7a - 3b$ **51.** $-2x + 5y$ **52.** $5x - y$ **53.** $-a + 8b$ **54.** $-3a + 9$ **55.** $-2b + 21$ **56.** 6 **57.** $12y - 34$ **58.** $5x + 24$ **59.** $-15x + 25$ **60.** D **61.** B **62.** $-\frac{5}{8}$ **63.** -2.1 **64.** 1000 **65.** $4a + 2b$

Understanding Through Discussion and Writing

1. The sum of each pair of opposites such as -50 and 50, -49 and 49, and so on is 0. The sum of these sums and the remaining integer, 0, is 0. **2.** The product of an even number of negative numbers is positive, and the product of an odd number of negative numbers is negative. Now $(-7)^8$ is the product of 8 factors of -7 so it is positive, and $(-7)^{11}$ is the product of 11 factors of -7 so it is negative. **3.** Consider $\frac{a}{b} = q$, where a and b are both negative numbers. Then $q \cdot b = a$, so q must be a positive number in order for the product to be negative. **4.** Consider $\frac{a}{b} = q$, where a is a negative number and b is a positive number. Then $q \cdot b = a$, so q must be a negative number in order for the product to be negative. **5.** We use the distributive law when we collect like terms even though we might not always write this step. **6.** Jake expects the calculator to multiply 2 and 3 first and then divide 18 by that product. This procedure does not follow the rules for order of operations.

Test: Chapter 1, p. 123

1. [1.1a] 6 **2.** [1.1b] $x - 9$ **3.** [1.2d] $>$ **4.** [1.2d] $<$ **5.** [1.2d] $>$ **6.** [1.2d] $-2 > x$ **7.** [1.2d] True **8.** [1.2e] 7 **9.** [1.2e] $\frac{9}{4}$ **10.** [1.2e] 2.7 **11.** [1.3b] $-\frac{2}{3}$ **12.** [1.3b] 1.4 **13.** [1.6b] $-\frac{1}{2}$ **14.** [1.6b] $\frac{7}{4}$ **15.** [1.3b] 8 **16.** [1.4a] 7.8 **17.** [1.3a] -8 **18.** [1.3a] $\frac{7}{40}$ **19.** [1.4a] 10 **20.** [1.4a] -2.5 **21.** [1.4a] $\frac{7}{8}$ **22.** [1.5a] -48 **23.** [1.5a] $\frac{3}{16}$ **24.** [1.6a] -9 **25.** [1.6c] $\frac{3}{4}$ **26.** [1.6c] -9.728 **27.** [1.8d] -173 **28.** [1.8d] -5 **29.** [1.3c], [1.4b] Up 15 points **30.** [1.4b] 14°F **31.** [1.5b] 16,080 **32.** [1.6d] -0.75°C each minute **33.** [1.7c] $18 - 3x$ **34.** [1.7c] $-5y + 5$ **35.** [1.7d] $2(6 - 11x)$ **36.** [1.7d] $7(x + 3 + 2y)$ **37.** [1.4a] 12 **38.** [1.8b] $2x + 7$ **39.** [1.8b] $9a - 12b - 7$ **40.** [1.8c] $68y - 8$ **41.** [1.8d] -4 **42.** [1.8d] 448 **43.** [1.2d] B **44.** [1.2e], [1.8d] 15 **45.** [1.8c] $4a$ **46.** [R.6a], [1.7e] $4x + 4y$

CHAPTER 2

Exercise Set 2.1, p. 130

1. Yes **3.** No **5.** No **7.** Yes **9.** Yes **11.** No **13.** 4 **15.** -20 **17.** -14 **19.** -18 **21.** 15 **23.** -14 **25.** 2 **27.** 20 **29.** -6 **31.** $6\frac{1}{2}$ **33.** 19.9 **35.** $\frac{7}{3}$ **37.** $-\frac{7}{4}$ **39.** $\frac{41}{24}$ **41.** $-\frac{1}{20}$ **43.** 5.1 **45.** 12.4 **47.** -5 **49.** $1\frac{5}{6}$ **51.** $-\frac{10}{21}$ **53.** -11 **54.** 5 **55.** $-\frac{5}{12}$ **56.** $\frac{1}{3}$ **57.** $-\frac{3}{2}$ **58.** -5.2 **59.** $-\frac{1}{24}$ **60.** 172.72 **61.** $\$83 - x$ **62.** $65t$ miles **63.** 342.246 **65.** $-\frac{26}{15}$ **67.** -10 **69.** All real numbers **71.** $-\frac{5}{17}$ **73.** $13, -13$

Exercise Set 2.2, p. 136

1. 6 **3.** 9 **5.** 12 **7.** -40 **9.** 1 **11.** -7 **13.** -6 **15.** 6 **17.** -63 **19.** -48 **21.** 36 **23.** -9 **25.** -21 **27.** $-\frac{3}{5}$ **29.** $-\frac{3}{2}$ **31.** $\frac{9}{2}$ **33.** 7 **35.** -7 **37.** 8 **39.** 15.9 **41.** -50 **43.** -14 **45.** $7x$ **46.** $-x + 5$ **47.** $8x + 11$ **48.** $-32y$ **49.** $x - 4$ **50.** $-5x - 23$ **51.** $-10y - 42$ **52.** $-22a + 4$ **53.** $8r$ miles **54.** $\frac{1}{2}b \cdot 10\ \text{m}^2$, or $5b\ \text{m}^2$ **55.** -8655 **57.** No solution **59.** No solution **61.** $\dfrac{b}{3a}$ **63.** $\dfrac{4b}{a}$

Calculator Corner, p. 141

1. Left to the student

Exercise Set 2.3, p. 145

1. 5 **3.** 8 **5.** 10 **7.** 14 **9.** -8 **11.** -8 **13.** -7 **15.** 12 **17.** 6 **19.** 4 **21.** 6 **23.** -3 **25.** 1 **27.** 6 **29.** -20 **31.** 7 **33.** 2 **35.** 5 **37.** 2 **39.** 10 **41.** 4 **43.** 0 **45.** -1 **47.** $-\frac{4}{3}$ **49.** $\frac{2}{5}$ **51.** -2 **53.** -4 **55.** $\frac{4}{5}$ **57.** $-\frac{28}{27}$ **59.** 6 **61.** 2 **63.** No solution **65.** All real numbers **67.** 6 **69.** 8 **71.** 1 **73.** All real numbers **75.** No solution **77.** 17 **79.** $-\frac{5}{3}$ **81.** -3 **83.** 2 **85.** $\frac{4}{7}$ **87.** No solution **89.** All real numbers **91.** $-\frac{51}{31}$ **93.** -6.5 **94.** -75.14 **95.** $7(x - 3 - 2y)$ **96.** $8(y - 11x + 1)$ **97.** -160 **98.** $-17x + 18$ **99.** $91x - 242$ **100.** 0.25 **101.** $-\frac{5}{32}$ **103.** $\frac{52}{45}$

Exercise Set 2.4, p. 153

1. **(a)** 57,000 Btu's; **(b)** $a = \dfrac{B}{30}$ **3.** **(a)** 1.6 mi; **(b)** $t = 5M$ **5.** **(a)** 1423 students; **(b)** $n = 15f$ **7.** 10.5 calories per ounce **9.** 42 games **11.** $x = \dfrac{y}{5}$ **13.** $c = \dfrac{a}{b}$ **15.** $m = n - 11$ **17.** $x = y + \dfrac{3}{5}$ **19.** $x = y - 13$ **21.** $x = y - b$ **23.** $x = 5 - y$ **25.** $x = a - y$ **27.** $y = \dfrac{5x}{8}$, or $\dfrac{5}{8}x$ **29.** $x = \dfrac{By}{A}$ **31.** $t = \dfrac{W - b}{m}$ **33.** $x = \dfrac{y - c}{b}$ **35.** $h = \dfrac{A}{b}$ **37.** $w = \dfrac{P - 2l}{2}$, or $\dfrac{1}{2}P - l$ **39.** $a = 2A - b$ **41.** $b = 3A - a - c$ **43.** $t = \dfrac{A - b}{a}$ **45.** $x = \dfrac{c - By}{A}$ **47.** $a = \dfrac{F}{m}$ **49.** $c^2 = \dfrac{E}{m}$ **51.** $t = \dfrac{3k}{v}$ **53.** 0.92 **54.** -90 **55.** -9.325 **56.** 44 **57.** -13.2 **58.** $-21a + 12b$ **59.** 0.031 **60.** 0.671 **61.** $\frac{1}{6}$ **62.** $-\frac{3}{2}$ **63.** **(a)** 1901 calories;

(b) $a = \dfrac{917 + 6w + 6h - K}{6}$;

$h = \dfrac{K - 917 - 6w + 6a}{6}$;

$w = \dfrac{K - 917 - 6h + 6a}{6}$

65. $b = \dfrac{Ha - 2}{H}$, or $a - \dfrac{2}{H}$; $a = \dfrac{2 + Hb}{H}$, or $\dfrac{2}{H} + b$ **67.** A quadruples. **69.** A increases by $2h$ units.

Mid-Chapter Review: Chapter 2, p. 157

1. False **2.** True **3.** True **4.** False

5.
$$\begin{aligned} x + 5 &= -3 \\ x + 5 - 5 &= -3 - 5 \\ x + 0 &= -8 \\ x &= -8 \end{aligned}$$

6.
$$\begin{aligned} -6x &= 42 \\ \frac{-6x}{-6} &= \frac{42}{-6} \\ 1 \cdot x &= -7 \\ x &= -7 \end{aligned}$$

7.
$$\begin{aligned} 5y + z &= t \\ 5y + z - z &= t - z \\ 5y &= t - z \\ \frac{5y}{5} &= \frac{t - z}{5} \\ y &= \frac{t - z}{5} \end{aligned}$$

8. 6 **9.** -12 **10.** 7 **11.** -10 **12.** 20 **13.** 5 **14.** $\frac{3}{4}$ **15.** -1.4 **16.** 6 **17.** -17 **18.** -9 **19.** 17 **20.** 21 **21.** 18 **22.** -15 **23.** $-\frac{3}{2}$ **24.** 1 **25.** -3 **26.** $\frac{3}{2}$ **27.** -1 **28.** 3 **29.** -7 **30.** 4 **31.** 2 **32.** $\frac{9}{8}$ **33.** $-\frac{21}{5}$ **34.** 9 **35.** -2 **36.** 0 **37.** All real numbers **38.** No solution **39.** $-\frac{13}{2}$ **40.** All real numbers **41.** $b = \dfrac{A}{4}$ **42.** $x = y + 1.5$ **43.** $m = s - n$ **44.** $t = \dfrac{9w}{4}$ **45.** $t = \dfrac{B + c}{a}$ **46.** $y = 2M - x - z$ **47.** Equivalent expressions have the same value for all possible replacements for the variable(s). Equivalent equations have the same solution(s). **48.** The equations are not equivalent because they do not have the same solutions. Although 5 is a solution of both equations, -5 is a solution of $x^2 = 25$ but not of $x = 5$.

49. For an equation $x + a = b$, add the opposite of a (or subtract a) on both sides of the equation. **50.** The student probably added $\frac{1}{3}$ on both sides of the equation rather than adding $-\frac{1}{3}$ (or subtracting $\frac{1}{3}$) on both sides. The correct solution is -2. **51.** For an equation $ax = b$, multiply by $1/a$ (or divide by a) on both sides of the equation. **52.** Answers may vary. A walker who knows how far and how long she walks each day wants to know her average speed each day.

Exercise Set 2.5, p. 163

1. 20% **3.** 150 **5.** 546 **7.** 24% **9.** 2.5 **11.** 5% **13.** 25% **15.** 84 **17.** 24% **19.** 16% **21.** $46\frac{2}{3}$ **23.** 0.8 **25.** 5 **27.** 40 **29.** \$16.1 **31.** \$2.1 **33.** About 12% **35.** \$2.646 billion **37.** \$390 **39.** (a) 16%; (b) \$29 **41.** (a) \$3.75; (b) \$28.75 **43.** (a) \$30; (b) \$34.50 **45.** About 85,821 acres **47.** About 22.6% **49.** 800% **51.** 10% **53.** About 144% **55.** 181.52 **56.** 0.4538 **57.** 12.0879 **58.** 844.1407 **59.** $a + c$ **60.** $7x - 9y$ **61.** -3.9 **62.** $-6\frac{1}{8}$ **63.** Division; subtraction **64.** Exponential; division; subtraction **65.** 6 ft 7 in.

Translating for Success, p. 178

1. B **2.** H **3.** G **4.** N **5.** J **6.** C **7.** L **8.** E **9.** F **10.** D

Exercise Set 2.6, p. 179

1. 3113 manatees **3.** 180 in.; 60 in. **5.** \$16.56 **7.** $699\frac{1}{3}$ mi **9.** 1204 and 1205 **11.** 41, 42, 43 **13.** 61, 63, 65 **15.** Length: 48 ft; width: 14 ft **17.** \$75 **19.** \$85 **21.** 11 visits **23.** 28°, 84°, 68° **25.** 33°, 38°, 109° **27.** \$350 **29.** \$852.94 **31.** 12 mi **33.** \$36 **35.** \$25 and \$50 **37.** -12 **39.** $-\frac{47}{40}$ **40.** $-\frac{17}{40}$ **41.** $-\frac{3}{10}$ **42.** $-\frac{32}{15}$ **43.** -10 **44.** 1.6 **45.** 409.6 **46.** -9.6 **47.** -41.6 **48.** 0.1 **49.** 120 apples **51.** About 0.65 in. **53.** \$9.17, not \$9.10

Exercise Set 2.7, p. 192

1. (a) Yes; (b) yes; (c) no; (d) yes; (e) yes
3. (a) No; (b) no; (c) no; (d) yes; (e) no

5.
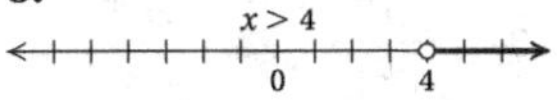

7.
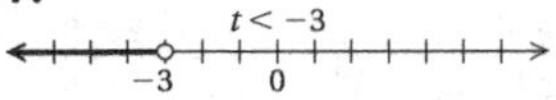

9.
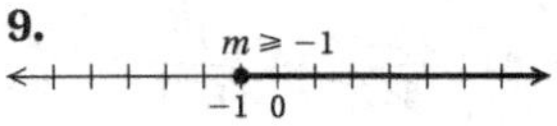

11.
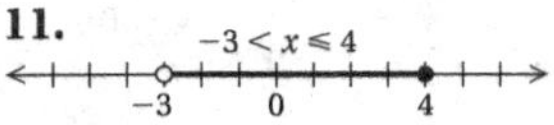

13.
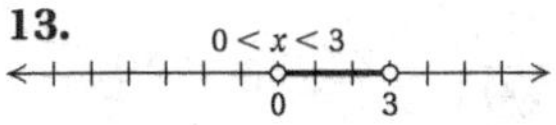

15. $\{x|x > -5\}$;

17. $\{x|x \leq -18\}$;
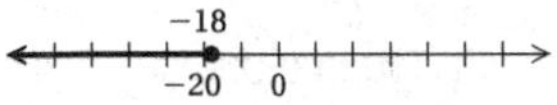

19. $\{y|y > -5\}$

21. $\{x|x > 2\}$ **23.** $\{x|x \leq -3\}$ **25.** $\{x|x < 4\}$ **27.** $\{t|t > 14\}$ **29.** $\{y|y \leq \frac{1}{4}\}$ **31.** $\{x|x > \frac{7}{12}\}$

33. $\{x|x < 7\}$;
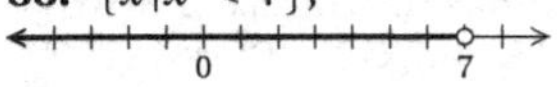

35. $\{x|x < 3\}$;
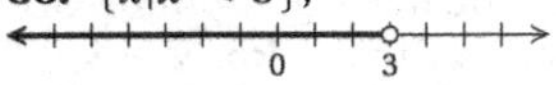

37. $\{y|y \geq - \geq \frac{2}{5}\}$ **39.** $\{x|x \geq -6\}$ **41.** $\{y|y \leq 4\}$ **43.** $\{x|x > \frac{17}{3}\}$ **45.** $\{y|y < -\frac{1}{14}\}$ **47.** $\{x|x \leq \leq \frac{3}{10}\}$ **49.** $\{x|x < 8\}$ **51.** $\{x|x \leq 6\}$ **53.** $\{x|x < -3\}$ **55.** $\{x|x > -3\}$ **57.** $\{x|x \leq 7\}$ **59.** $\{x|x > -10\}$ **61.** $\{y|y < 2\}$ **63.** $\{y|y \geq 3\}$ **65.** $\{y|y > -2\}$ **67.** $\{x|x > -4\}$ **69.** $\{x|x \leq 9\}$ **71.** $\{y|y \leq -3\}$ **73.** $\{y|y < 6\}$ **75.** $\{m|m \geq 6\}$ **77.** $\{t|t < -\frac{5}{3}\}$ **79.** $\{r|r > -3\}$ **81.** $\{x|x \geq -\frac{57}{34}\}$ **83.** $\{x|x > -2\}$ **85.** -74 **86.** 4.8 **87.** $-\frac{5}{8}$ **88.** -1.11 **89.** -38 **90.** $-\frac{7}{8}$ **91.** -9.4 **92.** 1.11 **93.** 140 **94.** 41 **95.** $-2x - 23$ **96.** $37x - 1$ **97.** (a) Yes; (b) yes; (c) no; (d) no; (e) no; (f) yes; (g) yes **99.** No solution

Exercise Set 2.8, p. 199

1. $n \geq 7$ **3.** $w > 2$ kg **5.** 90 mph $< s <$ 110 mph **7.** $w \leq 20$ hr **9.** $c \geq \$1.50$ **11.** $x > 8$ **13.** $y \leq -4$ **15.** $n \geq 1300$ **17.** $W \leq 500$ L **19.** $3x + 2 < 13$ **21.** $\{x|x \geq 84\}$ **23.** $\{C|C < 1063°\}$ **25.** $\{Y|Y \geq 1935\}$ **27.** $\{L|L \geq 5 \text{ in.}\}$ **29.** 15 or fewer copies **31.** 5 min or more **33.** 2 courses **35.** 4 servings or more **37.** Lengths greater than or equal to 92 ft; lengths less than or equal to 92 ft **39.** Lengths less than 21.5 cm **41.** The blue-book value is greater than or equal to \$10,625. **43.** It has at least 16 g of fat. **45.** Dates at least 6 weeks after July 1 **47.** Heights greater than or equal to 4 ft **49.** 21 calls or more **51.** Even **52.** Odd **53.** Additive **54.** Multiplicative **55.** Equivalent **56.** Addition principle **57.** Multiplication principle; is reversed **58.** Solution **59.** Temperatures between −15°C and $-9\frac{4}{9}$°C **61.** They contain at least 7.5 g of fat per serving.

Summary and Review: Chapter 2, p. 204

Concept Reinforcement

1. True **2.** True **3.** False **4.** True

Important Concepts

1. -12 **2.** All real numbers **3.** No solution **4.** $b = \dfrac{2A}{h}$

5.
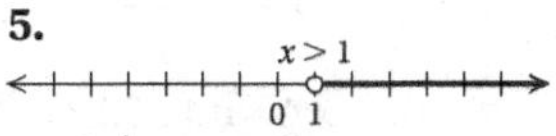

6.
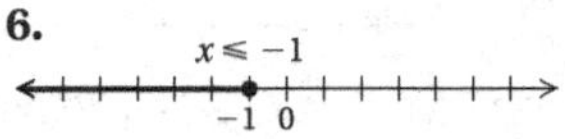

7. $\{y|y > -4\}$

Review Exercises

1. -22 **2.** 1 **3.** 25 **4.** 9.99 **5.** $\frac{1}{4}$ **6.** 7 **7.** -192 **8.** $-\frac{7}{3}$ **9.** $-\frac{15}{64}$ **10.** -8 **11.** 4 **12.** -5 **13.** $-\frac{1}{3}$ **14.** 3 **15.** 4 **16.** 16 **17.** All real numbers **18.** 6 **19.** -3 **20.** 28 **21.** 4 **22.** No solution **23.** Yes **24.** No **25.** Yes **26.** $\{y|y \geq -\frac{1}{2}\}$ **27.** $\{x|x \geq 7\}$ **28.** $\{y|y > 2\}$ **29.** $\{y|y \leq -4\}$ **30.** $\{x|x < -11\}$ **31.** $\{y|y > -7\}$ **32.** $\{x|x > -\frac{9}{11}\}$ **33.** $\{x|x \geq -\frac{1}{12}\}$

34.
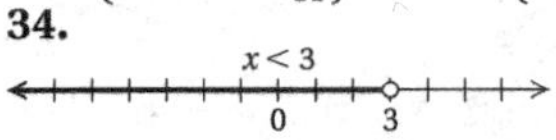

35.
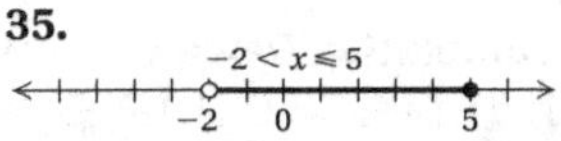

36.
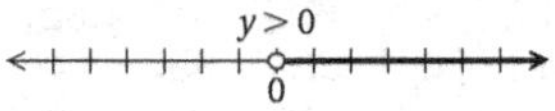

37. $d = \dfrac{C}{\pi}$ **38.** $B = \dfrac{3V}{h}$

39. $a = 2A - b$ **40.** $x = \dfrac{y - b}{m}$ **41.** Length: 365 mi; width: 275 mi **42.** 345, 346 **43.** \$2117 **44.** 27 subscriptions **45.** 35°, 85°, 60° **46.** 15 **47.** 18.75% **48.** 600 **49.** About 18% **50.** \$220 **51.** \$53,400 **52.** \$138.95 **53.** 86 **54.** $\{w|w > 17 \text{ cm}\}$ **55.** C **56.** A **57.** 23, −23 **58.** 20, −20 **59.** $a = \dfrac{y - 3}{2 - b}$

Understanding Through Discussion and Writing

1. The end result is the same either way. If s is the original salary, the new salary after a 5% raise followed by an 8% raise is $1.08(1.05s)$. If the raises occur the other way around, the new salary is $1.05(1.08s)$. By the commutative and associative laws of multiplication, we see that these are equal. However, it would be better to receive the 8% raise first, because this increase yields a higher salary initially than a 5% raise.
2. No; Erin paid 75% of the original price and was offered credit for 125% of this amount, not to be used on sale items. Now, 125% of 75% is 93.75%, so Erin would have a credit of 93.75% of the original price. Since this credit can be applied only to non-sale items, she has less purchasing power than if the amount she paid were refunded and she could spend it on sale items.

3. The inequalities are equivalent by the multiplication principle for inequalities. If we multiply on both sides of one inequality by -1, the other inequality results.
4. For any pair of numbers, their relative position on the number line is reversed when both are multiplied by the same negative number. For example, -3 is to the left of 5 on the number line $(-3 < 5)$, but 12 is to the right of -20 $(-3(-4) > 5(-4))$.
5. Answers may vary. Fran is more than 3 years older than Todd.
6. Let n represent "a number." Then "five more than a number" translates to the *expression* $n + 5$, or $5 + n$, and "five is more than a number" translates to the *inequality* $5 > n$.

Test: Chapter 2, p. 209

1. [2.1b] 8 **2.** [2.1b] 26 **3.** [2.2a] -6 **4.** [2.2a] 49
5. [2.3b] -12 **6.** [2.3a] 2 **7.** [2.3a] -8 **8.** [2.1b] $-\frac{7}{20}$
9. [2.3c] 7 **10.** [2.3c] $\frac{5}{3}$ **11.** [2.3b] $\frac{5}{2}$
12. [2.3c] No solution **13.** [2.3c] All real numbers
14. [2.7c] $\{x|x \le -4\}$ **15.** [2.7c] $\{x|x > -13\}$
16. [2.7d] $\{x|x \le 5\}$ **17.** [2.7d] $\{y|y \le -13\}$
18. [2.7d] $\{y|y \ge 8\}$ **19.** [2.7d] $\{x|x \le -\frac{1}{20}\}$
20. [2.7e] $\{x|x < -6\}$ **21.** [2.7e] $\{x|x \le -1\}$
22. [2.7b]
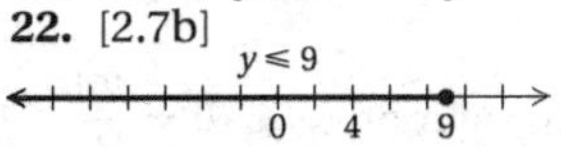

23. [2.7b, e]
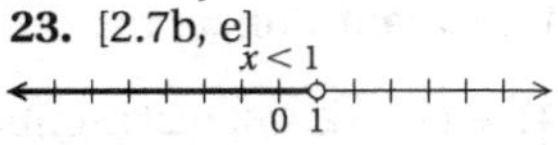

24. [2.7b]
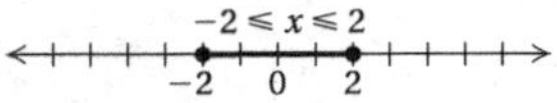

25. [2.5a] 18
26. [2.5a] 16.5% **27.** [2.5a] 40,000 **28.** [2.5a] About 25.8%
29. [2.6a] Width: 7 cm; length: 11 cm **30.** [2.5a] About \$310 billion
31. [2.6a] 2509, 2510, 2511 **32.** [2.6a] \$880 **33.** [2.6a] 3 m, 5 m
34. [2.8b] $\{l|l \ge 174 \text{ yd}\}$ **35.** [2.8b] $\{b|b \le \$105\}$
36. [2.8b] $\{c|c \le 143{,}750\}$ **37.** [2.4b] $r = \dfrac{A}{2\pi h}$
38. [2.4b] $x = \dfrac{y-b}{8}$ **39.** [2.5a] D **40.** [2.4b] $d = \dfrac{1-ca}{-c}$, or $\dfrac{ca-1}{c}$ **41.** [1.2e], [2.3a] 15, -15 **42.** [2.6a] 60 tickets

Cumulative Review: Chapters 1–2, p. 211

1. [1.1a] $\frac{3}{2}$ **2.** [1.1a] $\frac{15}{4}$ **3.** [1.1a] 0 **4.** [1.1b] $2w - 4$
5. [1.2d] $>$ **6.** [1.2d] $>$ **7.** [1.2d] $<$ **8.** [1.3b], [1.6b] $-\frac{2}{5}, \frac{5}{2}$
9. [1.2e] 3 **10.** [1.2e] $\frac{3}{4}$ **11.** [1.2e] 0 **12.** [1.3a] -4.4
13. [1.4a] $-\frac{5}{2}$ **14.** [1.5a] $\frac{5}{6}$ **15.** [1.5a] -105 **16.** [1.6a] -9
17. [1.6c] -3 **18.** [1.6c] $\frac{32}{125}$ **19.** [1.7c] $15x + 25y + 10z$
20. [1.7c] $-12x - 8$ **21.** [1.7c] $-12y + 24x$
22. [1.7d] $2(32 + 9x + 12y)$ **23.** [1.7d] $8(2y - 7)$
24. [1.7d] $5(a - 3b + 5)$ **25.** [1.7e] $15b + 22y$
26. [1.7e] $4 + 9y + 6z$ **27.** [1.7e] $1 - 3a - 9d$
28. [1.7e] $-2.6x - 5.2y$ **29.** [1.8b] $3x - 1$ **30.** [1.8b] $-2x - y$
31. [1.8b] $-7x + 6$ **32.** [1.8b] $8x$ **33.** [1.8c] $5x - 13$
34. [2.1b] 4.5 **35.** [2.2a] $\frac{4}{25}$ **36.** [2.1b] 10.9 **37.** [2.1b] $3\frac{5}{6}$
38. [2.2a] -48 **39.** [2.2a] $-\frac{3}{8}$ **40.** [2.2a] -6.2
41. [2.3a] -3 **42.** [2.3b] $-\frac{12}{5}$ **43.** [2.3b] 8 **44.** [2.3c] 7
45. [2.3b] $-\frac{4}{5}$ **46.** [2.3b] $-\frac{10}{3}$ **47.** [2.3c] All real numbers
48. [2.3c] No solution **49.** [2.7c] $\{x|x < 2\}$
50. [2.7e] $\{y|y < -3\}$ **51.** [2.7e] $\{y|y \ge 4\}$
52. [2.4b] $m = 65 - H$ **53.** [2.4b] $t = \dfrac{I}{Pr}$ **54.** [2.5a] 25.2
55. [2.5a] 45% **56.** [2.5a] \$363 **57.** [2.6a] \$24.60
58. [2.6a] \$45 **59.** [2.6a] \$1050
60. [2.6a] 50 m, 53 m, 40 m **61.** [2.8b] $\{s|s \ge 84\}$
62. [1.8d] C **63.** [2.6a] \$45,200 **64.** [2.6a] 30%
65. [1.2e], [2.3a] 4, -4 **66.** [2.3b] 3 **67.** [2.4b] $Q = \dfrac{2-pm}{p}$

CHAPTER 3

Exercise Set 3.1, p. 220

1. $3 \cdot 3 \cdot 3 \cdot 3$ **3.** $(-1.1)(-1.1)(-1.1)(-1.1)(-1.1)$
5. $\left(\frac{2}{3}\right)\left(\frac{2}{3}\right)\left(\frac{2}{3}\right)\left(\frac{2}{3}\right)$ **7.** $(7p)(7p)$ **9.** $8 \cdot k \cdot k \cdot k$
11. $-6 \cdot y \cdot y \cdot y \cdot y$ **13.** 1 **15.** b **17.** 1 **19.** -7.03
21. 1 **23.** ab **25.** a **27.** 27 **29.** 19 **31.** -81
33. 256 **35.** 93 **37.** 136 **39.** 10; 4 **41.** 3629.84 ft^2
43. $\dfrac{1}{3^2} = \dfrac{1}{9}$ **45.** $\dfrac{1}{10^3} = \dfrac{1}{1000}$ **47.** $\dfrac{1}{a^3}$ **49.** $8^2 = 64$ **51.** y^4
53. $\dfrac{5}{z^4}$ **55.** $\dfrac{x}{y^2}$ **57.** 4^{-3} **59.** x^{-3} **61.** a^{-5} **63.** 2^7
65. 8^{14} **67.** x^5 **69.** 9^{38} **71.** $(3y)^{12}$ **73.** $(7y)^{17}$
75. 3^3 **77.** 1 **79.** x^{17} **81.** $\dfrac{1}{x^{13}}$ **83.** $\dfrac{1}{a^{10}}$ **85.** s^3t^7
87. 7^3 **89.** y^8 **91.** $\dfrac{1}{16^6}$ **93.** $\dfrac{1}{m^6}$ **95.** $\dfrac{1}{(8x)^4}$ **97.** 1
99. x^2 **101.** x^9 **103.** $\dfrac{1}{z^4}$ **105.** x^3 **107.** 1 **109.** a^3b^2
111. $5^2 = 25; 5^{-2} = \frac{1}{25}; \left(\frac{1}{5}\right)^2 = \frac{1}{25}; \left(\frac{1}{5}\right)^{-2} = 25; -5^2 = -25;$ $(-5)^2 = 25; -\left(-\frac{1}{5}\right)^2 = -\frac{1}{25}; \left(-\frac{1}{5}\right)^{-2} = 25$ **113.** 8 in.; 4 in.
114. 228, 229 **115.** 25,543.75 ft^2 **116.** 51°, 27°, 102°
117. $\frac{23}{14}$ **118.** $\frac{11}{10}$ **119.** $4(x - 3 + 6y)$
120. $2(128 - a - 2b)$ **121.** No **123.** No **125.** y^{5x}
127. a^{4t} **129.** 1 **131.** $>$ **133.** $<$ **135.** $-\frac{1}{10{,}000}$
137. No; for example, $(3 + 4)^2 = 49$, but $3^2 + 4^2 = 25$.

Calculator Corner, p. 228

1. 1.3545×10^{-4} **2.** 3.2×10^5 **3.** 3×10^{-6} **4.** 8×10^{-26}

Exercise Set 3.2, p. 231

1. 2^6 **3.** $\dfrac{1}{5^6}$ **5.** x^{12} **7.** $\dfrac{1}{a^{18}}$ **9.** t^{18} **11.** $\dfrac{1}{t^{12}}$ **13.** x^8
15. a^3b^3 **17.** $\dfrac{1}{a^3b^3}$ **19.** $\dfrac{1}{m^3n^6}$ **21.** $16x^6$ **23.** $\dfrac{9}{x^8}$
25. $\dfrac{1}{x^{12}y^{15}}$ **27.** $x^{24}y^8$ **29.** $\dfrac{a^{10}}{b^{35}}$ **31.** $\dfrac{25t^6}{r^8}$ **33.** $\dfrac{b^{21}}{a^{15}c^6}$
35. $\dfrac{9x^6}{y^{16}z^6}$ **37.** $\dfrac{16x^6}{y^4}$ **39.** $a^{12}b^8$ **41.** $\dfrac{y^6}{4}$ **43.** $\dfrac{a^8}{b^{12}}$
45. $\dfrac{8}{y^6}$ **47.** $49x^6$ **49.** $\dfrac{x^6y^3}{z^3}$ **51.** $\dfrac{c^2d^6}{a^4b^2}$ **53.** 2.8×10^{10}
55. 9.07×10^{17} **57.** 3.04×10^{-6} **59.** 1.8×10^{-8}
61. 10^{11} **63.** 4.19854×10^8 **65.** $\$2.4 \times 10^9$
67. 87,400,000 **69.** 0.00000005704 **71.** 10,000,000
73. 0.00001 **75.** 6×10^9 **77.** 3.38×10^4
79. 8.1477×10^{-13} **81.** 2.5×10^{13} **83.** 5.0×10^{-4}
85. 3.0×10^{-21} **87.** Approximately 1.325×10^{14} ft^3
89. The mass of Jupiter is 3.18×10^2 times the mass of Earth.
91. 1×10^{22} **93.** 7.5×10^{-7} m **95.** 4.375×10^2 days
97. $9(x - 4)$ **98.** $2(2x - y + 8)$ **99.** $3(s + t + 8)$
100. $-7(x + 2)$ **101.** $\frac{7}{4}$ **102.** 2 **103.** $-\frac{12}{7}$ **104.** $-\frac{11}{2}$
105.
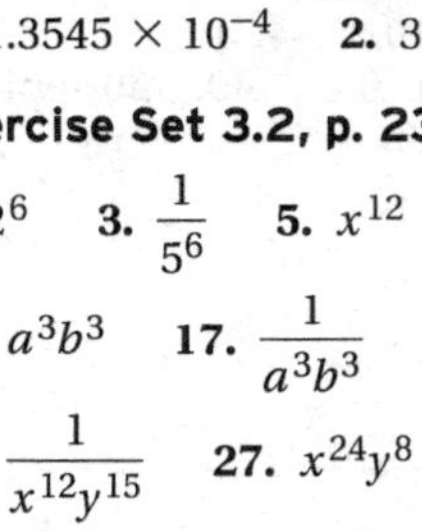

106.
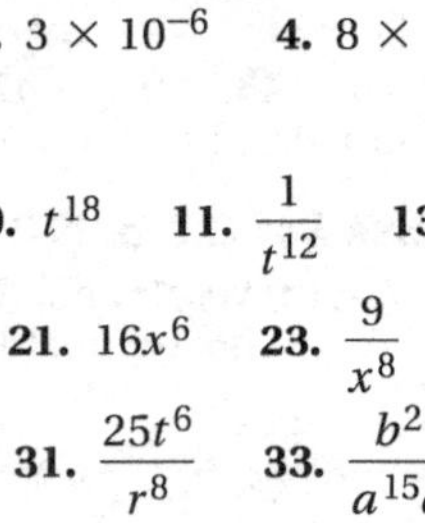

107. 2.478125×10^{-1} **109.** $\frac{1}{5}$ **111.** 3^{11} **113.** 7
115. $\frac{1}{0.4}$, or 2.5 **117.** False **119.** False **121.** True

Calculator Corner, p. 238

1. 3; 2.25; −27 **2.** 44; 0; 9.28

Exercise Set 3.3, p. 243

1. −18; 7 **3.** 19; 14 **5.** −12; −7 **7.** $\frac{13}{3}$; 5 **9.** 9; 1 **11.** 56; −2 **13.** 1112 ft **15.** \$18,750; \$24,000 **17.** −4, 4, 5, 2.75, 1 **19. (a)** 2728.4 billion kilowatt-hours; 3521.8 billion kilowatt-hours; 4315.2 billion kilowatt-hours; 5108.6 billion kilowatt-hours; 5902 billion kilowatt-hours; **(b)** left to the student **21.** 9 words **23.** 6 **25.** 15 **27.** 2, $-3x$, x^2 **29.** $-2x^4, \frac{1}{3}x^3, -x, 3$ **31.** $6x^2$ and $-3x^2$ **33.** $2x^4$ and $-3x^4$; $5x$ and $-7x$ **35.** $3x^5$ and $14x^5$; $-7x$ and $-2x$; 8 and −9 **37.** −3, 6 **39.** 5, $\frac{3}{4}$, 3 **41.** −5, 6, −2.7, 1; −2 **43.** $-3x$ **45.** $-8x$ **47.** $11x^3 + 4$ **49.** $x^3 - x$ **51.** $4b^5$ **53.** $\frac{3}{4}x^5 - 2x - 42$ **55.** x^4 **57.** $\frac{15}{16}x^3 - \frac{7}{6}x^2$ **59.** $x^5 + 6x^3 + 2x^2 + x + 1$ **61.** $15y^9 + 7y^8 + 5y^3 - y^2 + y$ **63.** $x^6 + x^4$ **65.** $13x^3 - 9x + 8$ **67.** $-5x^2 + 9x$ **69.** $12x^4 - 2x + \frac{1}{4}$ **71.** 1, 0; 1 **73.** 2, 1, 0; 2 **75.** 3, 2, 1, 0; 3 **77.** 2, 1, 6, 4; 6

79.

Term	Coefficient	Degree of the Term	Degree of the Polynomial
$-7x^4$	−7	4	
$6x^3$	6	3	
$-x^2$	−1	2	4
$8x$	8	1	
−2	−2	0	

81. x^2, x **83.** x^3, x^2, x^0 **85.** None missing **87.** $x^3 + 0x^2 + 0x - 27$; x^3 $-\ 27$ **89.** $x^4 + 0x^3 + 0x^2 - x + 0x^0$; x^4 $-\ x$ **91.** None missing **93.** Trinomial **95.** None of these **97.** Binomial **99.** Monomial **101.** 27 apples **102.** −19 **103.** $-\frac{17}{24}$ **104.** $\frac{5}{8}$ **105.** −2.6 **106.** $\frac{15}{2}$ **107.** $b = \frac{C + r}{a}$ **108.** 45%; 37.5%; 17.5% **109.** $3(x - 5y + 21)$ **111.** $3x^6$ **113.** 10 **115.** −4, 4, 5, 2.75, 1 **117.** 9

Calculator Corner, p. 252

1. Yes **2.** Yes **3.** No **4.** Yes **5.** No **6.** Yes

Exercise Set 3.4, p. 253

1. $-x + 5$ **3.** $x^2 - \frac{11}{2}x - 1$ **5.** $2x^2$ **7.** $5x^2 + 3x - 30$ **9.** $-2.2x^3 - 0.2x^2 - 3.8x + 23$ **11.** $6 + 12x^2$ **13.** $-\frac{1}{2}x^4 + \frac{2}{3}x^3 + x^2$ **15.** $0.01x^5 + x^4 - 0.2x^3 + 0.2x + 0.06$ **17.** $9x^8 + 8x^7 - 6x^4 + 8x^2 + 4$ **19.** $1.05x^4 + 0.36x^3 + 14.22x^2 + x + 0.97$ **21.** $5x$ **23.** $x^2 - \frac{3}{2}x + 2$ **25.** $-12x^4 + 3x^3 - 3$ **27.** $-3x + 7$ **29.** $-4x^2 + 3x - 2$ **31.** $4x^4 - 6x^2 - \frac{3}{4}x + 8$ **33.** $7x - 1$ **35.** $-x^2 - 7x + 5$ **37.** −18 **39.** $6x^4 + 3x^3 - 4x^2 + 3x - 4$ **41.** $4.6x^3 + 9.2x^2 - 3.8x - 23$ **43.** $\frac{3}{4}x^3 - \frac{1}{2}x$ **45.** $0.06x^3 - 0.05x^2 + 0.01x + 1$ **47.** $3x + 6$ **49.** $11x^4 + 12x^3 - 9x^2 - 8x - 9$ **51.** $x^4 - x^3 + x^2 - x$ **53.** $\frac{23}{2}a + 12$ **55.** $5x^2 + 4x$ **57.** $(r + 11)(r + 9)$; $9r + 99 + 11r + r^2$, or $r^2 + 20r + 99$ **59.** $(x + 3)(x + 3)$, or $(x + 3)^2$; $x^2 + 3x + 9 + 3x$, or $x^2 + 6x + 9$ **61.** $\pi r^2 - 25\pi$ **63.** $18z - 64$ **65.** 6 **66.** −19 **67.** $-\frac{7}{22}$ **68.** 5 **69.** 5 **70.** 1 **71.** $\frac{39}{2}$ **72.** $\frac{37}{2}$ **73.** $\{x \mid x \geq -10\}$ **74.** $\{x \mid x < 0\}$ **75.** $20w + 42$ **77.** $2x^2 + 20x$ **79.** $y^2 - 4y + 4$ **81.** $12y^2 - 23y + 21$ **83.** $-3y^4 - y^3 + 5y - 2$

Mid-Chapter Review: Chapter 3, p. 257

1. True **2.** False **3.** False **4.** True **5.** $4w^3 + 6w - 8w^3 - 3w = (4 - 8)w^3 + (6 - 3)w = -4w^3 + 3w$ **6.** $(3y^4 - y^2 + 11) - (y^4 - 4y^2 + 5) = 3y^4 - y^2 + 11 - y^4 + 4y^2 - 5 = 2y^4 + 3y^2 + 6$ **7.** z **8.** 1 **9.** −32 **10.** 1 **11.** 5^7 **12.** $(3a)^9$ **13.** $\frac{1}{x^3}$ **14.** 1 **15.** 7^4 **16.** $\frac{1}{x^2}$ **17.** w^8 **18.** $\frac{1}{y^4}$ **19.** 3^{15} **20.** $\frac{x^{18}}{y^{12}}$ **21.** $\frac{a^{24}}{5^6}$ **22.** $\frac{x^2z^4}{4y^6}$ **23.** 2.543×10^7 **24.** 1.2×10^{-4} **25.** 0.000036 **26.** 144,000,000 **27.** 6×10^3 **28.** 5×10^{-7} **29.** 16; 1 **30.** −16; 9 **31.** $-2x^5 - 5x^2 + 4x + 2$ **32.** $8x^6 + 2x^3 - 8x^2$ **33.** 3, 1, 0; 3 **34.** 1, 4, 6; 6 **35.** Binomial **36.** Trinomial **37.** $8x^2 + 5$ **38.** $5x^3 - 2x^2 + 2x - 11$ **39.** $-4x - 10$ **40.** $-0.4x^2 - 3.4x + 9$ **41.** $3y + 3y^2$ **42.** The area of the smaller square is x^2, and the area of the larger square is $(3x)^2$, or $9x^2$, so the area of the larger square is nine times the area of the smaller square. **43.** The volume of the smaller cube is x^3, and the volume of the larger cube is $(2x)^3$, or $8x^3$, so the volume of the larger cube is eight times the volume of the smaller cube. **44.** Exponents are added when powers with like bases are multiplied. Exponents are multiplied when a power is raised to a power. **45.** $3^{-29} = \frac{1}{3^{29}}$ and $2^{-29} = \frac{1}{2^{29}}$. Since $3^{29} > 2^{29}$, we have $\frac{1}{3^{29}} < \frac{1}{2^{29}}$. **46.** It is better to evaluate a polynomial after like terms have been collected, because there are fewer terms to evaluate. **47.** Yes; consider the following: $(x^2 + 4) + (4x - 7) = x^2 + 4x - 3$.

Calculator Corner, p. 262

1. Correct **2.** Correct **3.** Not correct **4.** Not correct

Exercise Set 3.5, p. 263

1. $40x^2$ **3.** x^3 **5.** $32x^8$ **7.** $0.03x^{11}$ **9.** $\frac{1}{15}x^4$ **11.** 0 **13.** $-24x^{11}$ **15.** $-2x^2 + 10x$ **17.** $-5x^2 + 5x$ **19.** $x^5 + x^2$ **21.** $6x^3 - 18x^2 + 3x$ **23.** $-6x^4 - 6x^3$ **25.** $18y^6 + 24y^5$ **27.** $x^2 + 9x + 18$ **29.** $x^2 + 3x - 10$ **31.** $x^2 + 3x - 4$ **33.** $x^2 - 7x + 12$ **35.** $x^2 - 9$ **37.** $x^2 - 16$ **39.** $3x^2 + 11x + 10$ **41.** $25 - 15x + 2x^2$ **43.** $4x^2 + 20x + 25$ **45.** $x^2 - 6x + 9$ **47.** $x^2 - \frac{21}{10}x - 1$ **49.** $x^2 + 2.4x - 10.81$ **51.** $(x + 2)(x + 6)$, or $x^2 + 8x + 12$ **53.** $(x + 1)(x + 6)$, or $x^2 + 7x + 6$

55.

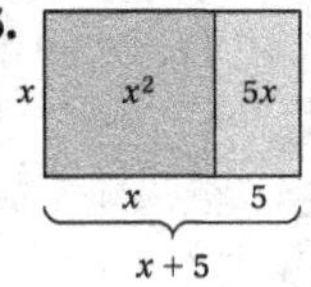

57.

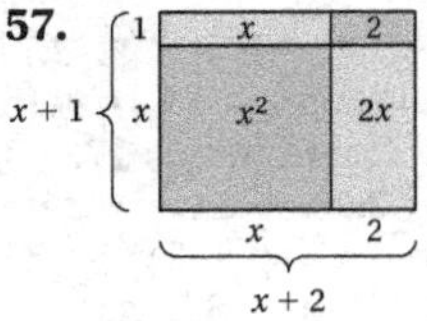

59.

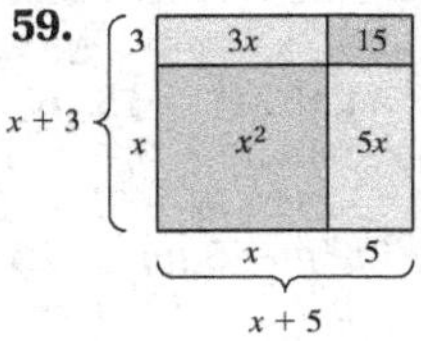

61. $x^3 - 1$ **63.** $4x^3 + 14x^2 + 8x + 1$ **65.** $3y^4 - 6y^3 - 7y^2 + 18y - 6$ **67.** $x^6 + 2x^5 - x^3$ **69.** $-10x^5 - 9x^4 + 7x^3 + 2x^2 - x$ **71.** $-1 - 2x - x^2 + x^4$ **73.** $6t^4 + t^3 - 16t^2 - 7t + 4$ **75.** $x^9 - x^5 + 2x^3 - x$ **77.** $x^4 - 1$ **79.** $x^4 + 8x^3 + 12x^2 + 9x + 4$ **81.** $2x^4 - 5x^3 + 5x^2 - \frac{19}{10}x + \frac{1}{5}$ **83.** $-\frac{3}{4}$ **84.** 6.4 **85.** 96 **86.** 32 **87.** $3(5x - 6y + 4)$ **88.** $4(4x - 6y + 9)$ **89.** $-3(3x + 15y - 5)$ **90.** $100(x - y + 10a)$

91.

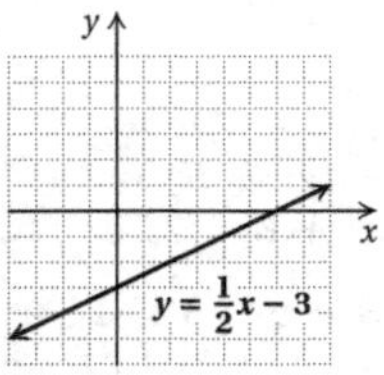

92. $\frac{23}{19}$ **93.** $75y^2 - 45y$
95. $V = (4x^3 - 48x^2 + 144x)$ in^3; $S = (-4x^2 + 144)$ in^2
97. 5 **99.** $(x^3 + 2x^2 - 210)$ m^3 **101.** 0 **103.** 0

Visualizing for Success, p. 272

1. E, F **2.** B, O **3.** K, S **4.** G, R **5.** D, M **6.** J, P
7. C, L **8.** N, Q **9.** A, H **10.** I, T

Exercise Set 3.6, p. 273

1. $x^3 + x^2 + 3x + 3$ **3.** $x^4 + x^3 + 2x + 2$ **5.** $y^2 - y - 6$
7. $9x^2 + 12x + 4$ **9.** $5x^2 + 4x - 12$ **11.** $9t^2 - 1$
13. $4x^2 - 6x + 2$ **15.** $p^2 - \frac{1}{16}$ **17.** $x^2 - 0.01$
19. $2x^3 + 2x^2 + 6x + 6$ **21.** $-2x^2 - 11x + 6$
23. $a^2 + 14a + 49$ **25.** $1 - x - 6x^2$ **27.** $\frac{9}{64}y^2 - \frac{5}{8}y + \frac{25}{36}$
29. $x^5 + 3x^3 - x^2 - 3$ **31.** $3x^6 - 2x^4 - 6x^2 + 4$
33. $13.16x^2 + 18.99x - 13.95$ **35.** $6x^7 + 18x^5 + 4x^2 + 12$
37. $8x^6 + 65x^3 + 8$ **39.** $4x^3 - 12x^2 + 3x - 9$
41. $4y^6 + 4y^5 + y^4 + y^3$ **43.** $x^2 - 16$ **45.** $4x^2 - 1$
47. $25m^2 - 4$ **49.** $4x^4 - 9$ **51.** $9x^8 - 16$ **53.** $x^{12} - x^4$
55. $x^8 - 9x^2$ **57.** $x^{24} - 9$ **59.** $4y^{16} - 9$ **61.** $\frac{25}{64}x^2 - 18.49$
63. $x^2 + 4x + 4$ **65.** $9x^4 + 6x^2 + 1$ **67.** $a^2 - a + \frac{1}{4}$
69. $9 + 6x + x^2$ **71.** $x^4 + 2x^2 + 1$ **73.** $4 - 12x^4 + 9x^8$
75. $25 + 60t^2 + 36t^4$ **77.** $x^2 - \frac{5}{4}x + \frac{25}{64}$ **79.** $9 - 12x^3 + 4x^6$
81. $4x^3 + 24x^2 - 12x$ **83.** $4x^4 - 2x^2 + \frac{1}{4}$ **85.** $9p^2 - 1$
87. $15t^5 - 3t^4 + 3t^3$ **89.** $36x^8 + 48x^4 + 16$
91. $12x^3 + 8x^2 + 15x + 10$ **93.** $64 - 96x^4 + 36x^8$
95. $t^3 - 1$ **97.** 25; 49 **99.** 56; 16 **101.** $a^2 + 2a + 1$
103. $t^2 + 10t + 24$ **105.** Lamps: 500 watts; air conditioner: 2000 watts; television: 50 watts **106.** $\frac{28}{27}$ **107.** $-\frac{41}{7}$
108. $\frac{27}{4}$ **109.** $y = \dfrac{3x - 12}{2}$, or $y = \frac{3}{2}x - 6$
110. $a = \dfrac{5d + 4}{3}$, or $a = \frac{5}{3}d + \frac{4}{3}$ **111.** $30x^3 + 35x^2 - 15x$
113. $a^4 - 50a^2 + 625$ **115.** $81t^{16} - 72t^8 + 16$ **117.** -7
119. First row: 90, −432, −63; second row: 7, −18, −36, −14, 12, −6, −21, −11; third row: 9, −2, −2, 10, −8, −8, −8, −10, 21; fourth row: −19, −6 **121.** Yes **123.** No

Exercise Set 3.7, p. 281

1. −1 **3.** −15 **5.** 240 **7.** −145 **9.** 3.715 L **11.** 205.9 m
13. 44.46 in^2 **15.** 63.78125 in^2 **17.** Coefficients: 1, −2, 3, −5; degrees: 4, 2, 2, 0; 4 **19.** Coefficients: 17, −3, −7; degrees: 5, 5, 0; 5 **21.** $-a - 2b$ **23.** $3x^2y - 2xy^2 + x^2$ **25.** $20au + 10av$
27. $8u^2v - 5uv^2$ **29.** $x^2 - 4xy + 3y^2$ **31.** $3r + 7$
33. $-b^2a^3 - 3b^3a^2 + 5ba + 3$ **35.** $ab^2 - a^2b$
37. $2ab - 2$ **39.** $-2a + 10b - 5c + 8d$
41. $6z^2 + 7zu - 3u^2$ **43.** $a^4b^2 - 7a^2b + 10$ **45.** $a^6 - b^2c^2$
47. $y^6x + y^4x + y^4 + 2y^2 + 1$ **49.** $12x^2y^2 + 2xy - 2$
51. $12 - c^2d^2 - c^4d^4$ **53.** $m^3 + m^2n - mn^2 - n^3$
55. $x^9y^9 - x^6y^6 + x^5y^5 - x^2y^2$ **57.** $x^2 + 2xh + h^2$
59. $9a^2 + 12ab + 4b^2$ **61.** $r^6t^4 - 8r^3t^2 + 16$
63. $p^8 + 2m^2n^2p^4 + m^4n^4$ **65.** $3a^3 - 12a^2b + 12ab^2$
67. $m^2 + 2mn + n^2 - 6m - 6n + 9$ **69.** $a^2 - b^2$
71. $4a^2 - b^2$ **73.** $c^4 - d^2$ **75.** $a^2b^2 - c^2d^4$
77. $x^2 + 2xy + y^2 - 9$ **79.** $x^2 - y^2 - 2yz - z^2$
81. $a^2 + 2ab + b^2 - c^2$
83. $3x^4 - 7x^2y + 3x^2 - 20y^2 + 22y - 6$ **85.** IV **86.** III
87. I **88.** II

89.

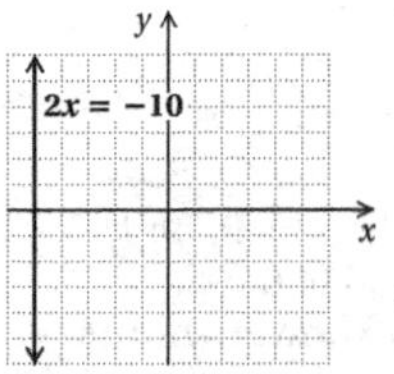

90.

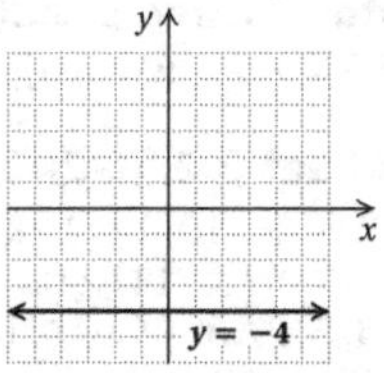

91.

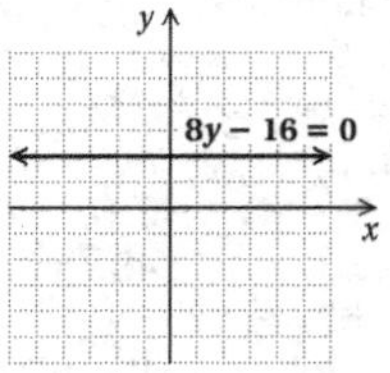

92.

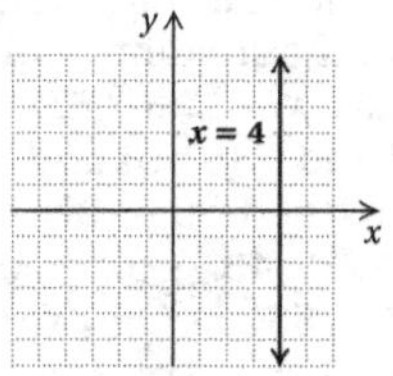

93. $4xy - 4y^2$ **95.** $2xy + \pi x^2$
97. $2\pi nh + 2\pi mh + 2\pi n^2 - 2\pi m^2$ **99.** 16 gal
101. $12,351.94

Summary and Review: Chapter 3, p. 286

Concept Reinforcement

1. True **2.** False **3.** False **4.** True

Important Concepts

1. z^8 **2.** a^2b^6 **3.** $\dfrac{y^6}{27x^{12}z^9}$ **4.** 7.63×10^5 **5.** 0.0003
6. 6×10^4 **7.** $2x^4 - 4x^2 - 3$ **8.** $3x^4 + x^3 - 2x^2 + 2$
9. $x^6 - 6x^4 + 11x^2 - 6$ **10.** $2y^2 + 11y + 12$ **11.** $x^2 - 25$
12. $9w^2 + 24w + 16$ **13.** $-2a^3b^2 - 5a^2b + ab^2 - 2ab$
14. $y^2 - 4y + \frac{8}{5}$

Review Exercises

1. $\dfrac{1}{7^2}$ **2.** y^{11} **3.** $(3x)^{14}$ **4.** t^8 **5.** 4^3 **6.** $\dfrac{1}{a^3}$ **7.** 1
8. $9t^8$ **9.** $36x^8$ **10.** $\dfrac{y^3}{8x^3}$ **11.** t^{-5} **12.** $\dfrac{1}{y^4}$
13. 3.28×10^{-5} **14.** 8,300,000 **15.** 2.09×10^4
16. 5.12×10^{-5} **17.** 1.54468×10^{10} slices **18.** 10
19. $-4y^5, 7y^2, -3y, -2$ **20.** x^2, x^0 **21.** 3, 2, 1, 0; 3
22. Binomial **23.** None of these **24.** Monomial
25. $-2x^2 - 3x + 2$ **26.** $10x^4 - 7x^2 - x - \frac{1}{2}$
27. $x^5 - 2x^4 + 6x^3 + 3x^2 - 9$
28. $-2x^5 - 6x^4 - 2x^3 - 2x^2 + 2$ **29.** $2x^2 - 4x$
30. $x^5 - 3x^3 - x^2 + 8$ **31.** Perimeter: $4w + 6$; area: $w^2 + 3w$
32. $(t + 3)(t + 4)$, $t^2 + 7t + 12$ **33.** $x^2 + \frac{7}{6}x + \frac{1}{3}$
34. $49x^2 + 14x + 1$ **35.** $12x^3 - 23x^2 + 13x - 2$
36. $9x^4 - 16$ **37.** $15x^7 - 40x^6 + 50x^5 + 10x^4$
38. $x^2 - 3x - 28$ **39.** $9y^4 - 12y^3 + 4y^2$ **40.** $2t^4 - 11t^2 - 21$
41. 49 **42.** Coefficients: 1, −7, 9, −8; degrees: 6, 2, 2, 0; 6
43. $-y + 9w - 5$ **44.** $m^6 - 2m^2n + 2m^2n^2 + 8n^2m - 6m^3$
45. $-9xy - 2y^2$ **46.** $11x^3y^2 - 8x^2y - 6x^2 - 6x + 6$
47. $p^3 - q^3$ **48.** $9a^8 - 2a^4b^3 + \frac{1}{9}b^6$ **49.** $5x^2 - \frac{1}{2}x + 3$
50. B **51.** D **52.** $-28x^8$ **53.** $\frac{94}{13}$
54. $x^4 + x^3 + x^2 + x + 1$ **55.** 80 ft by 40 ft

Understanding Through Discussion and Writing

1. 578.6×10^{-7} is not in scientific notation because 578.6 is not a number greater than or equal to 1 and less than 10.
2. When evaluating polynomials, it is essential to know the order in which the operations are to be performed.

3. We label the figure as shown.

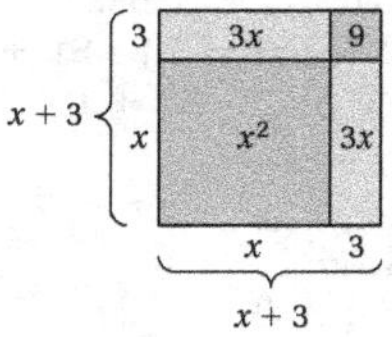

Then we see that the area of the figure is $(x + 3)^2$, or $x^2 + 3x + 3x + 9 \neq x^2 + 9$. **4.** Emma did not divide *each* term of the polynomial by the divisor. The first term was divided by $3x$, but the second was not. Multiplying Emma's "quotient" by the divisor $3x$, we get $12x^3 - 18x^2 \neq 12x^3 - 6x$. This should convince her that a mistake has been made. **5.** Yes; for example, $(x^2 + xy + 1) + (3x - xy + 2) = x^2 + 3x + 3$. **6.** Yes; consider $a + b + c + d$. This is a polynomial in 4 variables but it has degree 1.

Test: Chapter 3, p. 292

1. [4.1d, f] $\frac{1}{6^5}$ **2.** [4.1d] x^9 **3.** [4.1d] $(4a)^{11}$ **4.** [4.1e] 3^3 **5.** [4.1e, f] $\frac{1}{x^5}$ **6.** [4.1b, e] 1 **7.** [4.2a] x^6 **8.** [4.2a, b] $-27y^6$ **9.** [4.2a, b] $16a^{12}b^4$ **10.** [4.2b] $\frac{a^3b^3}{c^3}$ **11.** [4.1d], [4.2a, b] $-216x^{21}$ **12.** [4.1d], [4.2a, b] $-24x^{21}$ **13.** [4.1d], [4.2a, b] $162x^{10}$ **14.** [4.1d], [4.2a, b] $324x^{10}$ **15.** [4.1f] $\frac{1}{5^3}$ **16.** [4.1f] y^{-8} **17.** [4.2c] 3.9×10^9 **18.** [4.2c] 0.00000005 **19.** [4.2d] 1.75×10^{17} **20.** [4.2d] 1.296×10^{22} **21.** [4.2e] 1.5×10^4 files **22.** [4.3a] -43 **23.** [4.3d] $\frac{1}{3}, -1, 7$ **24.** [4.3g] 3, 0, 1, 6; 6 **25.** [4.3i] Binomial **26.** [4.3e] $5a^2 - 6$ **27.** [4.3e] $\frac{7}{4}y^2 - 4y$ **28.** [4.3f] $x^5 + 2x^3 + 4x^2 - 8x + 3$ **29.** [4.4a] $4x^5 + x^4 + 2x^3 - 8x^2 + 2x - 7$ **30.** [4.4a] $5x^4 + 5x^2 + x + 5$ **31.** [4.4c] $-4x^4 + x^3 - 8x - 3$ **32.** [4.4c] $-x^5 + 0.7x^3 - 0.8x^2 - 21$ **33.** [4.5b] $-12x^4 + 9x^3 + 15x^2$ **34.** [4.6c] $x^2 - \frac{2}{3}x + \frac{1}{9}$ **35.** [4.6b] $9x^2 - 100$ **36.** [4.6a] $3b^2 - 4b - 15$ **37.** [4.6a] $x^{14} - 4x^8 + 4x^6 - 16$ **38.** [4.6a] $48 + 34y - 5y^2$ **39.** [4.5d] $6x^3 - 7x^2 - 11x - 3$ **40.** [4.6c] $25t^2 + 20t + 4$ **41.** [4.7c] $-5x^3y - y^3 + xy^3 - x^2y^2 + 19$ **42.** [4.7e] $8a^2b^2 + 6ab - 4b^3 + 6ab^2 + ab^3$ **43.** [4.7f] $9x^{10} - 16y^{10}$ **44.** [4.8a] $4x^2 + 3x - 5$

Cumulative Review: Chapters 1–3, p. 294

1. [1.1a] $\frac{5}{2}$ **2.** [4.3a] -4 **3.** [4.7a] -14 **4.** [1.2e] 4 **5.** [1.6b] $\frac{1}{5}$ **6.** [1.3a] $-\frac{11}{60}$ **7.** [1.4a] 4.2 **8.** [1.5a] 7.28 **9.** [1.6c] $-\frac{5}{12}$ **10.** [4.2d] 2.2×10^{22} **11.** [4.2d] 4×10^{-5} **12.** [1.7a] -3 **13.** [1.8b] $-2y - 7$ **14.** [1.8c] $5x + 11$ **15.** [1.8d] -2 **16.** [4.4a] $2x^5 - 2x^4 + 3x^3 + 2$ **17.** [4.7d] $3x^2 + xy - 2y^2$ **18.** [4.4c] $x^3 + 5x^2 - x - 7$ **19.** [4.4c] $-\frac{1}{3}x^2 - \frac{3}{4}x$ **20.** [1.7c] $12x - 15y + 21$ **21.** [4.5a] $6x^8$ **22.** [4.5b] $2x^5 - 4x^4 + 8x^3 - 10x^2$ **23.** [4.5d] $3y^4 + 5y^3 - 10y - 12$ **24.** [4.7f] $2p^4 + 3p^3q + 2p^2q^2 - 2p^4q - p^3q^2 - p^2q^3 + pq^3$ **25.** [4.6a] $6x^2 + 13x + 6$ **26.** [4.6c] $9x^4 + 6x^2 + 1$ **27.** [4.6b] $t^2 - \frac{1}{4}$ **28.** [4.6b] $4y^4 - 25$ **29.** [4.6a] $4x^6 + 6x^4 - 6x^2 - 9$ **30.** [4.6c] $t^2 - 4t^3 + 4t^4$ **31.** [4.7f] $15p^2 - pq - 2q^2$ **32.** [4.8a] $6x^2 + 2x - 3$ **33.** [2.1b] -1.2 **34.** [2.2a] -21 **35.** [2.3a] 9 **36.** [2.2a] $-\frac{20}{3}$ **37.** [2.3b] 2 **38.** [2.1b] $\frac{13}{8}$ **39.** [2.3c] $-\frac{17}{21}$ **40.** [2.3b] -17 **41.** [2.3b] 2 **42.** [2.7e] $\{x|x < 16\}$ **43.** [2.7e] $\{x|x \leq -\frac{11}{8}\}$ **44.** [2.4b] $x = \frac{A - P}{Q}$ **45.** [2.5a] \$3.50 **46.** [2.6a] 18 and 19 **47.** [2.6a] 20 ft, 24 ft **48.** [2.6a] 10° **49.** [4.1d, f] y^4 **50.** [4.1e, f] $\frac{1}{x}$ **51.** [4.2a, b] $-\frac{27x^9}{y^6}$ **52.** [4.1d, e, f] x^3 **53.** [4.1a, f] $3^2 = 9, 3^{-2} = \frac{1}{9}, (\frac{1}{3})^2 = \frac{1}{9}, (\frac{1}{3})^{-2} = 9, -3^2 = -9, (-3)^2 = 9, (-\frac{1}{3})^2 = \frac{1}{9}, (-\frac{1}{3})^{-2} = 9$ **54.** [4.1d], [4.2a, b], [4.4a] $12x^5 - 15x^4 - 27x^3 + 4x^2$ **55.** [4.4a], [4.6c] $5x^2 - 2x + 10$ **56.** [2.3b], [4.6a, c] $\frac{11}{7}$ **57.** [1.2e], [2.3a] $-5, 5$

CHAPTER 4

Exercise Set 4.1, p. 305

1. x **3.** x^2 **5.** 2 **7.** $17xy$ **9.** x **11.** x^2y^2 **13.** $x(x - 6)$ **15.** $2x(x + 3)$ **17.** $x^2(x + 6)$ **19.** $8x^2(x^2 - 3)$ **21.** $2(x^2 + x - 4)$ **23.** $17xy(x^4y^2 + 2x^2y + 3)$ **25.** $x^2(6x^2 - 10x + 3)$ **27.** $x^2y^2(x^3y^3 + x^2y + xy - 1)$ **29.** $2x^3(x^4 - x^3 - 32x^2 + 2)$ **31.** $0.8x(2x^3 - 3x^2 + 4x + 8)$ **33.** $\frac{1}{3}x^3(5x^3 + 4x^2 + x + 1)$ **35.** $(x + 3)(x^2 + 2)$ **37.** $(3z - 1)(4z^2 + 7)$ **39.** $(3x + 2)(2x^2 + 1)$ **41.** $(2a - 7)(5a^3 - 1)$ **43.** $(x + 3)(x^2 + 2)$ **45.** $(x + 3)(2x^2 + 1)$ **47.** $(2x - 3)(4x^2 + 3)$ **49.** $(3p - 4)(4p^2 + 1)$ **51.** $(x - 1)(5x^2 - 1)$ **53.** $(x + 8)(x^2 - 3)$ **55.** $(x - 4)(2x^2 - 9)$ **57.** $\{x|x > -24\}$ **58.** $\{x|x \leq \frac{14}{5}\}$ **59.** 27 **60.** $p = 2A - q$ **61.** $y^2 + 12y + 35$ **62.** $y^2 + 14y + 49$ **63.** $y^2 - 49$ **64.** $y^2 - 14y + 49$

65.

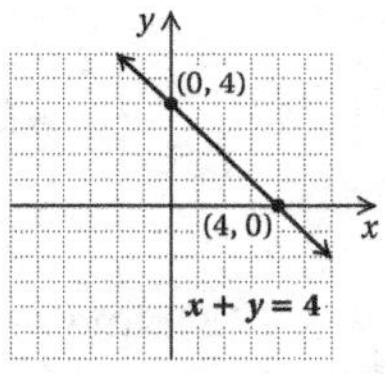

66.

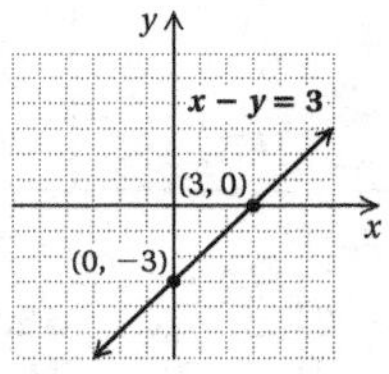

67.

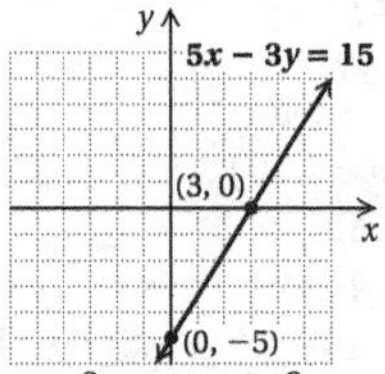

68.

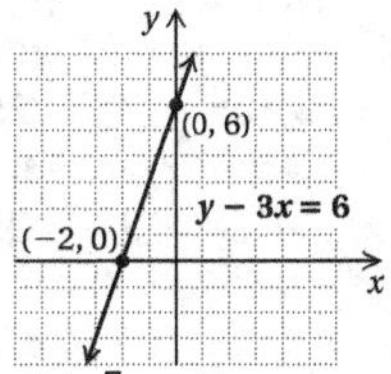

69. $(2x^2 + 3)(2x^3 + 3)$ **71.** $(x^5 + 1)(x^7 + 1)$ **73.** Not factorable by grouping

Exercise Set 4.2, p. 313

1.

Pairs of Factors	Sums of Factors
1, 15	16
−1, −15	−16
3, 5	8
−3, −5	−8

$(x + 3)(x + 5)$

3.

Pairs of Factors	Sums of Factors
1, 12	13
−1, −12	−13
2, 6	8
−2, −6	−8
3, 4	7
−3, −4	−7

$(x + 3)(x + 4)$

5.

Pairs of Factors	Sums of Factors
1, 9	10
−1, −9	−10
3, 3	6
−3, −3	−6

$(x - 3)^2$

7.

Pairs of Factors	Sums of Factors
−1, 14	13
1, −14	−13
−2, 7	5
2, −7	−5

$(x + 2)(x - 7)$

9.

Pairs of Factors	Sums of Factors
1, 4	5
−1, −4	−5
2, 2	4
−2, −2	−4

$(b + 1)(b + 4)$

11.

Pairs of Factors	Sums of Factors
$\frac{1}{3}, \frac{1}{3}$	$\frac{2}{3}$
$-\frac{1}{3}, -\frac{1}{3}$	$-\frac{2}{3}$
$1, \frac{1}{9}$	$\frac{10}{9}$
$-1, -\frac{1}{9}$	$-\frac{10}{9}$

$(x + \frac{1}{3})^2$

13. $(d - 2)(d - 5)$ **15.** $(y - 1)(y - 10)$ **17.** Prime
19. $(x - 9)(x + 2)$ **21.** $x(x - 8)(x + 2)$
23. $y(y - 9)(y + 5)$ **25.** $(x - 11)(x + 9)$
27. $(c^2 + 8)(c^2 - 7)$ **29.** $(a^2 + 7)(a^2 - 5)$
31. $(x - 6)(x + 7)$ **33.** Prime **35.** $(x + 10)^2$
37. $2z(z - 4)(z + 3)$ **39.** $3t^2(t^2 + t + 1)$
41. $x^2(x - 25)(x + 4)$ **43.** $(x - 24)(x + 3)$
45. $(x - 9)(x - 16)$ **47.** $(a + 12)(a - 11)$ **49.** $3(t + 1)^2$
51. $w^2(w - 4)^2$ **53.** $-1(x - 10)(x + 3)$, or $(-x + 10)(x + 3)$, or $(x - 10)(-x - 3)$
55. $-1(a - 2)(a + 12)$, or $(-a + 2)(a + 12)$, or $(a - 2)(-a - 12)$ **57.** $(x - 15)(x - 8)$
59. $-1(x + 12)(x - 9)$, or $(-x - 12)(x - 9)$, or $(x + 12)(-x + 9)$ **61.** $(y - 0.4)(y + 0.2)$
63. $(p + 5q)(p - 2q)$ **65.** $-1(t + 14)(t - 6)$, or $(-t - 14)(t - 6)$, or $(t + 14)(-t + 6)$ **67.** $(m + 4n)(m + n)$
69. $(s + 3t)(s - 5t)$ **71.** $6a^8(a + 2)(a - 7)$
73. $16x^3 - 48x^2 + 8x$ **74.** $28w^2 - 53w - 66$
75. $49w^2 + 84w + 36$ **76.** $16w^2 - 88w + 121$
77. $16w^2 - 121$ **78.** $y^3 - 3y^2 + 5y$
79. $6x^2 + 11xy - 35y^2$ **80.** $27x^{12}$ **81.** $\frac{8}{3}$ **82.** $-\frac{7}{2}$
83. 1743 arrests **84.** 100°, 25°, 55°
85. 15, −15, 27, −27, 51, −51 **87.** $\left(x + \frac{1}{4}\right)\left(x - \frac{3}{4}\right)$
89. $(x + 5)\left(x - \frac{5}{7}\right)$ **91.** $(b^n + 5)(b^n + 2)$
93. $2x^2(4 - \pi)$

Mid-Chapter Review: Chapter 4, p. 317

1. True **2.** False **3.** True **4.** False
5. $10y^3 - 18y^2 + 12y = 2y \cdot 5y^2 - 2y \cdot 9y + 2y \cdot 6$
$= 2y(5y^2 - 9y + 6)$
6. $a \cdot c = 2 \cdot (-6) = -12$;
$-x = -4x + 3x$;
$2x^2 - x - 6 = 2x^2 - 4x + 3x - 6$
$= 2x(x - 2) + 3(x - 2)$
$= (x - 2)(2x + 3)$
7. x **8.** x^2 **9.** $6x^3$ **10.** 4 **11.** $5x^2y$ **12.** x^2y^2
13. $x(x^2 - 8)$ **14.** $3x(x + 4)$ **15.** $2(y^2 + 4y - 2)$
16. $t^3(3t^3 - 5t - 2)$ **17.** $(x + 1)(x + 3)$ **18.** $(z - 2)^2$
19. $(x + 4)(x^2 + 3)$ **20.** $8y^3(y^2 - 6)$ **21.** $(z - 1)(z + 5)$
22. $(w - 5)(w - 3)$ **23.** $(x - 6y)(x - 4y)$
24. $3x(x + 2)(x + 5)$ **25.** $(y + 2)(y + 4)$ **26.** $(x - 7)(x^2 + 4)$
27. $-1(y - 4)(y + 1)$, or $(-y + 4)(y + 1)$, or $(y - 4)(-y - 1)$
28. $y(y + 6)(y + 3)$ **29.** $(y - 4z)(y + 5z)$
30. $(m - 8n)(m + 2n)$ **31.** $2(w - 3)^2$
32. $(t - 2)(t + 7)$ **33.** $(2t - 5)^2$ **34.** $(t - 2)(t + 6)$
35. $-1(y - 6)(y + 2)$, or $(-y + 6)(y + 2)$, or $(y - 6)(-y - 2)$

Exercise Set 4.3, p. 325

1. Yes **3.** No **5.** No **7.** Yes **9.** $(x - 7)^2$
11. $(x + 8)^2$ **13.** $(x - 1)^2$ **15.** $(x + 2)^2$ **17.** $(y + 6)^2$
19. $(t - 4)^2$ **21.** $(q^2 - 3)^2$ **23.** $(4y + 7)^2$ **25.** $2(x - 1)^2$
27. $x(x - 9)^2$ **29.** $3(2q - 3)^2$ **31.** $(7 - 3x)^2$, or $(3x - 7)^2$
33. $5(y^2 + 1)^2$ **35.** $(1 + 2x^2)^2$ **37.** $(2p + 3q)^2$
39. $(a - 3b)^2$ **41.** $(9a - b)^2$ **43.** $4(3a + 4b)^2$ **45.** Yes
47. No **49.** No **51.** Yes **53.** $(y + 2)(y - 2)$
55. $(p + 3)(p - 3)$ **57.** $(t + 7)(t - 7)$
59. $(a + b)(a - b)$ **61.** $(5t + m)(5t - m)$
63. $(10 + k)(10 - k)$ **65.** $(4a + 3)(4a - 3)$
67. $(2x + 5y)(2x - 5y)$ **69.** $2(2x + 7)(2x - 7)$
71. $x(6 + 7x)(6 - 7x)$ **73.** $\left(\frac{1}{4} + 7x^4\right)\left(\frac{1}{4} - 7x^4\right)$
75. $(0.3y + 0.02)(0.3y - 0.02)$ **77.** $(7a^2 + 9)(7a^2 - 9)$
79. $(a^2 + 4)(a + 2)(a - 2)$ **81.** $5(x^2 + 9)(x + 3)(x - 3)$
83. $(1 + y^4)(1 + y^2)(1 + y)(1 - y)$
85. $(x^6 + 4)(x^3 + 2)(x^3 - 2)$ **87.** $\left(y + \frac{1}{4}\right)\left(y - \frac{1}{4}\right)$
89. $\left(5 + \frac{1}{7}x\right)\left(5 - \frac{1}{7}x\right)$ **91.** $(4m^2 + t^2)(2m + t)(2m - t)$
93. −11 **94.** 400 **95.** $-\frac{5}{6}$ **96.** −0.9 **97.** 2 **98.** −160
99. $x^2 - 4xy + 4y^2$ **100.** $\frac{1}{2}\pi x^2 + 2xy$ **101.** y^{12}
102. $25a^4b^6$
103.

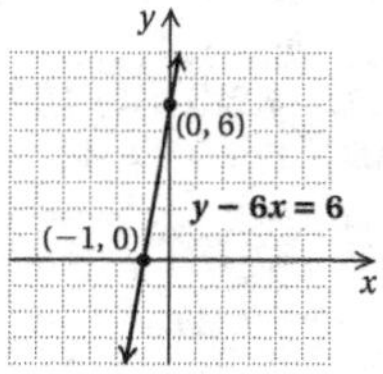

104.

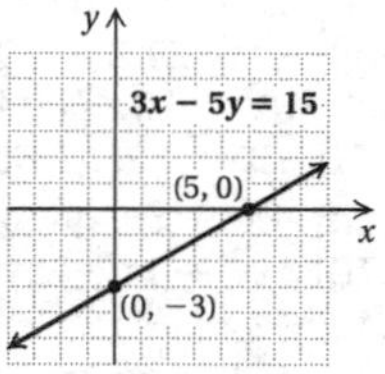

105. Prime **107.** $(x + 11)^2$ **109.** $2x(3x + 1)^2$
111. $(x^4 + 2^4)(x^2 + 2^2)(x + 2)(x - 2)$
113. $3x^3(x + 2)(x - 2)$ **115.** $2x\left(3x + \frac{2}{5}\right)\left(3x - \frac{2}{5}\right)$
117. $p(0.7 + p)(0.7 - p)$ **119.** $(0.8x + 1.1)(0.8x - 1.1)$
121. $x(x + 6)$ **123.** $\left(x + \frac{1}{x}\right)\left(x - \frac{1}{x}\right)$
125. $(9 + b^{2k})(3 - b^k)(3 + b^k)$ **127.** $(3b^n + 2)^2$
129. $(y + 4)^2$ **131.** 9 **133.** Not correct **135.** Not correct

Summary and Review: Chapter 4, p. 329

Concept Reinforcement

1. False **2.** True **3.** False **4.** True

Important Concepts

1. $4xy$ **2.** $9x^2(3x^3 - x + 2)$ **3.** $(z - 3)(z^2 + 4)$
4. $(x + 2)(x + 4)$ **5.** $(2x + 1)^2$ **6.** $2(3x + 2)(3x - 2)$

Review Exercises

1. $5y^2$ **2.** $12x$ **3.** $5(1 + 2x^3)(1 - 2x^3)$ **4.** $x(x - 3)$
5. $(3x + 2)(3x - 2)$ **6.** $(x + 6)(x - 2)$ **7.** $(x + 7)^2$
8. $(x + 1)(x^2 + 3)$ **9.** $(x^2 + 9)(x + 3)(x - 3)$
10. $2(x + 5)(x - 5)$ **11.** $(4x^2 + 1)(2x + 1)(2x - 1)$
12. Prime **13.** $x(x - 6)(x + 5)$ **14.** $(2x + 5)(2x - 5)$
15. $(x - 3)^2$ **16.** $3(x + 3)(x - 3)$ **17.** $(x - 5)(x - 3)$
18. $(5x - 2)^2$ **19.** $(xy + 4)(xy - 3)$
20. $(m + 5)(m + t)$ **21.** $32(x^2 - 2y^2z^2)(x^2 + 2y^2z^2)$

Test: Chapter 4, p. 332

1. [5.1a] $4x^3$ **2.** [5.2a] $(x - 5)(x - 2)$ **3.** [5.5b] $(x - 5)^2$
4. [5.1c] $(x + 1)(x^2 + 2)$ **5.** [5.1b] $x(x - 5)$
6. [5.2a] $x(x + 3)(x - 1)$ **7.** [5.5d] $(2x + 3)(2x - 3)$
8. [5.2a] $(x - 4)(x + 3)$ **9.** [5.5d] $3(w + 5)(w - 5)$
10. [5.5d] $3(x^2 + 4)(x + 2)(x - 2)$ **11.** [5.5b] $(7x - 6)^2$
12. [5.5d] $5(4 + x^2)(2 + x)(2 - x)$

Cumulative Review: Chapters 1–4, p. 333

1. [1.2d] $<$ **2.** [1.2d] $>$ **3.** [1.4a] 0.35 **4.** [1.6c] -1.57
5. [1.5a] $-\frac{1}{14}$ **6.** [1.6c] $-\frac{6}{5}$ **7.** [1.8c] $4x + 1$ **8.** [1.8d] -8
9. [4.2a, b] $\frac{8x^6}{y^3}$ **10.** [4.1d, e] $-\frac{1}{6x^3}$
11. [4.4a] $x^4 - 3x^3 - 3x^2 - 4$ **12.** [4.7e] $2x^2y^2 - x^2y - xy$
13. [4.6c] $4t^2 - 12t + 9$ **14.** [4.6b] $x^4 - 9$
15. [4.6a] $6x^2 + 4x - 16$
16. [4.5b] $2x^4 + 6x^3 + 8x^2$ **17.** [4.5d] $4y^3 + 4y^2 + 5y - 4$
18. [4.6b] $x^2 - \frac{4}{9}$ **19.** [5.2a] $(x + 4)(x - 2)$
20. [5.5d] $(2x + 5)(2x - 5)$ **21.** [5.5b] $(x - 13)^2$
22. [5.5d] $3(x^4 + 4y^4)(x^2 + 2y^2)(x^2 - 2y^2)$
23. [2.3b] 15 **24.** [2.7e] $\{y | y < 6\}$
25. [2.3a] 0.2 **26.** [2.7e] $\{x | x \le 20\}$
27. [2.3c] All real numbers **28.** [2.4b] $m = \frac{y - b}{x}$
29. [2.6a] 50, 52 **30.** [2.6a] 30 m, 60 m, 10 m
31. [2.5a] \$29 **32.** [2.3b] 22

APPENDIX

Exercise Set, p. 337

1. $\{3, 4, 5, 6, 7, 8\}$ **3.** $\{41, 43, 45, 47, 49\}$ **5.** $\{-3, 3\}$
7. False **9.** True **11.** True **13.** True **15.** True
17. False **19.** {c, d, e} **21.** $\{1, 10\}$ **23.** { }, or $\varnothing$
25. {a, e, i, o, u, q, c, k} **27.** $\{0, 1, 7, 10, 2, 5\}$
29. {a, e, i, o, u, m, n, f, g, h} **31.** $\{x | x \text{ is an integer}\}$
33. $\{x | x \text{ is a real number}\}$ **35.** { }, or $\varnothing$
37. **(a)** A; **(b)** A; **(c)** A; **(d)** { }, or $\varnothing$ **39.** True

Glossary

A

Abscissa The first coordinate in an ordered pair of numbers

Absolute value The distance that a number is from 0 on the number line

***ac*-method** A method for factoring trinomials of the type $ax^2 + bx + c, a \neq 1$, involving the product, ac, of the leading coefficient a and the last term c

Additive identity The number 0

Additive inverse A number's opposite; two numbers are additive inverses of each other if their sum is 0

Algebraic expression An expression consisting of variables, constants, numerals, operation signs, and/or grouping symbols

Area The number of square units that fill a plane region

Arithmetic numbers The whole numbers and the positive fractions. All these numbers can be named with fraction notation $\frac{a}{b}$, where a and b are whole numbers and $b \neq 0$.

Ascending order When a polynomial is written with the terms arranged according to degree from least to greatest, it is said to be in ascending order.

Associative law of addition The statement that when three numbers are added, regrouping the addends gives the same sum

Associative law of multiplication The statement that when three numbers are multiplied, regrouping the factors gives the same product

Average A center point of a set of numbers found by adding the numbers and dividing by the number of items of data; also called the *arithmetic mean* or *mean*

Axes Two perpendicular number lines used to identify points in a plane

B

Base In exponential notation, the number being raised to a power

Binomial A polynomial composed of two terms

C

Circumference The distance around a circle

Coefficient The numerical multiplier of a variable

Commutative law of addition The statement that when two numbers are added, changing the order in which the numbers are added does not affect the sum

Commutative law of multiplication The statement that when two numbers are multiplied, changing the order in which the numbers are multiplied does not affect the product

Complementary angles Angles whose sum is 90°

Completing the square Adding a particular constant to an expression so that the resulting sum is a perfect square

Complex fraction expression A rational expression that has one or more rational expressions within its numerator and/or denominator

Complex rational expression A rational expression that has one or more rational expressions within its numerator and/or denominator

Complex-number system A number system that contains the real-number system and is designed so that negative numbers have defined square roots

Composite number A natural number, other than 1, that is not prime

Conjugates Pairs of radical terms, like $\sqrt{a} + \sqrt{b}$ and $\sqrt{a} - \sqrt{b}$ or $c + \sqrt{d}$ and $c - \sqrt{d}$, for which the product does not have a radical term

Consecutive even integers Even integers that are two units apart

Consecutive integers Integers that are one unit apart

Consecutive odd integers Odd integers that are two units apart

Constant A known number

Constant of proportionality The constant in an equation of direct or inverse variation

Coordinates The numbers in an ordered pair

Cube root The number c is called a cube root of a if $c^3 = a$.

D

Decimal notation A representation of a number containing a decimal point

Degree of a polynomial The degree of the term of highest degree in a polynomial

Degree of a term The sum of the exponents of the variables

Denominator The bottom number in a fraction

Descending order When a polynomial is written with the terms arranged according to degree from greatest to least, it is said to be in descending order.

Diameter A segment that passes through the center of a circle and has its endpoints on the circle

Difference of cubes Any expression that can be written in the form $A^3 - B^3$

Difference of squares Any expression that can be written in the form $A^2 - B^2$

Direct variation A situation that translates to an equation described by $y = kx$, with k a positive constant

Discriminant The radicand, $b^2 - 4ac$, from the quadratic formula

Distributive law of multiplication over addition The statement that multiplying a factor by the sum of two numbers gives the same result as multiplying the factor by each of the two numbers and then adding

Distributive law of multiplication over subtraction The statement that multiplying a factor by the difference of two numbers gives the same result as multiplying the factor by each of the two numbers and then subtracting

Domain The set of all first coordinates of the ordered pairs in a function

E

Elimination method An algebraic method that uses the addition principle to solve a system of equations

Empty set The set without members

Equation A number sentence that says that the expressions on either side of the equals sign, =, represent the same number

Equation of direct variation An equation described by $y = kx$, with k a positive constant, used to represent direct variation

Equation of inverse variation An equation described by $y = k/x$, with k a positive constant, used to represent inverse variation

Equivalent equations Equations with the same solutions

Equivalent expressions Expressions that have the same value for all allowable replacements

Equivalent inequalities Inequalities that have the same solution set

Evaluate To substitute a value for each occurrence of a variable in an expression

Exponent In expressions of the form a^n, the number n is an exponent. For n a natural number, a^n represents n factors of a.

Exponential notation A representation of a number using a base raised to a power

F

Factor *Verb*: To write an equivalent expression that is a product. *Noun*: A multiplier

Factorization of a polynomial An expression that names the polynomial as a product

FOIL To multiply two binomials by multiplying the First terms, the Outside terms, the Inside terms, and then the Last terms

Formula An equation that uses numbers or letters to represent a relationship between two or more quantities

Fraction equation An equation containing one or more rational expressions; also called a *rational equation*

Fraction expression A quotient, or ratio, of polynomials; also called a *rational expression*

Fraction notation A number written using a numerator and a denominator

Function A correspondence that assigns to each member of a set called the domain *exactly one* member of a set called the range

G

Grade The measure of a road's steepness

Graph A picture or diagram of the data in a table; a line, curve, or collection of points that represents all the solutions of an equation

Greatest common factor (GCF) The common factor of a polynomial with the largest possible coefficient and the largest possible exponent(s)

H

Hypotenuse In a right triangle, the side opposite the 90° angle

I

Identity Property of 1 The statement that the product of a number and 1 is always the original number

Identity Property of 0 The statement that the sum of a number and 0 is always the original number

Index In the radical $\sqrt[n]{a}$, the number n is called the index.

Inequality A mathematical sentence using $<$, $>$, $\leq$, $\geq$, or $\neq$

Input A member of the domain of a function

Integers The whole numbers and their opposites

Intercept The point at which a graph intersects the x- or y-axis

Intersection of sets *A* and *B* The set of all elements that are common to both A and B

Inverse variation A situation that translates to an equation described by $y = k/x$, with k a positive constant

Irrational number A real number that cannot be named as a ratio of two integers

L

Leading coefficient The coefficient of the term of highest degree in a polynomial

Least common denominator (LCD) The least common multiple of the denominators of two or more fractions

Least common multiple (LCM) The smallest number that is a multiple of both numbers

Legs In a right triangle, the two sides that form the right angle

Like radicals Radicals that have the same radicand

Like terms Terms that have exactly the same variable factors

Line of symmetry A line that can be drawn through a graph such that the part of the graph on one side of the line is an exact reflection of the part on the opposite side

Linear equation Any equation that can be written in the form $y = mx + b$ or $Ax + By = C$, where x and y are variables

Linear function A function that can be described by an equation of the form $y = mx + b$, where x and y are variables

Linear inequality An inequality whose related equation is a linear equation

M

Mean A center point of a set of numbers found by adding the numbers and dividing by the number of items of data; also called the *average*

Median In a set of data listed in order from smallest to largest, the middle number if there is an odd number of data items, or the average of the two middle numbers if there is an even number of data items

Mode The number or numbers that occur most often in a set of data

Monomial An expression of the type ax^n, where a is a real number constant and n is a nonnegative integer

Motion problem A problem that deals with distance, speed (or rate), and time

Multiple A product of a number and some natural number

Multiplication property of 0 The statement that the product of 0 and any real number is 0

Multiplicative identity The number 1

Multiplicative inverses Reciprocals; two numbers whose product is 1

N

***n*th root** The number c is the nth root of a if $c^n = a$.

Natural numbers The counting numbers: 1, 2, 3, 4, 5, . . .

Negative integers The integers to the left of zero on the number line

Nonnegative rational numbers The whole numbers and the positive fractions. All these numbers can be named with fraction notation $\frac{a}{b}$, where a and b are whole numbers and $b \neq 0$.

Numerator The top number in a fraction

O

Opposite The opposite, or additive inverse, of a number a is denoted $-a$. Opposites are the same distance from 0 on the number line but on different sides of 0.

Opposite of a polynomial To find the opposite of a polynomial, replace each term with its opposite—that is, change the sign of every term.

Ordered pair A pair of numbers of the form (h, k) for which the order in which the numbers are listed is important

Ordinate The second coordinate in an ordered pair of numbers

Origin The point on a graph where the two axes intersect

Output A member of the range of a function

P

Parabola A graph of a quadratic equation

Parallel lines Lines in the same plane that never intersect. Two lines are parallel if they have the same slope.

Parallelogram A four-sided polygon with two pairs of parallel sides

Percent notation A representation of a number as parts per 100

Perfect square A rational number p for which there exists a number a for which $a^2 = p$

Perfect-square trinomial A trinomial that is the square of a binomial

Perimeter The distance around a polygon, or the sum of the lengths of its sides

Perpendicular lines Lines that form a right angle

Pi (π) The number that results when the circumference of a circle is divided by its diameter; $\pi \approx 3.14$, or 22/7

Point–slope equation An equation of the form $y - y_1 = m(x - x_1)$, where m is the slope and (x_1, y_1) is a point on the line

Polygon A closed geometric figure with three or more sides

Polynomial A monomial or a combination of sums and/or differences of monomials

Polynomial equation An equation in which two polynomials are set equal to each other

Positive integers The natural numbers or the integers to the right of zero on the number line

Prime factorization A factorization of a composite number as a product of prime numbers

Prime number A natural number that has *exactly two different factors*: itself and 1
Prime polynomial A polynomial that cannot be factored using only integer coefficients
Principal square root The positive square root of a number
Principle of zero products The statement that an equation $ab = 0$ is true if and only if $a = 0$ is true or $b = 0$ is true, or both are true
Proportion An equation stating that two ratios are equal
Proportional numbers Two pairs of numbers having the same ratio
Pythagorean theorem In any right triangle, if a and b are the lengths of the legs and c is the length of the hypotenuse, then $a^2 + b^2 = c^2$.

Q

Quadrants The four regions into which the axes divide a plane
Quadratic equation An equation equivalent to an equation of the type $ax^2 + bx + c = 0$, where $a \neq 0$
Quadratic formula The solutions of $ax^2 + bx + c = 0$, $a \neq 0$, are given by the equation $x = \dfrac{-b \pm \sqrt{b^2 - 4ac}}{2a}$.
Quadratic function A second-degree polynomial function in one variable

R

Radical equation An equation in which a variable appears in one or more radicands
Radical expression An algebraic expression written under a radical
Radical symbol The symbol $\sqrt{\ }$; also called *square root*
Radicand The expression under the radical
Radius A segment with one endpoint on the center of a circle and the other endpoint on the circle
Range The set of all second coordinates of the ordered pairs in a function
Rate The ratio of two different kinds of measure
Ratio The quotient of two quantities
Rational equation An equation containing one or more rational expressions; also called a *fraction equation*
Rational expression A quotient, or ratio, of two polynomials; also called a *fraction expression*
Rational number A number that can be written in the form a/b, where a and b are integers and $b \neq 0$
Rationalizing the denominator A procedure for finding an equivalent expression without a radical in the denominator
Real numbers All rational and irrational numbers; the set of all numbers corresponding to points on the number line
Reciprocal A multiplicative inverse. Two numbers are reciprocals if their product is 1.
Rectangle A four-sided polygon with four right angles
Relation A correspondence between a first set called the domain, and a second set called the range, such that each member of the domain corresponds to *at least one* member of the range
Repeating decimal A decimal in which a number pattern repeats indefinitely
Right triangle A triangle that includes a 90° angle
Rise The change in the second coordinate between two points on a line
Roster notation A way of naming sets by listing all the elements in the set
Rounding Approximating the value of a number; used when estimating
Run The change in the first coordinate between two points on a line

S

Scientific notation A representation of a number of the form $M \times 10^n$, where n is an integer, $1 \leq M < 10$, and M is expressed in decimal notation
Set A collection of objects
Set-builder notation The naming of a set by describing basic characteristics of the elements in the set
Similar triangles Triangles in which corresponding angles have the same measure and the lengths of corresponding sides are proportional
Simplest fraction notation A fraction written with the smallest numerator and denominator
Simplify To rewrite an expression in an equivalent, abbreviated, form
Slope The ratio of the rise to the run for any two points on a line
Slope–intercept equation An equation of the form $y = mx + b$, where x and y are variables
Solution A replacement for the variable that makes an equation or inequality true
Solution of a system of equations An ordered pair that makes both equations true
Solution set The set of all solutions of an equation, an inequality, or a system of equations or inequalities
Solve To find all solutions of an equation, an inequality, or a system of equations or inequalities; to find the solution(s) of a problem
Square A four-sided polygon with four right angles and all sides of equal length
Square of a number A number multiplied by itself
Square root The number c is a square root of a if $c^2 = a$.
Square root symbol The symbol $\sqrt{\ }$; also called *radical symbol*
Subsets Sets that are a part of other sets
Substitute To replace a variable with a number
Substitution method A nongraphical method for solving systems of equations
Sum of cubes An expression that can be written in the form $A^3 + B^3$

Sum of squares An expression that can be written in the form $A^2 + B^2$
Supplementary angles Angles whose sum is 180°
System of equations A set of two or more equations that are to be solved simultaneously

T

Term A number, a variable, or a product or a quotient of numbers and/or variables
Terminating decimal A decimal that can be written using a finite number of decimal places
Triangle A three-sided polygon
Trinomial A polynomial that is composed of three terms
Trinomial square The square of a binomial expressed as three terms

U

Union of sets *A* and *B* The set of all elements belonging to either A or B

V

Value The numerical result after a number has been substituted into an expression
Variable A letter that represents an unknown number
Variation constant The constant in an equation of direct or inverse variation
Vertex The point at which the graph of a quadratic equation crosses its line of symmetry
Vertical-line test The statement that a graph represents a function if it is impossible to draw a vertical line that intersects the graph more than once
Volume The number of cubic units that fill a solid region

W

Whole numbers The natural numbers and 0: 0, 1, 2, 3, . . .

X

***x*-intercept** The point at which a graph crosses the x-axis

Y

***y*-intercept** The point at which a graph crosses the y-axis

Index

SUPPLEMENTARY ELEMENTARY ALGEBRA EXERCISES

Introduction

The course objectives of Math 017 Elementary Algebra include concepts and material that may not be sufficiently covered in the main portion of this text. The Community College of Philadelphia Mathematics Department provides exercises in this supplement that we hope will provide adequate coverage to help students meet the course objectives. These exercises are drawn from the text *Elephant Math 017 Materials with Exercises* available at the departmental website: http://faculty.ccp.edu/dept/math/developmental.html. The exercises are organized according to the lessons in that text. We list the major topics in each lesson below as well in each section header to assist in locating relevant exercises. We hope you find this supplement useful and informative.

Contents

Ex.1 Fill in blanks using the following words 'variable', 'algebraic expression', 'number(s)' as appropriate.

$3x+2$, y^2, $\dfrac{a+bc}{2}$, $(-2a+1)^3$ are examples of ________________.

Ψ x, y, a, b, c are examples of ________________ but also examples of ________________.

Variables represent ________________.

If we know the value of x, we can evaluate $3x+2$, and as a result we get a ________________.

Ex.2 How are the following expressions read?

a) a^2 b) a^3 c) a^{12} d) 2^m

e) $-y$ f) cd g) $a-b$ h) $\frac{2}{5}x$

Ex.3 Rewrite the following expressions, inserting a multiplication sign whenever multiplication is implied. Whenever there is no operation of multiplication, clearly say so using the phrase "there is no multiplication performed in this expression".

a) $7n$ b) $-5km$ c) $-x-y$

d) $-x(-y)$ e) $\dfrac{3x}{2}$ f) $2x-yz+w(-t)$

Ex.4 The operation that is indicated in the algebraic expression $a+b$ is, of course, addition. Name the operation that is to be performed in the following algebraic expressions.

a) ab b) $\dfrac{q}{s}$ c) x^5

d) $3 \div x$ e) $3-x$ f) $3(-x)$

Ex.5 In the following expressions parentheses are needed. Explain why they are needed.

a) $x+(-b)$ b) $\left(\dfrac{m}{n}\right)^8$ c) $3b(-c)$

d) $(-a)^4$ e) $y(-x)$ f) $a \div (-b)$

Ex.6 Determine which expression is raised to the *n*-th power.

a) $(-s)^n$ b) $-s^n$ c) $(st)^n$

d) st^n e) $\dfrac{x^n}{y}$ f) $\left(\dfrac{x}{y}\right)^n$

g) $x(st)^n$ h) $xy-s^n$ i) $x(y-s)^n$

Ex.7 Fill in the blanks.

a) It is customary to write ________ instead of $1 \cdot x$.

b) It is customary to write ________ instead of $-1 \cdot x$.

c) When one writes ab, it is understood that the operation that is to be performed is ____________.

Ex.8 Fill in the blanks with numbers to make the statement true.

a) ______ $\cdot x = x$

b) ______ $\cdot x = -x$

c) ______ $\cdot x = 0$

Ex.9 Write an algebraic expression representing the opposite number of (do not remove parentheses).

a) $-x$

b) $\dfrac{x^3}{y}$

c) $-\dfrac{x^3}{y}$

d) $\dfrac{-x^3}{-y}$

Ex.10 Use the letter y to represent a number and write the following phrases as algebraic expressions.
a) Half of a number
b) Three fourths of a number
c) A quantity increased by 5
d) A number subtracted from v
e) A quantity squared
f) Three more than a number
g) A number decreased by x
h) The product of x and a number
i) A number doubled

Ex.11 Write the following phrases as algebraic expressions. Remember to place parentheses when needed (place them only when needed). Do not simplify.
a) The sum of a and $-b$
b) The difference of a and $-b$
c) The product of a and $-b$
d) The opposite of C
f) The opposite of $-C$
g) The opposite of $\dfrac{-a}{-b}$
h) The product of v, $-t$, and $-p$
i) The quotient of c and $-B$
j) $-x$ raised to m-th power
k) $\dfrac{x}{y}$ raised to m-th power

Ex.12 Give your answer in the form of an algebraic expression.
a) Carlos is x years old at this moment. How old will Carlos be in 10 years?
b) An items in a store costs x dollars. What is the price of the item, if after a discount, its price was reduced to two thirds of the original one?
c) You have x dollars to divide equally among 3 kids. How much will each child get?
d) You have $100 to divide equally among x kids. How much will each child get?
e) Charles bought 2 more lamps for his apartment today. If there are x lamps in Charles' apartment now, how many lamps were in his apartment before the purchase?
f) There are 30 books on each shelf. How many books are on x shelves?
g) There are x students in a classroom. How many students are still in the classroom, if 3 students leave?
h) John is 5 years older than Tom. If John is x years old, how old is Tom?

Ex.13 Let d be a variable representing the distance driven by a car, and let t represent the time it took to drive that distance. Write the following phrase as an algebraic expression: The distance divided by time.

Ex.14 Let m be a variable representing the mass of a given body, and let a represent its acceleration. Use m and a to write the following phrase as an algebraic expression: The product of the mass of a body and its acceleration.

Ex.15 Let h be a variable representing the height of a triangle, and b represent the base of the triangle. Use h and b to write the following statement as an algebraic expression: One half of the product of the base of a triangle and its height.

Ex.16 Let $x = 3$. Rewrite the expression replacing the variable with its value and evaluate, if possible. If evaluation is not possible, explain why it is not possible.

a) $x+5$
b) $x-2$
c) $\frac{x}{3}$
d) $4x$
e) x^2
f) $\frac{6}{x}$

Ex.17 If $x = 0$ the expression $\frac{1}{x}$ cannot be evaluated. Why not? Can $\frac{1}{x-5}$ be evaluated when $x = 0$? What if $x = 5$? Find another example of an algebraic expression and a value of a variable(s) for which evaluation is not possible.

Ex.18 Let $x = 0$. Rewrite the expression replacing the variable with its value and evaluate, if possible. If evaluation is not possible, explain why it is not possible.

a) $3x$
b) $x-2$
c) $\frac{4}{x}$
d) $\frac{x}{7}$
e) $\frac{2}{x-3}$
f) $\frac{0}{x}$

Ex.19 Let $x = 2$. Rewrite the expression replacing the variable with its value and evaluate, if possible. Otherwise, write "undefined".

a) 3^x
b) x^3
c) x^x

Ex.20 Evaluate $-A$, if

a) $A = 2$
b) $A = -2$

Ex.21 Substitute $x = 6$ in the following expressions and then evaluate, if possible. Otherwise, write "undefined".

a) $x-8$
b) $-10-x$
c) $-4+x$
d) $x-6$
e) $-2+x-6$

Ex.22 Substitute $x=-2$ in the following expressions and then evaluate, if possible. Otherwise, write "undefined".

a) $2+x$
b) $2-x$
c) $-2-x$
d) $-5-x+4$
e) $6+x-10-x$

Ex.23 Substitute $x=10$ in the following expressions and then evaluate, if possible. Otherwise, write "undefined".

a) $3x$
b) $-5x$
c) $\frac{-200}{x}$
d) $-\frac{x}{2}$
e) $-5\div x$
f) x^4

Ex.24 Substitute $x=-12$ in the following expressions and then evaluate, if possible. Otherwise, write "undefined".

a) $-1000x$
b) $\frac{x}{6}$
c) $-5x$
d) $\frac{6}{x+12}$
e) $-24\div x$
f) x^2

Ex.25 Substitute $x=\frac{2}{3}$ in the following expressions and then evaluate, if possible. Otherwise, write "undefined".

a) $\frac{5}{3}+x$
b) $x+\frac{1}{5}$
c) $-x+\frac{2}{7}$
d) $-\frac{5}{12}-x$
e) $2+x$
f) $-x-3$

Ex.26 Substitute $x=-\frac{3}{5}$ in the following expressions and then evaluate, if possible. Otherwise, write "undefined".

a) $\frac{3}{10}-x$
b) $-\frac{1}{7}-x$
c) $2\frac{1}{5}+x$
d) $-1\frac{1}{4}-x$
e) $-x-3\frac{1}{2}$

Ex.27 Substitute $x = \frac{2}{7}$ in the following expressions and then evaluate, if possible. Otherwise, write "undefined".

a) $2x$

b) $-7x$

c) $-\frac{14}{3}x$

d) $\frac{5}{28} \div x$

e) $\frac{5}{x}$

f) $\frac{-x}{2}$

Ex.28 Substitute $x = -\frac{3}{4}$ in the following expressions and then evaluate, if possible. Otherwise, write "undefined".

a) x^2

b) $\frac{4}{3}x$

c) $\frac{-x}{1\frac{2}{3}}$

d) $-1\frac{1}{8} \div x$

e) $\frac{x}{-3}$

f) $\frac{0}{x}$

Ex.29 Substitute $x = 0.2$ in the following expressions and then evaluate, if possible. Otherwise, write "undefined".

a) $x + 3.21$

b) $35.01 - x$

c) $\frac{x}{4}$

d) $-40x$

e) $0.3x$

f) $\frac{-x}{0.04}$

Ex.30 Substitute $x = -0.6$ in the following expressions and then evaluate, if possible. Otherwise, write "undefined".

a) $-x - 4.5$

b) $-2.7 - x$

c) $\frac{1.2}{-x}$

d) $-600x$

e) $0.001x$

f) x^3

Ex 31 Substitute $x = -1.5$ in the following expressions and then evaluate, if possible. Otherwise, write "undefined".

a) $x - 0.08$

b) $-3 - x + 0.4$

c) $x \div 0.15$

d) $-0.2x$

e) $\frac{-30}{x}$

Ex. 32 If possible, evaluate $x+y$ when

a) $x=\frac{3}{5}, y=\frac{2}{3}$

b) $x=\frac{2}{7}, y=-\frac{9}{14}$

c) $x=-0.2, y=-1.08$

Ex. 33 If possible, evaluate $x-y$ when

a) $x=\frac{3}{5}, y=\frac{2}{3}$

b) $x=\frac{2}{7}, y=-\frac{9}{14}$

c) $x=-0.2, y=-1.08$

Ex. 34 If possible, evaluate xy when

a) $x=\frac{2}{11}, y=\frac{22}{9}$

b) $x=-4, y=-\frac{9}{10}$

c) $x=-0.2, y=0.01$

Ex. 35 If possible, evaluate $\frac{x}{y}$ when

a) $x=\frac{2}{11}, y=\frac{22}{9}$

b) $x=-4, y=-\frac{9}{10}$

c) $x=-0.2, y=0.01$

Ex. 36 If possible, evaluate $(-x)^m$ when

a) $x=10, \quad m=7$

b) $x=-2, \quad m=4$

c) $x=\frac{1}{2}, \quad m=3$

d) $x=-0.1, \quad m=5$

Ex. 37 Use the letter x to represent a number and write the following statements as algebraic expressions. Then evaluate each expression when $x=-\frac{1}{2}$.

a) A number doubled
b) Three fourth of a number
c) A number raised to the second power

Ex.38 Evaluate $-t$, when $t = 1$, $t = -1$

Based on your results, which of the following are true?

a) $-t$ is always positive

b) $-t$ is always negative

c) $-t$ may be positive or negative depending on the value of t

Ex.1 Write the algebraic expression representing the following.

a) $m-2n$ subtracted from x
b) the opposite of $m-2n$
c) $m-2n$ multiplied by 7
d) $3a$ subtracted from $m-2n$
e) the opposite of k^2-3k+1
f) 4 divided by $-4x+y$ (use "÷" symbol in your answer)

Ex.2 Write the following phrases as algebraic expressions. Remember to place parentheses where needed (please, place them only when needed).

a) Multiply 3 by x, and then add y
b) Multiply the sum of a and b by 4
c) The opposite of x, then raise it to the sixth power
d) Subtract 3 from y, and then multiply the result by z
e) Raise x to the third power, and then multiply the result by 9
f) Multiply x by 9, and then raise the result to the third power
g) The difference of a and b, then divided by c
h) Divide 3 by y, and then add x
i) The opposite of the sum of M and 3
j) Raise $-x$ to the third power, raise y to the seventh power, and then add them together

Ex.3 Use the letter x to represent a number and write the following as an algebraic expression.

a) A number decreased by 7, and then doubled
b) Add c to a number, and then take two thirds of the sum
c) Take one fourth of a number, and then subtract 5 from it
d) Multiply a number by 9, and then subtract it from c
e) A number, first divided by 2, and then raised to the third power.
f) The opposite of a number, then multiplied by 4
g) A quantity raised to the third power, and then increased by 6
h) A number decreased by 4, and then the result multiplied by y
i) Subtract a number from y and then take the opposite of the result
j) A number multiplied by the sum of the same number and 5
k) The opposite of a number, then raised to one hundred and twenty first power
l) Square a number, and then take the opposite of it

Ex.4 Let C be a variable representing the temperature in Celsius. Write the following phrase as an algebraic expression: Nine fifths of the Celsius temperature plus 32.

Ex.5 Let L be a variable representing the length of a rectangle, and W its width. Use L and W to write the following phrase as an algebraic expression: The sum of the length of a rectangle and its width, then multiplied by 2.

Ex.6 Let m represents mass, and c speed of light. Use m and c to write the following phrase as an algebraic expression: The product of mass and the square of speed of light.

Ex.7 In the following expressions circle the arithmetic operation, together with its operands, that has to be performed first. Write the name of the operation next to your expression. For example, in $4+3x$, multiplication of 3 and x has to be performed first, thus the answer is

$4 \quad + \boxed{3x}$ multiplication

a) $a+b^5$ b) $(a+b)^5$

c) $-x^8$ d) $(-x)^8$

e) $\dfrac{a-b}{c}$ f) $a \div b \times c$

g) $4-7y$ h) $3+a \div b$

Ex.8 There are two operations in the algebraic expression $a+3b$, addition and multiplication. In order to evaluate $a+3b$, we would have to perform them according to the order of operations. First multiply 3 and b, and then add a.
List, according to the order of operations, operations that are in the following algebraic expressions.

a) $4x-y$ b) $\dfrac{a+3}{x}$

c) $(x+3)y$ d) $\dfrac{s}{t}+2$

e) $3x^2$ f) $(3x)^2$

g) $(a+c)^4$ h) $a+c^4$

Ex.9 Determine if, in the following algebraic expressions, parentheses are necessary, i.e. they change or do not change the order of operations. To this end, determine if the first operation that should be performed is the same as if the expression were written without any parentheses. If the operation is different, write "parentheses are needed', otherwise rewrite the expression without any changes.

a) $(2-a)x$ b) $(c-3)-a$

c) $(3a)+x$ d) $a-(c+b)$

e) $x \div (2ab)$ f) $\dfrac{(-c+d)}{a}$

g) $(a+2)^4$ h) $y(x)^8$

i) $(ab)^4$ j) $(a+d) \div c$

Ex.10 Evaluate, if possible.

a) $2x+1$, if $x=\dfrac{1}{2}$

b) $2a+1$, if $a=\dfrac{1}{2}$

c) $2y+1$, if $y=\dfrac{1}{2}$

d) Did you get the same answer for a, b, and c? Can you explain why it is so?

e) If $\dfrac{4x^3+x}{x-1}=-2$ when $x=\dfrac{1}{2}$, evaluate $\dfrac{4a^3+a}{a-1}$ when $a=\dfrac{1}{2}$. You should be able to arrive at your answer without performing any evaluation.

Ex. 11 Let $x = 3$. Rewrite the expression replacing the variable with its value and evaluate, if possible. Otherwise, write "undefined".

a) $-2x-5$

b) $-4+x^2$

c) $\dfrac{x}{x-3}$

d) $(-x)^2$

e) $-x^2$

f) $\dfrac{3-x}{4+x}$

g) x^x

Ex. 12 Let $x = 4$. Rewrite the expression replacing the variable with its value and evaluate, if possible. Otherwise, write "undefined".

a) -2^x

b) $(-2)^x$

c) $(-x)^2$

d) $-x^2$

Ex. 13 Let $x = -1$. Rewrite the expression replacing the variable with its value and evaluate, if possible. Otherwise, write "undefined".

a) $-x+x$

b) $-x-x$

c) $(-x)(-x)$

d) x^2

e) $-x^2$

Ex. 14 Substitute $A = \dfrac{1}{2}$ and then evaluate the following expressions, if possible. Otherwise, write "undefined".

a) $\dfrac{1}{A}$

b) $\dfrac{1}{A}+A$

c) $(-A)^2$

d) $-A^2$

Ex. 15 Let $x = -0.3$. Rewrite each expression replacing the variable with its value and evaluate, if possible. Otherwise, write "undefined".

a) x^2-x

b) $\dfrac{x}{0.1}-2$

c) $\dfrac{0.3-x}{x-0.3}$

d) $1000x-100x+10x$

Ex.16 The expression $\frac{3-x}{y-5}$ cannot be evaluated for which of the following values of x and y? Explain why.

a) $x=3,\quad y=-5$ b) $x=-3,\quad y=5$
c) $x=3,\quad y=5$ d) $x=-3,\quad y=-5$
e) $x=3,\quad y=0$ f) $x=0,\quad y=5$

Ex.17 If possible, evaluate when $m=-2,\quad n=5$. Otherwise, write "undefined". Before evaluating, rewrite the expressions substituting the numerical values of m and n.
a) $2m-3n$
b) $2m(-3n)$
c) $2(m-3n)$
d) $(2m-3)n$
e) $2(m-3)n$

Ex.18 If possible, evaluate when $m=-\frac{1}{8}, n=\frac{4}{5}$. Otherwise, write "undefined". Before evaluating, rewrite the expressions substituting the numerical values of m and n.
a) $8m-10n$
b) $10mn$
c) $2(n-m)$
d) $-8m^2+n$
e) $n\div(\frac{1}{8}+m)$
f) $n\div\frac{3}{10}+m$

Ex.19 If possible, evaluate when $A=\frac{1}{3},\quad B=-\frac{2}{3}$. Otherwise, write "undefined". Before evaluating, rewrite the expressions substituting the numerical values of A and B.
a) $2A^4$
b) B^4
c) $-B^4$
d) $\frac{A+B}{A-B}$
e) $\frac{A(-B)}{A\div B}$

Ex.20 Evaluate the following expressions: $a^3,\ 4^n,\ ab^2,\ (ab)^2,\ -a^n,\ a^{n+m}$ if $a=-1,\ b=\frac{1}{3}$, $n=3,\quad m=2$. If evaluation is not defined, write "undefined".

Ex.21 Let $x=2$, $y=-0.1$, and $z=-1$. If possible, evaluate the following expressions. Otherwise, write "undefined".
a) $x(z+y)$
b) $xz+y$

Ex.22 Let $a=0.1$, $b=-0.2$, $c=-1$. If possible (otherwise, write "undefined"), evaluate the following expressions. Before evaluating, rewrite the expressions substituting the numerical values of variables.
a) $a-bc$
b) a^{-c}
c) b^{10a}

Ex.23 Find the value of $2a^2-(2a)^2$ if
a) $a=1$
b) $a=-1$

Ex.24 Find the value of $2A-B$, if
a) $A=-1,\ B=3$
b) $A=-2,\ B=-4$
c) $A=0.3,\ B=-0.7$
d) $A=\frac{2}{8},\ B=-1$
e) $A=1\frac{5}{6},\ B=\frac{4}{5}$
f) $A=-\frac{3}{10},\ B=-\frac{5}{7}$

Ex.25 Find the value of $-(A+3B)$, if
a) $A=-1,\ B=-1$
b) $A=2,\ B=-3$
c) $A=0.1,\ B=-0.2$
d) $A=-2,\ B=-1\frac{2}{3}$
e) $A=\frac{2}{7},\ B=-\frac{1}{6}$
f) $A=-4,\ B=-\frac{5}{9}$

Ex.26 Find the value of $\frac{0.1x}{y}$, if
a) $x=2,\ y=0.02$
b) $x=-200,\ y=0.4$
c) $x=0.1,\ y=-0.2$

Ex.27 Evaluate the following expressions, if $m=-1$, $n=2$, and $p=-3$. Before evaluating, rewrite the expressions substituting the numerical values of variables.
a) $m-(n+p)$
b) $m-n+p$

Ex.28 In the following expressions, identify the first operation that should be performed according to the order of operations and anytime it is a numerical operation, perform it.

a) $3+4+x$

b) $3+4x$

c) $3(4)x$

d) $(3+4)x$

e) $x \cdot 2^3$

f) $\dfrac{2-3}{x}$

Ex.29 Write the following phrases as algebraic expressions and then evaluate them when $x=-3$.

a) 3 multiplied by *x*, and then squared

b) -4 subtracted from *x*, and then divided by 0.2

c) 9 divided by x, and then cubed

Ex. 1 Write a word to complete each sentence.

In the expression $4x^2 \times 2y$, $4x^2$ and $2y$ are called _______________ .

In the expression $4x^2 + 2y$, $4x^2$ and $2y$ are called _______________ .

Ex. 2 List all terms of the following expressions.

a) $3 + x$ b) $ab - cd$

c) $\frac{xy}{2} + 2y^2 - 1$ d) $-(2-b)^2 + \frac{x}{y} - z$

Ex. 3 Is 2+8 equal to 8+2? Is $x + 8$ equal to $8 + x$? How about $\frac{2a}{b} + \frac{cd}{2}$ and $\frac{cd}{2} + \frac{2a}{b}$? Why?

Ex. 4 a) Evaluate $m - n$ and $n - m$ when $m = 2$ and $n = 3$. Based on this evaluation, can you determine if the two expressions are equivalent?
b) Is it true that $m - n = -n + m$?

Ex. 5 For each of the following expressions
- List all its terms
- Using the fact that changing the order of terms results in an equivalent expression, rewrite the following expressions in their equivalent form by rearranging the terms. Use the equal sign to indicate that the resulting expressions are equivalent (for example, the expression $A + 9$ should be rewritten as $A + 9 = 9 + A$).

a) $2m + z$ b) $x - 2$

c) $-3c + 2$ d) $-2x^2 - \frac{y^3}{2}$

e) $c(d - f) + y^2$ f) $-(x - y)^2 + \frac{s+2}{3}$

Ex. 6 Fill in the blanks to make a true statement.

a) $x - mn + 2 = -mn + 2$ __________

b) $3 - (2a - 3b) + 4x = 4x$ __________

Ex. 7 List all terms, and then, by changing the order of these terms, create two new equivalent expressions for each of the following .

a) $-x^2 + x - x^3$

b) $-a^2 - 2bc + \frac{3x}{2}$

Ex.8 For each of the following expressions (1)-(5) find an expression equivalent to it among expression (A)-(E). Rewrite each matched pair with the equal sign between them to indicate their equivalence.

(1) $s+t+u$	(A) $t-u+s$
(2) $-t+s+u$	(B) $-s-t+u$
(3) $-u+s+t$	(C) $t+s+u$
(4) $u-t-s$	(D) $s-u-t$
(5) $s-t-u$	(E) $s+u-t$

Ex. 9 Rewrite the following expressions placing the multiplication sign '×' whenever (according to the convention) it was omitted. Then, identify all explicit factors.

a) $2a$

b) $3(a+b)$

c) $-3x\frac{2}{y}$

d) $4(x+y)(b-c)$

Ex.10 Rewrite each of the following expressions in its equivalent form using $xy = yx$. Use the equal sign to indicate that the resulting expression is equivalent to the original one (for example, the expression $9A$ should be rewritten as $9A = A \cdot 9$). Remember about parentheses.

a) mn

b) -5×7

c) $-cd$

d) $-c(a+d)$

Ex.11 a) Rewrite the expression vst in its equivalent form by changing the order of its factors to create three new equivalent expressions. Indicate their equivalence by using the equal sign (for example, one of the answers might be $vst = tsv$).

b) Repeat the above exercise for $v(x-y)t$.

Ex.12 a) Is AB equivalent to BA? How about $-3AB$ and $-3BA$, $-3AB$ and $BA(-3)$? Why?

b) Is $-3AB$ equivalent to $BA-3$? Why? Support your answer by evaluating both expressions when $A=1$ and $B=2$.

Ex.13 Is $ab+2$ equivalent to $2+ab$? How about $ab+2$ and $2+ba$? Why? How about $(mn+4)(a+b)$ and $(b+a)(4+nm)$? Why?

Ex. 14 According to the rules for adding and subtracting fractions, we have $\frac{a+b}{c}=\frac{a}{c}+\frac{b}{c}$ and $\frac{a-b}{c}=\frac{a}{c}-\frac{b}{c}$ (assume $c \neq 0$) Rewrite each of the expressions below as a sum or a difference of two expressions. Use equal signs to indicate that the resulting expressions are equivalent to the original ones (for example, the expression $\frac{2-t}{3}$ should be rewritten as $\frac{2-t}{3}=\frac{2}{3}-\frac{t}{3}$).

a) $\frac{2-5}{7}$

b) $\frac{a+6}{3}$

c) $\frac{a-2}{a+b}$

d) $\frac{b^2+c}{ab^2-c}$

Ex. 15 Using the fact that $\frac{a+b}{c}=\frac{a}{c}+\frac{b}{c}$ and $\frac{a-b}{c}=\frac{a}{c}-\frac{b}{c}$ (assume $c \neq 0$), rewrite the following expressions as a single fraction. Do not simplify.

a) $\frac{m}{4}+\frac{n}{4}$

b) $\frac{7m}{4}-\frac{n^2}{4}$

c) $\frac{5m}{4c-2}-\frac{2n^2}{4c-2}$

d) $\frac{A}{x}-\frac{B+2C}{x}$

Ex. 16 Write the following expressions as a single fraction using the fact that $\frac{a}{d}+\frac{b}{d}+\frac{c}{d}=\frac{a+b+c}{d}$

a) $\frac{4}{5}-\frac{7}{5}+\frac{2}{5}$

b) $\frac{7m}{4x}+\frac{n^2}{4x}-\frac{3}{4x}$

c) $\frac{m}{s-1}-\frac{3}{s-1}-\frac{t}{s-1}$

Ex. 17 According to the rule for multiplication of fractions the following is true: $\frac{3x}{7}=\frac{3}{7}x$. We can say that the quotient $\frac{3x}{7}$ was written as a product of a numerical factor $\frac{3}{7}$ and an algebraic expression x. Write the following expressions as a product of a numerical factor and an algebraic expression.

a) $\frac{2x}{3}$

b) $\frac{2x^2}{y}$

c) $\frac{-2x^2}{3}$

d) $\frac{-2(a+2b)}{y}$

e) $\frac{x}{3}$

f) $\frac{a+2b}{3}$

Ex.18 Using the rule for multiplication of fractions $a\frac{x}{y}=\frac{ax}{y}$, rewrite each of the following expressions in their equivalent form as a single fraction (for example, $2\cdot\frac{x}{y}=\frac{2x}{y}$). Remember to use parentheses when needed.

a) $3\cdot\frac{m}{n}$

b) $3\cdot\frac{-m}{n}$

c) $a\left(\frac{-b}{4}\right)$

d) $-a\left(\frac{-b}{4}\right)$

e) $(s-4)\frac{t}{n}$

f) $4\cdot\frac{-a}{n-1}$

g) $3\frac{m+n}{t}$

h) $a\cdot\frac{-x+1}{x^2}$

Ex.19 Students were to write an answer to the following problem: Using algebraic symbols, write an opposite number to $\frac{s}{t}$.

Student A gave the answer: $-\frac{s}{t}$

Student B gave the answer: $\frac{-s}{t}$

Student C gave the answer: $\frac{s}{-t}$

Who was right? Why?

Ex.20 You know that $-\frac{x}{y}=\frac{-x}{y}=\frac{x}{-y}$. By placing the minus sign differently, write each expression in two additional equivalent ways. Use parentheses when needed.

a) $-\frac{2a}{b}$

b) $\frac{2a+c}{-2d}$

Ex.21 Write each of the following expressions in their equivalent form as a single fraction. Do not simplify.

a) $\frac{2}{3}x+\frac{4}{3}y$

b) $\frac{2}{3}x-\frac{1}{3}y$

c) $2x\cdot\frac{1}{3}-7\cdot\frac{y}{3}$

d) $\frac{3}{t}x-\frac{1}{t}y$ *(continues on the next page)*

e) $-2\frac{x}{t}+3\frac{y}{t}$

f) $-\frac{1}{k+t}-2\frac{n}{k+t}$

g) $3\frac{a-b}{t}+2\frac{cd-1}{t}$

h) $-\frac{2+a}{xy}-3\frac{m-n}{xy}$

Ex.22 Fill in the blanks to make a true statement.

a) $\frac{3x}{y}=x\cdot$ ____________

b) $\frac{3x}{y}=3\cdot$ ____________

c) $\frac{3x}{y}=\frac{1}{y}\cdot$ ____________

d) $\frac{a+b}{y}=\frac{1}{y}\cdot$ ____________

Ex.23 Perform all numerical operations that are possible. If none is possible, write "not possible".

a) $4+a-8$

b) $4a(-8)$

c) $\frac{8a}{4}$

d) 8^2x

e) $8x^2$

f) $4-2x$

g) $(4-2)x$

h) $-(-2x)$

i) $(5-2)^m$

j) $2x^2\left(\frac{1}{2}\right)$

k) $-0.1x(10y^2)$

l) $5-2^m$

m) $10\cdot\frac{x}{5}$

n) $2\cdot(6-5)x$

o) $4\cdot\frac{2}{5}-x$

p) $\frac{12y}{2xz}$

q) $-\frac{1}{2}-x-\frac{1}{2}$

r) $\frac{3bd}{9ac}$

s) $(0.2xy)(-0.3z)$

t) $\frac{4x}{-1}$

Ex.24 Is $\left(\left(-\frac{1}{2}\right)^2+\frac{3}{4}\right)x$ equivalent to x? Is $x\left(\left(-\frac{1}{2}\right)^2+\frac{3}{4}\right)$ equivalent to x?

Ex.25 Is $(x+y)(1+a)$ equivalent to $x+y(1+a)$? Explain your answer.

Ex.26 Replace Ψ with expressions such that the resulting statement is true. Use parentheses when needed.

a) $a-2b+c=c-2b+\Psi$

b) $x=\frac{x}{\Psi}\cdot 4$

c) $\frac{xy}{4}=\frac{1}{4}x\Psi$

d) $a\div 2=\frac{\Psi}{2}$

e) $\frac{x+y}{3}=\frac{x}{3}+\Psi$

f) $z-c=-c+\Psi$

g) $-xyz=yz\Psi$

h) $\frac{ab}{2}=a\cdot\Psi$

Ex.27 Determine which of the following expressions are equivalent to $-m$

$\frac{m}{-1}$, $-\frac{m}{1}$, $m(-1)$, $m-1$, $-\frac{1}{m}$

Ex.28 Determine which of the following expressions are equivalent to $m-n$:

$n-m$, $m(-n)$, $m-(n)$, $-nm$, $-n+m$, $(-1)n-m$

Ex.29 Determine which of the following are equivalent to $-a-c+b+d$.

$-a+b-c+d$, $-a+b-c-d$, $d+b-c-a$, $a+c-b-d$

Ex.30 Determine which of the following are equivalent to $-\frac{a}{b}$.

$\frac{-a}{b}$, $-a\cdot\frac{1}{b}$, $-b\cdot\frac{1}{a}$, $-\frac{2a}{2b}$, $\frac{a}{-b}$, $\frac{-a}{-b}$

Ex.31 Determine which of the following expressions are equivalent to $\frac{5x}{6}$.

$5\cdot\frac{x}{6}$, $\frac{5}{6}x$, $x\cdot\frac{5}{6}$, $\frac{5}{6x}$, $\frac{10x}{12}$, $\frac{1}{6}\cdot 5x$

Ex.32 Determine which of the following expressions are equivalent to $x\div 2$.

$\frac{x}{2}$, $2x$, $2\div x$, x^2, $\frac{4x}{8}$, $\frac{-x}{-2}$

Ex.33 Determine which of the following expressions are equivalent to $3+8a$.

$11a$, $8a+3$, $3+a\cdot 8$, $11+a$, $2\cdot\dfrac{3+8a}{2}$

Ex.34 Determine which of the following expressions are equivalent to $\dfrac{3a-b}{6}$.

$\dfrac{b-3a}{6}$, $\dfrac{1}{6}(3a-b)$, $\dfrac{3a}{6}-b$, $\dfrac{3a}{6}-\dfrac{b}{6}$, $\dfrac{-b+3a}{6}$, $(3a-b)\dfrac{1}{6}$

Ex.35 Determine which of the following are equivalent to $\dfrac{m}{3}-\dfrac{n}{3}$.

$\dfrac{n}{3}-\dfrac{m}{3}$, $\dfrac{m-n}{3}$, $\dfrac{1}{3}\cdot m-\dfrac{1}{3}n$, $(m-n)\cdot\dfrac{1}{3}$, $\dfrac{-n+m}{3}$

Ex.36. The correct answer to a problem is $\dfrac{vt^2}{2}$. John's answer is $\dfrac{1}{2}vt^2$. Is John right? How about Mary whose answer is $\dfrac{t^2}{2}\cdot v$?

Ex.37 Show that $(-x)^4$ is not equivalent to $-x^4$ by evaluating both expressions when $x=-1$ and demonstrating that the values are not the same.

Ex.38 Show that x^2+y^2 is not equivalent to $(x+y)^2$ by evaluating both expressions when $x=-1$, $y=2$ and demonstrating that the values are not the same.

Ex.39 Show that $m-n+p$ is not equivalent to $m-(n+p)$ by evaluating both expressions when $m=2$, $n=5$, and $p=1$ and demonstrating that the values are not the same.

Ex.40 Evaluate $(-1)^m$ and -1^m when

a) $m=1$
b) $m=3$
c) $m=5$
d) $m=7$
e) Based on the above, can you determine if $(-1)^m$ and -1^m are equivalent?
f) Evaluate $(-1)^m$ and -1^m when $m=2$. Can you now determine if $(-1)^m$ and -1^m are equivalent?

Ex.1 In the expression $3x^m$, 3 is called the__________________, m is called the__________ or __________ and x is called the______________.

Ex.2 Fill in the blanks.

a) An expression x raised to the________ power is equal to itself.

b) An expression x raised to the________ power is equal to 1.

Ex.3 a) In the expression ab^m the exponent pertains to ______________.

b) In the expression $(ab)^n$ the exponent pertains to ______________.

c) In the expression $c(de)^n$ the exponent pertains to ______________.

d) In the expression $(-a)^n$ the exponent pertains to ______________.

e) In the expression $-a^n$ the exponent pertains to ______________.

f) In the expression $\left(\frac{2x}{y}\right)^m$ the exponent pertains to ______________.

Ex.4 Write the following statements as algebraic expressions using parentheses where appropriate.

a) The quotient of a and 2, then raised to the fourth power

b) Two thirds of a, then raised to the third power

c) c cubed, and then divided by 7

d) The product of a and 5, then raised to the second power

e) Raise a to the second power, and then multiply the result by 8.

f) The opposite of x, then raised to the fifth power.

g) Raise x to the tenth power, and then take the opposite of the result.

Ex.5 In each of the following expressions, identify the base, exponent and numerical coefficient.

a) $3x^4$

b) $-x^m$

c) $\frac{2x^3}{3}$

d) $-(a-bc)^2$

e) $\left(\frac{x}{y}\right)^m$

f) $\frac{(x+y)^7}{4}$

g) $\frac{3}{4}\left(\frac{3x+z}{w}\right)^7$

h) $-\frac{(ab)^5}{2}$

Ex.6 Write using exponential notation whenever it is possible.

a) $6\times6\times6\times6\times6$

b) $zzzz$

c) $3a\cdot3a\cdot3a\cdot a$

d) $-xyxyxxx$

e) $-a-aaaa$

f) $xxy-yyx$

g) $(a+b)(a+b)(a+b)$

h) $(2t^3)(2t^3)(2t^3)(2t^3)$

(continues on the next page)

i) $m+nn+m$

j) $\frac{kkk}{n}\cdot k$

k) $\frac{-z-z-z}{zzzz}$

l) $\frac{(-z)(-z)(-z)}{z+z+z}$

m) $x\cdot\frac{x}{2}\cdot x\cdot x$

n) $(3-x)(-x+3)(3-x)$

o) $\left(\frac{2a}{b}\right)\left(2\frac{a}{b}\right)\left(\frac{2a}{b}\right)$

p) $\left(-\frac{3}{x}\right)\left(\frac{-3}{x}\right)\left(\frac{3}{-x}\right)$

q) $\frac{1}{(w+2v)(2v+w)(2v+w)}$

r) $\left(\frac{x}{m}-\frac{y}{m}\right)\left(\frac{x-y}{m}\right)\left(\frac{x-y}{m}\right)$

s) $(m+n)(m+n)m+n$

t) $(m+p-n)(p+m-n)(n+m-p)$

Ex.7 Write the following expressions without using exponential notation.

a) $(-4)^5$

b) -4^5

c) $(-m)^3$

d) $-m^3$

e) $(2a)^3$

f) $2a^3$

g) $(a+b)^2$

h) $a+b^2$

Ex.8 Simplify by raising to the indicated power.

a) $(3x)^0$

b) $3x^0$

c) 3^0x

d) $a(b+c)^0$

e) abc^0

f) $(abc)^0$

g) $ab+c^0$

h) $a^0b^0c^0$

Ex. 9 While copying expressions from a blackboard, John kept forgetting to copy parentheses.

a) $(x)^3$ John copied as x^3

b) $(-x)^4$ John copied as $-x^4$

c) $-(x)^7$ John copied as $-x^7$

d) $a+(2b)^3$ John copied as $a+2b^3$

e) $(a+2b)^3$ John copied as $a+2b^3$

f) $a+2(b)^3$ John copied as $a+2b^3$

g) $a(bc)^m$ John copied as abc^m

h) $\left(\frac{2x}{y}\right)^4$ John copied as $\frac{2x^4}{y}$

Determine if what was on the board and what John copied has the same meaning, i.e. are the parentheses necessary. Write "same" or "different" for each.

Ex.10 Evaluate when $x=100$. Explain why you did not get the same result.

a) $2x^3$

b) $(2x)^3$

Ex. 11 Fill in the blanks, each time using one of the following words: add, subtract, multiply, divide.

a) To multiply exponential expressions with the same bases one needs to __________ the exponents.
b) To ______________ exponential expressions with the same bases one needs to ____________ their exponents.
c) To raise an exponential expression to another power one needs to __________ the exponents.

Ex. 12 Write as a single exponential expression.

a) $n^3 \cdot n^{20}$
b) $(s^7)^2$
c) $\dfrac{x^8}{x^2}$
d) $b^7 b$
e) $(-4x)^2$
f) $2m^4 m^5$
g) $\dfrac{1}{b} \cdot b^2$
h) $\dfrac{x}{x}$
i) $\dfrac{9a^{20}}{a^4}$
j) $x^3 x^4 x^5$
k) $\dfrac{a^4}{2a^2}$
l) $x^4 \cdot \dfrac{3}{x}$
m) $6a^{11} \cdot a^3 \cdot a^{18}$
n) $\dfrac{0.5s^{12}}{0.1s}$
o) $-5(t^3)^4$
p) $(2x^7)^3$

Ex. 13 Write as an algebraic expression using parentheses where appropriate, then remove the parentheses and simplify.
a) The product of m^2 and $-2m$
b) The quotient of $3x^5$ and $18x^3$
c) The expression $2a^5$ raised to the third power

Ex. 14 Simplify the following expressions first, and then evaluate when $a = 2$.

a) $\dfrac{a^7}{a^6}$
b) $2a^2 a^2$
c) $(2a)(-\dfrac{1}{2}a^2)$
d) $\dfrac{1}{(a^2)^3} \cdot a^8$

Ex. 15 Simplify the following expressions first, and then evaluate when $m = -1$.

a) $m^3 m^5$
b) $\dfrac{m^3}{-2m^2}$
c) $\dfrac{(m^2)^{14}}{3}$
d) $2m^7 m^{50}$

Ex.16 Simplify the following expression $\frac{-x^{10}}{x^8}$, and then evaluate when

a) $x = 7$

b) $x = -7$

c) $x = -\frac{2}{3}$

d) $x = -0.07$.

Ex.17 Rewrite in its equivalent form as a single exponential expression without parentheses. Identify the numerical coefficient of the final expression.

a) $(-B)^5$

b) $(-B)^8$

c) $(-B)^5 B^3$

d) $-B^2(-B)^2$

Ex.18 Perform the indicated operations and simplify.

a) $-4x^2(-2x)$

b) $(-4x)^2(-2x)$

c) $(3x)(-2)(x^3)$

d) $(3x^2)(4x^5x)$

e) $\frac{a^4}{(2a)^2}$

f) $\frac{3x^5}{(3x)^2}$

g) $\frac{(4x)^3}{-x}$

h) $\frac{(-a)^3}{2a^2}$

i) $-2a \cdot \frac{a^7}{(-2a)^2}$

j) $\frac{-2x^3x^5}{x^4}$

k) $\frac{(3x^2)^3}{x^4}$

l) $\frac{a^2}{a^4} \cdot a^2$

m) $\left(\frac{1}{v}\right)^2 v^7$

n) $(3aa^2)^2$

o) $\left(\frac{2}{3}x^4\right)\left(-\frac{3}{5}x^2\right)$

p) $-\left(\frac{x^3}{0.4}\right)^2$

Ex.19 Write as an algebraic expression using parentheses where appropriate, then remove the parentheses and simplify.

a) The product of $-3x$ and x^2, then raised to the third power

b) The quotient of $4a^{12}$ and a^2, then raised to the second power

c) $-a^3$ raised to seventh power, then multiplied by a

Ex.20 Perform the indicated operations and simplify.

a) $(x^5y^3)^2$

b) $\left(\frac{x^2y}{x}\right)^3$

c) $3a(b^5)^2$

d) $3(ab^2)^2$

e) $-\left(\frac{a^3}{4b^2}\right)^2$

f) $x^2y(-x^3)y^4$

(continues on the next page)

g) $\dfrac{-ab^7a}{ba^2b^6}$

h) $x^2 \cdot \dfrac{s^2x}{(4s)^2}$

i) $\dfrac{2(x^2)^3y^2}{x} \cdot y$

j) $4(m-n)^2(m-n)^3$

k) $\dfrac{(a+b)^8}{2(a+b)^4}$

l) $\dfrac{a^{13}b^2c^4}{a^5c^2b}$

Ex.21 Write as an algebraic expression using parentheses where appropriate, then remove the parentheses and simplify.

a) xy^7 raised to the fifth power, then divided by y^3

b) $3ab^3$ squared, and then multiplied by b

Ex.22 Simplify the following expressions, and then evaluate when $m=-2$ and $n=1$.

a) $\dfrac{m^2n^5}{mn}$

b) $\dfrac{(mn^2)^3}{m(n^2)^3}$

c) $\dfrac{(m+n)^4}{(m+n)^2}$

d) $(2m-n)^0$

Ex.23 Circle all expressions that are equivalent to $\dfrac{2}{5}y^2$.

$\dfrac{4}{25}y^2$ $\qquad \dfrac{2y^2}{5}$ $\qquad y \cdot \dfrac{2}{5} \cdot y$ $\qquad \left(\dfrac{2}{5}y\right)^2$ $\qquad \dfrac{2}{5}yy$

Ex.24 Circle all expressions that are equivalent to $\left(\dfrac{a}{3}\right)^{20}$.

$\dfrac{a^{20}}{3}$ $\qquad \dfrac{a^{20}}{3^{20}}$ $\qquad \dfrac{(a^{12})^8}{3^{20}}$ $\qquad \dfrac{a^{12}a^8}{3^{20}}$ $\qquad \dfrac{(a^4)^5}{3^{20}}$

Ex.25 Circle all expressions that are equivalent to $4x^3y^2$.

$4y^2x^3$, $\qquad (2y)^2x^3$, $\qquad (-2)y^2(-2)x^3$, $\qquad (4xy)^2x$, $\qquad 4(xy)^2x$

Ex.26 Circle all expressions that are equivalent to $2a^6b^3c^2$.

$2a^6c^2b^3$, $\qquad 2a^2b^3c^2a^3$, $\qquad 2(abc)^{11}$, $\qquad \dfrac{7c^2b^3a^6}{14}$, $\qquad 2(a^3c)^2b^3$

Ex.27 Replace Ψ with a number so the following are equal.

a) $81^4 = 9^\Psi$

b) $7^\Psi = 49^5$

c) $16^{100} = 2^\Psi$

d) $27^4 = 3^\Psi$

e) $\left(\dfrac{1}{4}\right)^7 = \left(\dfrac{1}{2}\right)^\Psi$

f) $0.2^\Psi = (0.04)^5$

Ex.28 Evaluate the following expressions.

a) $\dfrac{15^{248}}{15^{247}}$

b) $\dfrac{3^{21}\cdot 3^{10}}{3^{29}}$

c) $\dfrac{(12^3)^6}{-12^{17}}$

d) $\dfrac{0.5^{10}\times 0.5^6}{(0.5^7)^2}$

e) $\dfrac{64^5}{4^{13}}$

f) $-\dfrac{4^{15}}{2^{27}}$

In all exercises of this lesson, we assume that denominators are different from zero.

Ex. 1 The Distributive Law states that $c(a+b)=ca+cb$. Explain how we can use it to write an equivalent expression without parentheses. from the expression $(a+b)c$.

Ex. 2 Write an equivalent expression without parentheses.

a) $2(L+W)$
b) $R(1-x)$
c) $P(1+rt)$
d) $(R^2-r^2)s$
e) $-(3+xy)$
f) $(x^2-7z)x$
g) $c(2a+c-c^5)$
h) $-(-a+a^2-2)$

Ex. 3 The Distributive Law applied to the product of two sums states.

$(x+y)(b+c)=xb+yb+xc+yc$

Can we instead state it as $(x+y)(b+c)=xb+xc+yb+yc$? Why? Reformulate the Distributive Law in four different ways.

Ex. 4 Write an equivalent expression without parentheses.

a) $\frac{5}{9}(F-18)$
b) $3y(6y^4+8y^3)$
c) $(x^2-2x)x^4$
d) $-\frac{2}{3}(3c-33d)$
e) $a(a^2+ab+ab^2)$
f) $(2x^3y+\frac{3}{7}-xy^4)xy$
g) $(x-y)(z+w)$
h) $(a-\frac{2}{5}b)(10-a^3)$
i) $(a+b-g)(c-d)$
j) $(x^3+x^2+x+1)(y-1)$
k) $\frac{1}{4}(4x-8)(2y+3)$
l) $(2a-1)(1-b)(c-2)$

Ex. 5 First write each of the following statements as an algebraic expression using parentheses where appropriate, and then rewrite it again in its equivalent form without parentheses.

a) The product of x^2-y and 5
b) The opposite of $-4x+1$
c) The product a and $-c+1$
d) The product of $2y$ and $-a+2b+d$
e) The product of $x-1$ and y^3+2
f) The opposite of $x-x^2+2x^4$

Ex. 6 Write the following expressions in five different equivalent ways.

a) $3(a+b)$
b) $(2-y)z$

Ex.7 Circle all expressions that are equivalent to $m(n+p)$.

$mn+mp$ $(n+p)m$ $pm+nm$ $mn+p$ $mp+nm$

Ex.8 Circle all expressions that are equivalent to $-(x-y+z)$.

$(-1)(x-y+z)$ $(x-y+z)(-1)$ $-1(x-y+z)$ $(x-y+z)-1$

$-x+y-z$ $-x-y+z$ $-x+y+z$ $-(x+z-y)$

Ex.9 a) After factoring a common factor from a two term expression, how many terms should you have inside parentheses?

b) After factoring a common factor from a three term expression, how many terms should you have inside parentheses?

c) After factoring a common factor from an m-term expression, how many terms should you have inside parentheses?

Ex.10 Factor

a) 5 from the expression $5x+5y$

b) 7 from the expression $7-49a$

c) c from the expression $3c-2c^2$

d) y from the expression $-8xy^6+y$

e) $11t$ from the expression $-11t+44t^3$

f) 2 from the $2lw+2lh+2wh$

g) x from the expression $4x^3-5x^2+5x$

Ex.11 Factor xy from the following expressions

a) $2xy-a^2xy$ b) $-x^2y+xy^2$ c) $axy+xby-yx$

Ex.12 Factor -1 from

a) $3+x$ b) $-a+b+1$ c) $a-\dfrac{x+y-z}{2}$

Ex.13 Factor

a) $5a$ from the following expression $10a-15a^2$

b) $11t$ from the following expression $-\dfrac{11}{2}t^2+44t$

c) $5x^3$ from the following expression $15x^5+5x^3$

d) $-4y^5$ from the following expression $-8xy^6+4y^5$

e) c^2d^2 from the following expression $8c^2d^2-ac^2d^3$

f) $3x^2y$ from the following expression $-3x^2y+9x^3y^2$

g) $\dfrac{x}{y}$ from the following expression $\dfrac{2x}{y}+a\dfrac{x}{y}$

h) $\dfrac{1}{a+b}$ from the following expression $\dfrac{1}{a+b}+s\dfrac{1}{a+b}$

Ex. 14 Factor

a) $\frac{2}{3}$ from the following expression $\frac{2}{3}x^2y-\frac{4}{3}z$

b) $\frac{1}{5}$ from the following expression $\frac{1}{5}x-\frac{1}{25}$

c) 0.6 from the following expression $3.6x-6y+0.6$

Ex. 15 Factor $a+b$ from the following expressions

a) $6(a+b)-x(a+b)$

b) $4(a+b)-3(a+b)^2$

Ex. 16 Factor

a) $2xy$ from the following expression $2xy-2xy^2+4x^2y^2$

b) a^3b^3 from the following expression $a^3b^4+5b^3a^7-a^3b^3$

c) $17xy$ from the following expression $17x^5y^3+34x^3y^2+51xy$

d) a^3b^3 from the following expression $a^3b^4+5b^3a^7-a^3b^3$

e) $4ac^3$ from the following expression $-16ac^3+8ac^7-12ac^8d$

f) $7ab^2$ from the following expression $35ab^3-14a^2b^4+21ab^2$

g) $x-2y$ from the following expression $-2(x-2y)+(x-2y)z^2$

h) $(c+d)^2$ from the following expression $(c+d)^2-4a(c+d)^3$

Ex. 17 Factor a from the following expression $a-a^2+3$

Ex. 18 From the expression $4-x$, factor the following.

a) 2

b) x

c) $2x$

d) $4x$

Ex. 19 List all terms of the denominator and numerator of the following algebraic fraction. For each such term list all its explicit factors. Find all factors that are common to all terms. If you were asked to simplify the fraction, what would be the expression by which you would divide the numerator and denominator to simplify it?

a) $\frac{t}{2t-ty}$

b) $\frac{x+xy}{2ax}$

c) $\frac{3ab}{ab-a^2}$

Ex. 20 In the expression $\frac{7x}{x-5}$, can x be viewed as a factor of the denominator? Can x be viewed as a factor of the numerator? Can we "cancel x". If not, why? If yes, what is the resulting expression?

Ex.21 In the expression $\frac{7x}{x^2y}$, can x be viewed as a factor of the denominator? Can x be viewed as a factor of the numerator? Can we "cancel x". If not, why? If yes, what is the resulting expression?

Ex.22 In the expression $\frac{a(a+x)}{a}$, can a be viewed as a factor of the denominator? Can a be viewed as a factor of the numerator? Can we "cancel a". If not, why? If yes, what is the resulting expression?

Ex.23 In the expression $\frac{-ab}{ab^2+c}$, can ab be viewed as a factor of the denominator? Can ab be viewed as a factor of the numerator? Can we "cancel ab". If not, why? If yes, what is the resulting expression?

Ex.24 Simplify, if possible. Otherwise write "not possible". Also, name the expression by which you divide the numerator and denominator.

a) $\frac{3xy}{9yx}$ b) $\frac{2abc}{8ab}$

c) $\frac{-a^2}{b^2a^2}$ d) $\frac{5xy^4}{20y^3}$

e) $\frac{15x(a-b)}{25x}$ f) $\frac{a^2(b-c)}{2a}$

g) $\frac{4x(-5x^2)}{x}$ h) $\frac{bc(b+e)}{b}$

i) $\frac{a+b}{7(a+b)}$ j) $\frac{2x+3}{2x}$

Ex.25 Simplify, if possible. Otherwise write "not possible".

a) $\frac{2}{2x+2y}$ b) $\frac{xy+xz}{3x}$

c) $\frac{4x-5x^2}{x}$ d) $\frac{3x+3x^2}{6x}$

e) $\frac{3x}{3x-9x^2}$ f) $\frac{a^3b-4b^4a^4}{a}$

g) $\frac{a-3b}{-3b+a}$ h) $\frac{x^2}{2x^2-x^5}$

i) $\frac{a+b+c}{a+b}$ j) $\frac{xy}{xy+xy^2}$

k) $\frac{12x-4}{3x}$ l) $\frac{-4x+12y+8z}{4}$

m) $\frac{xy-xy^2+x^2y}{3yx}$ n) $\frac{u+2v-s}{s-2v-u}$

o) $\frac{4uv^2-6vu^2+2vu}{2uv}$ p) $\frac{xy}{3x^4y-6x^2y^2z}$

Ex. 1 Which of the following rows consists of all like terms?

a) $-\frac{1}{2}x,\ \ 4x^2,\ \ 0.5x^2,\ \ -\frac{1}{6}x^2,\ \ 3x$

b) $-3xy,\ \ 8yx,\ \ -0.6xy,\ \ 2xy,\ \ -\frac{3}{7}xy$

c) $5x,\ \ 5x^2,\ \ 5x^3,\ \ 5x^4,\ \ 5$

d) $-2a,\ \ -5a,\ \ 7a,\ \ 29a,\ \ a,\ \ -11a$

Ex. 2 Are x and $-x$ like terms?

Ex. 3 Are any of the following like terms: $7x^2y$, $7xy^2$, and $7(xy)^2$?

Ex. 4 Circle all terms that are like $6x^2y$.

$6x^2y^2$ $\qquad -2x^2y$ $\qquad 5xy$ $\qquad 0.3yx^2$

Ex. 5 Circle all terms that are like $-\frac{3}{7}a^2b$.

$5(ab)^2$ $\qquad 2a^2b$ $\qquad -\frac{3}{7}ab^2$ $\qquad \frac{ba^2}{7}$

Ex. 6 Circle all expressions that are like x^2y^3.

y^3x^2 $\qquad xy^3x$ $\qquad 2x^3y^2$ $\qquad y^2xx$ $\qquad yyxxy$

Ex. 7 Circle all expressions that are like a^5b^3.

$a^2b^5a^3$ $\qquad -b^2a^5b$ $\qquad (ab)^3b^3$ $\qquad 2(ab)^3a^2$ $\qquad a^3b^5$

Ex. 8 If possible, add (or subtract) the following expressions. Otherwise, write "not possible".

a) $4x-2x$

b) a^2-a

c) $y-y$

d) $a+ab$

e) $st+ts$

f) ac^2+cac

g) ac^2+6ca^2

h) $7mhv-hmv$

i) $2xy^3z^5+y^3z^5x$

j) $3m^3n+6m^2nm$

k) $7xy^3z^5-xy^4z^5$

l) $9a^2b^2-7(ab)^2$

Ex.9 Collect like terms by first factoring x.

a) $3x - 4x$

b) $\frac{1}{3}x - \frac{2}{7}x$

c) $\frac{2}{11}x - \frac{3x}{22}$

d) $0.3x - 0.5x$

e) $-\frac{7}{9}x - \frac{2x}{5}$

f) $\frac{x}{5} - \frac{2}{3}x + \frac{3x}{10}$

Ex.10 If possible, collect like terms. Otherwise, write "not possible".

a) $7x - 8x$

b) $2a - 7a$

c) $\frac{1}{2}x + \frac{1}{2}x$

d) $\frac{1}{2}x - \frac{3}{2}x$

e) $ab - 8ba$

f) $4 - 7x$

g) $5c^3 - 10c^4$

h) $-0.4x^2y - 0.8yx^2$

Ex.11 Rewrite by grouping all like terms together. Then collect like terms. For example, $3x - 7y + 2x - 2y = 3x + 2x - 7y - 2y = 5x - 9y$.

a) $-3x + 8y - 8x - 2x$

b) $-5a - 3b - 2b - 7a$

c) $-2ab - 4ba + 2 + 3ab - 1$

Ex.12 Simplify by collecting all like terms.

a) $3j - 4j + 2j$

b) $2 + a - \frac{2}{3}a$

c) $0.2z - 0.5z + z$

d) $2 - 7m - 4$

e) $-x^3 + x^4 - x^3$

f) $2x + y + x - 2y$

g) $-\frac{3x}{2} + \frac{1}{2}x - 1$

h) $-3y + \frac{1}{2}x - x + 4y$

i) $\frac{cd}{3} + \frac{1}{3}dc - d + c$

j) $a^2b^3 - 4b^2a^3 - 6a^2b^3$

k) $x^4y - 2x + 3yx^4 - 5x$

l) $\frac{3}{38}ab - \frac{7}{19}ba + 2\frac{3}{4} + 3\frac{1}{8}$

Ex.13 Students were asked to simplify the expression $-2(a-b) + 3a - 3b$. The following answers were given.
Student A: $a - b$
Student B: $b - a$
Student C: $-b + a$
Student D: $-a + b$

List all students who gave the right answer.

Ex. 14 Collect like terms, and only then evaluate $-3x+2y-\frac{2}{3}y+4x-\frac{y}{3}$ when

a) $x=-1, \quad y=-3$

b) $x=-2, \quad y=\frac{1}{5}$

c) $x=0.5, \quad y=-3.2$

Ex. 15 Evaluate $\frac{2}{5}x+\frac{1}{2}x+\frac{x}{10}$ when

a) $x=4$

b) $x=-10$

c) $x=\frac{2}{3}$.

If you have not done this yet, simplify the expression by collecting like terms. Compare the obtained expression with the results of the evaluations.

Ex. 16 Write an equivalent expression without parentheses and then collect like terms

a) $(6a-2)+12a$

b) $4a+7a+2(8a+1)$

c) $y-3(-y+2)$

d) $-100(t-0.1)+102t$

e) $\frac{2x}{5}-(2x-1)$

f) $a-0.1(2-3a)$

g) $-(x-1)-x$

h) $(q+6)(-8)-21q$

i) $3a-9b-(4a-\frac{4}{5}b)$

j) $2x-5y-4(3x+y)$

k) $-6(\frac{2}{3}d-\frac{1}{2}a)-a-d$

l) $3a^2-1-(4a^2+2)$

m) $-3xy+7yx-(xy+3)$

n) $-3cb+abc-2(a+bc)$

o) $\frac{1}{3}a-b-\frac{1}{3}(a-2b)$

p) $(6x^4+3x^3-1)-(3x^3-3x^2-3)$

q) $(1+4x+6x^2+7x^3)+(5-4x+6x^2-7x^3)$

r) $-(0.2m+0.03)-(2.3m-4)$

Ex. 17 a) Students were asked to write $(A+B)^2$ in its equivalent form without parentheses and collect like terms of the resulting expression. One student claimed that the answer was A^2+B^2, the other one that it was $A^2+2AB+B^2$. Was either of them right?
b) If you were asked to write $(A-B)^2$ in its equivalent form without parentheses and then collect like terms, what would be your answer?

Ex. 18 Write an equivalent expression without parentheses, and then collect like terms.

a) $(x^4+2)^2$

b) $(3x-1)^2$ *(continues on the next page)*

c) $(a-2)(a+4)$

d) $(3b-c)\left(b+\frac{1}{2}c\right)$

e) $\frac{1}{3}(3c-x)+2(5x-c)$

f) $(1+x-2x^2)(2-x)$

g) $(a^3+b)(a^2-2b)$

h) $\left(\frac{2}{3}-2x\right)^2$

i) $-(a-3b+c)-(c-a)$

j) $-2(-x+2y)-3(5x-3y)$

k) $3x+(4-x)(x+2)$

l) $5-a^2-(3+2a)^2$

m) $6x^2-(x+1)(3x-2)-2$

n) $4-m-2(m-1)^2$

o) $3k^2-3k-(k-2)(2k+3)$

p) $x^4+9-(x^2-3)^2-6x^2$

Ex.19 Write each of the following expressions using algebraic symbols, then rewrite it in its equivalent form without parentheses and, if necessary, collect like terms.

a) Subtract $-2xy$ from $3yx$

b) The sum of $3x-1$ and $-4x+2$

c) The difference of $-4a^3+2a$ and $4a^3-2$

d) Subtract $-2b+a$ from $-a+2+3b$

e) The product of $a-\frac{1}{3}$ and $\frac{2}{5}-2a$

f) The product of $2x^2-y$ and $3y-x^2$

g) The sum of $-mnk$, $4nmk$, and $-3mn$

h) The sum of $3x$ and 2, then raised to the second power

i) The difference of $2a$ and b, then raised to the second power

j) The product of 2 and $-4x+1$, then added to $5x+2$

Ex.20 Rewrite the expression $-a-2(a-b)-5b$ in its equivalent form without parentheses, collect like terms, and only then evaluate if

a) $a=-1,\quad b=-2$

b) $a=\frac{3}{14},\quad b=\frac{2}{7}$

c) $a=-2.4,\quad b=0.6$

Ex.21 Rewrite the expression $4x^2-xy-2(yx-1+2x^2)-2$ in its equivalent form without parentheses, collect like terms, and only then evaluate when

a) $x=-1,\quad y=-3$

b) $x=-2,\quad y=\frac{1}{6}$

c) $x=0.5,\quad y=-0.2$

Ex.1 If $x^2 = 10$, evaluate the following.

a) $2x^2$

b) $\left(\frac{1}{30}x^2\right)^3$

c) $-3x^2 - 2$

Ex.2 If $A^5 = -3$, evaluate the following.

a) $-2A^5$

b) $-(2A^5)^2$

c) $-2-2A^5$

d) $3A^3A^2$

Ex.3 Evaluate the following expressions, if $\frac{a+b}{c} = -2$.

a) $\frac{a+b}{c} - 2$

b) $-\left(\frac{a+b}{c}\right)^2$

c) $\left(-\frac{a+b}{c}\right)^2$

Ex.4 If $x + y = -2$, evaluate.

a) $7x + 7y$

b) $\frac{x}{7} + \frac{y}{7}$

c) $-x - y$

d) $(-x - y)^2$

Ex.5 If $\frac{1}{A} = -\frac{2}{7}$, evaluate.

a) $1 \div A$

b) $\frac{-1}{A}$

c) $\frac{1}{-A}$

d) $\frac{1}{A^2}$

Ex.6 Evaluate the following expressions, if $2a + b - c = -7$.

a) $-c + b + 2a$

b) $-2a - b + c$

c) $-(-2a - b + c)$

d) $2a - (c - b)$

e) $a + b - c + a$

Ex.7 Evaluate the following expressions, if $GHJ = -1$.

a) $-JHG$

b) $\frac{1}{GHJ}$

c) $G(-2)H(-1)J$

d) $G^3(HJ)^3$

Ex.8 Evaluate the following expressions, if $\frac{a}{b} = 3$.

a) $\left(\frac{a}{b}\right)^2$

b) $-\frac{a}{b}$

c) $a \div b$

d) $\frac{b}{a}$

e) $a \cdot \frac{2}{b}$

f) $\frac{a^2 a}{b^3}$

Ex.9 Evaluate the following expressions, if $\frac{xy}{z} = -\frac{1}{3}$.

a) $\frac{yx}{z}$

b) $\frac{xy}{-z}$

c) $-\frac{x^2y^2}{z^2}$

d) $\frac{1}{z} \cdot xy$

e) $\frac{z}{xy}$

f) $xy \div z$

Ex.10 Evaluate the following expressions, if $a + b = -2 \quad c - d = 3$.

a) $a + b + c - d$

b) $2(a - d + c + b)$

c) $9(a + b)^2 - d + c$

Ex.11 Evaluate the following expressions, if $x^2y = -0.2, \quad x - z = 0.6$

a) $\frac{x-z}{x^2y}$

b) $-(x - z) - x^2y$

c) $y(x - z)x^2$

Ex.12 Evaluate the following expressions, if $xy = -1, \quad zt = -3$.

a) $-4xyzt$

b) $-zxty$

c) $-xy + zt$

d) $\frac{yx - tz}{xy}$

Ex.13 Evaluate the following expressions, if $x^3y^4z^6 = -\frac{2}{3}$.

a) $-z^6y^4x^3$

b) $x^3(y^2z^3)^2$

c) $-\frac{x^3y^4}{3}\cdot z^6$

d) $z^6(-2)y^4(-3)x^3$

Ex.14 Evaluate the following expressions, if $x^2 + y^2 = 0.1$

a) $y^2 - 0.3 + x^2$

b) $\frac{x^2}{0.2} + \frac{y^2}{0.2}$

c) $\frac{1}{2}x^2 + \frac{1}{2}y^2$

d) $\frac{1}{x^2 + y^2}$

Ex.15 Simplify the following expressions, and then evaluate when $x = 2,\ z = -3$.

a) $\frac{3x + 3z}{3}$

b) $4x - (z + 4x)$

Ex.16 Rewrite the expression $\frac{3a}{2}$ in terms of x, if it is given that $a = 2x$. Simplify.

Ex.17 Let $C = -3x,\ \ D = \frac{x}{2}$. Express the following expression in terms of x. Simplify.

a) CD

b) $C - D$

c) $3C^2D$

d) $\frac{C - 2D}{4}$

Ex.18 Rewrite the expression a^2 in terms of x for each of the following. Write your answer without parentheses.

a) $a = x$

b) $a = 5x$

c) $a = -x$

d) $a = -5x$

e) $a = x + 1$

f) $a = x^3$

Ex.19 Rewrite the expression $a^2 - 2ab + b^2$ in terms of x, if

a) $a = 1,\ b = x$

b) $a = 3x,\ b = 2x$

c) $a = \frac{x}{2},\ b = -x$

d) $a = b = x$

Ex.20 Let $P = 3x^2 - 2x + 1$, $Q = -6x^2 + x - 2$, and $R = -3x^2 - 1$. Express the following in terms of x. Remove parentheses and simplify.

a) $P + R$

b) $2R - Q$

c) $2P + Q$

Ex.21 Express the following expression in terms of s, if $x = s^3$, $y = 2s$. Simplify, if possible.

a) $2x - y$

b) $x^2 y$

c) $2x + y^3$

d) $\frac{xy^2}{4}$

Ex.22 Express ab in terms of x, if $a = \frac{5x}{126}$, $b = \frac{126}{5}$. Simplify.

Ex.23 Express the expression $(mn)^2 - mn^2$ in terms of

a) m, if $n = m$. Simplify.
b) s, if $m = 2s$, $n = s$. Simplify

Ex.24 Express the expression $m^3 n - 2m^2 n^2$ in terms of s, if

a) $m = s$, $n = -2s$
b) $m = 2s^2$, $n = s^4$
c) $n = m = s$

Ex.25 Express the expression $(m-n)^2 + (m+n)^2$ in terms of

a) s, if $m = 2s$, $n = 3s$
b) m, if $n = m$
c) m, if $n = -m$

Ex.26 The following is true: $(a+b)^4 = a^4 + 4a^3 b + 6a^2 b^2 + 4ab^3 + b^4$

a) Express $(a+b)^4$ in terms of b, if $a = b$.
b) Express $a^4 + 4a^3 b + 6a^2 b^2 + 4ab^3 + b^4$ in terms of b, if $a = b$. Simplify.
c) Compare the results of (a) and (b).
d) Express $(a+b)^4$ in terms of b, if $a = -b$.
e) Express $a^4 + 4a^3 b + 6a^2 b^2 + 4ab^3 + b^4$ in terms of b, if $a = -b$. Simplify.
f) Compare the results of (d) and (e).

Ex.27 Rewrite the expression $a - 2b + 3c + 4d$ in terms of x, if it is given that $a + 3c = 5x$ and $4d - 2b = -x$. Simplify.

Ex.28 Express the following expression in terms of m, if $ab = m$

a) $-3ba$

b) $\frac{a}{2} b$

c) $(6^a)^b$

d) $a^3 b^3$

e) $(-2b)(-\frac{1}{2}a)$

f) $a \div \frac{1}{b}$

Ex.29 Express the following expression in terms of y, if $\frac{x}{z} = -y$, $\frac{t}{z} = 2y$. Simplify.

a) $\frac{x}{z} - \frac{t}{z}$

b) $\left(\frac{x}{z}\right)^2 - \left(\frac{t}{z}\right)^2$

c) $\frac{x+t}{z}$

d) $\frac{1}{z}x - \frac{2}{z}t$

Ex.30 Rewrite the expression $(a-b)(a+b)$ in terms of x, if it is given that $a = 5x$ and $b = 2 - x$. Simplify.

Ex. 1 Fill in the blanks using the following words: 'equation', 'algebraic expression', 'solution' as appropriate.

One can solve a(n)____________ but not a(n) ________________ .

If the left hand side of an equation is equal to the right hand side of the equation for $x = 7$, then 7 is called a ______________ .

The __________(s) of an equation are all values of variables that make the equation true.

The statement that contains two quantities separated by an equal sign is called a(n) ___________ .

A(n) ______________ always makes the ______________ true.

Ex. 2 Determine whether the following mathematical sentences represent an equation or an algebraic expression. In the case of an equation, circle the right-hand side of the equation.

a) $5x$

b) $5x = 2$

c) $x^2 = 36$

d) $\dfrac{x-1}{2} + x$

e) $x = -4 + 2x$

Ex. 3 Tom found the solution of an equation to be $x = 3$, but the teacher gave as a correct solution $3 = x$. Is Tom's answer right? Mary's answer to the same question is $-x = -3$. Did Mary correctly solve the equation? Tell why or why not for both Tom and Mary.

Ex. 4 Does $x = 7$ make the statement $2(x+1) - x = 7$ true or false? Does that mean that 7 is, or is not a solution of $2(x+1) - x = 7$?

Ex. 5 Determine if any of the following numbers $-2,\ 16,\ \dfrac{1}{2},\ 2$ is a solution of the equation. $-x^4 = 16$. How about the equation $x^4 = 16$?

Ex. 6 Is $x = -1$ a solution of

a) $(-x)(-x) = 2$

b) $-x - x = 2$

Ex. 7 Is $x = 2$ a solution of

a) $6^x = 36$ b) $-6^x = 36$ c) $(-6)^x = 36$

Ex.8 Does $a = \frac{2}{5}$ make the following statements true or false?

a) $-a^2 = \frac{4}{25}$

b) $a - \left(-\frac{3}{5}\right) = 1$

c) $-\frac{a}{2} = -5$

d) $-a = -\frac{12}{5} + 5a$

Ex.9 Determine if $y = 0.3$ is a solution of any of the following equations.

a) $0.027 = y^3$

b) $\frac{y}{1-y} = \frac{3}{7}$

c) $(-y - 0.7)^{26} = -1$

Ex.10 Determine whether the following mathematical sentences represent an equation or an algebraic expression. In the case of an equation, determine whether or not $x = -3$ is a solution of it.

a) $\frac{x}{x+3}$

b) $\frac{x}{x+3} = 0$

c) $-x = x^2 - 12$

d) $x^2 = -2x$

e) $x^2 - 2x$

f) $x^3 = x^2 + x$

Ex.11 Determine whether the following mathematical sentences represent an equation or an algebraic expression. In the case of an equation, determine whether or not $x = 0.6$ is a solution of it.

a) $-10x^2$

b) $-3.6 = -10x^2$

c) $(0.5 - x)^2 = 0.01$

d) $(0.5 - x)^2$

e) $\frac{12}{-x} = -20$

f) $\frac{-x + 0.6}{x} = 0.6$

Ex.12 Determine whether the following mathematical sentences represent an equation or an algebraic expression. In the case of an equation, guess one of its solutions.

a) $2x^3 = -2$

b) $2x + 3x^3$

c) $x^2 + 5 = x + 5$

d) $\frac{4}{x} = 4$

e) $-8x^7$

f) $3(x - 7) = 0$

Ex.13 Find a number that makes the equation $\frac{1}{x} = -\frac{1}{2}$ a) true

b) false

Ex.14 Find a number that is a) a solution of $-x = 5$

b) not a solution of $-x = 5$

Ex.15 Check each of the following to determine whether or not it is a solution of the equation

$$(4-x)(2x+5)(x+3)x = 0$$

a) $x = -3$ b) $x = 0$

c) $x = -\frac{5}{2}$ d) $x = \frac{5}{2}$

e) $x = -4$ f) $x = 4$

Ex.16 Guess four solutions of the equation $-(2-x) = -2 + x$.

Ex.17 Mr. X tried to solve the following equation $x = 2x$ by dividing each side by x. As a result, he obtained the equation $1 = 2$ and concluded that the equation $x = 2x$ has no solution. The correct solution of this equation is $x = 0$. What did Mr. X do wrong?

Ex.18 Solve the following linear equations and check your solution.

a) $x + 4 = 1$ b) $3x = 18$

c) $-7 + x = -2$ d) $-5 = \frac{x}{4}$

e) $-10 = 0.2x$ f) $-5 = -2 + x$

g) $4 = -2x$ h) $-x = 8$

Ex.19 Solve the following equations and check your solution.

a) $2x + 15 = 7$ b) $4x - 7 = 5$

c) $9 = 3 - 2x$ d) $-5x + 4 = 0$

e) $-x - 13 = 5$ f) $10 = -3x - 5$

Ex.20 Solve the following equations.

a) $-4x = x + 12$
b) $3x = 5 - 4x$
c) $6x = 15x$
d) $-4x + 2 = 3x$
e) $3 - 7x = x$
f) $3 = -1 - 4x$

Ex.21 Solve the following equations.

a) $4(x - 3) = 12$
b) $0 = 2(1 + x)$
c) $-6 = 2(x + 5)$
d) $-(x + 3) = 2x$
e) $-2(x - 3) = -x$
f) $x - 4 = -(x + 2)$

Ex.22 Determine which of the following equations has no solution, exactly one solution, or solution consisting of all real numbers.

a) $x - 8 = x - 9$
b) $-x = 0$
c) $x - x = 0$
d) $4(x + 2) = 2 + 4x$
e) $3x + 1 = 3\left(x + \frac{1}{3}\right)$

Ex.23 Solve the following equations.

a) $6x = -12$
b) $\frac{a}{4} = -15$
c) $-x = -7$
d) $-x = 0$
e) $\frac{1}{6}a + 4 = 4$
f) $3x - 7 = 8$
g) $0.8y - 0.1 = 1.5$
h) $22 - 5y = y$
i) $-x - 4x = -2x$
j) $x - 5 = 3x + 7$
k) $4x + 3 = 1 - x$
l) $2.3a - 5 = 1.8a$
m) $3(2B + 5) = 16$
n) $-3x = 12 - 7x$
o) $-3(x - 2) = 6 - 3x$
p) $x - 7 = -3(x + 5)$
q) $3 - 7x = 2 - 4x$
r) $3(2m - 4) = 6m + 6$
s) $-(x + 3) = 2x + 3(1 - x)$
t) $-2(4x - 1) + 7x = 4 - x$

In exercises 7-18 of this lesson, we assume that all denominators (divisors) are different from zero.

Ex. 1 Solve the following equations.

a) $\frac{x-2}{4}=-5$

b) $-1=8x-\frac{x}{2}$

c) $-3x-\frac{x}{5}-1=0$

d) $\frac{x-1}{3}=1-\frac{x}{2}$

e) $\frac{1}{5}y-\frac{1}{5}=\frac{3}{10}y$

f) $\frac{x}{2}+\frac{2}{3}=\frac{3}{4}$

Ex. 2 Solve the following equations.

a) $8x-2=3x+5(x+2)$

b) $-x+(2-x)=5x-12x$

c) $1-\frac{2}{3}a=\frac{5}{6}$

d) $\frac{3x}{2}-\frac{3}{4}=-1$

e) $4(3x-1)=12x-2$

f) $4x-2=3x-(1-5x)$

g) $2(x-3)+4=x-2$

h) $-\frac{3x}{2}=-1+\frac{3x}{5}$

i) $3(4-x)=-2(x-6)-x$

j) $\frac{5}{8}x-\frac{7}{12}=x-\frac{3}{4}$

k) $3(4-7x)=1-5(3+x)$

l) $-(x+2)+2(x-1)=3x+5$

Ex. 3 Let $A=2x,\quad B=-x$. Find x, so the following are true (Hint: Substitute algebraic expressions for A and B. Then solve for x).

a) $A+B=0$

b) $A-3B=1$

c) $\frac{A}{3}=\frac{B}{8}$

Ex. 4 Let $P=3(x-1),\quad Q=4x+5$. Find x such that the following is true (Hint: Substitute algebraic expressions for P and Q. Then solve for x).

a) $P=Q$

b) $P=-Q$

c) $\frac{Q}{2}=P$

Ex. 5 Let $x=-3a+2,\quad y=2a+1,\quad z=2-a$. Find a, so the following are true (Hint: Substitute algebraic expressions for $x, y,$ and z. Then solve for a).

a) $x+y=z$

b) $2x=y+z$

c) $\frac{x}{8}+\frac{y}{2}=\frac{z}{4}$

Ex.6 Does the following statement make sense: "Solve $\frac{x+1}{2}-5y$ for x? ". Why or why not?

Ex.7 Solve for x. a) $\frac{x}{2}=7$ b) $\frac{x}{a}=b$

Ex.8 Solve for x. a) $x+3=8$ b) $x+a=b$

Ex.9 Solve for x. a) $3x-7=11$ b) $ax-b=c$

Ex.10 Solve for x. a) $5x-2x-6=0$ b) $ax-bx-c=0$

Ex.11 Solve for x. a) $4x=2(x+1)$ b) $ax=b(x+c)$

Ex.12. Solve for the indicated variable. Simplify your answer whenever possible.

a) $-x=a$ for x

b) $\frac{b}{a}=ac$ for b

c) $\frac{a}{b^3}=\frac{b}{c}$ for a

d) $ax+b=4b$ for a

e) $\frac{a^2}{u}=a$ for u

f) $abc^2=(ac)^3$ for b

g) $\frac{2m}{n^2}=4n$ for m

h) $2x+y=t+3x$ for y

i) $x^3+xy=2x^3$ for y

j) $AX-A=1-X$ for A

k) $s(x-1)=s^2$ for x

l) $ax-by=3ax+4by$ for a

m) $3(v-t)=s$ for v

n) $ax+x(a+2)=1$ for x

o) $\frac{m-2n}{x}=2n-m$ for x

p) $mb+2mb^2=3b$ for m

Ex.13 Solve the following equation $\frac{x}{y}=d+e$ for

a) d b) x c) y

Ex.14 Solve the following equation $3at + b = 2at + t$ for

a) b b) a c) t

Ex.15. Solve $\frac{x}{a^3} = a^6$ for x, and then evaluate, if $a = -1$.

Ex.16. Solve $3mn = mn - 2m^2$ for n, and then evaluate, if $m = -4$.

Ex.17. If b represents the base of a triangle, h its height, and A is the area of the triangle, then the following is true: $A = \frac{bh}{2}$.

a) Solve the above formula for h

b) Find the height of a triangle with base $b = 2$ inches and the area $A = 4$ square inches

Ex.18. If L represents the length of a rectangle and W its width, then the perimeter P of the rectangle is given by the formula $P = 2(L + W)$

a) Solve the above formula for W.

b) Find the value of W when $P = 4$, and $L = 1$.

c) Find the width of a rectangle with perimeter 10 inches and length equal to 3 inches.

Ex. 1 List two numbers satisfying $x < 5$. List two numbers satisfying $a < 5$. Is the second question different from the first one? How about asking: List two numbers satisfying $5 > x$?

Ex. 2 Which of the following statements has the same meaning as $x < -2$.

a) $-2 > x$

b) $-2 \le x$

c) $x > -2$

d) $x \le -2$ and $x \ne -2$

e) All numbers x that are at least -2.

f) All numbers x that are no more than -2.

Ex. 3 Name three numbers that satisfy the condition $x \le -1$

Ex. 4 Find a number that satisfies $x \ge \frac{2}{3}$ but does not satisfy $x > \frac{2}{3}$.

Ex. 5 Circle all numbers that satisfy the following inequality $x > -3$

-3, -2, -1, 0, 1, 2, 3, 4, 5

Ex. 6 Determine which of the following numbers do not satisfy the inequality $x > -3$

-3, -2, -1, 0, 1, 2, 3, 4, 5

Ex. 7 Determine which of the following numbers satisfies the inequality $x \le -0.6$.

$\frac{-1}{2}$, $-.666$, -6, -0.6 $-.5999$, 0

Ex. 8 Describe the following sets of numbers using inequality signs.

a) All negative numbers x.

b) All non-positive numbers x.

c) All numbers x that are at least equal to 6.

d) All numbers x that are at most equal to 6.

e) All numbers x that are not more than 6

Ex.9 Graph the following sets on a number line provided. Assume that all marks on the line are equally spaced.

a) $x < -4$

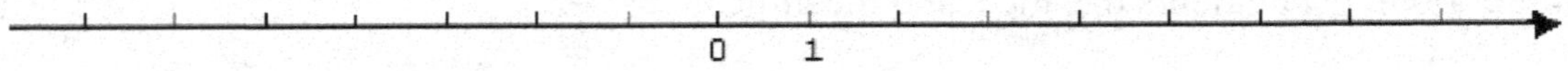

b) $x \geq 1\frac{2}{3}$

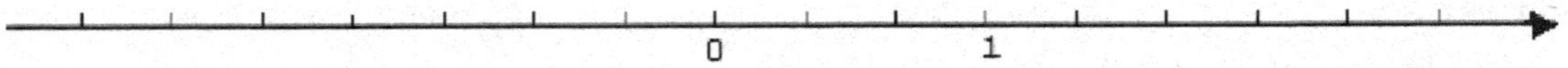

c) $-4 < x$

d) $x \geq 2$

e) $x > \frac{4}{3}$

f) $x \leq -\frac{5}{2}$

Ex.10 Graph the following number sets on a number line.

a) All numbers that are no less than -2

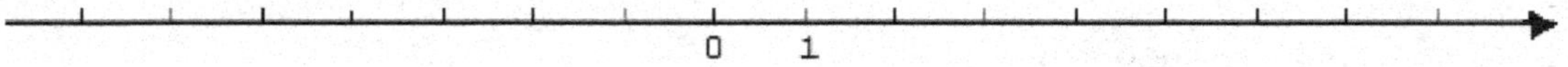

b) All numbers no more than 4

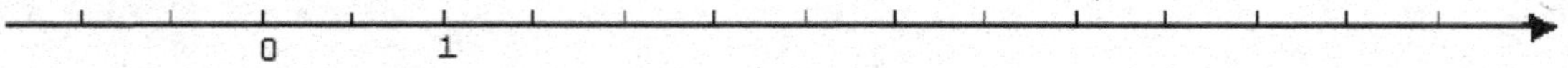

c) All non-negative numbers

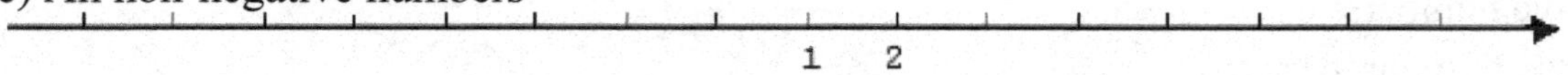

d) All numbers that are at most -1

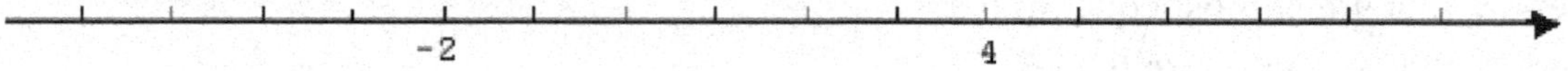

Ex. 11 Using inequality symbols, describe the set that is graphed below.

a)

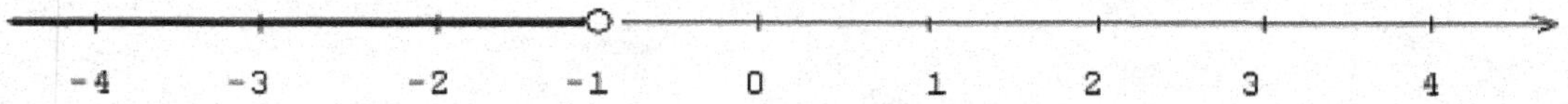

b)

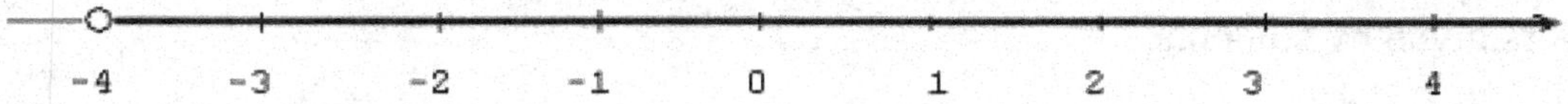

c)

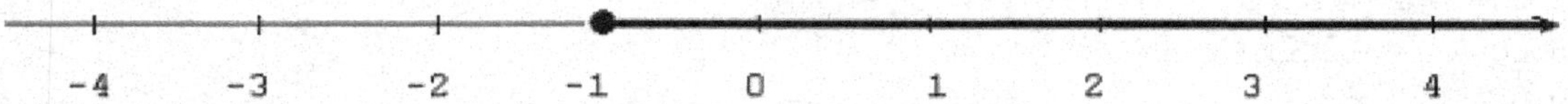

d)

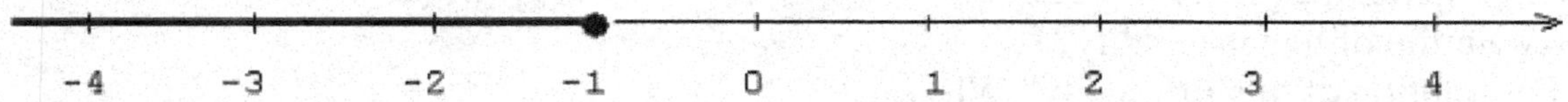

Ex. 12 Graph $x \geq \frac{2}{3}$ and $x \leq \frac{2}{3}$ on one number line, and then find a number that satisfies $x \geq \frac{2}{3}$ and also satisfies $x \leq \frac{2}{3}$.

Ex. 13 Plot the points in part (a) and (b) on separate number lines. Then write an inequality for each that is satisfied by all points from the set.

a) 3, 4, 6
b) -2, -1, 3

Ex. 14 Plot the points in part (a) and (b) on separate number lines. Then write an inequality for each that is *not* satisfied by any of these points.

a) 0, 1, 4

b) $-\frac{1}{2}$, $1\frac{1}{2}$ 2

Ex. 15 Find an inequality that is satisfied by -1 but not by 3 (if it helps, you might plot the points).

Ex. 16 Find an inequality that is satisfied by $\frac{3}{4}$ but not by 5 (if it helps, you might plot the points).

Ex.17 The number -5 is a solution of which of the following inequalities. Determine your answer without solving the inequality. Show your work.
a) $x+2<4$
b) $-x+8\geq 13$
c) $-x+3<1$
d) $3x>-15$

Ex.18 The solution of an inequality is $x\geq 2$
Here are the answers given by students.
Student A: $x>2$
Student B: $2\leq x$
Student C: $-x\geq -2$
Student D: $-2\leq x$
Student E: $x>3$
List all students who correctly solved the inequality.

Ex.19 The solution of a given inequality is $x\geq 0$.
a) Is $x=2$ *a* solution of this inequality?
b) Is $x=2$ *the* solution of this inequality? Why?
c) How many solutions does this inequality have?
d) List three solutions of the inequality.
e) List three numbers that are not solutions of this inequality.
f) If we write the solution of the inequality as $0\leq x$, would that also be correct? Why?
g) If we write the solution of the inequality as $0<x$, would that also be correct? Why?
h) Would it be right to say that the solution consists of all positive numbers?
i) Would it be right to say that the solution consists of all non-negative numbers?

Ex.20 Determine which of the following operations requires the change of inequality sign.
a) Multiplying both sides of an inequality by -2.
b) Multiplying both sides of an inequality by 2.
c) Adding 2 to both sides of an inequality.
d) Subtracting $\frac{1}{2}$ from both sides of an inequality.
e) Dividing both sides of an inequality by -2.

Ex.21 Name the operation that must be performed on both sides of an inequality to isolate z on one side. Determine if the operation requires the change of inequality sign (indicate it in writing), and then perform the operation, reversing the inequality sign, if needed (for example, to isolate z in the inequality $z-1<3$, 1 must be added to both sides, the operation of adding 1 does not require the change of sign, the resulting inequality is $z<4$).
a) $z+5<8$
b) $-2+z<1$
c) $-12<4z$
d) $-z>-3$
e) $-\frac{z}{3}>1$

Ex.22 Knowing $x < -10$, which of the following inequalities must also be true?

a) $x + 10 < 0$ b) $-2x > -20$

c) $\frac{x}{2} > -5$ d) $-\frac{3}{10}x > 3$

Ex.23 Knowing $-2x \geq 0$, which of the following inequalities must also be true?

a) $x \geq 2$ b) $x \leq 0$

c) $x \leq -2$ d) $2x \leq 0$

Ex.24 Solve the following inequalities and graph their solutions.

a) $-2x > 8$ b) $x - 1 \leq x$

c) $-0.3x \leq 0.6$ d) $3 > 2a - 11$

e) $-6 - x < 4$ f) $2a - 1 \leq 3$

Ex.25 Solve the following inequalities. Each time you perform the operation on both sides of inequality, name the operation together with the operand (for example write "adding 2 to both sides", "dividing both sides by 3", and so on).

a) $4 > -3 - a$ b) $3x + 1 < 6$

c) $\frac{3x}{4} < -15$ d) $-5 \geq \frac{-x}{4}$

e) $\frac{x}{4} + 1 \geq -1$ f) $\frac{x+1}{4} \geq -1$

Ex.26 Solve the following inequalities.

a) $-3x > 18$ b) $\frac{-x}{2} > 1$

c) $2 - 3x \leq 14$ d) $x \leq x$

e) $x < x$ f) $-3 - a > 4a$

g) $4x - 1 \leq 7x - 5$ h) $-x + 1 > 6x - 2$

i) $\frac{3}{2}x > -1$ j) $x - 8 > x - 9$

k) $2 - a > 4a - 5a - 2$ l) $4x - 1 \leq 2(x - 5)$

m) $-3(x + 2) \leq -3x + 2$ n) $3x + 1 < 3(x + \frac{1}{3})$

o) $3(2x + 5) > 6x + 16$ p) $3(2x - 1) < 2(x - 2)$

q) $\frac{-x-2}{4} \leq -5$ r) $\frac{-y}{2} - \frac{y+3}{3} \leq -1$

s) $\frac{2a-3}{5} - 1 > -5a + \frac{2}{3}$ t) $3 - 2(3a - 5) < -6a$

Ex.1 The expression $\left(y-\frac{3}{4}\right)^2$ is written in the form $(y-a)^2$. What is the value of a?

Ex.2 The following expressions are written in the form $ax+by$. What are the values of a and b in these representations?

a) $3x+4y$

b) $-4x+\frac{2}{3}y$

Ex.3 The expression $-3+x$ is written

a) in the form $p+x$. Determine the value of p in this representation.

b) in the form $-p+x$. Determine the value of p in this representation

Ex.4 The expression x^{-2+5} is written in the form x^{a+b}. What are the values of a and b?

Ex.5 The expression $(-7)^2x$ is written in the form a^2x. What is the value of a?

Ex.6 The expression $4x-2y$ is written in the form $A-2B$. What algebraic expression represents A and B.

Ex.7 The following expressions are written in the form XY^2 For each of them determine what algebraic expression represents X and Y.

a) $3ab^2$

b) $3(ab)^2$

Ex.8 The following expressions are written in the form $\frac{c^9}{b}$. For each of expressions identify (without rewriting the expression) what algebraic expression represents c and b.

a) $\frac{(x-1)^9}{2}$

b) $\frac{x^9}{y^9}$

Ex. 9 For each of the following expressions (1-6) indicate if they match A, B, C, D, E or F. Each time identify a and b.

(1) $x^3 - 1^3$ (A) $(a-b)^3$

(2) $(x-1)^2$ (B) $a^2 - b^2$

(3) $(8+x)(64-8x+x^2)$ (C) $(a-b)(a+b)$

(4) $(3x-5y)^3$ (D) $(a+b)(a^2-ab+b^2)$

(5) $(3x)^2-(5y)^2$ (E) a^3-b^3

(6) $(3-y)(3+y)$ (F) $(a-b)^2$

Ex. 10 Among the expressions below identify those that are written in the form $A-B$ and those that are in the form $A+B$, where A and B are any expressions except 0. Those that are in the form $A-B$ rewrite as $A+B$, those that are in the form $A+B$ rewrite as $A-B$ (In other words, rewrite sums as differences and differences as sums).

a) $5-(-n)$

b) $5+n$

c) $5+(-n)$

d) $5-n$

Ex. 11 Rewrite the following expressions in the form ax^3+b, where a and b are any numbers. Identify a and b in your representation.

a) $-x^3+3$ b) $2x^3-3$

c) $1-\frac{x^3}{2}$ d) $\frac{4x^3+3}{2}$

e) $\frac{3-2x^3}{2}$ f) $(2x)^3+4$

Ex. 12 Write the following expressions in the form a^2, where a is any algebraic expression or a number. In each case state what a is equal to.

a) 36 b) 400

c) 0.16 d) $\frac{9}{49}$

e) $25y^2$ f) $\frac{b^2}{100}$

g) $0.49c^2$ h) X^4

i) $4x^6$ j) $81x^2y^8$

Ex. 13 Write the following expressions in the form a^3, where a is any algebraic expression or a number. In each case state what a is equal to.

a) -1

b) 27

c) 0.027

d) $\frac{8}{125}$

e) $-z^3$

f) $64x^3$

g) $\frac{-x^3}{8}$

h) y^6

i) $1000x^9$

j) $\frac{x^{15}}{8y^3}$

Ex. 14 Write the expressions x^{24} in the following forms.

a) a^4

b) a^6

c) a^{12}

Ex. 15 Write the following expressions in the form A^7. Identify A in your representation.

a) $-x^7$

b) x^{14}

c) $x^{14}y^{21}$

d) $\frac{y^{21}}{z^{70}}$

Ex. 16 Write the following expressions in the form a^m, where a is any algebraic expression and m is a positive integer different from 1. Identify a and m in your representation.

a) x^2x^3

b) $s^7(tv)^7$

c) $b(b^3)^2$

d) $\frac{B^3}{C^3}$

e) $\left(\frac{x+y}{z}\right)^3\frac{x+y}{z}$

f) $64x^2$

Ex. 17 Write the following equations in the form $ax^2+by^2=0$, where a and b are any numbers. Identify a and b in your representation.

a) $x^2-2y^2=0$

b) $3x^2=y^2$

c) $\frac{x^2}{2}-(y^2-6)=6$

d) $x^2=0$

e) $\frac{3x^2+y^2}{4}=0$

f) $-x^2=\frac{8x^2-5y^2}{2}$

Ex.18 Write in the form $Ax + By + Cz$, where A, B, C are any numbers. Identify A, B, and C.

a) $-x + \frac{3}{2}z - \frac{y}{4}$

b) $-3(2x + y) + z$

c) $\frac{3x - 2y + z}{4}$

d) $x - y$

e) $\frac{x + 3y}{4} - x + 2z$

f) $\frac{z}{3} - \frac{2}{5}z$

Ex.19 Write the following equations to match the form $y = mx + b$, where m and b are any numbers. In each case determine the value of m and b.

a) $y = 3x - 2$

b) $y = x$

c) $y = \frac{x}{5}$

d) $y + 3x - 2 = 0$

e) $3y = 6x - 1$

f) $y - x = -x - 5$

g) $3 - y = 3$

h) $\frac{-y + 4x + 2}{2} = 4$

Ex.20 Recall the formula for the square of the sum $(a + b)^2 = a^2 + 2ab + b^2$. The following expressions are written in the form $(a + b)^2$. For each such expression, identify *a* and *b*, and then substitute their values in $a^2 + 2ab + b^2$. Simplify.

a) $(3 + b)^2$

b) $(2x + 3y)^2$

c) $\left(y^2 + \frac{2}{5}\right)^2$

Ex.21 Determine if the following equations are linear equations in one variable. If so, express it in the form $ax + b = 0$, where *b* is any real number, *a* is any real number except zero, and x is unknown. Determine the values of *a*, and *b* in your representation.

a) $3x^2 - 9 = 0$

b) $\frac{x}{3} - 1 = 0$

c) $-x = 0$

d) $\frac{x + 8}{8} = 0.1$

e) $x(x + 1) = x^2 - 2$

f) $-3x + 7 = x$

g) $-(x + 2) = 0.5$

h) $\frac{x}{5} = 2x - \frac{1}{2}$

Ex.22 The equation $4x+2=0$ is a linear equation written in the form $ax+b=0$. Record the values of a and b in this representation. Obtain an equivalent equation by multiplying both side of the equation by 3. What are the values of a and b in the new representation?

Ex.23 Using the formula for the difference of two squares $a^2-b^2=(a-b)(a+b)$, factor the following expressions. Simplify your answer, if possible.

a) x^2-1

b) $4-9x^2$

c) y^2-100a^2

d) $25s^2-64t^2$

e) $x^4-\frac{1}{9}$

f) $x^2y^2-0.25$

g) $\frac{a^2}{b^2}-36$

h) $m^2-(2m+1)^2$

i) $(x+1)^2-(3x+5)^2$

j) $(2a-3)^2-9a^2$

Ex.24 The following formula is true $a^3-b^3=(a-b)(a^2+ab+b^2)$. Factor each of the following expressions using the above formula. To this end

- rewrite each expression to match the left-hand side of the equation
- identify the value of a and b in your representation
- replace a and b in $(a-b)(a^2+ab+b^2)$ with their representation
- simplify, if possible

a) x^3-64

b) $1-8y^3$

c) $8x^3-27y^3$

d) $x^6-\frac{1}{27}$

Ex.25 The following formulas are true

$$a^2-b^2=(a-b)(a+b)$$
$$a^3+b^3=(a+b)(a^2-ab+b^2).$$
$$a^3-b^3=(a-b)(a^2+ab+b^2)$$

Factor each of the following expressions using one of the above formulas. To this end, you must first match each expression with one of the above formulas, then identify the value of a and b in your representation, and finally replace a and b in the right-hand side of the used formula, Please, simplify your answer..

a) $8x^3+y^3$

b) $36x^2-0.01y^2$

c) x^3-27y^3

d) $64a^3-b^3c^3$

Ex.26 Calculate $10.7^2 - 9.3^2$ using $a^2 - b^2 = (a-b)(a+b)$ (Show how you matched to the given identity in order to arrive at your answer).

Ex.27 The following formula is true (you are not asked to check it, although you certainly can; you have enough knowledge to do so)

$$(a+b)^4 = a^4 + 4a^3b + 6a^2b^2 + 4ab^3 + b^4$$

Use the above formula to calculate 11^4. Hint: Use the fact that $11 = 10+1$ to write 11^4 to match the form $(a+b)^4$.

Solutions to these arithmetic review questions are on page 62.

Compute if possible or write '*undefined.*' Make sure that you use the '=' sign correctly

1. $-12+17$
2. $-5-8$
3. $-2+5-8+4$
4. $-3+(-6)-(-4)+1$
5. $(-7)(-8)$
6. $(-2)(-6)(-5)$
7. $\frac{18}{-3}$
8. $(-48)\div(-3)$
9. $\frac{3}{10}+\frac{5}{6}$
10. $-\frac{2}{7}+\frac{3}{8}$
11. $\frac{2}{3}-\frac{7}{12}+\frac{3}{4}$
12. $-\frac{5}{16}+2$
13. $\frac{25}{3}-3$
14. $-\frac{5}{12}\times(-8)$
15. $-24\times\frac{2}{15}$
16. $\frac{3}{16}\times\left(\frac{24}{15}\right)\times\frac{10}{27}$
17. $\left(-\frac{8}{25}\right)\times\frac{15}{16}\times\left(-\frac{4}{9}\right)$
18. $\frac{\left(\frac{3}{8}\right)}{\left(-\frac{2}{3}\right)}$
19. $\frac{7}{24}\div\frac{35}{42}$
20. $\frac{\left(\frac{12}{35}\right)}{-4}$
21. $-15\div\frac{10}{11}$
22. $-18-(-18)$
23. $-5\div0$
24. $-0.03\times1{,}000$
25. $-13\div(-100)$
26. $317.2\div(-100)$
27. $\left(-\frac{2}{3}\right)\div\left(\frac{8}{9}\right)\times\left(-\frac{8}{3}\right)$
28. $-3\times5-7$
29. $6+(-8)\div(-2)$
30. $(-6)\times(-5)\div(-3)\times(-2)$
31. $2.35-6$
32. $-7.03+6.3$

33. $-2.1 \times (-101)$

34. 1.01×0.3

35. $\dfrac{0.33}{1.1}$

36. $32.5 \div 0.05$

37. $(-0.02)^3$

38. $-(-3^4)$

39. $\left(-\dfrac{2}{3}\right)^4$

40. $2\dfrac{1}{3}+3\dfrac{1}{2}$

41. $6\dfrac{2}{7}-7\dfrac{1}{6}$

42. $-2\dfrac{1}{3}\times 3\dfrac{1}{2}$

43. $1\dfrac{2}{5}\div 2\dfrac{1}{5}$

44. $1-2(1-2)^2$

45. $-(5-3)^2-(5-2)^3$

46. $\left(\dfrac{7}{8}-\dfrac{1}{4}\right)^2 \div \left(-\dfrac{1}{2}\right)$

47. $\dfrac{12\div 4-2}{8\div 4}$

48. $\dfrac{(-0.6+0.5)^2}{0.2}$

49. $-0.7+2(-0.3+0.2)$

50. $\dfrac{2-5}{4}\div\left(-\dfrac{1}{8}\right)$

1.	5	2.	-13
3.	-1	4.	-4
5.	56	6.	-60
7.	-6	8.	16
9.	$\frac{17}{15}$ *or* $1\frac{2}{15}$	10.	$\frac{5}{56}$
11.	$\frac{5}{6}$	12.	$\frac{27}{16}$ *or* $1\frac{11}{16}$
13.	$\frac{16}{3}$ *or* $5\frac{1}{3}$	14.	$\frac{10}{3}$ *or* $3\frac{1}{3}$
15.	$-\frac{16}{3}$ *or* $-3\frac{1}{5}$	16.	$\frac{1}{15}$
17.	$\frac{2}{15}$	18.	$-\frac{9}{16}$
19.	$\frac{7}{20}$	20.	$-\frac{3}{35}$
21.	$-\frac{33}{2}$ *or* $-16\frac{1}{2}$	22.	0
23.	*undefined*	24.	-30
25.	0.13	26.	-3.172
27.	2	28.	-22
29.	10	30.	20
31.	-3.65	32.	-0.73
33.	212.1	34.	0.303

35. 0.3

36. 650

37. 0.000008

38. 81

39. $\frac{16}{81}$

40. $\frac{35}{6}$ *or* $5\frac{5}{6}$

41. $-\frac{37}{42}$

42. $-\frac{49}{6}$ *or* $-8\frac{1}{6}$

43. $\frac{7}{11}$

44. -1

45. -31

46. $-\frac{25}{32}$

47. $\frac{1}{2}$

48. $\frac{1}{20}$ *or* 0.05

49. -0.9

50. 6

Lesson 1

1 $3x+2$, y^2, $\frac{a+bc}{2}$, $(-2a+1)^3$ are examples of <u>algebraic expressions</u>. Ψ x, y, a, b, c are examples of <u>variables</u> but also examples of <u>algebraic expressions</u>. Variables represent <u>unknown numbers</u>. If we know the value of x, we can evaluate $3x+2$, and as a result we get a <u>number</u>.

2 a) "a squared" or "a raised to the second power." b) "a cubed" or "a raised to the third power." c) "a raised to the twelfth power." d) "2 to the m" or " 2 raised to the m-th power." e) "minus y" or "the opposite of y" f) "the product of *c* and *d*" or "c times d" g) "a minus b" h) "two-fifth times x" or "two-fifth x"

3 a) $7\times n$ b) $-5\times k\times m$ c) "there is no multiplication performed" d) $-x\times(-y)$ e) $\frac{3\times x}{2}$ f) $2\times x-y\times z+w\times(-t)$

4 a) multiplication b) division c) exponentiation d) division e) subtraction f) multiplication

5 a) Any time two operation signs are next to each other, parentheses are needed. b) If parentheses are removed, only *m* would be raised to the fourth power. c) Any time two operation signs are next to each other, parentheses are needed, even if the multiplication sign is not explicitly displayed d) If parentheses are removed, only *a* would be raised to the fourth power. e) Any time two operation signs are next to each other, parentheses are needed, even if the multiplication sign is not explicitly displayed f) Any time two operation signs are next to each other, parentheses are needed

6 a) $-s$ b) s c) st d) t e) x f) $\frac{x}{y}$ g) st h) s i) $y-s$

7 a) x b) $-x$ c) multiplication

8 a) $1\cdot x = x$; b) $-1\cdot x = -x$ c) $0\cdot x = 0$

9 a) $-(-x)$ b) $-\frac{x^3}{y}$ c) $-\left(-\frac{x^3}{y}\right)$ d) $-\left(\frac{-x^3}{-y}\right)$

10 a) $\frac{1}{2}y$ b) $\frac{3}{4}y$ c) $y+5$ d) $v-y$ e) y^2 f) $y+3$ g) $y-x$ h) xy i) $2y$

11 a) $a+(-b)$ b) $a-(-b)$ c) $a(-b)$ d) $-C$ f) $-(-C)$ g) $-\frac{-a}{-b}$

h) $v(-t)(-p)$ i) $\frac{c}{-B}$ j) $(-x)^m$ k) $\left(\frac{x}{y}\right)^m$

12 a) $x+10$ b) $\frac{2}{3}x$ c) $\frac{x}{3}$ d) $\frac{100}{x}$ e) $x-2$ f) $30x$ g) $x-3$ h) $x-5$

13 $\frac{d}{t}$

14 ma

15 $\frac{1}{2}(bh)$ or $\frac{1}{2}bh$

16 a) $3+5=8$ b) $3-2=1$ c) $\frac{3}{3}=1$ d) $4\times 3=12$ e) $3^2=9$ f) $\frac{6}{3}=2$

17 $\frac{1}{x}$ can not be evaluated with $x = 0$, because the denominator of a fraction can not be 0.

If $x = 0$, $\frac{1}{x-5}$ can be evaluated: $\frac{1}{x-5} = \frac{1}{0-5} = -\frac{1}{5}$, but if $x = 5$ then $\frac{1}{x-5} = \frac{1}{5-5} = -\frac{1}{0}$ is undefined. Another example could be: $\frac{3}{y+4}$ cannot be evaluated with $y = -4$. (answers vary)

18 a) $3 \cdot 0 = 0$ b) $0 - 2 = -2$ c) undefined d) $\frac{0}{7} = 0$ e) $\frac{2}{0-3} = -\frac{2}{3}$ f) undefined

19 a) $3^2 = 9$ b) $2^3 = 8$ c) $2^2 = 4$

20 a) $-A = -2$ b) $-A = 2$

21 a) $6 - 8 = -2$ b) $-10 - 6 = -16$ c) $-4 + 6 = 2$ d) $6 - 6 = 0$ e) $-2 + 6 - 6 = -2$

22 a) $2 + (-2) = 0$ b) $2 - (-2) = 4$ c) $-2 - (-2) = 0$ d) $-5 - (-2) + 4 = 1$ e) $6 + (-2) - 10 - (-2) = -4$

23 a) $3(10) = 30$ b) $-5(10) = -50$ c) $\frac{-200}{10} = -20$ d) $-\frac{10}{2} = -5$

e) $-5 \div 10 = -0.5$ or $-\frac{1}{2}$ f) $10^4 = 10{,}000$

24 a) $-1000(-12) = 12{,}000$ b) $\frac{-12}{6} = -2$ c) $-5(-12) = 60$

d) $\frac{6}{-12+12}$ "not possible" e) $-24 \div (-12) = 2$ f) $(-12)^2 = 144$

25 a) $\frac{7}{3}$ or $2\frac{1}{3}$ b) $\frac{13}{15}$ c) $-\frac{8}{21}$ d) $-\frac{13}{12}$ e) $\frac{8}{3}$ or $2\frac{2}{3}$ f) $-\frac{11}{3}$ or $-3\frac{2}{3}$

26 a) $\frac{9}{10}$ b) $\frac{16}{35}$ c) $\frac{8}{5}$ *or* $1\frac{3}{5}$ d) $-\frac{13}{20}$ e) $-\frac{29}{10}$ *or* $-2\frac{9}{10}$

27 a) $\frac{4}{7}$ b) -2 c) $-\frac{4}{3}$ d) $\frac{5}{8}$ e) $\frac{35}{2}$ *or* $17\frac{1}{2}$ f) $-\frac{1}{7}$

28 a) $\frac{9}{16}$ b) -1 c) $\frac{9}{20}$ d) $\frac{3}{2}$ e) $\frac{1}{4}$ f) 0

29 a) 3.41 b) 34.81 c) 0.05 d) -8 e) 0.06 f) -5

30 a) -3.9 b) -2.1 c) 2 d) 360 e) -0.0006 f) -0.216

31 a) -1.58 b) -1.1 c) -10 d) 0.3 e) 20

32 a) $\frac{19}{15}$ *or* $1\frac{4}{15}$ b) $-\frac{5}{14}$ c) -1.28

33 a) $-\frac{1}{15}$ b) $\frac{13}{14}$ c) 0.88

34 a) $\frac{4}{9}$ b) $\frac{18}{5}$ *or* $3\frac{3}{5}$ c) -0.002

35 a) $\frac{9}{121}$ b) $\frac{40}{9}$ c) -20

36 a) $-10{,}000{,}000$ b) 16 c) $-\frac{1}{8}$ d) 0.00001 or $\frac{1}{100{,}000}$

37 a) $2x = 2\left(-\frac{1}{2}\right) = -1$ b) $\frac{3}{4}x = \frac{3}{4}\left(-\frac{1}{2}\right) = -\frac{3}{8}$ c) $\left(-\frac{1}{2}\right)^2 = \frac{1}{4}$

38 $-t = -1$ if $t = 1$, $-t = -(-1) = 1$ if $t = -1$; $-t$ may be positive or negative depending on the value of t

Lesson 2

1 a) $x-(m-2n)$ b) $-(m-2n)$ c) $(m-2n)\cdot 7$ d) $m-2n-3a$ e) $-(k^2-3k+1)$ f) $4\div(-4x+y)$

2 a) $3x+y$ b) $4(a+b)$ c) $(-x)^6$ d) $z(y-3)$ *or* $(y-3)z$ e) $9x^3$

f) $(9x)^3$ g) $\frac{a-b}{c}$ h) $\frac{3}{y}+x$ i) $-(M+3)$ j) $(-x)^3+y^7$

3 a) $2(x-7)$ b) $\frac{2}{3}(x+c)$ c) $\frac{1}{4}x-5$ d) $c-9x$ e) $\left(\frac{x}{2}\right)^3$ f) $4(-x)$

g) x^3+6 h) $y(x-4)$ i) $-(y-x)$ j) $x(x+5)$ k) $(-x)^{121}$ l) $-x^2$

4 $\frac{9}{5}C+32$

5 $2(L+W)$

6 mc^2

7 a) $a+b^5$ exponentiation b) $(a+b)^5$ addition

c) $-x^8$ exponentiation d) $(-x)^8$ opposite of x

e) $\frac{a-b}{c}$ subtraction f) $a\div b\times c$ division

g) $4-7y$ multiplication h) $3+a\div b$ division

8 a) Multiply x by 4 and then subtract y. b) Add a and 3 and then divide the result by x.
c) Add x and 3 and then multiply the result by y. d) Divide s by t and then add 2 to the result.
e) Square x and then multiply by 3. f) Multiply x by 3 and then square the result.
g) Add a and c and then raise the result to the 4th power. h) Raise c to the 4th power and then add the result to a.

9 a) parentheses are needed b) $c-3-a$ c) $3a+x$ d) parentheses are needed e) parentheses are needed

f) $\frac{-c+d}{a}$ g) parentheses are needed h) yx^8 i) parentheses are needed j) parentheses are needed

10 a) 2 b) 2 c) 2 d) Yes, because we performed the same operations. e) −2

11 a) $-2\times3-5=-11$ b) $-4+3^2=5$ c) $\frac{3}{3-3}$ cannot be performed

d) $(-3)^2=9$ e) $-3^2=-9$ f) $\frac{3-3}{4+3}=0$ g) $3^3=27$

12 a) $-2^4=-16$ b) $(-2)^4=16$ c) $(-4)^2=16$ d) $-4^2=-16$
13 a) $(-(-1))+(-1)=0$ b) $(-(-1))-(-1)=2$ c) $(-(-1))(-(-1))=1$ d) $(-1)^2=1$ e) $-(-1)^2=-1$
14 a) $\frac{1}{\frac{1}{2}}=2$ b) $\frac{1}{\frac{1}{2}}+\frac{1}{2}=2\frac{1}{2}=\frac{5}{2}$ c) $\left(-\frac{1}{2}\right)^2=\frac{1}{4}$ d) $-\left(\frac{1}{2}\right)^2=-\frac{1}{4}$

15 a) 0.39 b) −5 c) −1 d) −273
16 b) c) and f) We would have 0 in the denominator in these cases.
17 a) −19 b) 60 c) −34 d) −35 e) −50
18 a) $8\times\left(-\frac{1}{8}\right)-10\times\frac{4}{5}=-9$ b) $10\left(-\frac{1}{8}\right)\left(\frac{4}{5}\right)=-1$ c) $2\left(\frac{4}{5}+\left(-\frac{1}{8}\right)\right)=\frac{37}{20}$

d) $-8\left(-\frac{1}{8}\right)^2+\frac{4}{5}=\frac{27}{40}$ e) $\frac{4}{5}\div\left(\frac{1}{8}+\left(-\frac{1}{8}\right)\right)$ cannot be performed .f) $\frac{4}{5}\div\frac{3}{10}+\left(-\frac{1}{8}\right)=\frac{61}{24}$

19 a) $2\times\left(\frac{1}{3}\right)^4=\frac{2}{81}$ b) $\left(-\frac{2}{3}\right)^4=\frac{16}{81}$ c) $-\left(-\frac{2}{3}\right)^4=-\frac{16}{81}$

d) $\dfrac{\frac{1}{3}-\frac{2}{3}}{\frac{1}{3}+\frac{2}{3}}=-\frac{1}{3}$ e) $\dfrac{\frac{1}{3}\times\left(-\left(-\frac{2}{3}\right)\right)}{\frac{1}{3}+\left(-\frac{2}{3}\right)}=-\frac{4}{9}$

20 a) −1 b) 64 c) $-\frac{1}{9}$ d) $\frac{1}{9}$ e) 1 f) −1

21 a) −2.2 b) −2.1

22 a) −0.1 b) 0.1 c) −0.2

23 a) −2 b) −2

24 a) −5 b) 0 c) 1.3 d) $1\frac{1}{2}=\frac{3}{2}$ e) $2\frac{13}{15}=\frac{43}{15}$ f) $\frac{4}{35}$

25 a) 4 b) 7 c) 0.5 d) 7 e) $\frac{3}{14}$ f) $\frac{17}{3}=5\frac{2}{3}$

26 a) 10 b) −50 c) −0.05

27 a) 0 b) −6

28 a) addition, 7+x b) multiplication c) multiplication, 12x d) addition, 7x

e) exponentiation, $x \cdot 8$ f) subtraction $\frac{-1}{x}$

29 a) $(3x)^2 = 81$ b) $\frac{x-(-4)}{0.2} = 5$ c) $\left(\frac{9}{x}\right)^3 = -27$

Lesson 3

1 In the expression $4x^2 \times 2y$, $4x^2$ and $2y$ are called factors. In the expression $4x^2 + 2y$, $4x^2$ and $2y$ are called terms.

2 a) $3, \quad x$ b) $ab, \quad -cd$ c) $\frac{xy}{2}, \quad 2y^2, -1$ d) $-(2-b)^2, \quad \frac{x}{y}, \quad -z$

3 All these expressions are equal (equivalent) because of the commutative property of addition.

4 a) $m-n=-1$, $n-m=1$; they are not equivalent. b) True

5 a) Terms: $2m, z$; $2m+z=z+2m$ b) Terms: $x, -2$; $x-2=-2+x$ c) Terms: $-3c, 2$; $-3c+2=2-3c$

d) Terms: $-2x^2, -\frac{y^3}{2}$ $-2x^2-\frac{y^3}{2}=-\frac{y^3}{2}-2x^2$ e) Terms: $c(d-f), y^2$; $c(d-f)+y^2=y^2+c(d-f)$

f) Terms: $-(x-y)^2, \quad \frac{s+2}{3}$; $-(x-y)^2+\frac{s+2}{3}=\frac{s+2}{3}-(x-y)^2$

6 a) $x-mn+2=-mn+2+x$ b) $3-(2a-3b)+4x=4x+3-(2a-3b)$

7 a) Terms: $-x^2, x-x^3$; $-x^2+x-x^3=x-x^2-x^3=-x^3+x-x^2$ (answers vary)

b) Terms: $-a^2, -2bc, \frac{3x}{2}$; $-a^2-2bc+\frac{3x}{2}=\frac{3x}{2}-a^2-2bc=\frac{3x}{2}-2bc-a^2$ (answers vary)

8 (1) -- (C), (2) -- (E), (3) --(A), (4) --(B), (5)-- (D

9 a) $2\times a$; factors: 2, a b) $3\times(a+b)$; factors: 3, $(a+b)$

c) $-3\times x\times\frac{2}{y}$; factors: -3, x, $\frac{2}{y}$ d) $4\times(x+y)\times(b-c)$; factors: 4, $(x+y)$, $(b-c)$

10 a) $mn=nm$ b) $-5\times7=7(-5$ c) $-cd=d(-c)$ d) $-c(a+d)=(a+d)(-c)$

11 a) $vst=stv=svt=tsv$ b) $v(x-y)t=vt(x-y)=(x-y)vt=(x-y)tv$.

12 a) All these expressions are equal (equivalent) because of the commutative property of multiplication
b) $-3AB=-3\times1\times2=-6$; $BA-3=2\times1-3=-1$ when $A=1$ and $B=2$, thus they are not equivalent,

13 They are all equivalent because of the commutative property of addition and multiplication

14 a) $\frac{2-5}{7}=\frac{2}{7}-\frac{5}{7}$ b) $\frac{a+6}{3}=\frac{a}{3}+\frac{6}{3}$ c) $\frac{a-2}{a+b}=\frac{a}{a+b}-\frac{2}{a+b}$ d) $\frac{b^2+c}{ab^2-c}=\frac{b^2}{ab^2-c}+\frac{c}{ab^2-c}$

15 a) $\frac{m+n}{4}$ b) $\frac{7m-n^2}{4}$ c) $\frac{5m-2n^2}{4c-2}$ d) $\frac{A-B+2C}{x}$

16 a) $\frac{4-7+2}{5}$ b) $\frac{7m+n^2-3}{4x}$ c) $\frac{m-3-t}{s-1}$

17 a) $\frac{2}{3}x$ b) $2\frac{x^2}{y}$ c) $\frac{-2}{3}x^2$ d) $-2\cdot\frac{(a+2b)}{y}$ e) $\frac{1}{3}x$ f) $\frac{1}{3}(a+2b)$

18 a) $\frac{3m}{n}$ b) $\frac{3(-m)}{n}$ c) $\frac{a(-b)}{4}$ d) $\frac{-a(-b)}{4}$ e) $\frac{(s-4)t}{n}$ f) $\frac{4(-a)}{n-1}$ g) $\frac{3(m+n)}{t}$ h) $\frac{a(-x+1)}{x^2}$

19 The opposite to $\frac{s}{t}$ is $-\frac{s}{t}$ or equivalently $\frac{-s}{t}$, $\frac{s}{-t}$. All students were right.

20 a) $-\frac{2a}{b}=\frac{-2a}{b}=\frac{2a}{-b}$ b) $\frac{2a+c}{-2d}=\frac{-(2a+c)}{2d}=-\frac{2a+c}{2d}$

21 a) $\frac{2x+4y}{3}$ b) $\frac{2x-y}{3}$ c) $\frac{2x-7y}{3}$ d) $\frac{3x-y}{t}$ e) $\frac{-2x+3y}{t}$ f) $\frac{-1-2n}{k+t}$

g) $\frac{3(a-b)+2(cd-1)}{t}$ h) $\frac{-(2+a)-3(m-n)}{xy}$

22 a) $\frac{3x}{y}=x\cdot\frac{3}{y}$ b) $\frac{3x}{y}=3\cdot\frac{x}{y}$ c) $\frac{3x}{y}=\frac{1}{y}\cdot 3x$ d) $\frac{a+b}{y}=\frac{1}{y}\cdot(a+b)$

23 a) $-4+a$ b) $-32a$ c) $2a$ d) $64x$ e) not possible f) not possible g) $2x$ h) $2x$
i) 3^m j) x^2 k) $-xy^2$ l) not possible m) $2x$ n) $2x$

o) $\frac{8}{5}-x$ p) $\frac{6y}{xz}$ q) $-1-x$ r) $\frac{bd}{3ac}$ s) $-0.06xyz$ t) $-4x$

24 Yes, both are equivalent.

25 $(x+y)(1+a)$ and $x+y(1+a)$ are not equivalent. In $(x+y)(1+a)$ the entire expression of $(x+y)$ is multiplied with $(1+a)$ and in $x+y(1+a)$ only y is multiplied with $(1+a)$.

26 a) $a-2b+c=c-2b+a$ b) $x=\frac{x}{4}\cdot 4$ c) $\frac{xy}{4}=\frac{1}{4}xy$ d) $a\div 2=\frac{a}{2}$

e) $\frac{x+y}{3}=\frac{x}{3}+\frac{y}{3}$ f) $z-c=-c+z$ g) $-xyz=yz(-x)$ h) $\frac{ab}{2}=a\cdot\frac{b}{2}$

27 $\frac{m}{-1}$, $-\frac{m}{1}$, $m(-1)$ are equivalent to $-m$.

28 $m-(n)$ and $-n+m$ are equivalent to $m-n$:

29 $-a+b-c+d$ and $d+b-c-a$ are equivalent to $-a-c+b+d$.

30 $\frac{-a}{b}$, $-a\cdot\frac{1}{b}$, $-\frac{2a}{2b}$, $\frac{a}{-b}$ are equivalent to $-\frac{a}{b}$.

31 All of the expressions are equal to $\frac{5x}{6}$ except $\frac{5}{6x}$

32 $\frac{x}{2}$, $\frac{4x}{8}$, and $\frac{-x}{-2}$ are equivalent to $x\div 2$

33 $8a+3$, $3+a\cdot 8$, $2\cdot\frac{3+8a}{2}$ are equivalent to $3+8a$

34 $\frac{1}{6}(3a-b)$, $\frac{3a}{6}-\frac{b}{6}$, $\frac{-b+3a}{6}$, and $(3a-b)\frac{1}{6}$ are equivalent to $\frac{3a-b}{6}$.

35 $\frac{m-n}{3}$, $\frac{1}{3}\cdot m-\frac{1}{3}n$, $(m-n)\cdot\frac{1}{3}$ *and* $\frac{-n+m}{3}$ are equivalent to $\frac{m}{3}-\frac{n}{3}$.

36 Both John and Mary are right.

37 $(-x)^4=1$, $-x^4=-1$. Since $-1\neq 1$ the expressions are not equivalent.

38 $x^2+y^2=5$, $(x+y)^2=1$, when $x=-1$, $y=2$. Since $5\neq 1$ the expressions are not equivalent.

39 $m-n+p=-2$, $m-(n+p)=-4$, when $m=2$, $n=5$ $n=5$, and $p=1$. Since $-2\neq -4$ the expressions are not equivalent.

40 a) $(-1)^m=-1$, $-1^m=-1$, when $m=1$ b) $(-1)^m=-1$, $-1^m=-1$, when $m=3$

c) $(-1)^m=-1$, $-1^m=-1$, when $m=5$ d) $(-1)^m=-1$, $-1^m=-1$, when $m=7$

e) No, we cannot. Even if the expressions have the same answers in a-d, we cannot conclude that the expression will always be equivalent. f) $(-1)^m=1$, $-1^m=-1$, when $m=2$. Yes, we can, they are not equivalent. It is enough to find **one** set of values of variables for which two expressions are not equal to determine that they are not equivalent.

Lesson 4

1 coefficient, exponent or power, the base.

2 a) first b) zero

3 a) *b* b) *ab* c) *de* d) $-a$ e) *a* f) $\left(\frac{2x}{y}\right)$

4 a) $\left(\frac{a}{2}\right)^4$ b) $\left(\frac{2}{3}a\right)^3$ c) $\frac{c^3}{7}$ d) $(5a)^2$ e) $8a^2$ f) $(-x)^5$ g) $-x^{10}$

5

	base	exponent	coefficient
a)	x	4	3
b)	x	m	-1
c)	x	3	$\frac{2}{3}$
d)	$a-bc$	2	-1
e)	$\frac{x}{y}$	m	1
f)	$x+y$	7	$\frac{1}{4}$
g)	$\frac{3x+z}{w}$	7	$\frac{3}{4}$
h)	ab	5	$-\frac{1}{2}$

6 a) 6^5 b) z^4 c) $3^3 \cdot a^4$ d) $-x^5y^2$ e) $-a-a^4$ f) x^2y-xy^2 g) $(a+b)^3$ h) $(2t^3)^4$

i) $m+n^2+m$ j) $\frac{k^3}{n}\cdot k = \frac{k^4}{n}$ k) $\frac{-z-z-z}{z^4}$ l) $\frac{(-z)^3}{z+z+z}$ m) $x^3 \cdot \frac{x}{2} = \frac{x^4}{2}$ n) $(3-x)^3$

o) $\left(\frac{2a}{b}\right)^3$ p) $\left(-\frac{3}{x}\right)^3$ q) $\frac{1}{(w+2v)^3}$ r) $\left(\frac{x-y}{m}\right)^3$ s) $(m+n)^2m+n$ t) $(m+p-n)^2(n+m-p)$

7 a) $(-4)(-4)(-4)(-4)(-4)$ b) $-4\cdot4\cdot4\cdot4\cdot4$ c) $(-m)(-m)(-m)$ d) $-m\cdot m\cdot m$
e) $(2a)(2a)(2a)$ f) $2\cdot a\cdot a\cdot a$ g) $(a+b)(a+b)$ h) $a+b\cdot b$

8 a) 1 b) 3 c) x d) a e) ab f) 1 g) $ab+1$ h) 1

9 a) x^3 b) $(-x)^4$, necessary c) $-x^7$ d) $a+(2b)^3$, necessary

e) $(a+2b)^3$, necessary f) $a+2b^3$ g) $a(bc)^m$, necessary h) $\left(\frac{2x}{y}\right)^4$, necessary

10 a) 2,000,000 b) 8,000,000 The answers are different, since the order of operations is different. In part b, we must first complete operations within parentheses.

11 a) To multiply exponential expressions with the same bases one needs to add the exponents.

b) To divide exponential expressions with the same bases one needs to subtract their exponents

c) To raise an exponential expression to another power one needs to multiply exponents.

12 a) n^{23} b) s^{14} c) x^6 d) b^8 e) $16x^2$ f) $2m^9$ g) b h) $x^0 = 1$

i) $9a^{16}$ j) x^{12} k) $\frac{1}{2}a^2$ l) $3x^3$ m) $6a^{32}$ n) $5s^{11}$ o) $-5t^{12}$ p) $8x^{21}$

13 a) $m^2(-2m) = -2m^3$ b) $\frac{3x^5}{18x^3} = \frac{1}{6}x^2$ or $\frac{x^2}{6}$ c) $(2a^5)^3 = 8a^{15}$

14 a) $a = 2$ b) $2a^4 = 32$ c) $-a^3 = -8$ d) $a^2 = 4$

15 a) $m^8 = 1$ b) $-\frac{1}{2}m = \frac{1}{2}$ c) $\frac{1}{3}m^{28} = \frac{1}{3}$ d) $2m^{57} = -2$

16 a) $-x^2 = -49$ b) -49 c) $-\frac{4}{9}$ d) -0.0049

17 a) $-B^5$ nc: -1 b) B^8 nc: 1 c) $-B^8$ nc: -1 d) $-B^4$ nc: -1

18 a) $8x^3$ b) $-32x^3$ c) $-6x^4$ d) $12x^8$ e) $\frac{1}{4}a^2$ f) $\frac{1}{3}x^3$ g) $-64x^2$ h) $-\frac{1}{2}a$

i) $-\frac{1}{2}a^6$ j) $-2x^4$ k) $27x^2$ l) 1 m) v^5 n) $9a^6$ o) $-\frac{2}{5}x^6$ p) $-\frac{x^6}{0.16}$

19 a) $(-3xx^2)^3 = -27x^9$ b) $\left(\frac{4a^{12}}{a^2}\right)^2 = 16a^{20}$ c) $(-a^3)^7 \cdot (a) = -a^{22}$

20 a) $x^{10}y^6$ b) x^3y^3 c) $3ab^{10}$ d) $3a^2b^4$ e) $-\frac{a^6}{16b^4}$ f) $-x^5y^5$

g) -1 h) $\frac{1}{16}x^3$ i) $2x^5y^3$ j) $4(m-n)^5$ k) $\frac{1}{2}(a+b)^4$ l) a^8bc^2

21 a) $\frac{(xy^7)^5}{y^3} = x^5y^{32}$ b) $(3ab^3)^2 b = 9a^2b^7$

22 a) $mn^4 = -2$ b) $m^2 = 4$ c) $(m+n)^2 = 1$ d) 1

23 $\frac{4}{25}y^2$, $\frac{2y^2}{5}$, $y \cdot \frac{2}{5} \cdot y$, $\left(\frac{2}{5}y\right)^2$, $\frac{2}{5}yy$

24 $\frac{a^{20}}{3}$, $\frac{a^{20}}{3^{20}}$, $\frac{(a^{12})^8}{3^{20}}$, $\frac{a^{12}a^8}{3^{20}}$, $\frac{(a^4)^5}{3^{20}}$

25 $4y^2x^3$, $(2y)^2x^3$, $(-2)y^2(-2)x^3$ $(4xy)^2x$, $4(xy)^2x$

26 $2a^6c^2b^3$, $2a^2b^3c^2a^3$, $2(abc)^{11}$, $\frac{7c^2b^3a^6}{14}$, $2(a^3c)^2b^3$

27 a) Ψ= 8 b) Ψ =10 c) Ψ = 400 d) Ψ = 12 e) Ψ = 14 f) Ψ = 10

28 a) 15 b) $3^2 = 9$ c) −12 d) $05^2 = 0.25$ e) $4^2 = 16$ f) $-2^3 = -8$

Lesson 5

1 Based on the Commutative Law of Multiplication: $(a+b)c = c(a+b)$, and from here we can apply the Distributive Law: $c(a+b) = ca + cb$.

2 a) $2L+2W$ b) $R-Rx$ c) $P+\Pr t$ d) R^2s-r^2s e) $-3-xy$ f) x^3-7zx g) $2ac+c^2-c^6$ h) $a-a^2+2$

3 Based on the Commutative Law of Addition $xb + yb + xc + yc = xb + xc + yb + yc$, so the two answers are equivalent. Some other ways (answers vary):

$(x + y)(b + c) = xb + xc + yc + yb = yc + yb + xb + xc = yc + xc + yb + xb = xc + xb + yc + yb$

4 a) $\frac{5}{9}F-10$ b) $18y^5+24y^4$ c) x^6-2x^5 d) $-2c+22d$ e) $a^3+a^2b+a^2b^2$

f) $2x^4y^2+\frac{3}{7}xy-x^2y^5$ g) $xz-yz+xw-yw$ h) $10a-4b-a^4+\frac{2}{5}a^3b$

i) $ac+bc-gc-ad-bd+gd$ j) $x^3y+x^2y+xy+y-x^3-x^2-x-1$

k) $2xy-4y+3x-6$ l) $2ac-c-2abc+bc-4a+2+4ab-2b$

5 a) $(x^2-y)\cdot 5 = 5x^2-5y$ b) $-(-4x+1) = 4x-1$ c) $a(-c+1) = -ac+a$

d) $2y(-a+2b+d) = -2ya+4yb+2yd$ e) $(x-1)(y^3+2) = xy^3-y^3+2x-2$

f) $-(x-x^2+2x^4) = -x+x^2-2x^4$

6 a) $3a+3b = 3b+3a = (a+b)\cdot 3 = a\cdot 3+b\cdot 3 = b\cdot 3+a\cdot 3$ (answers vary)

b) $2z-yz = -yz+2z = z(2-y) = z\cdot 2-zy = 2z-zy$ (answers vary)

7 $mn+mp$ (circled) $(n+p)m$ (circled) $pm+nm$ (circled) $mn+p$ $mp+nm$ (circled)

8 $(-1)(x-y+z)$ (circled) $(x-y+z)(-1)$ (circled) $-1(x-y+z)$ (circled) $(x-y+z)-1$

$-x+y-z$ (circled) $-x-y+z$ $-x+y+z$ $-(x+z-y)$ (circled)

9 a) 2 b) 3 c) m

10 a) $5(x+y)$ b) $7(1-7a)$ c) $c(3-2c)$ d) $y(-8xy^5+1)$

e) $11t(-1+4t^2)$ f) $2(lw+lh+wh)$ g) $x(4x^2-5x+5)$

11 a) $xy(2-a^2)$ b) $xy(-x+y)$ c) $xy(a+b-1)$

12 a) $-1(-3-x)$ b) $-1(a-b-1)$ c) $-1\left(-a+\frac{x+y-z}{2}\right)$

13 a) $5a(2-3a)$ b) $11t\left(-\frac{1}{2}t+4\right)$ c) $5x^3(3x^2+1)$ d) $-4y^5(2xy-1)$

e) $c^2d^2(8-ad)$ f) $3x^2y(-1+3xy)$ g) $\frac{x}{y}(2+a)$ h) $\frac{1}{a+b}(1+s)$

14 a) $\frac{2}{3}(x^2y-2z)$ b) $\frac{1}{5}\left(x-\frac{1}{5}\right)$ c) $0.6(6x-10y+1)$

15 a) $(a+b)(6-x)$ b) $(a+b)[4-3(a+b)]$

16 a) $2xy((1-y+2xy)$ b) $a^3b^3(b+5a^4-1)$ c) $17xy(x^4y^2+2x^2y+3)$ d) $a^3b^3(b+5a^4-1)$

e) $4ac^3(-4+2c^4-3c^5d)$ f) $7ab^2(5b-2ab^2+3)$ g) $(x-2y)(-2+z^2)$ h) $(c+d)^2[1-4a(c+d)]$

17 $a\left((1-a+\frac{3}{a}\right)$

18 a) $2(2-\frac{x}{2})$ b) $x\left(\frac{4}{x}-1\right)$ c) $2x\left(\frac{2}{x}-\frac{1}{2}\right)$ d) $4x\left(\frac{1}{x}-\frac{1}{4}\right)$

19 a) Numerator: One term, *t*. (can be viewed as two factors, 1 and *t*) Denominator: two terms: 2*t* (with factors 2 and *t*) and —*ty* (with factors —1, *t* and *y*). Therefore *t* is a common factor of ALL terms (numerator and denominator.) We can divide the numerator and the denominator by *t*.

b) Numerator: two terms, *x* (with factors 1 and *x*) and *xy* (with factors *x* and *y*) Denominator: one term, 2a*x* (with factors 2, *a* and *x*). ALL terms in the numerator AND in the denominator have a common factor, *x*. We can therefore divide both the numerator and denominator by *x*.

c) Numerator: one term, 3*ab* (with three factors 3, *a* and *b*). Denominator: two terms, *ab* (with factors *a* and *b*) and $-a^2$ (with factors —1 and a^2). ALL terms in the numerator AND in the denominator have a common factor, *a*. We can therefore divide both the numerator AND the denominator by *a*.

20 *x* is NOT a factor in the denominator, but it can be viewed as a factor in the numerator. We can NOT cancel *x*, because it is not a factor in the denominator.

21 *x* IS a factor in BOTH the numerator and the denominator, therefore we can cancel *x*.. The result is $\frac{7}{xy}$

22 *a* IS a factor in BOTH the numerator and denominator, thus we can cancel it. The result: $a+x$.

23 *ab* IS a factor in the denominator, but NOT in the denominator, therefore we cannot cancel it.

24 a) $\frac{1}{3}$; 3xy b) $\frac{c}{4}$; 2ab c) $\frac{-1}{b^2}$; a^2 d) $\frac{xy}{4}$; $5y^3$ e) $\frac{3(a-b)}{5}$; $5x$

f) $\frac{a(b-c)}{2}$; a g) $-20x^2$; x h) $c(b+e)$; b i) $\frac{1}{7}$; $(a+b)$ j) not possible

25 a) $\frac{1}{x+y}$ b) $\frac{y+z}{3}$ c) $4-5x$ d) $\frac{1+x}{2}$ e) $\frac{1}{1-3x}$ f) $a^2b-4b^4a^3$ g) 1

h) $\frac{1}{2-x^3}$ i) not possible j) $\frac{1}{1+y}$ k) not possible l) $-x+3y+2z$

m) $\frac{1-y+x}{3}$ n) -1 o) $2v-3u+1$ p) $\frac{1}{3x^3-6xyz}$

Lesson 6

1 b) and d)
2 Yes.
3 No. (All three are unlike)

4 $6x^2y^2$ $\quad$ $-2x^2y$ (circled) $\quad$ $5xy$ $\quad$ $0.3yx^2$ (circled)

5 $5(ab)^2$ $\quad$ $2a^2b$ (circled) $\quad$ $-\frac{3}{7}ab^2$ $\quad$ $\frac{ba^2}{7}$ (circled)

6 y^3x^2 (circled) $\quad$ xy^3x (circled) $\quad$ $2x^3y^2$ $\quad$ y^2xx $\quad$ $yyxxy$ (circled)

7 $a^2b^5a^3$ $\quad$ $-b^2a^5b$ (circled) $\quad$ $(ab)^3b^3$ $\quad$ $2(ab)^3a^2$ (circled) $\quad$ a^3b^5

8 a) $2x$ b) not possible c) 0 d) not possible e) $2st$ or $2ts$ f) $2ac^2$ g) not possible

h) $6hmv$ i) $3xy^3z^5$ j) $9m^3n$ k) not possible l) $2a^2b^2$

9 a) $(3-4)x=-x$ b) $\left(\frac{1}{3}-\frac{2}{7}\right)x=\frac{1}{21}x$ c) $\left(\frac{2}{11}-\frac{3}{22}\right)x=\frac{1}{22}x$

d) $(0.3-0.5)x=-0.2x$ e) $\left(-\frac{7}{9}-\frac{2}{5}\right)x=-\frac{53}{45}x$ f) $\left(\frac{1}{5}-\frac{2}{3}+\frac{3}{10}\right)x=-\frac{1}{6}x$

10 a) $-x$ b) $-5a$ c) x d) $-x$ e) $-7ab$ f) not possible g) not possible h) $-1.2x^2y$

11 a) $-3x-8x-2x+8y=-13x+8y$ b) $-5a-7a-3b-2b=-12a-5b$

c) $-2ab-4ba+3ab+2-1=-3ab+1$

12 a) j b) $2+\frac{1}{3}a$ c) $0.7z$ d) $-2-7m$ e) $-2x^3+x^4$ f) $3x-y$ g) $-x-1$

h) $y-\frac{1}{2}x$ i) $\frac{2}{3}cd-d+c$ j) $-4b^2a^3-5a^2b^3$ k) $4yx^4-7x$ l) $-\frac{11}{38}ab+5\frac{7}{8}$

13 Student A and C.

14 $x+y$ a) -4 b) $-\frac{9}{5}$ c) -2.7

15 x; a) 4 b) -10 c) $\frac{2}{3}$.

16 a) $18a-2$ b) $27a+2$ c) $4y-6$ d) $2t+10$ e) $-\frac{8}{5}x+1$ f) $1.3a-0.2$ g) $-2x+1$ h) $-29q-48$

i) $-a-\frac{41}{5}b$ j) $-10x-9y$ k) $2a-5d$ l) $-a^2-3$ m) $3xy-3$

n) $-5bc+abc-2a$ o) $-\frac{1}{3}b$ p) $6x^4+3x^2+2$ q) $12x^2+6$ r) $-2.5m+3.97$

17 a) The student claiming that $(A+B)^2=A^2+2AB+B^2$ was right. b) $(A-B)^2=A^2-2AB+B^2$

18 a) x^8+4x^4+4 b) $9x^2-6x+1$ c) a^2+2a-8 d) $3b^2+\frac{1}{2}bc-\frac{1}{2}c^2$ e) $-c+\frac{29}{3}x$

f) $2x^3-5x^2+x+2$ g) $a^5-2a^3b+a^2b-2b^2$ h) $\frac{4}{9}-\frac{8}{3}x+4x^2$ i) $3b-2c$ j) $-13x+5y$

k) $-x^2+5x+8$ l) $-5a^2-12a-4$ m) $3x^2-x$ n) $-2m^2+3m+2$ o) k^2-2k+6 p) 0

19 a) $3yx-(-2xy)=5xy$ b) $(3x-1)+(-4x+2)=-x+1$

c) $(-4a^3+2a)-(4a^3-2)=-8a^3+2a+2$ d) $(-a+2+3b)-(-2b+a)=-2a+5b+2$

e) $\left(a-\frac{1}{3}\right)\left(\frac{2}{5}-2a\right)=-2a^2+\frac{16}{15}a-\frac{2}{15}$ f) $(2x^2-y)(3y-x^2)=-2x^4+7x^2y-3y^2$

g) $-mnk+4nmk+(-3mn)=3mnk-3mn$ h) $(3x+2)^2=9x^2+12x+4$

i) $(2a-b)^2=4a^2-4ab+b^2$ j) $(5x+2)+2(-4x+1)=-3x+4$

20 $-3a-3b$; a) 9 b) $-\frac{3}{2}$ or $-1\frac{1}{2}$ c) 5.4

21 $-3xy$; a) -9 b) 1 c) 0.3

Lesson 7

1	a) 20	b) $\frac{1}{27}$	c) -32			
2	a) 6	b) -36	c) 4	d) -9		
3	a) -4	b) -4	c) 4			
4	a) -14	b) $-\frac{2}{7}$	c) 2	d) 4		
5	a) $-\frac{2}{7}$	b) $\frac{2}{7}$	c) $\frac{2}{7}$	d) $\frac{4}{49}$		
6	a) -7	b) 7	c) -7	d) -7	e) -7	
7	a) 1	b) -1	c) -2	d) -1		
8	a) 9 b) -3	c) 3	d) $\frac{1}{3}$	e) 6	f) 27	
9	a) $-\frac{1}{3}$	b) $\frac{1}{3}$	c) $-\frac{1}{9}$	d) $-\frac{1}{3}$	e) -3	f) $-\frac{1}{3}$
10	a) 1	b) 2	c) 39			
11	a) -3	b) -0.4	c) -0.12			
12	a) -12	b) -3	c) -2	d) -2		
13	a) $\frac{2}{3}$	b) $-\frac{2}{3}$	c) $\frac{2}{9}$	d) -4		
14	a) -0.2	b) $\frac{1}{2}$	c) 0.05 or $\frac{1}{20}$	d) 10		
15	a) $x+z=-1$	b) $-z=3$				
16	a) $\frac{6x}{2}=3x$					
17	a) $\frac{-3x^2}{2}$ *or* $-\frac{3}{2}x^2$	b) $-\frac{7}{2}x$	c) $\frac{27}{2}x^3$	d) $-x$		
18	a) x^2	b) $25x^2$	c) x^2	d) $25x^2$	e) x^2+2x+1	f) x^6

19 a) $1-2x+x^2$ b) x^2 c) $\frac{x^2}{4}+x^2+x^2=\frac{9}{4}x^2$ d) 0

20 a) $-2x$ b) $-x$ c) $-3x$

21 a) $2s^3-2s$ b) $2s^7$ c) $10s^3$ d) s^5

22 x

23 a) m^4-m^3 b) $4s^4-2s^3$

24 a) $-10s^4$ b) $8s^{10}-8s^{12}$ c) $-s^4$

25 a) $26s^2$ b) $4m^2$ c) $4m^2$

26 a) $(2b)^4=16b^4$ b) $16b^4$ c) equal d) 0 e) $b^4-4b^4+6b^4-4b^4+b^4=0$ f) equal

27 $4x$

28 a) $-3m$ b) $\frac{m}{2}$ c) 6^m d) m^3 e) m f) m

29 a) $-3y$ b) $-3y^2$ c) y d) $-5y$

30 $(6x-2)(4x+2)$

Lesson 8

1 One can solve an equation but not an algebraic expression. If the left hand side of an equation is equal to the right hand side of the equation for $x=7$, then 7 is called a solution. The solutions of an equation are all values of variables that make the equation true. The statement that contains two quantities separated by an equal sign is called an equation. A solution always makes the equation true.

2 Equations: b) $5x=2$ c) $x^2=36$ e) $x=-4+2x$

3 Both Tom's and Mary's answers are correct, because $x=3$ is equivalent to both $3=x$ and $-x=-3$.

4 False. 7 is not a solution of $2(x+1)-x=7$.

5 None of the numbers is a solution of $-x^4=16$. The number 2 and -2 are solutions of $x^4=16$.

6 a) No b) Yes

7 a) Yes b) No c) Yes

8 a) No b) Yes c) No d) Yes

9 a) Yes b) Yes c) No

10 a) algebraic expression b) equation; −3 is a solution c) equation; −3 is not a solution

d) equation; −3 is not a solution e) algebraic expression f) equation; −3 is a solution

11 a) algebraic expression b) equation; 0.6 is a solution c) equation; 0.6 is a solution
d) algebraic expression e) equation; 0.6 is a solution f) equation; 0.6 is not a solution

12 a) equation; −1 b) algebraic expression c) equation; 0 or 1 d) equation; 1

e) algebraic expression f) equation; 7

13 a) −2 b) 3 (answers vary; any number different from −2)

14 a) -5 b) 5 (answers vary; any number different from −5.)

15 a) a solution b) a solution c) a solution d) not a solution e) not a solution f) a solution

16 For example, −2, −1, 0, 1 (answers vary; every number is a solution of this equation)

17 We can only divide by a variable if we assume it is not 0. It is better if we always try to avoid dividing by a variable or by an algebraic expression. A better way to solve this equation is: $x=2x$; $x-2x=-2x-2x$; $x=0$;

18 a) $x=-3$ b) $x=6$ c) $x=5$ d) $x=-20$

e) -50 f) $x=-3$ g) $x=-2$ h) $x=-8$

19 a) $x=-4$ b) $x=3$ c) $x=-3$ d) $x=\frac{4}{5}$ e) $x=-18$ f) $x=-5$

20 a) $x=-\frac{12}{5}$ b) $x=\frac{5}{7}$ c) $x=0$ d) $x=\frac{2}{7}$ e) $x=\frac{3}{8}$ f) $x=-1$

21 f) $x=6$ g) $x=-1$ c) $x=-8$ h) $x=-1$ e) $x=6$ f) $x=1$

22 a) no solution b) $x=0$ (exactly one solution) c) all real numbers d) no solution e) all real numbers

23 a) $x=-2$ b) $a=-60$ c) $x=7$ d) $x=0$ e) $a=0$ f) $x=5$ g) $y=2$
h) $y=\frac{22}{6}=\frac{11}{3}$ i) $x=0$ j) $x=-6$ k) $x=-\frac{2}{5}$ l) $a=10$ m) $B=\frac{1}{6}$ n) $x=3$
o) all real numbers p) $x=-2$ q) $x=\frac{1}{3}$ r) no solution s) no solution t) no solution u) $x=\frac{7}{5}$ v) $x=2$

Lesson 9

1 a) $x=-18$ b) $x=-\frac{2}{15}$ c) $x=-\frac{5}{16}$ d) $x=\frac{8}{5}$ e) $y=-2$ f) $x=\frac{1}{6}$

2 a) no solution b) $x=-\frac{2}{5}$ c) $a=\frac{1}{4}$ d) $x=-\frac{1}{6}$ e) no solution f) $x=-\frac{1}{4}$

g) $x=0$ h) $x=\frac{10}{21}$ i) all real numbers j) $x=\frac{4}{9}$ k) $x=\frac{13}{8}$ l) $x=-\frac{9}{2}$

3 a) $x=0$ b) $x=\frac{1}{5}$ c) $x=0$

4 a) $x=-8$ b) $x=-\frac{2}{7}$ c) $x=\frac{11}{2}$

5 a) no solution b) $a=\frac{1}{7}$ c) $a=-\frac{2}{7}$

6 No. $\frac{x+1}{2}-5y$ is not an equation, so we can not solve it.

7 a) $x=14$ b) $x=ab$

8 a) $x=5$ b) $x=b-a$

9 a) $x=6$ b) $x=\frac{c+b}{a}$

10 a) $x=2$ b) $x=\frac{c}{a-b}$

11 a) $x=1$ b) $x=\frac{bc}{a-b}$

12 a) $x=-a$ b) $b=a^2c$ c) $a=\frac{b^4}{c}$ d) $a=\frac{3b}{x}$ e) $u=a$ f) $b=a^2c$ g) $m=2n^3$

h) $y=t+x$ i) $y=x^2$ j) $A=\frac{1-x}{x-1}=\frac{-(x-1)}{x-1}=-1$ k) $x=s+1$ l) $a=-\frac{5by}{2x}$

m) $v=\frac{s}{3}+t$ or $v=\frac{s+3t}{3}$ n) $x=\frac{1}{2a+2}$ o) $x=\frac{m-2n}{2n-m}=-1$ p) $m=\frac{3b}{b+b^2}=\frac{3}{1+b}$

13 a) $d=\frac{x}{y}-e$ b) $x=y(d+e)$ c) $y=\frac{x}{d+e}$

14 a) $b=t-at$ b) $a=\frac{t-b}{t}$ or $a=1-\frac{b}{t}$ c) $t=\frac{b}{1-a}$ or $t=\frac{-b}{a-1}$

15 $x=a^9=-1$

16 $n=-m=4$

17 a) $h = \frac{2A}{b}$ b) $h = 4$ inches

18 a) $W = \frac{P-2L}{2}$ or $W = \frac{P}{2} - L$ b) $W = 1$ c) $W = 2$ inches

Lesson 10

1 For example $x = 3$ or $x = -2$ (answers vary). The same numbers could be solutions for the other inequality. Both x<5 and 5>x state the same condition (are equivalent)

2 a) and d)

3 For example $x = -1$ or $x = -3$ or $x = -10$ (answers vary.)

4 $x = \frac{2}{3}$

5. -3, -2, -1, 0, 1, 2, 3, 4, 5

6. -3, -2, -1, 0, 1, 2, 3, 4, 5

7 $-.666$, -6, -0.6

8 a) $x < 0$ b) $x \le 0$ c) $x \ge 6$ d) $x \le 6$ e) $x \le 6$

9

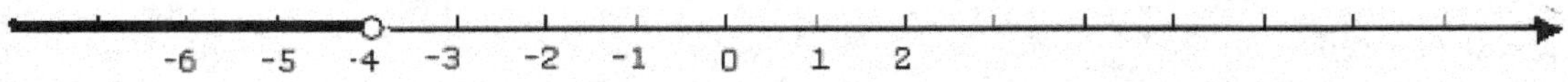

b)

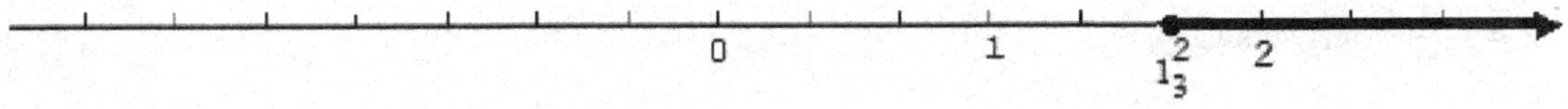

c)

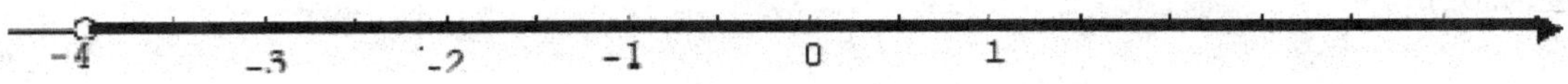

d)

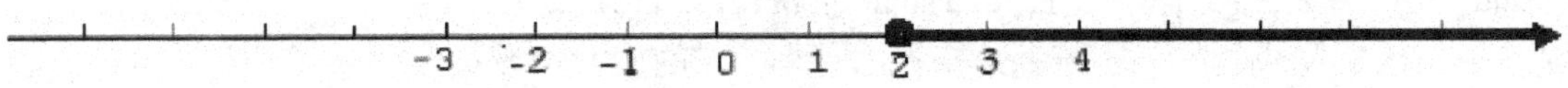

e)

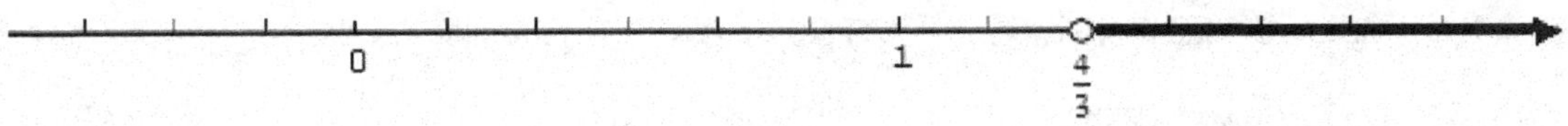

f)

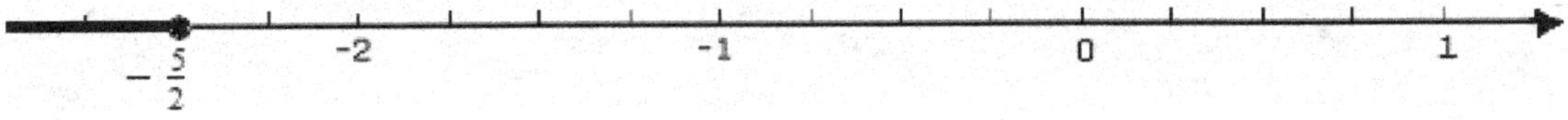

10

a)

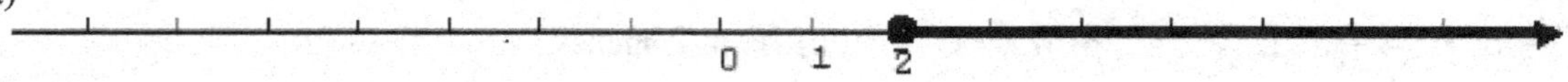

b)

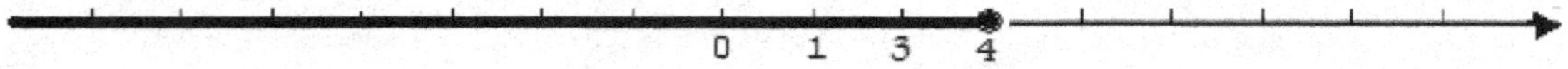

c)

d)

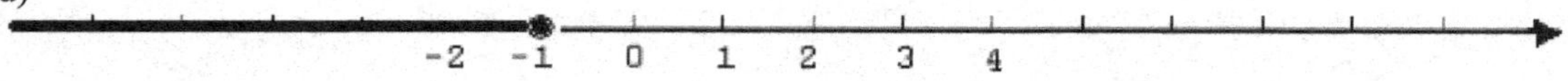

11 a) $x < -1$ b) $x > -4$ c) $x \geq -1$ d) $x \leq -1$

12 $x = \frac{2}{3}$ is the value that satisfies both inequalities.

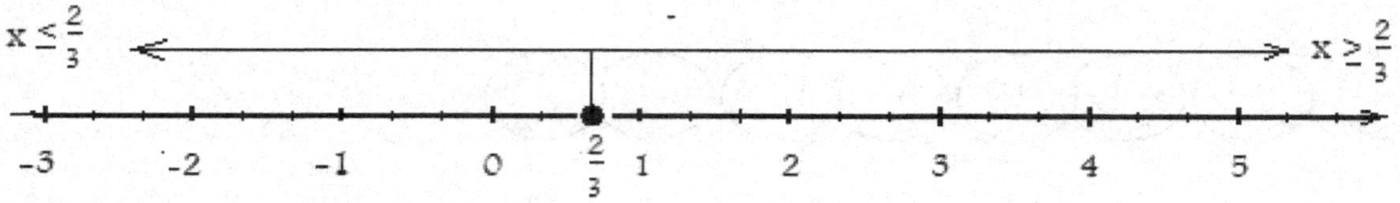

13 a) $x \geq 3$ or $x < 7$ (answers vary)

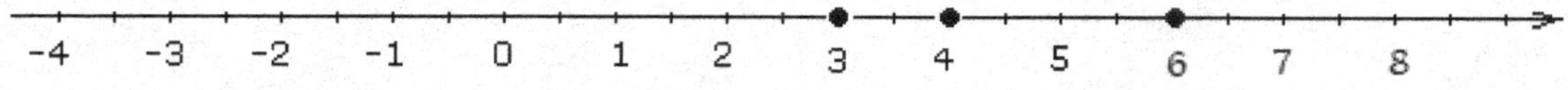

b) $x \geq -2$ or $x \leq 3$ (answers vary)

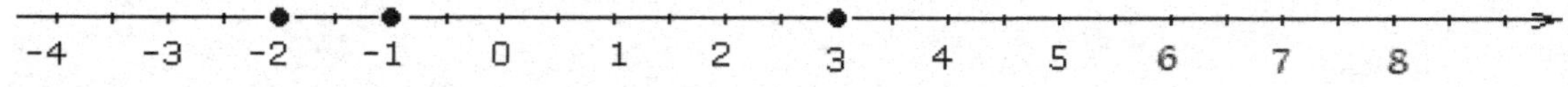

14 a) $x > 4$ or $x < 0$ (answers vary)

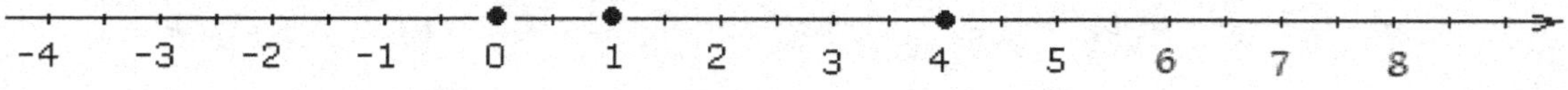

b) $x > 2$ or $x < -\frac{1}{2}$ (answers vary)

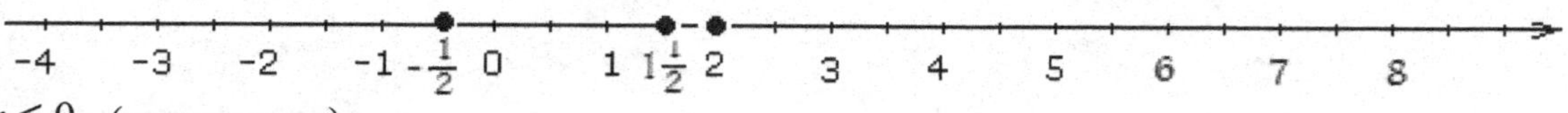

15 $x \leq 0$ (answers vary.)

16 $x \leq 4$ (answers vary)

17 a) $-5+2<4$ and b) $5+8 \geq 13$; -5 is not a solution of (c) and (d) $-3<4$ $13 \geq 13$

18 Only student B

19 a) yes b) no (there are infinitely many solutions) c) infinitely many
d) 1, 10, 100 e) -1, -3, -5 (answers vary.) f) yes g) no h) no i) yes

20 a) and e)

21 a) subtract 5; no sign change; $z < 3$ b) add 2; no sign change; $z < 3$ c) divide by 4; no sign change; $z > -3$
d) divide or multiply by -1; sign changes; $z < 3$ e) multiply by -3; sign changes; $z < -3$

22 a) and d)

23 b) and d)

24 a) $x < -4$

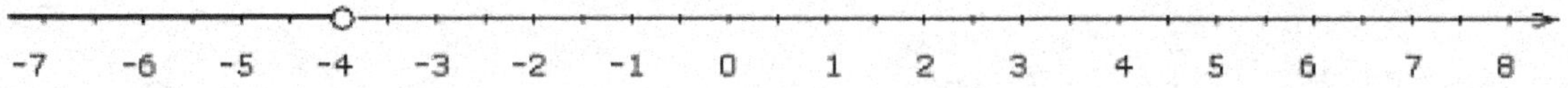

b) All real numbers

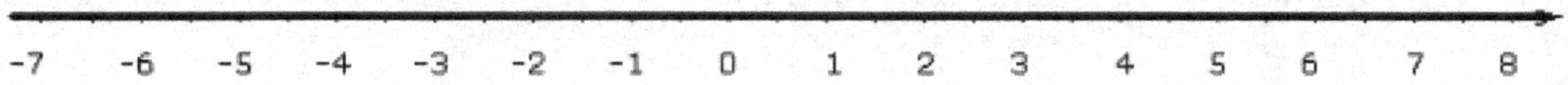

c) $x \geq -2$

d) $a < 7$

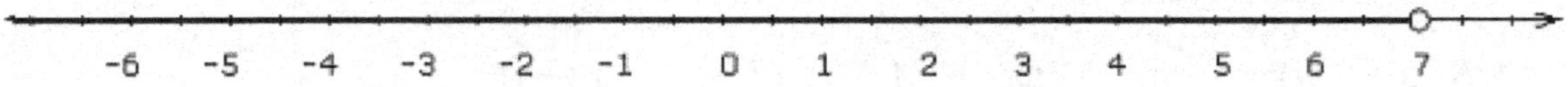

e) $x > -10$

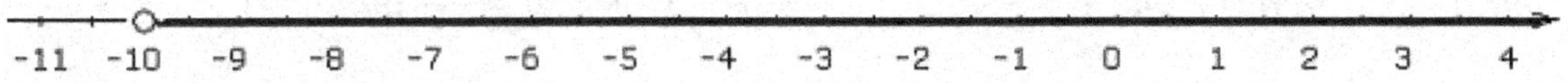

f) $a \leq 2$

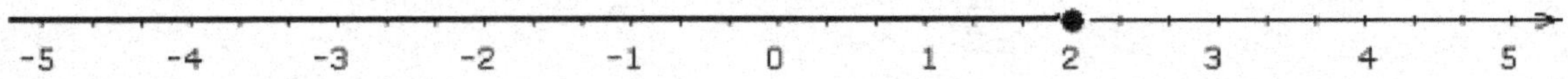

25 a) "add 3 to both sides", "divide each side by -1"; $a > -7$

b) "subtract 1 from both sides", "divide each side by 3"; $x < \frac{5}{3}$

c) "multiply each side by 4", "divide each side by 3"; $x < -20$

d) "multiply each side by 4", "divide each side by -1"; $x \geq 20$

e) "subtract 1 from both sides", "multiply each side by 4"; $x \geq -8$

f) "multiply each side by 4", "subtract 1 from both sides"; $x \geq -5$

26 a) $x < -6$ b) $x < -2$ c) $x \geq -4$ d) all real numbers e) no solution f) $a < -\frac{3}{5}$ g) $x \geq \frac{4}{3}$

h) $x < \frac{3}{7}$ i) $x > -\frac{2}{3}$ j) all real numbers k) all real numbers l) $x \leq -\frac{9}{2}$ m) all real numbers

n) no solution o) no solution p) $x < -\frac{1}{4}$ q) $x \geq 18$ r) $y \geq 0$ s) $a > \frac{34}{81}$ t) no solution

Lesson 11

1 $a = \frac{3}{4}$

2 a) $a = 3$ and $b = 4$ b) $a = -4$ and $b = \frac{2}{3}$

3 a) $p = -3$ b) $p = 3$

4 $a = -2$ and $b = 5$

5 $a = -7$

6 $A = 4x$ and $B = y$

7 a) $X = 3a$ and $Y = b$ b) $X = 3$ and $Y = ab$

8 a) $c = x - 1$ and $b = 2$ b) $c = x$ and $b = y^9$

9 (1)-E; $a = x$ and $b = 1$ (2)-F; $a = x$ and $b = 1$ (3)-D; $a = 8$ and $b = x$

(4)-A; $a = 3x$ and $b = 5y$ (5)-B; $a = 3x$ and $b = 5y$ (6)-C; $a = 3$ and $b = y$

10 a) form of $A - B$; $5 - (-n) = 5 + n$ b) form of $A + B$; $5 + n = 5 - (-n)$

c) form of $A + B$; $5 + (-n) = 5 - n$ d) form of $A - B$; $5 - n = 5 + (-n)$

11 a) $a = -1$ *and* $b = 3$ b) $a = 2$ *and* $b = -3$ c) $-\frac{1}{2}x^3 + 1$; $a = -\frac{1}{2}$ *and* $b = 1$

d) $2x^3 + \frac{3}{2}$; $a = 2$ *and* $b = \frac{3}{2}$ e) $-x^3 + \frac{3}{2}$; $a = -1$ *and* $b = \frac{3}{2}$ f) $8x^3 + 4$ $a = 8$, $b = 4$

12 a) 6^2; $a = 6$ b) 20^2; $a = 20$ c) 0.4^2; $a = 0.4$ d) $\left(\frac{3}{7}\right)^2$; $a = \frac{3}{7}$ e) $(5y)^2$; $a = 5y$ f) $\left(\frac{b}{10}\right)^2$; $a = \frac{b}{10}$

g) $(0.7c)^2$; $a = 0.7c$ h) $(X^2)^2$; $a = X^2$ i) $(2x^3)^2$; $a = 2x^3$ j) $(9xy^4)^2$; $a = 9xy^4$

13 a) $(-1)^3$; $a = -1$ b) 3^3; $a = 3$ c) 0.3^3; $a = 0.3$ d) $\left(\frac{2}{5}\right)^3$; $a = \frac{2}{5}$ e) $(-z)^3$; $a = -z$

f) $(4x)^3$; $a = 4x$ g) $\left(-\frac{x}{2}\right)^3$; $a = -\frac{x}{2}$ h) $(y^2)^3$; $a = y^2$ i) $(10x^3)^3$; $a = 10x^3$ j) $\left(\frac{x^5}{2y}\right)^3$; $a = \frac{x^5}{2y}$

14 a) $(x^6)^4$; $a = x^6$ b) $(x^4)^6$; $a = x^4$ c) $(x^2)^{12}$; $a = x^2$

15 a) $(-x)^7$; $A = -x$ b) $(x^2)^7$; $A = x^2$ c) $(x^2y^3)^7$; $A = x^2y^3$ d) $\left(\frac{y^3}{z^{10}}\right)^7$; $A = \frac{y^3}{z^{10}}$

16 a) x^5; $a = x$; $m = 5$ b) $(stv)^7$; $a = stv$; $m = 7$ c) b^7; $a = b$; $m = 7$

d) $\left(\frac{B}{C}\right)^3$; $a = \frac{B}{C}$; $m = 3$ e) $\left(\frac{x+y}{z}\right)^4$; $a = \frac{x+y}{z}$; $m = 4$ f) $(8x)^2$; $a = 8x$; $m = 2$

17 a) $x^2 + (-2)y^2 = 0$; $a = 1$; $b = -2$ b) $3x^2 + (-1)y^2 = 0$; $a = 3$; $b = -1$

c) $\frac{1}{2}x^2 + (-1)y^2 = 0$; $a = \frac{1}{2}$; $b = -1$ d) $1x^2 + 0y^2 = 0$; $a = 1$; $b = 0$

e) $\frac{3}{4}x^2 + \frac{1}{4}y^2 = 0$; $a = \frac{3}{4}$; $b = \frac{1}{4}$ or $3x^2 + y^2 = 0$ if you were to multiply both sides by 4, then $a = 3$, $b = 1$

f) $10x^2 + (-5)y^2 = 0$; $a = 10$; $b = -5$ or $-10x^2 + 5y^2 = 0$; $a = -10$; $b = 5$

18 a) $(-1)x+\left(-\frac{1}{4}\right)y+\frac{3}{2}z;\ A=-1;\ B=-\frac{1}{4};\ C=\frac{3}{2}$ b) $-6x+(-3)y+z;\ A=-6;\ B=-3;\ C=1$

c) $\frac{3}{4}x+\left(-\frac{1}{2}\right)y+\frac{1}{4}z;\ A=\frac{3}{4};\ B=-\frac{1}{2};\ C=\frac{1}{4}$ d) $1x+(-1)y+0z;\ A=1;\ B=-1;\ C=0$

e) $-\frac{3}{4}x+\frac{3}{4}y+2z;\ A=-\frac{3}{4};\ B=\frac{3}{4};\ C=2$ f) $0x+0y+\left(-\frac{1}{15}\right)z;\ A=0;\ B=0;\ C=-\frac{1}{15}$

19 a) $y=3x+(-2);\ m=3;\ b=-2$ b) $y=1x+0;\ m=1;\ b=0$ c) $y=\frac{1}{5}x+0;\ m=\frac{1}{5};\ b=0$

d) $y=-3x+2;\ m=-3;\ b=2$ e) $y=2x+\left(-\frac{1}{3}\right);\ m=2;\ b=-\frac{1}{3}$

f) $y=0x+(-5);\ m=0;\ b=-5$ g) $y=0x+0;\ m=0;\ b=0$ h) $y=4x+(-6);\ m=4;\ b=-6$

20 a) $a=3;\ b=b;\ 3^2+2(3)b+b^2=9+6b+b^2$

b) $a=2x;\ b=3y;\ (2x)^2+2(2x)(3y)+(3y)^2=4x^2+12xy+9y^2$

c) $a=y^2;\ b=\frac{2}{5};\ (y^2)^2+2(y^2)\frac{2}{5}+\left(\frac{2}{5}\right)^2=y^4+\frac{4}{5}y^2+\frac{4}{25}$

21 a) not linear b) $\frac{1}{3}x+(-1)=0;\ a=\frac{1}{3};\ b=-1$ c) $-1x+0=0;\ a=-1;\ b=0$

d) $\frac{1}{8}x+0.9=0;\ a=\frac{1}{8};\ b=0.9$ or $x+7.2=0;\ a=1;\ b=7.2$ e) $x+2=0,\ a=1,\ b=2$

f) $-4x+7=0;\ a=-4;\ b=7$ or $4x+(-7)=0;\ a=4;\ b=-7$ g) $-x+(-2.5)=0;\ a=-1;\ b=-2.5$

h) $18x+(-5)=0;\ a=18;\ b=-5$ or $-18x+5=0;\ a=-18;\ b=5$

22 $a=4;\ b=2$; $12x+6=0$ where $a=12;\ b=6$

23 a) $(x-1)(x+1)$ b) $(2-3x)(2+3x)$ c) $(y-10a)(y+10a)$ d) $(5s-8t)(5s+8t)$

e) $\left(x^2-\frac{1}{3}\right)\left(x^2+\frac{1}{3}\right)$ f) $(xy-0.5)(xy+0.5)$ g) $\left(\frac{a}{b}-6\right)\left(\frac{a}{b}+6\right)$

h) $[m-(2m+1)][m+(2m+1)]=(-m-1)(3m+1)$

i) $[(x+1)-(3x+5)][(x+1)+(3x+5)]=(-2x-4)(4x+6)$

j) $[(2a-3)-3a][(2a-3)+3a]=(-a-3)(5a-3)$

24 a) $x^3-4^3;\ a=x;\ b=4;\ (x-4)(x^2+4x+16)$ b) $1^3-(2y)^3;\ a=1;\ b=2y;\ (1-2y)(1+2y+4y^2)$

c) $(2x)^3-(3y)^3;\ a=2x;\ b=3y;\ (2x-3y)(4x^2+6xy+9y^2)$

d) $(x^2)^3-\left(\frac{1}{3}\right)^3;\ a=x^2;\ b=\frac{1}{3};\ \left(x^2-\frac{1}{3}\right)\left(x^4+\frac{1}{3}x^2+\frac{1}{9}\right)$

25 a) $(2x+y)(4x^2-2xy+y^2)$ b) $(6x-0.1y)(6x+0.1y)$

c) $(x-3y)(x^2+3xy+9y^2)$ d) $(4a-bc)(16a^2+4abc+b^2c^2)$

26 $10.7^2-9.3^2=(10.7-9.3)(10.7+9.3)=1.4\times 20=28$

27 $(10+1)^4=10^4+4\times 10^3\times 1+6\times 10^2\times 1^2+4\times 10\times 1^3+1^4=14641$